DENIAL
IS NOT A RIVER IN EGYPT

OVERCOME
ADDICTION,
COMPULSION
& FEAR WITH
DR. STOCKWELL'S
SELF-HYPNOSIS
SYSTEM

SHELLEY STOCKWELL, PH.D.

DENIAL IS NOT A RIVER IN EGYPT

Overcome Addiction, Compulsion and Fear with Dr. Stockwell's Self-Hypnosis System

Cover Design:	Bryce Stockwell, Laura Wagg, Wendy Quintanilla
Cover Photo:	Jon Nicholas
Illustrations:	Shelley Stockwell, Wallace Keown, Carin Robinson, Ormond McGill and Clark Dunbar
Book Design:	Wendy Quintanilla
Editorial Consultant:	Lt. Col. O.J. Vogl, Nica Lee
Other Photos:	Jon Nicholas, Shelley Stockwell, Joann Kelly, Pam Bourne, Stan Hillis, Bryce Stockwell, Neredah Bradstreet, Carol Kozlovich, Mary Bontempo, John Bruecker, Almarie Clifford, Rayma Ditson, Grant Stockwell, Gerry Lumian, James Wanless, Nica Lee, Tamara Thomas, Janus Welton, and Richard Vogl.

DENIAL IS NOT A RIVER IN EGYPT

Published January 2003

30819 CASILINA DRIVE
RANCHO PALOS VERDES, CALIFORNIA 90275
United States Of America
Phone: (310) 541-4844
e-mail sstockwell@earthlink.net
www.hypnosisfederation.com

Library of Congress Catalog Card Number: 2002092142
ISBN: 0-912559-22-5

Printed in the United States of America

Cover Her-Ass

Photo by JoAnn Kelly

This book educates the reader on ways to cope with out-of-control behavior, mood states and the potential danger of many socially accepted, legal and illegal drugs, remedies, treatments, cures, "foods," "supplements," "additives" and medical procedures. It is based on personal observation, experience, case studies and research of the author who is not a medical or naturopathic doctor (and says, "who needs that aggravation").

This book is intended to be informational and not a substitute for those who have been hypnotized by their culture, subculture, advertisers, the law, or any individual to rely upon the advice and prescriptions of a paid up and licensed medical adviser, drug dealer or manufacturer. Anyone who is taking prescription medications, over-the-counter drugs, or self-medicating with caffeine, tobacco, sugar, processed food, supplements, street drugs or other similarly dangerous substances, should seek professional advice on the best way to remedy their situation.

The author and publisher of this book expressly disclaim responsibility for any adverse effects arising from the use or application of the information contained in this book.

The author and the publisher of this book expressly claim responsibility for all good effects arising from the use or application of the information contained in this book.

"Your book could help a lot of people."

Dr. Bernie Siegel, M.D.
Author, *Love, Medicine and Miracles*

"I very much enjoyed what you wrote."

Leo Buscaglia, Ph.D.
Author, College Professor

"Your book is a fantastic pyramid scheme."

Steve Bhaerman, aka Swami Beyondananda
Author: *Driving Your Own Karma*

"Shelley gives you the power to hire your higher self and master your life! There's no biz like grow biz."

Raleigh Pinskey
Author: *101 Ways to Promote Yourself*

"Thank you Shelley! Your love, humor and compassionate intelligence gives people tools to release pain, heal addiction and create joy and fulfillment in their lives."

Suzy Prudden, CHt.
Author: *Take-Two: Two Minutes to Heal You Life*

"If you've ever felt depressed, out-of-control or off-center, this book will put you on a balanced laugh track. There's a twist around every turn of the page. As you release limiting habits, it ties a love knot around your heart."

Frank Garfield, CHt.
Author: *Dreams: The Real Windows to Your Life*

"Thank you. You put a fresh layer of rubber on my spinning wheels. Feels good to have some traction for a change."

Michael P.

"Rock on, Mom."

Bryce Stockwell, Computer Artist

"Humor with recovery."

Jon Nicholas, Hypnotherapist

"A comprehensive piece of work that deserves every serious therapists attention. Dr. Stockwell's ease of style makes this book understandable to the lay person as well."

Richard Neves, Ph.D.
President, American Board of Hypnotherapy

"Compost happens. This book lets you blossom!"

James Wanless, Ph.D.
Creator of the Voyager Tarot Deck

"A spoonful of laughter, a pinch of insight and a gallon of love. The Stockwell System has the makings of a best-selling soufflé."

Dianna Whitley, C.Ht.

"This complete self-help guide is a true blessing to those seeking freedom of negative life patterns. This is a positive path on the journey to personal power, wholeness, peace, and prosperity."

Jillian LaVelle, C.Ht.
C.E.O. Int. Assoc. of Counselors and Therapists

"Shelley took something so BIG -life's problems- and gave us easy solutions. Her way warms even the most resistant. Shelley, you did it again!"

Josan Galletti, C.Ht.
Author: *Primer to the Light: A Spiritual Book For Beginners*

"I always excused my obsessive addictions as "exuberance." This book woke me up from rationalizing and liberated me to keep addiction in check."

Nica Lee
Executive Manager,
Creativity Unlimited Press

"I hold my heart in my hands and my heart is holding me."

Jen Walker
Age 11

"Hypnosis expert, Shelley Stockwell."

Chris Rodell
National Inquirer

Illustration by Wallace Keown

I Sphinx, Therefor I Am

Foreword

By Ormond McGill

Stockwell's *Denial Is Not a River in Egypt* is perfect!

Mysterious old Egyptian mummies unravel at her saucy humor. Even the Sphinx smiles.

Photo by Jon Nicholas

Shelley and Ormond

Shelley writes with wisdom both ancient and modern, with Egypt as her theme. She bares her heart and tells you how to transform your life from unhappiness to happiness. And, she does it in such a lighthearted way, you are entertained and entranced.

Transpersonal Hypnotherapist, Shelley Stockwell, Ph.D. considers this book to be her masterwork. It is a book that has to be lengthy as it has so much to say.

Hour after hour have gone into its production.

Each hour was a work of love.

Shelley tells you how to take a journey deep into the mysterious nature of yourself. Sometimes you will drop into the abyss of your subconscious mind. You may even slip into new dimensions beyond space and time. When you return, you will notice how the quality of your life has improved. In fact, you may scarcely recognize yourself.

Get with it, read and receive the gifts Shelley Stockwell gives you and remember: *Denial is not a river in Egypt.*

Ormond McGill, Ph.D., 2002 A.D.
The Dean of American Hypnosis,
Author of *The 21st Century Encyclopedia of Hypnotherapy*

Illustration by Shelley Stockwell

DENIAL IS NOT A RIVER IN EGYPT

Overcome Addiction Compulsion and Fear

This Book Shows You How to Transform:

Denial into Truth
Stress into Relaxation
Depression into Expression
Sadness into Joy
Pain into Pleasure
Anger into Kindness
Addiction into Health
Compulsion into Peace
Frightful into Insightful
Loneliness into Friendship, Love, Sex

▲

Yes
Joy
Free
Play
Love
Open
Calm
Move
Dream
Magic
Giggle
Laugh
Dive In
Believe
Imagine
Celebrate
Stay Loose
Moon baths

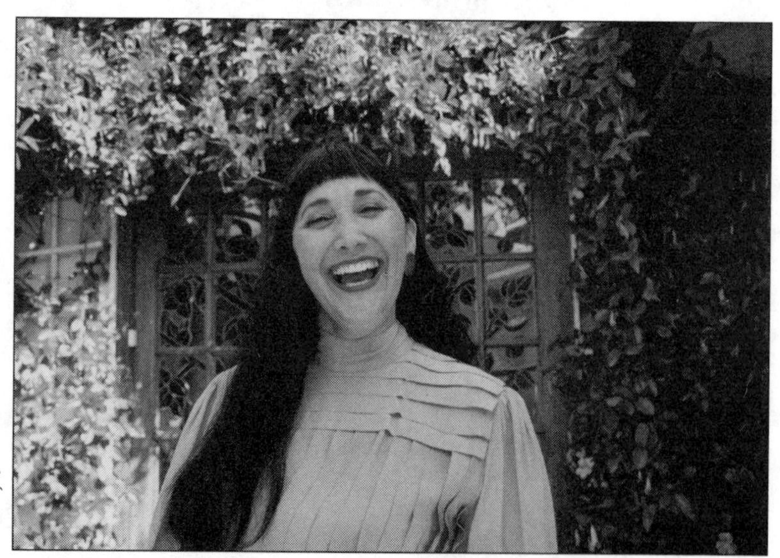

Photo by Jon Nicholas

SHELLEY STOCKWELL, Ph.D.

Photo by Jon Nicholas

Shelley Stockwell, Ph.D.

Shelley Stockwell, Ph.D., is a Transpersonal Hypnotherapist, Motivational Speaker, Trainer, Teacher, Healer, Poet, Artist, TV/Radio Personality, Trance Channel and Non-denominational Minister. She holds a Ph.D. in Transpersonal Psychology and is the spokesperson and founder of the International Hypnosis Federation and on the Board of Advisors for Canada's Hypnotherapy Board and The International Medical and Dental Hypnotherapy Association.

She is honored by the Hypnosis Hall of Fame, the International Association of Counselors and Therapists, The Medical and Dental Hypnotherapy Association, and Toastmasters International. Shelley's cable TV program "The Shelley Show" won an Angel Award of Excellence for Outstanding Cable Television.

Shelley is a popular radio and internet guest on shows worldwide. You may have seen her on one of her regularly appearances on television shows like The Other Side, The Phil Donahue Show, Good Morning Australia, Strange Universe, Mike and Maty, The Channel 9 News, The Channel 11 News, Live at Five News, Rise and Shine and Pajama Party. The National Enquirer and the Los Angeles Times call her: "hypnosis expert."

Shelley's training programs offer hands on transformational tools. She trains corporate executives, sales and marketing personnel here and abroad and certifies Hypnotists, Hypnotherapists, Behavioral Counselors, Addiction Counselors, MFT's, Nurses, Past Life Therapists, Stage Hypnotists, Motivational Speakers, Metaphysicians and Spiritual Counselors.

Shelley is author of thirty hypnosis tapes, seventeen songs, six videos and ten books. Her speaking tours have taken her across America, Japan, Bali, Australia, New Zealand and Egypt. Stockwell loves her family, friends, cats, America and you, her readers.

BOOKS BY SHELLEY STOCKWELL, Ph.D.:

Automatic Writing & Hieroscripting: Tap Unlimited Creativity and Guidance

Everything You Ever Wanted to Know About Everything
(Co-author: Ormond McGill)

Hypnosis: How to Put a Smile on Your Face and Money in Your Pocket

Insides Out: Self-Talk Poetry

Sex and Other Touchy Subjects: Transformational Poetry

Stockwell's Hypnosis for Weight Control: 10 Easy Steps To A New You

The Secrets of Hypnotizing Women
(Co-author: Ormond McGill)

The Search for Cosmic Consciousness: The Hypnosis Book Einstein Would Have Loved
(Co-author: Ormond McGill)

Time Travel: The Do-It-Yourself Past Life Journey Handbook

AUDIO TAPES

Automatic Writing
Entrancing Music
Great Golf
I Love to Exercise
Kundalini Rising
Lose Weight
Meet Your Angel
Mer-Ka-Ba
No More Alcohol
No More Sugar Junkie
Peace and Calm
Quit Smoking
Sex and Other Touchy Subjects
Sleep Beautiful Sleep
The Money Tape
The Wellness Tape
Time Travel
You Are What You Eat: Children's Songs
Yes I Can!

VIDEO TAPES

How to Time Travel: Past Life Regression/Future Life Progression

How to Hypnotize in 30 Seconds: Stockwell's Rapid & Instant Inductions

Hypnotically Yours: Stockwell interviews Ormond McGill

Joy Therapy

Stockwell's Hypnosis for Weight Control Seminar

Stockwell's Secrets of the Mind

The Secret Lives of Ormond McGill

Trance-Formations: Hypnosis, Channeling & Past Life Regression

---

To order Shelley's books, CD's, audio and videotapes see the back of this book or call (310) 541-4844 or email: sstockwell@earthlink.net www.hypnosisfederation.com

Dead•ication

Love to my, dear Angels, Fathers and Mothers:
Irving Lessin 1913-1966 and Irma Lessin 1915-1986
Ed and Winnie Self

Aunts and Uncles: Sarah and Charles Mandel, Helen and Joe Mitler, Hal Lessin, Mike Lessin, Ollie Lessin, and George Kapilese

Dear Friends: Lloyd Kaechele, John Odegard, Hanka and Jerze Makowski, Ellen Vogl, and Troy Garrison.

Alive•ication

To: Jon Nicholas, Bryce Stockwell, Nica Lee, Jim Vogl, Alex Lessin, Ormond McGill, Sophie Lessin, Florence Kaplan, Corinne Hartley, and Bernie Siegel.

My heartfelt love and appreciation for your comments, support and understanding. I couldn't have done it without you.

Thank you too to my friends and support team: Barbara McNurlin, Charlene Ackerman, Eliana Bar-El, Don and Ewa Carlsson-Bay, Steve and Trudie Bhaerman, Pam Bourne, Dr. Tom Bump, Rhonda Carpenter, Tom Cobb, Virginia Cologne, Betsy and Gordon Cowen, Solange Dunlop, Josan and Sam Galletti, Joel Gober, Shelby Harris, Lloyd Jones, Lois Kantor, Jillian LaVelle, Janet Lessin, Lynn Lofthouse, Gerry Lumian, Mary O'Maly, Leslie McGuirk, Lynn Morgan, Dr. Lilia Prado, Sandy Medearis, Richard Neves, Kathy Popoff, Suzy Prudden, Wendy & Cavin Quintanilla, Bob Rumph, Larry Savell, Jill and Clyde Searles, Gregory Soultanian, Jim and Joanna Schumacher, Hilda Schupps, George Papadakis, Rex Perkins, Pamela McHenry, Judy Umansky, Richard Vogl, Laura Waag, Judy and David Walker, Jae Webster, Judy Wolkovitch, Gilda Whited, Lisa and Anthony Zolezzi, and my Ph.D. advisor and friend, Dr. Irv Katz.

My gratitude goes to my precious Tuesday Night Friendship Group, Peninsula Toastmasters Club 174 and my wonderful hypnosis and channeling clients and friends. Your talent, stories, poetry and quotes enrich my life and bring clarity to my work. And of course, to my Egyptian friends whose warm hospitality, sense of humor and rich heritage made this book a delight to write.

Tomb It May Concern

☆ *"They say that there is always one weirdo on the bus. I've been on the bus many times and I've never seen him."*

—Jose Rodriguez

Dear Reader:

This book is your own magic carpet to fun. It is gleaned from my twenty-five years as a Hypnotherapist and over fifteen thousand hours of holding the mirror for others. Each step-by-step technique is the result of observation, research, case studies and experimentation. My inner guides expanded my perspective.

We all enter the land of denial (no lie). We trick and pretend to have fun, get ourselves through the night, cope, not hurt someone else's feelings and hope that painful things will turn out to be not what they seem. Blame games like "egypt me" keep us little and not in charge of life. Inner deception silently fogs joy, robs intimacy and makes life lackluster.

If you are addicted to a person, behavior or drug, you can physically "detox" in two weeks. But how do you mentally "detox?" How do you get your mind to stop tricking you with lies, rationales, cravings, pain and yearnings and bring you joy?

Asking the conscious mind to change a behavior that lives in the subconscious mind is like calling in a plumber to fix your electricity. It won't work. But change your subconscious and the lights come on 💡, your behavior changes and you feel good.

Change Your Mind and Change Your Life

Read the following words. Let their meaning sink into your brain, like earth soaks in rain. When you take suggestions into your deepest mind, you literally change your life.

My truth is as I create it to be.
I love and accept myself entirely.
I feel good. I am healthy.
My life works perfectly.
I do kind things for me.
I am happy. I am free.

What is it like for you to say such kind and affirmative things to yourself? Familiar? Foreign?

Affirm Success Exercises like these make life more joyous.

Into-Great Power Exercises use persuasive techniques like power learning, NLP, self-hypnosis, humor and conscious re-framing to bring you to life's promised land: Your Magnificent Self.

Inner-View Quizzes help you identify and shift negative patterns to positive ones.

Yes I'm Positive

Sunshine wonderful absolutely Yes!
I am feeling fine; complete, I am at my best.

I hear that you are crying, slashin' mental wrists.
Give your head a twist about. Put your grief to rest.
Once I was mistaken, sad, on overload.
Now I'm positively bent; and I'm not even stoned.

Sunshine wonderful absolutely Yes!
When you're happy, feeling fine, you can't be depressed.

Life is a conspiracy guaranteeing ecstasy.
Abundant love to satisfy all the needs of you and me.
Want it, watch it happen. Enjoy absurdity.
Giggle, chortle, laugh aloud, start slappin' at your knees.

Say sunshine wonderful, absolutely Yes
I am groovy, feeling fine, I am at my best!

I Love You,

Shelley Stockwell

Shelley Stockwell, Ph.D.

Photo by Pam Bourne

Shelley Stockwell, Giza, Egypt

P.S. I loved writing this book for you...
There's no denial!

The Structure of Denial Is Not A River in Egypt

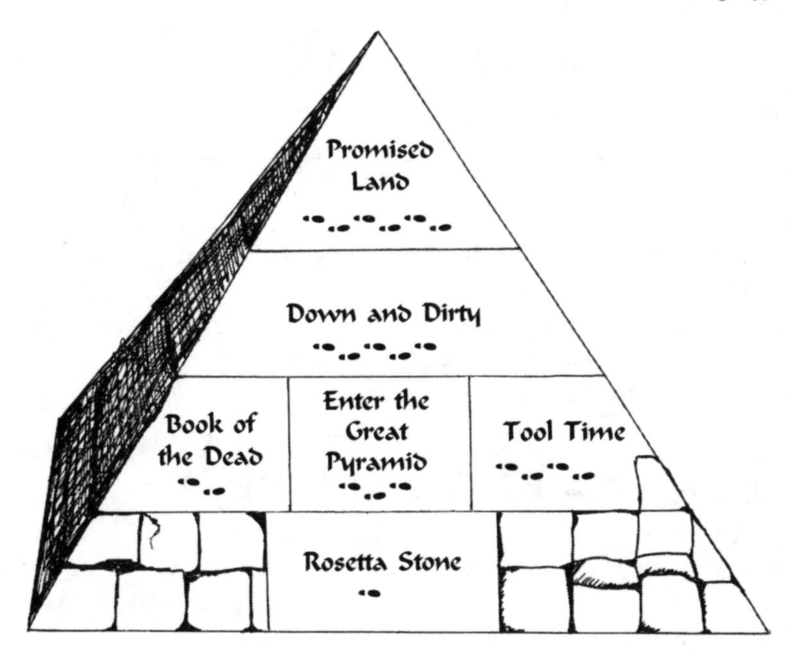

"Baby steps, take baby steps"
—Bill Murray in the movie, *What About Bob?*

Step One	**Rosetta Stone: Deciphering Denial and Truth** How You Got to Where You Are
Step Two	**Book of the Dead: Veil of Illusion** How & Why We Go Numb
Step Three	**Enter the Great Pyramid: Turn the Key of Life** How to Feel Terrific
Step Four	**Tool Time: Hammer it Home** How to Master Your Mind
Step Five	**Down & Dirty: Nitty Gritty City** How to Conquer Specific Problems
Step Six	**The Promised Land: Out Of Egypt** Pharaoh Thee Well!

The Stockwell System

Contents Cartouche

Step One •• ROSETTA STONE:

Deciphering Denial and Truth

Step Two ••.. BOOK OF THE DEAD

Veil of Illusion

Step Three ••..•• ENTER THE GREAT PYRAMID

Turn the Key of Life

Step Four •-•-•-•-•• TOOL TIME

Hammer it Home

Step Five •-•-•-•-•-• DOWN & DIRTY

Nitty Gritty City

Step Six •-•-•-•-•-•-•• THE PROMISED LAND

Out of Egypt

Step Seven •-•-•-•-•-•-•-• THE CHARIOT

Helpers on Your Journey

Illustration by Shelley Stockwell

INNER•VIEW QUIZ

Choose Your Life

Choose Poem 1 or 2—Which one best represents your life?

Poem 1
Mother loves me forever.
Father is there 'til the end.
Brothers and sisters, best buddies.
I'm never in need of a friend.

Truth is the mode of communing.
Laughter: the tone of the day.
My talents and dreams are encouraged.
"You're terrific" is what they all say.

My energy bubbles elation.
I relax right up to the soul.
Love and peace are so easy.
I am healthy, happy and whole.

Poem 2
Mother abandoned me early
Daddy beat me instead.
My sister and brother betrayed me.
I was sexually molested in bed.

Family secrets are sacred.
Survival: the tone of the day.
My talents and dreams are insulted.
"You're a loser" is what they all say.

My energy's always hysteric.
To stop the pain is my goal.
Shame, guilt, rage and heartache,
Keep me sad and out of control.

If you chose Poem 1, congratulate yourself. You have been blessed.
If you chose Poem 2, yet prefer Poem 1, choose Poem 3 and be blessed.

Poem 3
I become my own good mommy
And a daddy I love and adore.
I really am my best buddy
For that's what friends are for.

The truth is what has freed me
I laugh and smile and grin.
My talents and dreams are respected
I hear the voice within.

I do kind things for my body
I take back control at last.
I honestly express each emotion
I release and forgive the past.

Rosetta Stone

Step One

Rosetta Stone:

Deciphering Denial & Truth

How YOU Got To Where YOU Are

Up Your Egypt

The Rosetta Stone

A picture is worth a thousand words.

In 1798 one of Napoleon's soldiers found a very special black stone near the town of Rosetta. The stone was a royal announcement and was carved in Greek, hieroglyphics and demotic languages. In 1822, French scholar Jean Chamollion deciphered the 750 hieroglyphic signs. Thanks to Jean, we are able to understand hieroglyphics.

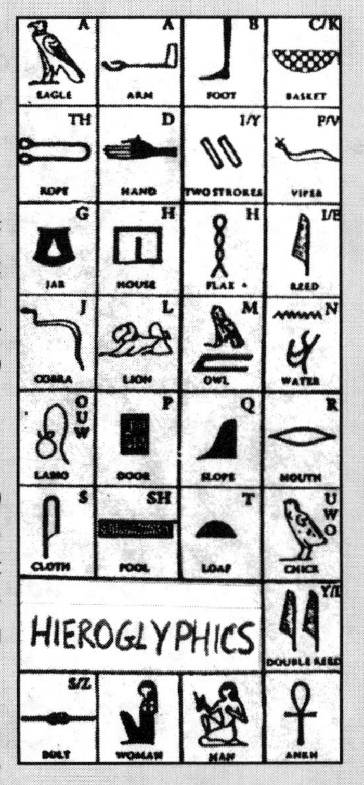

The oldest known writing, done over 5,200 years ago, hieroglyphics uses pictures to communicate words and sounds. The ancient Egyptians' African/Asian spoken language regularly used a rebus or riddle-like writing style that is similar to hieroglyphics.

An akin Indus script was used later in Pakistan and Sumaria. Numerous English words come from the Egyptian/Arabic language. The word "luxury" for example, comes from the rich and grand city of Luxor.

✿

You
Bravo.
Go for it
Brilliant.
Right on!!
Spectacular.
Excellent job.
You're a winner.
You're a treasure.
You're on top of it.
It's easy to love you.
Now is your moment.
Yes, I knew you could do it.
Everything's coming up roses.
I respect you. How lucky you are.
You're fantastic. You are on track.
How clever of you. Now you've got it.
Happy you. You've done it. You are a winner.
It's easy to love you. There's no where but up.
There is no stopping you. You are a grown up.

YOUR SUCCESS PYRAMID

Step One

Rosetta Stone:

Deciphering Denial & Truth

How YOU Got To Where YOU Are

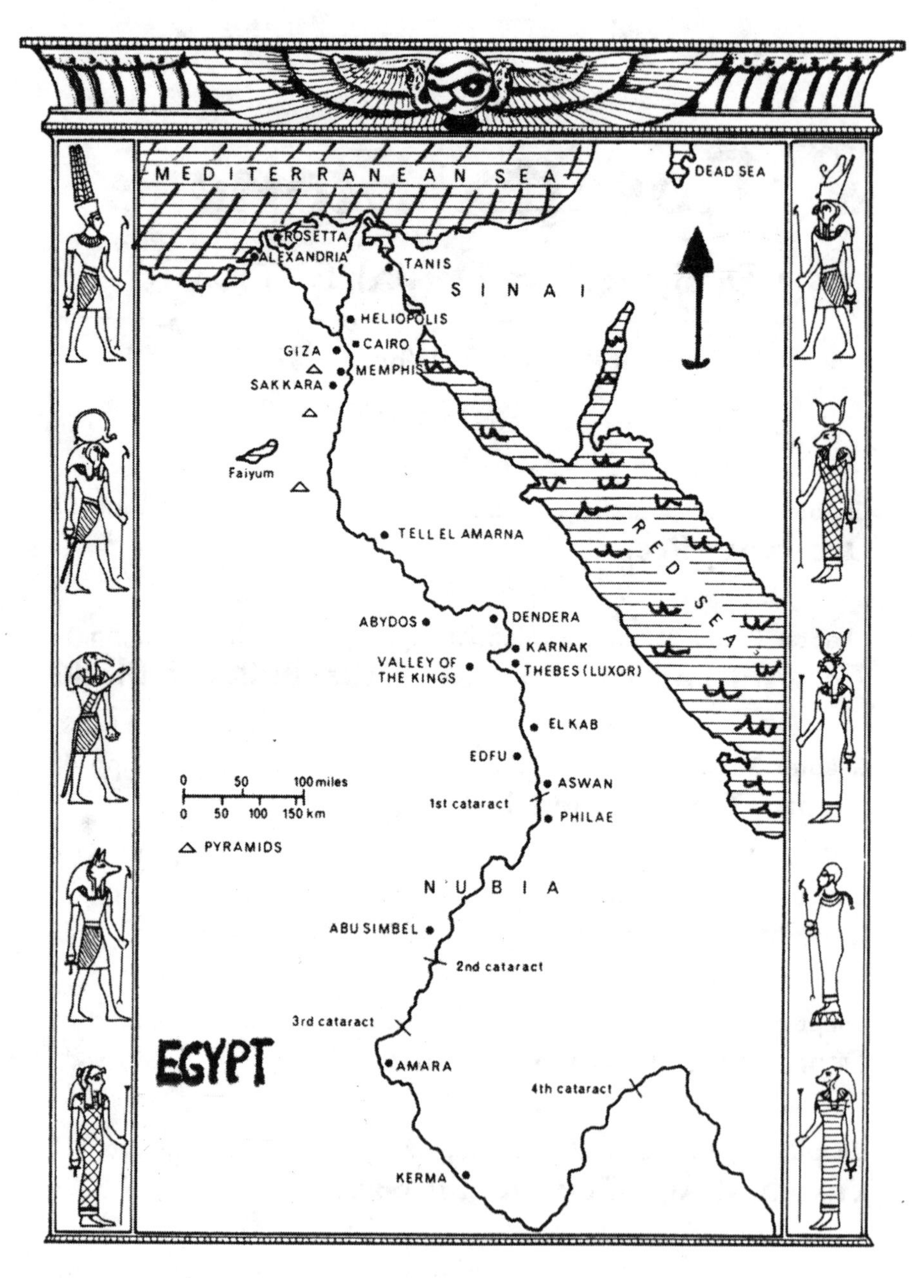
MEDITERRANEAN SEA
DEAD SEA
ROSETTA
ALEXANDRIA
TANIS
SINAI
HELIOPOLIS
GIZA
CAIRO
MEMPHIS
SAKKARA
Faiyum
TELL EL AMARNA
RED SEA
ABYDOS
DENDERA
KARNAK
VALLEY OF THE KINGS
THEBES (LUXOR)
EL KAB
EDFU
ASWAN
1st cataract
PHILAE
0 50 100 miles
0 50 100 150 km
PYRAMIDS
NUBIA
ABU SIMBEL
2nd cataract
3rd cataract
EGYPT
AMARA
4th cataract
KERMA

Map of Egypt

Chapter 1
Overview: Reed

▲ **Denial Triangle: Self Destruction**
▲ **Truth Pyramid: Reconstruction**

☆ *A sense of humor is a fun-drous thing*
When my day is bad, it relieves the sting.
So I keep my fun mirror on the nearest shelf,
When I can't spell relief...I laugh at myself.
—Kenneth Leonhardt

The Nile is the longest river in the world. It flows from Central Africa 4,145 miles (6,670km) north to the Mediterranean. If all its bends were straightened out, it would reach one third of the distance from the North to the South Pole!

Navigating the Nile's twists and turns is challenging.

Think of the Nile as your inner life: mystical, intriguing, challenging and sometimes convoluted. As you navigate your terrain of thought, you discover an endless labyrinth of feelings, ambitions, dreams and behavior. Fragments of potentials not yet recognized, instincts long forgotten, stories you tell yourself and boundless changes as you grow and ripen.

When you go with your flow, listen well to your inner wisdom and tell yourself the truth you mature and enjoy the twists and turns of your cruise through life.

Joy, peace, passion and truth are your compass!

If you have once sludged down the muddy river of denial, you now luxuriate in the Pharaoh's 1st class cabin of truth.

Royal barge ahead.

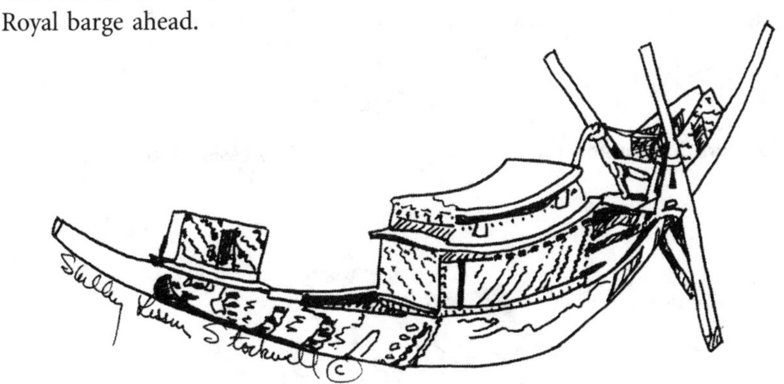

The Denial Triangle and Truth Pyramid are the basis of this book. Here is how the theory goes:

▲ The Denial Triangle: Self Destruction

☆ *Did you hear about the fountain pen that didn't have an inkling?*

Conflict, upset, boredom and confusion, make life feel like you are rowing backward and forward at the same time. You go nowhere and eventually stall out in denial and self-incriminations. If this happens, your brain chemistry goes out of balance and you experience depression and frustration.

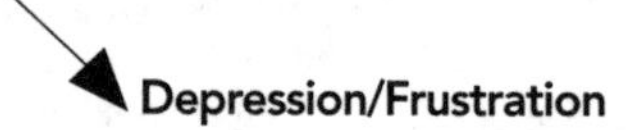

To balance your chemistry, feel good, relax, fit in, get high and deal with and/or forget problems, people numb with the self-destructive behaviors of addictions, compulsions and fear.

Addiction/Compulsion/Phobia 

Eventually, self-destructive behavior loses effectiveness and you feel worse than ever. Pain you avoid exaggerates and intensifies and your inner wisdom cries, "Stop hurting me."

If you answer, "Shut up" or "Not now," you go to the land of denial.

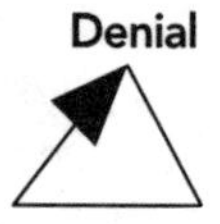

It takes pretending to hurt yourself. The more you lie to yourself, the more depressed you get.

Life becomes a never-ending saga of sadness, destruction and self-deception; a heartbreaking slow-motion suicide.

Horrors! In such a suicide, the murderer is also the victim.

Denial

Addiction/Compulsion/Phobia  Depression/Frustration

Enough already! 

In the truth pyramid, you contact the real you and get high with your higher self. You clean up your act, live your truth and your brain chemistry returns to balance. Destructive thoughts and behavior fall away. Here's how it works:

▲ The Truth Pyramid: Reconstruction

☆ *"The best mind altering drug is truth."*

—Lily Tomlin

The opposite of depression is honest expression. To heal and feel, GET REAL! Freedom begins when you wake up and tell yourself the truth, say good and kind things to yourself, and choose to be in harmony.

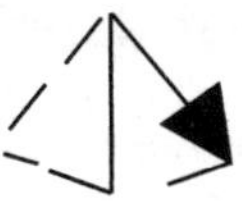

Expression/Balance

Nothing to hide, no need to numb. Positive patterns replace negative ones:

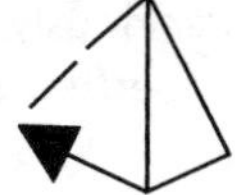

Awake and feeling physically well, you listen, hear and live your truth:

Welcome back to the land of the living: You are honest, good and feel terrific.

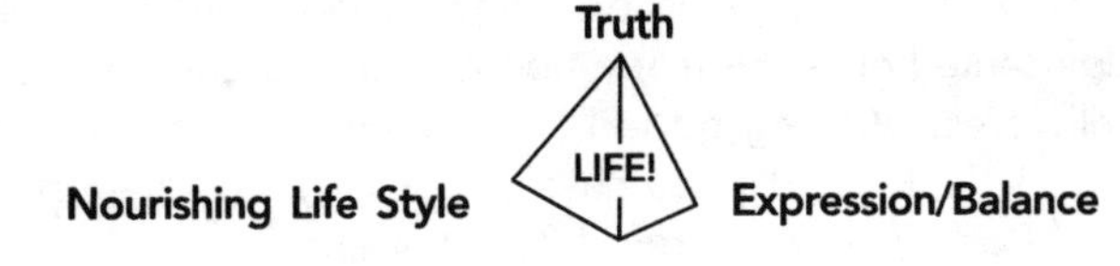

A TRUE STORY Shelley

"**I came from a dysfunctional family.** Dad had love affairs with other women. Mom had a love affair with ice cream, candy, pills, and house cleaning.

Seeds of addictions came early. During hypnosis regression, this is my recall of my birth:

'She's taking drugs again (crying). It hurts me inside. Stop hurting me. You're hurting me. I can't move. She must not like me very much. Why would she take drugs when I take them, too? Don't hurt me. I like it inside mommy with no drugs. She is pretty: pink, stretched smooth. I like it when daddy pats her. He's warm. I smell him. He smells good. She smells good with no drugs.

I have a bad taste in my mouth (crying). The drugs taste terrible, bitter. She doesn't take care of me. When she takes drugs, I can't move. She is throwing up. It hurts me. I can't move. I came out because she pushed me out. I can't help. I can't move. So tired...'

Sugar was my first drug. My mother fed me from a bottle with cow's milk and sugar (malto-dextrose). Later, my allowance went to buy candy. I could eat an entire cake at one sitting. Miraculously, I never got fat. To numb my feelings of worthlessness, I never stopped moving.

Mom was out-of-control. She woke up groggy from sleeping pills, made breakfast, sweetly bid my father, 'Have a nice day, Dear' and drank the first of some 20 cups of coffee. Somewhere between her coffee, orange juice and soft-boiled eggs, she took a diet pill and shifted into high hysteria. She cleaned the house with a vengeance and screamed:

'Your rooms are disgusting. You're pigs. What did I do to deserve you stupid kids? You don't clean your room. You are mean. Mean clear through. You can hide that mean streak, but we all know it's true.' If the phone rang, without missing a beat, she'd chirp in the dulcet tones of a nightingale, 'Hello.'

When she hung up, she'd continue where she left off:

'You'll pay, you slobs. I hope you have children just like you. Then you'll know how awful you are. You get back your meat as you measure: you cannot do wrong and get right...' And on and on, negative upon negative. Half an hour before Daddy came home she made up her face and shed her chenille bathrobe for a frilly dress. Waiting poised and perfumed at the door, she'd greet him sweetly: 'Hello, Dear, did you have a nice day?' For the rest of the evening, in front of Daddy, honey dripped from her lips.

Except the nights when Daddy 'worked late.'

'Shelley' she loudly wailed, 'help Mommy. Daddy doesn't love me. Nobody loves me.' There may have been good days with Mom but I barely remember.

To the world, I had a sunny disposition. Alone, I hurt. My secret pain spread resounding ripples through my world. Most nights I cried myself to sleep. I knew something was terribly wrong. I felt worthless. I was sure that there must be something wrong with me, something so toxic that Mommy hated and berated me. Even when she said kind things, I didn't believe her.

I fluctuated between defending and hating her: 'Poor mommy. Maybe if I'm nicer, she'll be nicer, happier...' Or secretly, 'I don't like the Mommy I got. I want a new one. I wish she were dead.' Mainly I wanted the pain to stop: 'I want to curl up and die.' I said to myself. And I did; I died a thousand silent deaths.

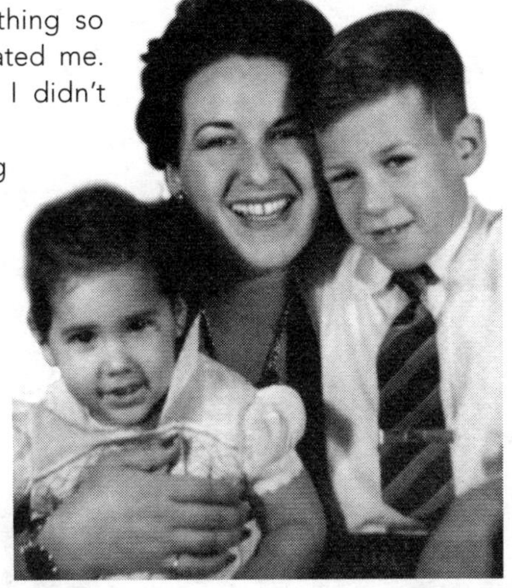

Irma Lessin with author, Shelley and her brother, Ollie—1950

I shut up. Honest expression was not an option in our house. Relatives secretly whispered about my mother. 'Crazy Irma' they called her. The neighbors minded their own business, too. They had enough of their own painful family secrets: incest, beatings and alcohol.

My older brother was my ally until one day, we heard my Father on the phone with his lover. 'If you tell anyone, I'll kill you,' my brother threatened. I believed him. At ten, mother asked, 'Shelley, do you think Dad is seeing another woman?' 'He wouldn't do that to you,' I lied.

It took me eleven years to get up the courage to tell Dad (whom I adored) that Mom yelled and I hated her. 'Don't ever say that again.' He said. 'Your Mother is going through changes. That happens to women. Someday you'll understand.' Dad was right. Someday I did understand. It took me 40 years to change myself, become clear, tell the truth and feel great. Forty years to understand that my mother's frustration, addiction and pain was about her—not about me.

Years of research, trial and error, successes and failures brought me joy, ecstasy and peace of mind. The skills that helped me become happy, now bring joy to my hypnosis clients and students. They will help you, too.

Photo by Shelley Stockwell

Chapter 2
✳Thought Patterns

Mental Blocks/Building Blocks

This chapter gives you an overview of attitudes and thoughts that positively or adversely influence success and happiness. At the end of this chapter, I'll stress stress, but don't be distressed. I'll teach you how to de-stress in chapters that follow.

- ▲ **Imprints: Footsteps on the Sands of Time**
- ▲ **Perish the Thought**
- ▲ **Nega-holics: Nay Sayers**
- ▲ **Up Tight: Bound and Determined**
- ▲ **How Did We Get Into This Mess, Ali?**
- ▲ **Adrenal Stress: Gland Plan Gone Awry**
- ▲ **De-Myth-Defy Stress**

☆ *NEVER ENOUGH*
How come when I bake cookies I never make enough?
I follow the directions and stir in all the stuff.
The recipe keeps saying, "I'll yield 36 or more."
But when the bowl is empty, I've made less than 24!

Do you suppose those little tastes of sweetness on my tongue?
The sample bites, the well licked spoons, each doughy little crumb
Has off set the equation written in the recipe book?
And I ate a bakers dozen before I even looked?

—Evie Streight and Shelley Stockwell

Ever noticed how you go on automatic pilot? Unconscious of your actions?

That's because mental patterns *automatically* determine every behavior and mood. Many patterns came with you when you arrived on this planet. Consider them your precious God given gifts. Effortlessly, these imprinted mental patterns allow you to learn, grow, mature, walk, talk and read these words.

Many behavior patterns are taught to you. The shoe you put on first, the way you tie laces, the phrases you use and the way you talk to yourself are learned and became automatic responses. Joy, peace, positive attitudes, unhappiness, frustration, negativity and loneliness are learned patterns.

Rules of caretakers, teachers and culture influence you. Even when rules change, and the reason for a pattern is taken away, it may remain imprinted in the meadow of your your mind as you unconsciously repeat it.

Radio, TV, advertising and what you read also influence your behavior.

What Are the "Golden Arches?"

What pops into your mind when you hear the words *golden arches*?

Do you imagine a McDonald's sign or a hamburger and fries? Does the thought of a big juicy hamburger make you salivate? Are you salivating now?

Words activate mental patterns that stimulate involuntary responses. Oprah Winfrey's remarks about hamburgers caused cattle growers to foam at the mouth. Mention hamburger to a vegetarian or a meat eater and you will evoke different automatic responses.

▲ Imprints: Footprints on the Sands of Time

☆ *"Childhood imprints are mythical tattoos written in indelible ink that become self fulfilling prophecies."*

—Jennifer Jennings

☆ *"And the Sphinx said; 'The desert is a grain of sand, and the sand is a desert; and now let us all be silent again.'"*

—Kahlil Gibran

Harness your mind and your possibilities are unlimited.

Everything begins as conscious and unconscious thought. What you hear, see, smell, taste, touch and perceive, and how you think and react to these experiences, reinforce old patterns and create new ones. Your mind makes, repeats and imprints mental and emotional patterns to keep you alive, active and balanced (in homeostasis).

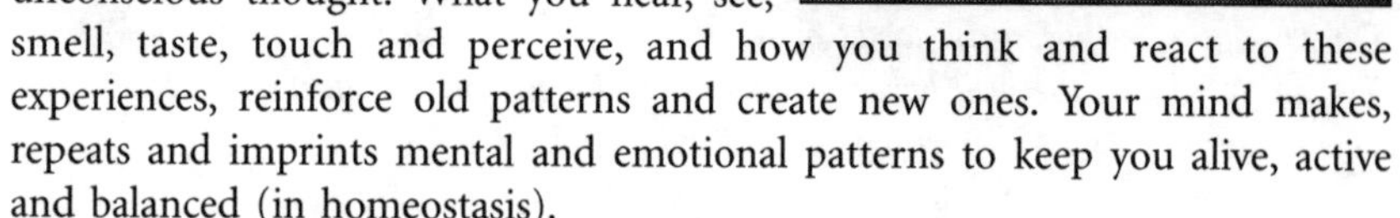

Most patterns begin in childhood as you instinctively imitate and model caretakers to survive, enjoy pleasure, contact, love and avoid rejection, abandonment or death. When life isn't a dream, many of us go to sleep.

Childhood teachings become life lessons and unchallenged, last a lifetime. Like a broken record we often recreate familiar roles. The way big people viewed you influences how you view yourself.

What role did you play in your families' movie?

Were you "The smart one?"
"The dumb one?"
"The graceful one?"
"The klutz?"
Were you "The peacemaker?"
"The troublemaker?"
Were you the diversion for Mom or Dad's frustration?
Were you invisible?
Daddy's little girl?
Mommy's little man?
Was it your job to live Dad's life or fulfill Mom's dreams?
Do you still act out these roles in your present life?

How Do You Feel About Food?

We all have imprints about food and eating. The following "roast" tale is often quoted:

A TRUE STORY

I asked my mother why I had to cut off both ends of the roast before cooking it. She said: "That's what Mom taught me."

So I asked grandma: "Why do you cut off both ends of the roast before baking it?" She said: " Because my mom taught me to do it that way."

So I asked great grandma: "Why do you cut off both ends of the roast before baking it?"

"The pan was too small." she answered.

What do you feel about eating?
Do you eat to "go home again" and comfort yourself?
Do you eat or not eat to assert your independence from family?
Are you consumed by what you consume?

If mother told you to finish everything on your plate (to help the starving children in __________ (fill in the blank), you may automatically "always finish everything on your plate." You don't think about it, you just do it. If the everything has led you to become rolley polley, this imprint isn't serving you well anymore. (Or perhaps it's serving you too well!) The original thought, "I always finish everything on my plate," planted in the garden of your unconscious mind with the best intentions, may have become an horrendous weed.

Chemical Tradition: Have an Apple Dearie

Both before and after your birth, big people create many of your chemical traditions, too.

Did Mom take drugs, drink, smoke or toke when you were in her womb?

Was yours a drugged birth?

Were you given shots and medicines at birth?

Were you encouraged to take drugs (aspirin, antacids, cough medicine, antibiotics, Ritalin, antidepressants) for anything that ailed you?

Was your food laced with hormones and chemical additives?

Was your environment clouded with pesticides, cigarette smoke and hair spray?

Were you rewarded with sugar and caffeine in the form of cake, candy, ice cream, soft drinks and chocolate?

If so, chemical initiation came early.

Do you still use substances to reward yourself, get high, numb out, elevate mood, feel grown up or "go home again?"

A TRUE STORY Sandy

"My mother rewarded me with food and berated me if I ate too much. She is, to this day, a drinking alcoholic.

I was bulimic at fifteen. It started in boarding school. We stuffed ourselves with carbs; pasta, peanut butter, soup and bread and then took turns throwing up.

By age forty, I was very, very sick and very, very scared. I was throwing up four and five times a day. I was afraid I was going to kill myself. After a book tour, I went on a seven-day vacation to California and bought all the groceries for the week. Usually I'd eat my week's worth of food right then. Out of control eating is like sliding down a greased shoot; you cannot stop. After, you feel horrifically guilty and absurd.

But this time, instead of bingeing, suddenly, out of nowhere, I had a free floating feel good. I felt wonderful.

"What do I have to do to feel this good all the time?" I asked myself.

"Stop throwing up." I answered.

I stopped my bulimia that very moment. It's been over ten years. My body naturally prefers vegetables, carbs and meat proteins. If I stick to that, my body does nice things and feels human. Last year, I got a grip and stopped drinking. I had to admit that I was acting just like my mother. I hypnotized myself to say; "I can drink if I want. I don't want to do that."

$$$

Money is a great example of unconscious patterns. Whatever you believe about money, you reinforce with your self-talk and behavior. Abundance or poverty mentality becomes your reality.

How do you feel about money? Do you deserve to have it? Do you believe that you're a financial failure? Or do you believe you easily create all the money you want and need? Where did you get these ideas?

A Bun Dance

Illustration by Jeff Bucchino

Imprints from Society: Tradition!

☆*"Around the world, people live in reality-tunnels which cause them to think that other reality-tunnels are insane or perverse. There are nudists and Buddhists and Russian Communists and Norse Socialists and French Existentialists and Samoan Shamans and New York Jewish Intellectuals and fundamentalist Christians and Shiite Moslems and all of them know, for sure, that they have the one correct reality-tunnel."*

—Robert Anton Wilson
(from Monsters and Magical Sticks)

Obsolete cultural patterns influence your life. Cleopatra shaved her legs with a sharp edged shell; now we remove "unwanted" hair. You can thank military leaders who wanted soldiers to stop wiping their noses on their shirts for buttons on suit jacket sleeves.

Whole nations adapt attitudes based on imprints. Cultural traits influence your attitudes, behavior and style. We spend thirty thousand on a school bus to haul our kids one mile and then build a million-dollar gym for them to get exercise. Denial, compulsion, addiction, fears and depression are often socially transmitted mental blocks.

Illustration by Shelley Stockwell

Four Bears

Up Your Egypt

Catty Remarks

Bast

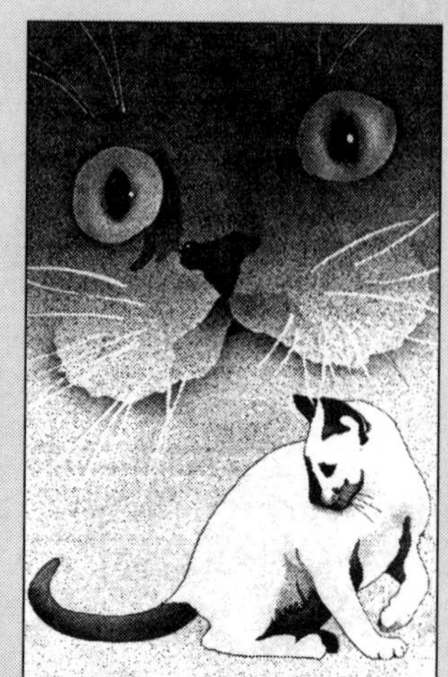

Cats were sacred animals in Ancient Egypt. As a sign of respect, Egyptians shaved off their eyebrows if their cat died. A favorite cat's collar was saved and buried with the pet owner. Cats were mummified for the afterlife. A cat cache near Karnak, Egypt contained 500,000 mummified cats and some mummified mice too. If in 4000 BC you killed a cat, even by accident, your crime was punishable by death!

The goddess Bast or Bastet was represented by a cat or cat-headed woman.

Illustration by Jeff Bucchino

Call in Reinforcements

☆ *Life is like a mirror reflecting what you do.*
And if you smile upon it, it will smile right back to you.

Patterns that serve you well, are good to reinforce. Patterns that disrupt and hurt, need to be recycled. When you repeat an old pattern, you reinforce it.

Self Talk

☆ *"Most folks are as happy as they make up their mind to be.'"*
—Abe Lincoln

☆ *"If you think you can or you can't, your correct."*
—Henry Ford

When an authority tells you something, you give it credence and it influences you. The more often the authority repeats the idea, the more you believe it.

Look in the mirror. The one looking back at you is the world's greatest authority on YOU. What you tell yourself makes a big impression upon you and creates your reality. How you behave creates your future reality.

Self-talk is powerful self-hypnosis. Self-talk is a self-fulfilling prophecy that you reinforce.

How do you talk to yourself? Do you say good, kind and loving things like;
"I'm terrific at making money,"
"I deserve to be happy," or
"I love to exercise?"

Practice tuning in to how you talk to yourself. If your mental conversation is negative, diligently direct your thoughts to the bright side. Say bright loving things to yourself. Light always over-rides shadows. Relate to yourself as you would to someone you deeply care about. Be your own best friend and kind coach. Once learned, mental self-regulation and positive mind chatter positively changes your whole life!

AWARENESS OF SELF TALK →POSITIVE CHOICE → POSITIVE ACTION →POSITIVE RESULTS

AFFIRM SUCCESS: Positive Self Talk
I am consciously aware of all self-talk and I easily change any negatives to positives. My self-talk determines how I perceive the outer world. How I talk to myself colors what my senses perceive, how I feel and what action I take. The stories I tell myself become what I believe as true. I refocus my beliefs into real, positive and beneficial truth. I tell myself the truth in a loving and positive way. I use positive discernment. I say good, kind, loving things to myself.

▲ Perish the Thought

☆ Basket Case: *A victim of a long drought felt a few drops of rain on his face and promptly fainted. They revived him by throwing a bucket of dust in his face.*

Behavior begins as thought:
"Alcohol gets my mind off my problems; down the hatch?"
"I feel better if I binge (starve, smoke, snort, obsess, yell or freak out)."
"A toke, (eating) helps me make it through the night."
"I can never sleep at night."

Hi, Go Trigger
What triggers self-destruction?

H unger	H abit
A nger	A ddiction
L onliness	B oredom
T iredness	I solation
	T ension
	S tress

Coping Mechanisms

☆ *"Some people believe things you wouldn't believe."*

—Mary O'Neill

When you want to feel good, resolve pain and escape difficulty, frustration, stress or upset, your brain searches for a familiar pattern of thinking to help. Like a jukebox, the mind punches "Pain 1" and the familiar imprint, like a record, plays the pattern you use to cope.

If you have healthy coping patterns, the record is a positive tune and that's great. You release pain and return to homeostasis or pleasure.

Ways We Block Joy

Negative thoughts and emotions
Limiting thoughts
Changing the subject
Clinging to faulty beliefs
Blindly accepting the dogma of others
Becoming the masks we wear
Having to be right
Flat-lining with no vitality
Burying or drowning underlying trauma
Hiding behind fear
Not accepting "YES" for an answer

Way to Joy

▲
Joy
▲
Release
▲
Pain

▲ Nega-holics: Nay Sayer

☆ *"The most powerful words of woman or man is Yes, Yes, Yes I can!"*

—Shelley Stockwell

Are you optimistic and positive?

Are you eager to learn new ways of living your life?

Do you cope well with stress?

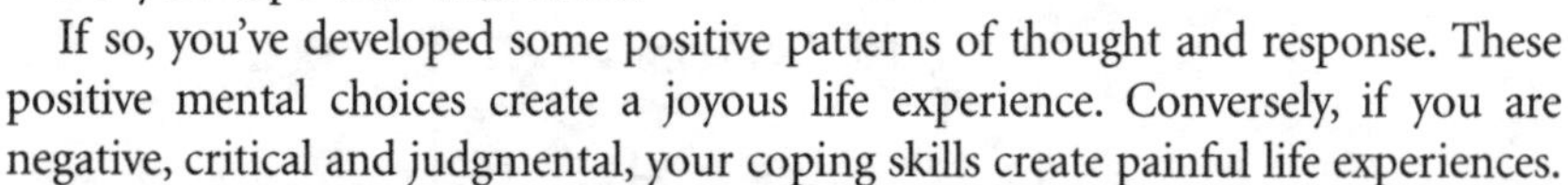

If so, you've developed some positive patterns of thought and response. These positive mental choices create a joyous life experience. Conversely, if you are negative, critical and judgmental, your coping skills create painful life experiences.

The power of positive thinking is well documented. If most of your 50,000 daily thoughts are positive or neutral, you create, expand and heal.

The more negative thoughts you indulge, the worse you feel. The average two-year-old receives many more negative statements than positive ones. No wonder it's called the *terrible twos.*

Were you trained to be negative? Was your name always proceeded with the word "no."? "No Johnny," "No Carol, no, no, no." No wonder the majority of fourteen-year-olds poled want to change their name.

Caretakers control and teach. If yours were negative, you may imitate them.

When a boss or teacher freaks out at mistakes and ignores successes, it forces negativity. In a study at UCLA, freshmen term papers had six negative red marks for every positive "atta boy."

We usually repeat negative patterns because we have a *payoff*. The payoff may be to take us home so we may feel close to those who taught us negative ways. Another payoff is the attention we get. Negativity keeps us from taking responsibility. Victims of circumstances don't have to move forward.

☆ YES! I'M POSITIVE

Sunshine wonderful, Absolutely yes!
When you're happy, feelin' fine, you can't be depressed.
I hear that you were crying, slashin' mental wrists.
Give your head a twist about; put your grief to rest.

Once I was mistaken, sad, on overload.
Now I'm positively bent; and I'm not even stoned.

Life is a conspiracy guaranteeing ecstasy,
Abundant love satisfies all the needs of you and I.
Want it, watch it happen and enjoy absurdities,
Giggle, chortle, laugh aloud, start slappin' at your knees.
Sunshine wonderful Absolutely yes!
I am feelin' fine complete. I am at my best.

—Shelley Stockwell

What Can Negativity Do for You?

Negativity Makes You Sick. Studies show that a person who engages in negative thinking is six times as likely to be infected with a cold virus and twice as likely to develop cold symptoms.

Negativity Can Wreck Your Marriage. *"Our marriage broke up over a stressful divorce."* Positive communication keeps marriages intact, say researchers. Couples that remain married say five times more positive than negative things about or to each other. Those that divorce said three negative remarks for every two positive ones while married.

Negativity Can Make You Depressed.

Negativity Can Make You Lonely. Habitual nega-holics and gripers destroy a positive environment and make others around them uncomfortable. Unpleasant people aren't fun to be around.

How Can You Cope With Someone Who is Negative?

☆ *"A pessimist is a man who thinks everybody [is] as nasty as himself, and hates them for it."*

—George Bernard Shaw

☆ *"Never join a club that would accept you as a member."*

—W.C. Fields

☆ *"Imagine a world without hypothetical situations."*

—Jon Nicholas

Negative folks don't wake up in the morning and proclaim, "I think I'll act like a jerk today." They feel unworthy and powerless. The best way to cope with one is to not join in. Resist slam-dunking them with negativity and sarcasm. Instead, ask them if something good came from their experience and guide the conversation to a positive subject. If they won't get off their gripe-a-thon, get away.

Up Your Egypt

Door Charms Bust the Boogie Man

To protect a house or temple from the entry of evil, Ancient Egyptians use a door charm known as the Pillars of Horus. Horus, The Hawk, was a form of the sun god Ra. Small tablets were engraved with hieroglyphic spells that kept bad spirits away. We get the word "hero" from "Horus".

Later, the Jews adopted this tradition in the form of the Mezuzah. The touching or the kissing of their door charm dates back to the Hindu custom of touching the doorpost figure of Kali for good luck.

Horus

Accentuate the Positive, Eliminate the Negative

Pay attention to your thoughts and actions.

Alone with thoughts, are you positive?

If not, revise or replace negative patterns. Change your self-talk. If you hear yourself saying negative or limiting things, change your internal dialog. You change limiting attitudes and behaviors as you reprogram and focus on positive and nourishing patterns.

Here's a perfect affirmation that positively gets you going. Repeat it out loud three times, twice a day for two weeks; you'll change and feel a lot better:

AFFIRM SUCCESS: Conquer Negativity

"I'm positive in thought, word and deed. I am optimistic. I trust and see the beauty in and around me. I'm so glad to be alive. I easily switch to the part of my mind that controls right thought. I am positive in my thoughts, actions and what I say out loud. I love myself more and more each day. I am worthy. I am positive. Yes! Yes! Yes! I feel terrific. As I read these words I feel happier and happier. I enjoy finding new ways to make myself feel terrific. As I continue reading this book, I re-affirm a terrific feeling of self-love and happiness."

Let Me Rephrase That!

THEN		NOW
"I'll start my diet tomorrow."	➔	"I eat healthy foods today & stop when I am physically full."
"I won't leave the house: I'm too fat."	➔	"I love going out & about."
"I'll just leave my coat on."	➔	"Take my wrap, dahling."
"I'll turn the light off first."	➔	"How beautiful we look."
"I'm huge."	➔	"I'm perfect just the way I am."
"I'm disgusting."	➔	"I love my body."
"I have no will power."	➔	"I've taken back control of my life."
"They won't see me eat this."	➔	"I live my truth."

Bury the Dead

☆ *"A rut is a grave with two sides knocked out of it."*

—Erskine

☆ *"The only one who LIKES change is a baby with a wet diaper."*

—Jim Vogl

Negative patterns die hard. Their staying power comes from denial and ignore•ance. It takes extra effort to change entrenched patterns. Change thrusts us into the unknown and is sometimes uncomfortable. That's why we may ignore the self-destructive damage we inflict upon ourselves. "At least things are familiar," we rationalize.

The way you label things in your head or out loud, create a biochemical response. Change your words and you change your mind.

Stubborn	➔	Open Minded
Selfish	➔	Self Actualized
Spoiled Brat	➔	Loved
Show Off	➔	Outgoing
Fat	➔	Opulent
Not Good Enough	➔	Perfect Just As I Am

A hypnotherapist, counselor, body worker or friend can assist your attitude adjustment.

INNER•VIEW QUIZ

Do Behaviors Run You?

___ Some behaviors run me.
___ I am out of control in certain areas of my life.
___ I'm enslaved by irresistible urges.
___ I'm possessed by my possessions.
___ I'm obsessed by my obsessions.
___ I feel yucky, not happy.
___ I'm unhealthy.
___ I feel stuck and/or disabled by guilt/shame.
___ Fear takes up a lot of my time and energy.
___ Fear affects my relationships and health.
___ I suffer from insomnia, panic attacks and/or compulsions.
___ My hands shake.
___ My pulse is rapid.
___ I get headaches.
___ I have blurred vision (not related to eyewear).
___ I stutter and stammer.
___ I am sometimes irrational, uneasy, tense and confused.

Answering "yes" to any of these questions means life is not working as well as it could. It's time to get a grip and get happy.

AFFIRM SUCCESS: Yes and Chuckle Up
Take a deep breath and get into center as you read these words:
I now live in the "moment of now." I honestly recognize how I create and perpetuate out-of-control defenses. I am in control. It is safe in my world.

I create a clear action plan for new positive habits. I positively change my mind. I tap my subconscious power. I imprint new, positive patterns that make life rewarding and fun. I do good, loving and nourishing things to and for my body. I choose joy and wellness. Change positively does me good. I speak respectfully to myself. I find new ways to love myself. In this moment, I think of one way to love myself more.
(Pause and think of a way to love yourself more before you read on.)

Hello inner wisdom, I'm listening to you. You are my council, mentor, guide and bigger picture.

A smile is the shortest distance between myself and joy. I smile and build a positive relationship with myself.

My mantra is the word "yes" chanted ten times. Yes. Yes. Yes. Yes. Yes. Yes. Yes. Yes. Yes. Yes. I am positive. Yes. Yes. Yes. Yes. Yes. Yes. Yes. Yes. Yes. Yes.

I laugh right now (even if I fake it). Ha, Ha. Chortle. Chuckle. I am joyous. I now tell myself three special things about me. (Pause)

1.__________ 2.__________ 3.__________

I count my blessings.

▲ Up Tight: Bound and Determined

☆ Question: *"Why didn't the skeleton cross the road?"*
Answer: *"He didn't have the guts."*

Did you ever notice how much more you get done when you're on a deadline or company is coming? Mild anxiety gives you extra energy and motivation. But, if you reach a deadline feeling dead or stressed to the max, it's proof that something's not working.

We all have bad moods, stress and frustration, and can be fickle, fretful, rude or insensitive. We want to increase thrills and avoid chills. We hide wounds to the psyche (traumas turned inward) with smoke screen behavior and convoluted thinking.

Death Is Nature's Way Of Telling You To Slow Down

Negative stress is life's most debilitating problem. It can occur suddenly from great disappointment like losing a loved one, arguing or getting laid off. Or, it can come as constant irritation like worry, pushing too hard or chronic thrill seeking. My friend recently spent two weeks with her angry teenage nephew and when he left, she started having panic attacks.

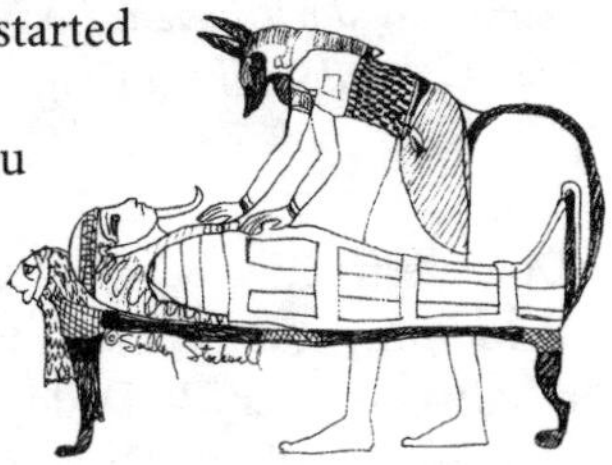

What do you do when tension mounts? Do you go outside yourself to make things better? Do you find healthy solutions? Deal with it? Wait for it to pass?

Or do you give your power to substances, habits, groups or an individual to get you through? Do you over do it? Eat uncontrollably? Smoke, drink coffee or eat sweets? Take antidepressants or go on a pill mill? Drink alcohol or coke? Do you ignore stress? Freak out? Get uptight?

Bury the Dead

Unsuccessful coping behaviors add stress.

▲ How Did We Get Into This Mess, Ali?

☆ A man picks up his new custom suit from the tailor. *"The right sleeve is too long."* He says.
"No problems" says the tailor *"Gather up the right shoulder and hold it under your chin."* And the man does.
"The left pant leg is too long." Says the man.
"No problem." says the tailor "*Reach across with your right arm and hand and grab it and pull it up.*" and the man does.
He leaves the shop; chin to shoulder, arm to pant leg. As he walks down the street two doctors pass. One says *"I wonder what's wrong with that guy?"* and the other answers *"I don't know but doesn't his suit fit nicely?"*

Self medication and avoidance often soothe, excite and gratify before they numb and steal life's zest.

But there isn't one problem that over-the-top behavior and self-destruction can't exacerbate.

Cope with hurt by hurting yourself and you amplify pain.

Poor eating habits weaken you and you get sick.

Temper tantrums and anxiety yields more stress and angst.

The short-lived high from toxic substances (alcohol, sugar, tobacco and caffeine) is replaced with even more depression from chemical stress and cause you to take more chemicals.

A biochemical *buzz* or *rush* lasts a few minutes...then you feel yucky and more stressed.

Historical Hysteria as a Cause

☆ Basic Training: *"If someone wants you to follow their train of thought, make sure they don't have a (loco) motive. Don't let them railroad you to the wrong track and de-rail your joy."*

—Shelley Stockwell

Does destructive behavior remind you of anyone in your family?

If Mommy numbed with food, you may also. Or you may do the opposite and starve yourself. If Daddy or Mommy raged, you may use outbursts and tizzies, just like them. Or you may adopt your own brand of anger by putting on a "nice" mask and dealing sneaky "gotchas."

Mommy, Daddy and others may be the role models you imitate. Their genetic legacy may fuel your behavior.

Why We Hurt Ourselves: The FAN Theory

Addictions, compulsions, obsessions, and phobias are unsuccessful attempts to

FEEL GOOD
AVOID
NUMB

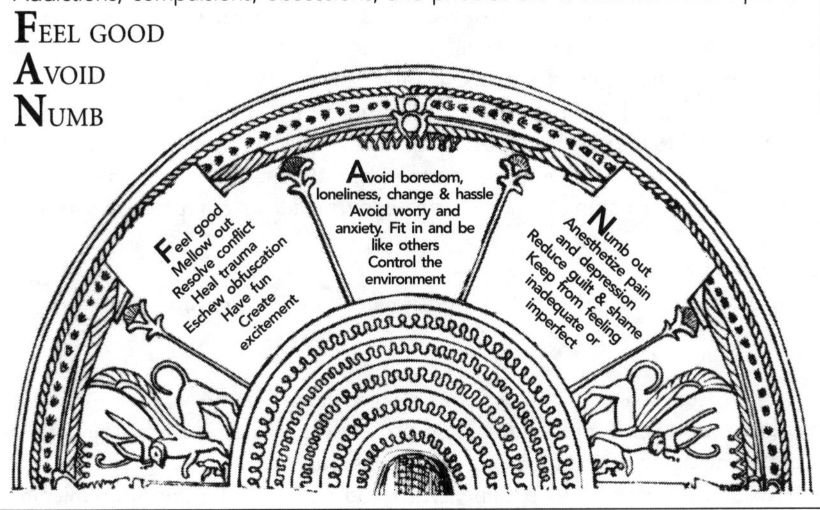

Trauma as Cause

☆ Question: *"Dear God, Why Me?"*
Answer: *"You piss me off."*

Anything real or imagined that shocks your central nervous system can set off a chain reaction of stress, insomnia, panic, compulsive behavior, guilt and depression. Hurt and trauma from being unloved, unprotected or abused upsets the nervous system.

What you see, hear, intuit or experience can off-center you.

Violence and natural disasters (earthquake, shipwreck and war) hurt. Vietnam vets suffer "flashbacks" or "shell shock." So do victims of tornadoes, childhood abuse, invasive surgery, drugs, toxic chemicals, fear and stress.

Trauma also results from the drugs and self-destructive behavior we use to cope. "I'm traumatized so I get drunk and traumatize myself even more." Hurt or trauma need a healthy release.

Neuro-biologists present compelling evidence that severe stress indelibly impacts changes in brain structure and function.

Avoiding Pain as Cause

☆ *"Never put off 'til tomorrow what you can do the day before tomorrow."*
—Shelley Stockwell

Pain is a self-perpetuating prophecy. The more distorted your response, the more distorted your response becomes.

"It hurts to be lonely; I'll drink to forget my loneliness."

"When I drink I feel more lonely; I'll drink some more."

"Drink makes me sick, (hung-over, antisocial) I need a drink to help me cope..."

"I need a 'hair of the dog that bit me' drink to make me feel better."

Pain that poor coping behaviors create, overshadows any pain we avoid.

Effect as Cause

☆ Question: *What's the world's most prolific manufacturer and user of drugs?*
Answer: *Your brain.*

One reason we get "hooked" on crazy behavior is an out-of-proportion pleasure and relief it gives. Adrenaline and endorphins are such big payoffs, we avoid thinking about painful long-term consequences.

From crazy thinking to cocaine, when you get carried away, your tolerance increases, and you must remain clueless to continue. If you paid attention, you'd give up toxic instant gratification for the greater good. Ben is a perfect example:

A TRUE STORY Ben

"Women go for guys who are buff. There's a guy named Tam at my gym who sculpted his body like Adonis. He was my hero. One day after working out, he turned me on to steroids. They worked great. I looked like Mr. America. Perfect definition. My girlfriend loved it. Then the roller coaster ride began. If I took too much, I became a raging bull. If I took too little, I felt like a complete wimp. And worst, I lost my sexual drive. I couldn't get it up. The very thing I used to enhance my masculinity made me impotent. It took two brawls and one arrest to help me get a grip. Hypnosis and acupuncture helped me get clean and sober."

Stress stimulates, activates and rewires emotional brain circuits to release too many or too few neurochemicals, which in turn, leaves your thoughts confused and off center.

Do you drink for *fun*? Do you use performance enhancers for *sport*? Your body tends to be hooked on pleasurable internal and external chemicals. The agreeable chemical rush may override the fact that these chemicals are toxic.

When hypnotized, I asked my subconscious mind "Why do I crave sugar?" it answered:

"Your confused brain thinks sugar is water.' You attempt to satisfy your thirst. You associate the sugar rush with the malto-dextrose formula your mommy fed you. Drink water and parent yourself instead. The sugar is killing you."

A physically hooked smoker may also be hooked on the "pleasure" response they get from the ritual associated with smoking. Here's how one of my hypnosis clients quit smoking.

"I didn't just quit smoking cigarettes, I had to give up my ritual of lighting up and holding those white devils, too. The way I did it was to interweave breathing fresh air while holding an imaginary cigarette and enjoying a 'quiet break' to reconnect with myself."

AFFIRM SUCCESS: The Great Brain Balancer
This affirmation will add some mental balance.
Positive, nourishing behavior stimulates my brain's natural neurochemistry. Positive thinking and healthy choices make me chemically balanced and feel great. The rush of an over-cranked brain is unpleasant. True pleasure is subtle and profoundly more rewarding. I love being balanced and mentally comfortable.

Belief as a Cause

☆ *"I've worked my way up from nothing to a state of extreme poverty."*
—Groucho Marx

Addictions, compulsions and phobias are symptoms of underlying beliefs that usually begin in childhood and reverberate throughout adult life. The following are some of the beliefs that cause us to "suffa:"

STUCK: You believe you're stuck, with no way out.
UNAWARE: You're unaware of how your behavior affects you or others.
FAMILIAR: You've done them so long; hurtful patterns feel natural or familiar.
FAMILY TRADITIONS: You believe what you were taught.
AFRAID: You fear change or think you can't change.

Stress and Overload As a Cause

☆ *You can't stay mad at someone who makes you laugh."*
—Jay Leno

☆ *"With mallet toward none."*
—The Carpenter

Some stress is normal. Positive stress motivates you to take action and get the results you want. Changing to a better job can send you into an upset tizzy until you adjust. Finding new ways to spend an incredible rise in salary can be positively stressful. A new love can be stressful. So can winning the lottery.

On the positive side, the adrenaline from stress forestalls boredom, gives pleasure and distracts. It gives us motivation to grow as an individual. It gives us interaction with other enthusiasts. It makes us feel passionate and on purpose.

Compelled hard core hobbyists are rewarded with a sense of autonomy, pride and stimulation. The Wall Street Journal (April 8, 1997) says that we receive as many as one hundred and seventy-eight messages everyday from telephone, faxes, voice mail, memos, solicitations, internet flags and e-mail. Combine this glut, with requests from billboards, radio, television, family and friends, and you may need to unload overload.

Are you frazzled and chronically fatigued? "There aren't enough hours in the day." "I don't have time." "I'm too impatient." "I feel like a 45 played on 78." "I have less and less time to do more and more."

In banking terms: deficit activity can make you feel overdrawn.

INNER•VIEW QUIZ

Is Dis•stress Killing You?

Find out if life is the way it's intended to be. Put "T" for true and true for T…

___ I am stressed, overwhelmed and anxious most of the time.
___ I'm stretched to the max.
___ I'm very competitive.
___ I have difficulty making decisions.
___ I often feel frustrated in relationships.
___ I'm not as sexually free as I'd like to be.
___ I worry about living up to others' expectations of me.
___ I worry about money.
___ I worry about worrying.
___ I'm compulsive or overindulge when worried.
___ I worry about being out of control or going crazy.
___ I'm irritated when things don't go my way.
___ If I feel inadequate or incompetent, I may withdraw, slam doors or yell.
___ I feel smothered, short of breath, dizzy, choked & swallow with difficulty.
___ I have heart palpitations or a rapid heart beat.
___ I shake, sweat, tremble, tingle and have chills, nausea and numbness.
___ I feel frustrated when the rules are unclear.
___ I'm painfully shy in many new situations.
___ I feel inadequate & uncomfortable sharing feelings.
___ I avoid social situations.
___ I'm overly sensitive to cold or pain.
___ Everyday tasks fall apart; work is undone, I'm distracted and disorganized.
___ Change upsets me.
___ I'm often concerned about what might happen.
___ I'm a nervous wreck.
___ I'm a compulsive thrill seeker.
___ Larry, you're killing me!
___ I find this quiz stressful.

The more trues, the stronger the possibility that you are overstressed and it is affecting you and your health.

> **Stress Buster**
> Speak s-l-o-w-l-y: It lowers your blood pressure and calms you.

Two Tents

☆ Man to psychiatrist: "*Sometimes I think I'm a teepee other times a wigwam. What's wrong with me?*"
Psychiatrist to Man: "*You're two tents.*"

Illustration by Jon & Shelley

Two Tents

The Siamese twins of chronic stress are stifled emotions and physical expression. Stifled tension makes you a pressure cooker ready to "explode." You let off steam when you tell your truth and move your body. Free trapped energy with positive action.

Stress Literally Gets on Your Nerves

Stress makes muscles tight (called muscle armoring) and puts you on edge by overtaxing the myelin sheaths that encase your nerve fibers. A University of Arizona study showed that people with arthritis hurt more when under stress.

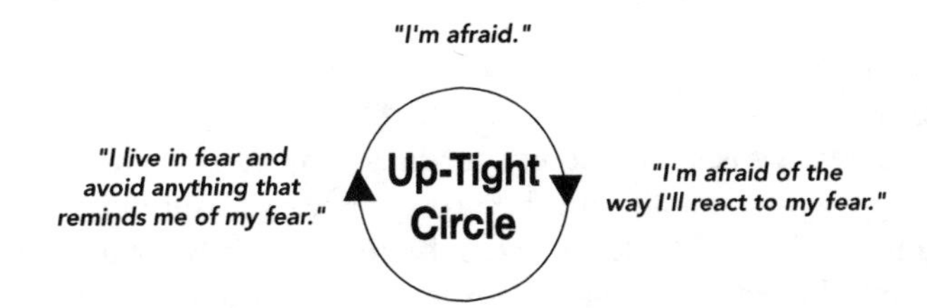

Forget It

Stress interferes with your ability to learn and remember. Cortisol may shrink nerve cells and your brain's hippocampus, the center of learning and memory. The older you are, the more increased cortisol effects memory. In women, increased cortisol decreases estrogen resulting in more forgetfulness.

Pounding Heart

Stress causes irregular heartbeat, which increases your risk of heart attack. Stress raises total cholesterol production and lowers your HDL (good cholesterol) levels.

Flushed Cheeks

Too much adrenaline constricts arteries so that fluid moves more slowly. This raises blood pressure, increasing the risk of stroke.

Blood Thickening

Stress thickens blood, increasing your chance of embolisms (an air bubble, detached clot, bacteria or foreign body that obstructs a blood vessel). If the embolism is in the heart, it can cause a heart attack; if it is in the brain, a stroke. The stickiness of blood platelet factors, increases the likelihood of blood clotting.

Distorted Body Sensations

Too much adrenaline distorts body sensations causing itches that can't be scratched.

Stress Can Make You Fat

When you are living on the edge, you gain weight, especially in your belly. Tension prompts your adrenal glands to secrete cortisol, which tells your body to store more fat in the abdomen in case of an emergency. Extra insulin makes you more sensitive to lipoprotein lipase, an enzyme that also makes you fat.

Tension

Too much adrenaline creates tension and migraine headaches and leads to fatigue, lethargy and sleeplessness. It even effects healing. In a Ohio State University study Phillip Marucha, a Doctor of Microbiology, found that students who had dental surgery during exam week took much longer to heal than those who had the same procedures during summer vacation.

Indigestion

Excess stress generates gastric juices that cause heartburn, nausea, diarrhea and ulcers.

Ear Wax

When you are frightened your ears produce more ear wax.

Vulnerable to Disease

Long-term stress weakens immunity to disease by robbing your body of vitamin C and magnesium. Too much cortisol appears to shrink glands that produce immune cells. As self-destructive behavior damages your thinking and body, you stop feeling well. There can be severe damage without your noticing. You may think you are OK, and only notice you're not OK when it's too late. Healthy living is your best revenge.

▲ Adrenal Stress: Gland Plan Gone Awry

ODE TO MY ADRENALS

Oh,
pyramid-
shaped organs
atop each kidney rest,
though I have overtaxed you
and you have made me stressed.
Thank you for awakening stimulating juices,
adrenaline and cortisone, a rush my body uses.
So I can build my tissue and keep me at the ready,
I will not fatigue you more with fear and panic petty.
Instead, I will caress you for your sweet and loving care.
And an easy-going life style together we will share.
Take that long vacation, you earned because you please me.
Refreshed, renewed and mellow, we will take it easy.

—Shelley Stockwell

Real or Imagined Danger

Your perception of an event determines your bio-energetic response. Thoughts, feelings and attitudes inform your cells whether or not they need to evoke a protective or an open posture.

Has a harmless pussycat startled you? Real or *imagined* situations release *real* adrenaline. During real or *imagined* danger, your instinctive self responds with "fright, fight, flight or excite." Your adrenal glands release adrenaline and heighten your senses so you can run like mad or stand and bare your teeth. If someone yells, "fire," and you believe them, your body rolls out its adrenaline panic pump.

This stress response lingers after an alarm reaction.

Stimulants, such as constant and regular loud music, caffeine, sugar, spicy foods, thrill seeking and uppers, add adrenaline and gives you a rush. Your body doesn't know if it is getting hyped up from external stimuli or an internal mechanism. Either way, you get the adrenaline flowing.

Alert, Divert and Disburse

Adrenaline has a lot to offer. It increases vitality, delays pain, diverts attention, stimulates the central nervous system and triggers hormones (catecholamines). Adrenaline gives you extra physical strength and euphoria.

Small doses of adrenaline are pleasurable. That's why thrilling novels, argumentative talk shows, horror movies, docu-dramas, graphic news (O.J. can you see?), "exciting" television shows and high speed chases are popular. This is why advertisers sell cars with slogans like "pure adrenaline" and "who needs caffeine?"

What Adrenaline Does for You

- Dilates your pupils so you let in more light for better vision.
- Increases respiration so your cells heat up and work faster.
- Changes temperature from hot or cold.
- Thickens your blood so you won't bleed easily.
- Heart pumps harder and faster, forcing blood to your brain so you think clearly .
- Stimulates your legs so you are strong and can react or run quickly.
- Stops digestion to allow more blood to go to the muscles.
- Releases glycogen from the liver, and converts it to glucose, for extra energy.
- Inhibits inflammatory reaction of lymph nodes.
- Brain races and your body jumps into motion.
- Adrenaline stimulate heart, kidneys, pancreas, stomach, adrenal glands and blood vessels.

Adrenal Meanies

It's ironic that the very hormones that save your life in an emergency, when overused, can kill. Hyper-alertness leaves no room for your body to relax and renew. Thrill seekers take extraordinary risks for the rush of it.

Stress creates adrenaline to be released and reabsorbed by your adrenal glands in *less than three minutes.* You then naturally come back to balance unless you panic. Or, you panic because you are panicking. Or, panic because you are afraid you'll panic. Or because you get hooked on the high from being hyper.

Adrenaline Addiction

Overloaded lifestyles and obsessive behavior addicts us to the adrenaline rush. If you are addicted, you may hysterically move from one activity or life drama to another. Or, seek bigger and better rushes; like bungee jumping on your motorcycle over the Grand Canyon.

A regular adrenaline order from your inner pharmacist creates a constant state of emergency and gets expensive. The price you pay is wear, tear, stress, weight gain and disease (adrenaline fatigue, chronic fatigue, hypoadrenia and worse). If you are addicted to adrenaline, your overtaxed body eventually demands payment for its services.

Adrenaline is as addictive as heroin. Over time, the highs become less high and more and better highs are needed to stay "up." When you unload overload, you may go through withdrawal.

Excitement Junkie Game

INNER•VIEW QUIZ

Are You an Excitement Junkie?

__ I crave the thrill of the chase.
__ I like high-risk sports.
__ I seek bigger and better high-risk challenges.
__ The pursuit of the unavailable turns me on.
__ Unstable, rejecting, on-again-off-again people intensely interest me.
__ I regularly make myself late and then freak out getting there.
__ It always excites me to gamble away everything I own.
__ I get a rush breaking the law.

If you answered yes to these ideas beware! Your intensity and stress may be cross wired with pain and distress.

Excitement junkies seek greater and greater thrills because they use adrenaline to substitute for boredom or as an escape.

Too much adrenaline is nerve-wracking and leaves you stressed and exhausted.

Doctors say that it takes over one and a half years for your body to renew and regenerate itself after running a marathon. Be patient. It takes a while for your body to mellow out. Though life may seem quiet at first, it is a much happier life to have small rich pleasures. When you decide to relax, your body may have to withdraw from adrenaline. This takes time. Develop new hobbies, passions, and find new, rewarding ways to have fun. Chill out.

Here's an affirmation to change stress:

AFFIRM SUCCESS: Adrenal Genie

I adjust and find large thrills in subtle things. My true self takes pleasure in the subtleties of life. I am calm, peaceful and clear minded. I find new, gentle ways to enjoy my life and myself.

Blood flows fully and freely within my brain and body. My right and left hemispheres are perfectly balanced and my body and mind are peaceful.

Stress Junky Game: Rushes

☆ *Speed in the fast lane*
Cursing rush hour
Fast food, Express Mail
Fax me my shower.

—Shelley Stockwell

Rushes

INNER•VIEW QUIZ

Are You On a Deadline?

__ Stop The clock I want to get off.
__ No matter how much I organize, I never have enough time.
__ I keep myself constantly busy.
__ I don't like being alone.
__ I have to work extremely hard to achieve anything.
__ It is most important never to waste time.
__ I don't slow down unless I am dead on my feet.
__ I only feel worthwhile if I am busy.
__ If I weren't crazy I'd go nuts?
__ Stress gives me a large charge.
__ I overtax and exhaust myself.

Yes to these means that you are in a frenzy. Busy-ness numbs underlying pain.

If you put sleep aside, compulsively risk your life, gamble your paycheck, live on the edge, never stop moving, worry and fret, do coke, speed, coffee, cola, tobacco, chocolate or sugar, you most likely are a stress junkie.

Burning the candle at both ends may make your face permanently waxen.

Here is what happened to one psychologist who was caught red-handed:

A TRUE STORY Ashley

"After a client left my office I felt wrung out. Like anyone who works hard, I needed release and escape. I had an adrenaline "rush" when I took something that didn't belong to me. My compulsion to steal used to overwhelm me. As a teenager, I used to steal because it was part of my neurotic patterns with my friends. I got caught but was never prosecuted. It put the fear of God into me. It was humiliating. I never took anything that wasn't mine again."

Panic is No Picnic

If you are afraid, frustrated or upset, your amazing alarm reaction stimulates your heart, kidneys, pancreas, stomach, adrenal glands and blood vessels. Your heart pounds, brain races and your body jumps into motion and you appear nervous and high strung. Repetitive or continuous stress exhausts your adrenal glands and you get sick and tired. When hysteria, stress or adrenaline runneth over, your cup explodeth.

What is Hypoadrenia?

Hypoadrenia is a stress disease where your lymph nodes shrink. Its symptoms are fear, nervousness, severe body weakness, weight loss, inability to sleep or sleeping too much, profound tiredness and a letdown feeling.

What is Chronic Fatigue?

☆ *"My marriage was terminated by death."*
"Whose death terminated it?'

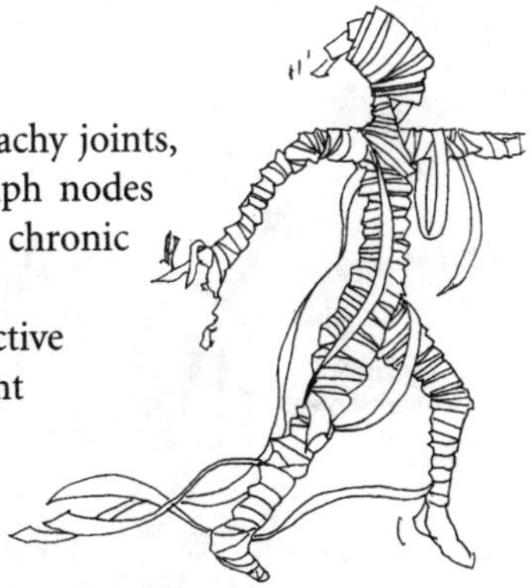

If you are exhausted but can't sleep, have achy joints, mind gaps, sores in your nose, swollen lymph nodes and out-of-control emotions, you may have chronic fatigue, Epstein Barr virus or Fibromyalgia.

Too much stress creates a skitterish overactive immune system and impaired ability to fight infection.

Repeated stress from toxins, like x-ray, alcohol, smoke, fumes, pollutants and poor eating, damage cells produced by the thymus gland, spleen and other organs. Unstable oxygen molecules, called free radicals, severely deplete vitamins and minerals like much needed magnesium. When free radicals are carried through the body via the lymph system, lymph nodes become damaged.

Illustration by Shelley Stockwell

"I keep going and going & going…I'm gone."

Chronic Fatigue and Epstein-Barr Virus are characterized by extreme fatigue, recurrent sore throats, swollen glands, muscle and joint pains, cognitive dysfunction and are thought to be related to herpes and mononucleosis. Sometimes referred to as "chronic mono," it is estimated that 75% are infected and that women are more susceptible than men.

Fatigue is often proceeded by stress and exposure to toxins. After the initial reaction, the virus remains dormant until reactivated by stress or toxins like: certain flowering plants, marking pens, solvents, jet fuel, gasoline, copy machine toner, furniture strippers, fast-drying paint, some foods and other viruses.

Chronic fatigue may be present regardless of blood test results.

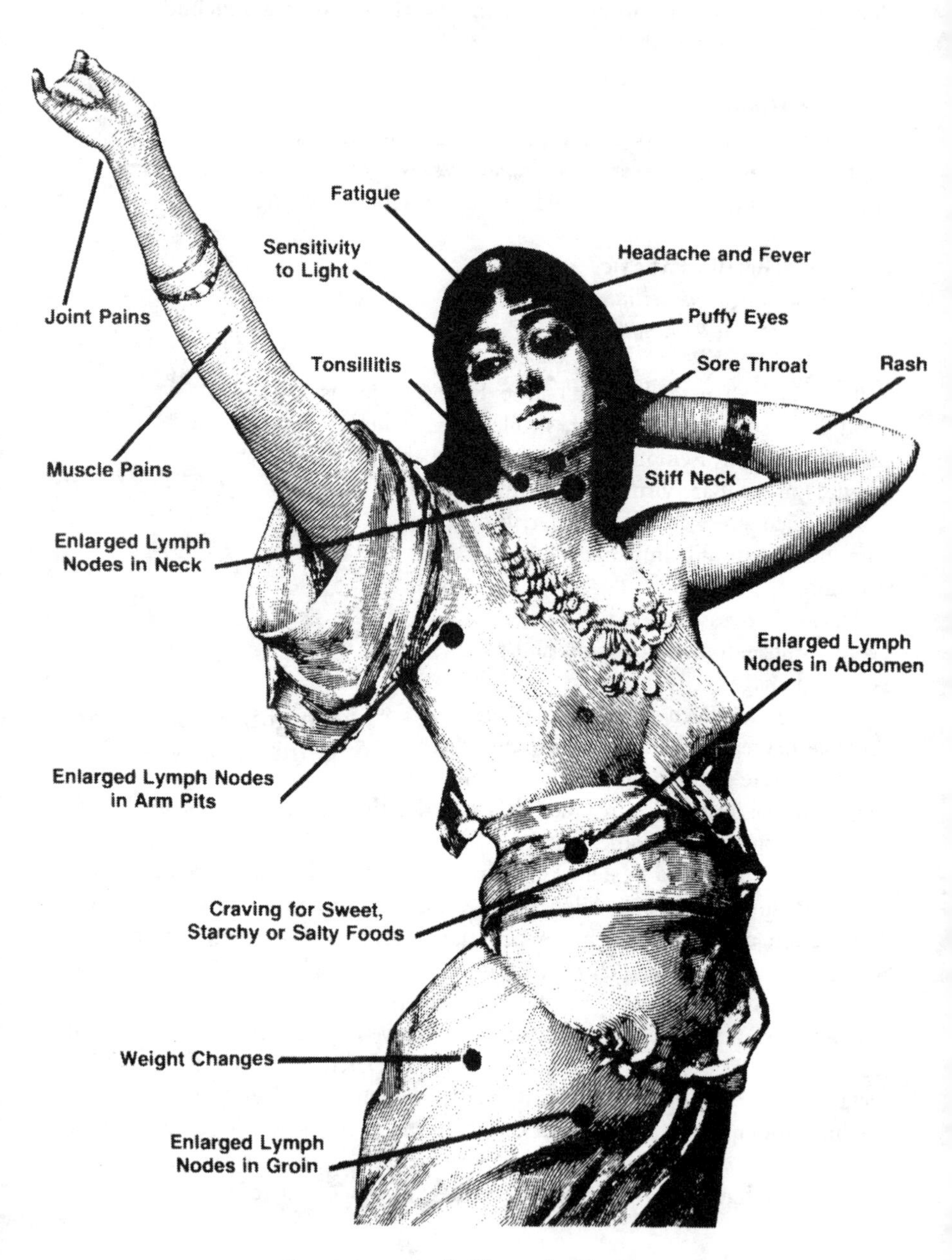

Symptoms of Chronic Fatigue

INNER•VIEW QUIZ

The Signs of Chronic Mono or Chronic Fatigue

The signs of chronic fatigue may include some or all of these symptoms:

- ___ Allergies
- ___ Alteration of taste, smell, hearing and vision
- ___ Chronic low grade fever (below 101 degrees F)
- ___ Cravings for sweet, starchy and salty foods
- ___ Difficult thought processes, mind gaps, forgetting, disorientation
- ___ Saying the wrong words
- ___ Difficulty moving your tongue
- ___ Eye sensitivity to strong light and night blindness
- ___ Fatigue (usually worse after exercise)
- ___ Headache (especially behind the eyes)
- ___ Herpes, canker sores, sores in the nose or shingles
- ___ Intolerance to alcohol
- ___ Irritable bowel syndrome
- ___ Joint pain
- ___ Light headedness, feeling spaced out
- ___ Mild to severe fatigue
- ___ Muscle aches and twitches
- ___ Nightmares
- ___ Night sweats
- ___ Palpitations and chest pain
- ___ Puffy eyes
- ___ PMS
- ___ Rashes
- ___ Sleep disturbances
- ___ Sore throat, tonsillitis
- ___ Stiff neck
- ___ Swollen glands in the neck, under the arms, in the groin and abdomen
- ___ Weight loss
- ___ Upper respiratory infection

So What's the Solution for Chronic Fatigue?

Get off processed foods. Healthy fresh fruits and vegetables are essential. Eat fish and avoid meat, cheese and dairy.

Stop using drugs and chemicals.

Get exercise and breathe well.

Drink a green drink (like Green Magma-Japan made from rice and barley greens and loaded with amino acids. You can order it in the back of this book.)

Vitamins help.

Stimulate your thymus gland by tapping your fingers on the middle of your breastbone for 5 minutes twice a day.

AFFIRM SUCCESS: Even Keel
Every day, in every way, I slow down. I have enough time to work, play and rest. I make my own choices about how I spend my time. I am responsible for my lifestyle.

I find pleasure in the subtleties of life. I am open to adventure. My body replenishes itself. My mind is learning new ways to think and understand. I am on an even keel. I choose how to spend my time. I choose a comfortable life style. I focus on this moment and the opportunities this day brings me. I tackle life's challenges one by one and come up with terrific solutions I can live with.

My work and my home enrich my life. They are separate from me. I am not my work, my possessions, the people in my life or my home. I am ME.

I choose to say yes or no. It is my right and responsibility. When I say yes or no, people respect and assist me in getting what I want. I take good care of myself.

I now visualize and imagine myself on a mental vacation. I am soothed by the sweet fragrance of flowers and a warm mist. My breath slows down. I am at peace. It is safe in my world.

▲ De•myth•defy Stress

Certain myths keep you jazzed and frazzed. Here are a few, along with antidotes for overcoming them:

Myth #1: "Adrenaline Makes You More Lively."

Some people increase adrenaline to feel alive and override numbness and boredom. In truth, too much adrenaline overtaxes, exhausts and deadens.

AFFIRM SUCCESS: Balanced
"Homeostasis and balance are normal. Hyperness is not. I will myself to be quiet. I am safe. I enjoy quiet. I enjoy my own thoughts and I easily embrace peace and harmony."

Myth #2: "If You Stay On Ready Alert, You Avoid Surprises."

A childhood with unpleasant surprises is usually the origin of this idea. To survive, did you learn to stay super-aware and anticipate everything? If you learn to pay diligent attention until the *other shoe drops*, the other shoe may be your ill health.

What you fear usually comes to pass.

AFFIRM SUCCESS: Blessed

The wind welcomes me with softness. The sun blesses me with warm hands. I fly so high and well that God joins me in laughter and sets me gently into the arms of Mother Earth.

I am safe. Everything is safe, protected and serene in my world. I am surrounded by positive energy; white light. I learn new ways to relax with myself and others. I yield to life's possibilities. I enjoy the surprises of the unknown. My life is a new adventure, unfolding afresh with each breath.

Myth #3: "Imitating Someone Who Was Stressed Makes You Close To Them."

We use this myth to go home again. "Just like _________ I never stop moving (worrying): Familiar stress makes you feel close for a while, then it just upsets you.

AFFIRM SUCCESS: Fun at Your Own Expanse

Read this affirmation slowly to yourself and let the meaning sink deeply into your mind. It will create a lot of fun for you:

The past is just a memory, tomorrow just a fantasy. In this moment, I choose my own innate rhythm. I no longer live to be close or distant from someone else. I live to be close to myself. I enjoy a comfortable rhythm of excitement and relaxation.

I am keenly aware of my thoughts and feelings; I come to my senses. My awareness of the bigger picture helps me take charge of my behavior. I expand my awareness in every way.

I am well adjusted in everything I think, say and do. I love solving my challenges and clarifying any confusion. I think clearly. I act positively. My actions benefit myself and others.

I do good and kind things for myself. I respect my body. I use right thinking, and right action follows. I expand my awareness in every way. I think big thoughts and cherish small pleasures.

INNER•VIEW QUIZ

Have You Been Abused?

Honestly answer True to the statements that are. If you are not sure, guess.

IN THE PAST:
___ I was mentally, physically, emotionally, sexually, and/or verbally abused.
___ I felt unloved.
___ Love was withheld as punishment.
___ I was often given the silent treatment.
___ My parents didn't want me.
___ My parents' absences hurt me.
___ The big people were too busy with their own lives to notice mine.
___ My every move was watched. I had no freedom.
___ I was hit, hurt and bruised.
___ I was a victim of someone's unpredictable rages.
___ I was insulted and/or yelled at.
___ In my family, other children and/or animals were mistreated.
___ Big people controlled me with guilt and shame.
___ My family was chaotic and the rules changed daily.
___ No matter how hard I tried, it wasn't good enough.

TODAY:
___ I'm abusive to others and/or myself.
___ I'm addictive and/or compulsive.
___ I maintain family secrets.
___ I have many fears.
___ I'm afraid others will discover my "awful, hidden flaws."
___ I fear intimacy and/or I have sexual problems.
___ I fear my sudden, angry and destructive impulses.
___ I am hostile toward authority figures.
___ I fear being controlled, engulfed or suffocated by others.
___ I like to control other people's behavior, feelings and responses.
___ I believe that men own women and children.
___ I believe that women control men.
___ I choose abusive or withdrawn partners.
___ I have unrealistic expectations of other people.
___ I have trouble expressing my needs.
___ I won't feel or express love.
___ I'm not able to maintain lasting relationships.
___ I'm ashamed of myself.
___ I'm a perfectionist.
___ I create chaos.
___ I have a nervous stomach and/or "bowel" problems.
___ I experience nagging feelings and emotions I cannot explain.

The more true answers, the greater your pain. If you answered true to any of these questions, there is a good chance you where abused.

Chapter 3

Victim Traps: Egypt Me

Abuse, Abandonment, Overprotection & Neglect

Photo by Jon Nicholas

This chapter traces the seeds of frustration in our life. We are all victims. Read this and learn how to become a victor.

- ▲ Trauma and Ritual Trances
- ▲ Abandonment and Neglect: Passover
- ▲ S-mothered: Overprotected
- ▲ Verbal Abuse: Babble On
- ▲ Emotional Abuse: Mortar-fied
- ▲ Physical Abuse: Defile the Nile
- ▲ Sexual Abuse: A Touchy Subject
- ▲ Healing Actions

☆ BECAUSE OF ME

If anyone is out there looking for me,
here I am.
If anyone can hear my cry, here I am.
If anyone can help me, here I am.

In the corner of my bedroom I tightly squeeze my knees,
not even letting go to wipe the tears from my cheeks.

He takes his belt. He buckles it in place.
Before he leaves, he says to me,
"You deserved it, you know you did."

—Neda Najibi

☆ *When is enough enough?*
When do I stop being tough?
When do I walk away and
enjoy the light of day?

—Shelley Stockwell

Victims are innocents who have been put upon.

Abuse is any thing that traumatizes you and results in negative repercussions like pain, hurt, numbness and self-destruction.

If you were neglected, abandoned, overprotected or abused; verbally, mentally, emotionally, physically or sexually, you may think that love is dangerous. Childhood hurts cause difficulties and challenges later in life.

Abuse distorts the way you love, how you hold boundaries and your self-esteem. Guilt, blame, hysteria, compulsions and self-destruction often result.

It is normal to adapt to your environment, no matter how crazy it was.

We recreate trauma as drama in a feeble attempt to right an original wrong. Or, abuse ourself as a way to vent rage and frustration. Do old coping mechanisms still haunt you? Jane's story is a perfect example of that:

A TRUE STORY Jane

"I ate myself into obesity. While bingeing I felt sad, lonely and different."

With hypnosis, I regressed to the first time I felt that way:

When Mommy died, people brought food over. Daddy got sick and was taken to the hospital and I was alone.

When I eat out-of-control, I recreate the identical feeling I had when Mommy and Daddy left me. Feeling sad, lonely and different is a kind of homecoming to that time.

I said, 'Enough. I choose health, joy, and healthy relationships for myself and others.' I now use food as fuel. With Shelley's help, I've happily lost 100 pounds."

Depraved Because You Were Deprived

If you imitate the brand of love your parents "sold" you, you may not know how to love yourself or another. How can you learn to positively cope if no one teaches you? If you were left alone, smothered or controlled, destructive behaviors may be your attempt to cope with painful memories. If you deny that you were abused, you may tolerate and rationalize abuse.

We deny and camouflage pained memory to protect our wounded inner child, go to school, or just function. We stifle cries, hold back anger and numb to protect ourselves and make it through.

And it may work...for a while.

Then, self-deceit hurts more than any pain you try to hide. Lying to yourself detaches you from your body, emotions and life. Denial causes stress and stress escalates defenses.

Photo by Joann Kelly

Blocked

Too-Darn Common

Reports of two million child abuse or neglect cases were filed in 1985, by the U.S. Child Protective Services. By 1989, that figure rose to two-and-one-half million. One thousand two hundred children reportedly died from abuse in one year.

Twenty-five percent of physically and sexually abused children were under five years old, sixty-percent between five and fourteen. What are the numbers now? Childhood abuse is the main cause of difficulties later in life.

▲ Trauma and Ritual Trances

Stress and shock cause us to "leave the body" or lose conscience awareness to cope with pain or disappointment. This is called a *trauma trance.*

Abusers enter into a *ritual trance* and robotically, act out their hurtful behavior. They disassociate or leave their body.

Ritual trance is about human contact, energy and stealing light. Abusers always steal the brightest light. If you were abused, it was because you are radiant. An abuser may make you believe that something is wrong with you. Nothing is wrong with you.

Trauma and ritual trances are held in the cells of the body. Even if you disassociate or leave your body, your cells and subconscious mind remember.

Memories of abuse come up so you can heal. Expose them to the light and they lift away from you and you lighten up! The trick is to release the past and move forward in your life. Forgive yourself, and if possible, those who hurt you.

Abusers

Perhaps the biggest cause of abuse is the lack of impulse control caused by drugs and alcohol. Those who abuse another suffer guilt and rage and feel despicable on a deep level. Even if they don't consciously recognize these feeling, their cells and subconscious mind does. Very, very sick people may have no regrets but they are *rare* exceptions.

An abuser needs tools to handle frustration, dump addictions and take control. Self-respect and respect for others is possible when angry people vent rage in healthy exercise, tell the truth, stay conscious and stop getting loaded.

Ritual Addicts

An abuser's thoughts and behavior are like an old, stuck record playing their ritual over and over. Most abusers recreate old patterns of abuse many, many times. The specific ritual an abuser performs, usually mirrors abuse *they* suffered. Many abusers are abuse victims themselves and have not learned appropriate ways to express and release their hurt.

If you abuse another (or yourself) you act out your own *trauma/ritual trance.* Your victim becomes a ritual object in a distorted attempt to resolve your under•lying pain.

▲ Abandonment and Neglect: Pass Over

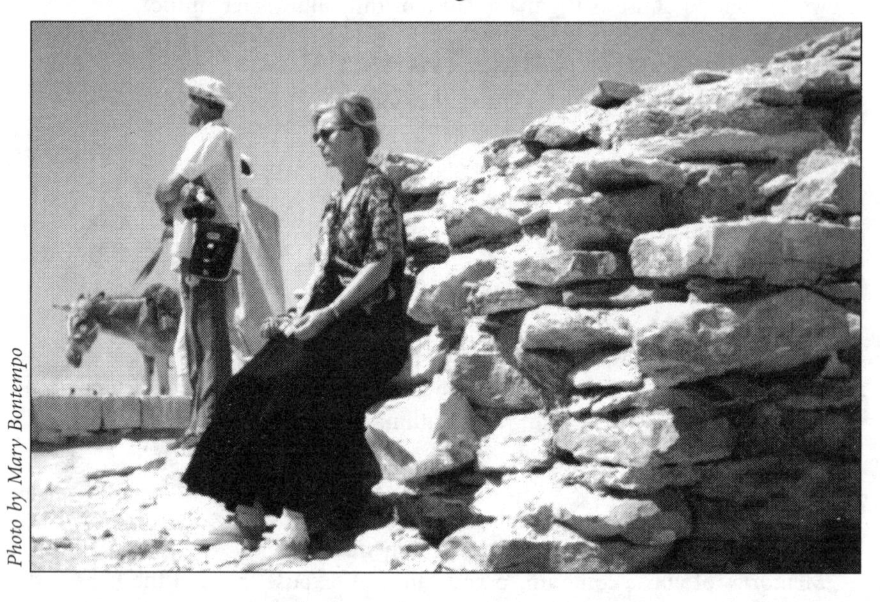

Photo by Mary Bontempo

Children suffer from neglect. If you survived infancy and babyhood without contact and attention, you are a "baby Green Beret." Like all human babies, you couldn't take care of yourself. If no one fed, warmed or held you, you might have died. In the 1950's, a shocking study proved that newborn babies die when not touched. If you are hypersensitive to being left or abandoned, you were most likely neglected.

You were neglected if:
You felt unwanted or ignored.
Your grownups were too preoccupied with themselves to notice you.
They disapproved of what you did or didn't do.
The big people withheld love as punishment.
You were a latch key kid who raised yourself.

Shut down parents who smother, ignore, or are emotionally unavailable, inadvertently wound their children.

INNER•VIEW QUIZ

Do You Have Abandonment Issues?

☆ *"If you don't leave me alone, I'll find someone else who will."*

Be truly honest with yourself and answer T to each true statement.

___ My main theme is, "Please don't leave me."
___ I am obsessed with keeping him or her.
___ No matter what they say, I think they really want to leave me.
___ I feel like I can't survive alone.
___ I stay in crummy relationships because it hurts more to be alone.
___ I keep "backup" people available in case, God forbid, I'm left alone.
___ I feel desperate when someone pulls away.
___ I detach, leave or withdraw to punish my partner for leaving me alone.
___ When alone, I feel anxious, detached or depressed.
___ I overreact to minor things my partner says or does.
___ People are unreliable.
___ Throughout my life, I have had disappointing friendships.
___ My relationships are a roller coaster ride.
___ I have often been left (right?).
___ I'm always worried that those I love will die.
___ I'm touchy/clutchy; a desperate cling•on.
___ I'm very jealous and possessive.
___ My obsession over my lover leaving drives them away.
___ My life is about keeping loved ones.
___ I avoid intimate relationships.
___ Chasing after someone who is partially available turns me on.
___ The less available they are, the more I pursue.
___ I choose mates who won't commit.
___ I choose non-relationship relationships with unstable or ambivalent partners.
___ I make sure I'm always alone.
___ I won't commit.
___ I leave them before they leave me.

Yes to these questions means that you are afraid of being abandoned or are reacting to being smothered. The more "yes's" the greater your fear.

Withdrawal is a natural part of relationships. All people withdraw from others occasionally, even in the best of relationships. If you have abandonment issues, your reactions are triggered by the slightest notion that someone is going to withdraw from you. It's time to embrace and not abandon yourself.

Suzuki's story is a perfect example of the impact of neglect. She was born in Japan after World War II. Her parents, like millions of other Japanese, worked hard to reconstruct their society. Suzuki's "home" was a box in the corner of one three-tatami-mat room, cordoned off by a curtain, so that her beautician mother could do people's hair and nails. Here's what she has to say:

A TRUE STORY Suzuki

"No one had time for me. Mother said, 'Be quiet. No customer wants to hear you. If you cry, we will not have food to eat.'

When a giant rat bit me, nobody heard me cry. Maybe I didn't cry at all.

Hypnotherapy helped me overcome bulimia and sleeplessness, which have tortured me all my life. I learned to re-parent myself by giving myself the attention I missed. I never felt like there was enough food, and I never felt calm enough to digest it. I now nourish myself, and I don't throw up any more. I am my own good mommy and daddy, and I will never abandon myself again."

☆ *THEN HE LEAVES ME*

"He loves me." Then he lies to me.
My heart has learned to cry.

"He loves me," Then he ignores me.
No attention can I buy.

"He loves me." Then he cheats on me.
Tear tracks etch my face.

"He loves me." Then he hits me;
Bruises my heart can't erase.

"He loves me." Then he yells at me.
His hateful words pierce my soul.

"He loves me." How can I tell him how he hurts me?
We will survive, I know we will. I love him still

"He loves me." Then he leaves me.
My heart has learned to die.

—Michele Borders

Karen's story demonstrates the chain of memory that sometimes leads us to break patterns of abuse and neglect:

A TRUE STORY Karen

"As long as I remember, I've felt paralyzed; like I can't move. This morning a memory came to me. I am 5 years old, and I'm standing in front of my kindergarten after school waiting to be picked up. I'm wearing a white hat and a thick woolen coat, and I'm crying. I'm cold and frightened. My sister and mother aren't here. I feel helpless and angry.

When mother comes, she says, 'You are stupid for crying. Of course someone will be here to take you home. You were not abandoned....'

'How stupid of me to get upset and cry,' I say to myself. 'I have no right to be angry. I have no right to feel LOST.'

I've been on that corner my whole life. I feel lost, confused, frightened and angry, as if I don't know where to turn. I wait. Only in that designated spot. I don't move or speak to anyone. But I can't cry anymore. I am too tired. Then I go numb.

During hypnosis with Shelley, I recalled being born. The doctor is saying 'hurry up' to my mother. 'It's late and I have to go. I have plans tonight.' My next memory is when I was very small in my crib. My father is hitting me saying, 'Shut up. Stop crying. You are bothering us.' I'm too little to even roll over. I just froze and couldn't let out a sound.

I realize now that I was trained to believe that I was a bother and to not let my feelings out. I am changing that now. Hypnosis and the truth are making me feel much better."

AFFIRM SUCCESS Abandon Abandonment with Great Abandon

I Take Back My Soul. I am whole. I take back my soul, I am holy. I stay conscious and present. I create new healthy rituals. My boundaries are healthy. I am in charge of my behavior. I'm responsible for my actions. I choose right action. I only allow right thought. My life begins afresh in this moment.

I release and forgive the past and am relieved. The past is just a memory. Tomorrow is a fantasy. My life is now and in this moment I choose joy and peace.

I'm resilient and flexible. I embrace my power. I'm secure in my own company and in intimate relationships. I am 100% responsible for running my own life. I run my life with joy and peace. I'm grown up. I stay conscious. I stay in my body. I like living here.

I have a natural need for human contact. I create healthy contact with others. I'm loveable. I'm loving. I pray for guidance.

If someone withdraws, I control my response. I am appropriate. I take charge of my thoughts and actions. I choose right thought and right action. I focus on the bigger picture. I think kind thoughts toward them and myself. I enjoy the ebb and flow of relationships. I notice feelings and let them move through me but I don't invite them to tea. My attention focuses on positive thoughts. Everyone else is just a mirror of my thoughts. I generate my thoughts. Every day I find new ways to develop myself. I choose new ways of coping with old feelings. I find healthy new ways to relate to others.

I am in charge of my behavior. I am my best friend. I am always there for myself. I listen and hear my inner self. I give myself what I need. I spend quality time with me. I enjoy honest and open communication with myself.

Detachment or threats from others no longer manipulate me. Normal separations from others give me a chance to breathe, develop my own interests, hobbies, talents and myself. I luxuriate in my own company. Even perfect relationships have a rhythm of interaction and separation. Little withdrawals allow my partner and me to regroup, recharge and re-ignite. Everyone is busy with his or her life. They call or write when they can. I give others "space."

I choose those who are there for me in healthy ways. I choose intimate, available people who take responsibility for their own life. I choose people who make commitments and honor them. I spend time with clean, sober and stable people. I choose people who are available and willing to spend time with me.

I am clean, sober, stable and willing to be in a committed relationship. I'm willing to spend time with another. I do not threaten others with abandonment or withdrawal.

In my heart and physical world, I honor friendship and love. I know that love lasts forever. Even if I choose to move on, I still love. If I choose to move on, it is because I have learned from that relationship what I needed to learn. I no longer move on because of a neurotic need to leave. I enjoy honest, open, loving contact with others.

▲ S•mothered: Over-Protected

INNER•VIEW QUIZ

Were You S•mothered?

____ I was over shadowed.
____ I was killed with kindness.
____ Doting, overboard caretakers devoted full energy to my welfare.
____ I was not allowed to leave my caretaker's side.
____ I was not allowed to think for myself.
____ I fear I will fail or make "mistakes?"
____ My father/mother/caretaker always knew best.
____ My job is to live my caretaker's plans for me.
____ The message was clear: Stifle thyself or die.
____ My parents/caretaker watched my every move and I had no freedom.

Yes to these ideas means that you may suffer from emotional constipation. Read on.

S•mothering is a masterful co-dependent game. The flip side of abandonment and over-protection may look friendly from the outside, but on the inside, you feel "non-personed," discounted and abandoned.

The main message from a smotherer, whether silent or loud is: "I'm right, you're wrong." "I know, you don't know." "I'm smart, you're stupid." "You are my shadow. Without me you are nothing."

A TRUE STORY Shelley

"Mother meant well, but she was a complete control freak. She bought my clothes. She told me what to think, how to act, and what to do with my time. If I had a problem with someone at school, she fought the battle for me. And I, the good little girl, yielded.

I felt secure in her oppressiveness and if she wasn't there when I got home from school, I stood by the gate and threw a tantrum. Yet, I developed the habit of dallying; walking the two blocks from school took me three hours. I slept long hours. And, I was always the last one to the dinner table.

Years later, I realized that both pleasing or avoiding Mommy caused me to go unconscious. It took me a long time to separate from my mother the warden. She was long dead but still quite alive in my head. When I let her go, I woke up to my peaceful self."

Cancel the Caterer

Dr. Spock encouraged permissive behavior and some thirty years later, retracted it, saying he had made a great error. "Too much catering does not build responsible, independent adults," he said.

▲ Verbal Abuse: Babble-On

INNER•VIEW QUIZ

!%#**!! I Swear!

____ I say insulting things to myself.
____ I use put-down humor.
____ *! %!!#** is a familiar expression from my childhood.
____ People insult me.
____ I am manipulated by guilt and shame.
____ I am critical and judgmental of others.
____ I swear.

☆ BEWARE!

You flare,
I scare, tear, go dumb,
sinking silent in the arms of numb.
I die and bleed;
hoping not to need
your care.
Beware!

—Shelley Stockwell

Photo by Joann Kelly

You Dirty Little Alabaster

Styles of verbal abuse vary from screaming rages, snide snipes, criticism, shame, threats of abandonment, jokes at another's expense, a steady diet of negativity. Verbally abusive people know very well how to attack weak spots. They know where you are vulnerable. To feel better about themselves, they put others down.

If someone criticizes you and you let it get to you, you feel bad and "less than." The hurt is even worse if you value your critic's opinion, because you experience loss.

Don't Dump On Your Darling

If you are critical, use Dr. Alex Lessin's approach. It works: Imagine what it would be like if you felt good no matter what your darling did. If they did what you prefer, you feel great. If they didn't do what you prefer, you still feel great: you win no matter what. Use this technique and appreciate your partner:

ATTITUDE:
Think of what you resent and how it makes you feel toward your love.
(Example: "You're late again, while I worry and get mad.")

BEHAVIOR:
How do you act toward them when you feel this pain or resentment?
(EXAMPLE: I demand, "You should come on time" or I withdraw, rage, snipe, or get even.)

WHAT ARE YOUR EMOTIONAL PAYOFFS?
What is your emotional payoff for having these feelings and behavior?
(EXAMPLE: I get to release trapped energy and rage).

WHAT ARE YOUR BEHAVIORAL PAYOFFS?
What are your behavioral payoffs?
(EXAMPLE: I get to feel control by making demands, just like Dad/Mom).

PREFERRED ATTITUDE:
Change your mind to your preferred feeling.
(EXAMPLE: Stop expecting your mate to make you happy. Choose to make yourself happy. Choose inner peace. Find new ways to be in control. Choose joy. Choose a loving relationship).

PREFERRED BEHAVIOR:
Divert your attention to something you like to do.
(EXAMPLE: Instead of fretting, do a favorite hobby or activity. Say, "You're late, dear. I did something I thoroughly enjoyed instead of getting angry, but next time, please come on time. Now let's enjoy...").
When you choose happy preferences, you stop dumping on your darling and allow yourself to get closer in your relationship.

Three Ways to Control Anger

1. Repeat an uplifting sound-bite to prevent negativity, such as: "Mellow out", "Calm and relaxed", "Kick back", "Chill out"
2. Take slow, deep breaths.
3. Count backwards slowly, from 10.

▲ Emotional Abuse: Mortar•Fied

All abuse is emotional abuse because it hurts you emotionally. Emotional abuse can be subtle and pervasively disabling.

Do others control and manipulate you with guilt trips? Were you not permitted to express feelings for fear of consequences; "It will upset Mom" or "cause Dad a heart attack." "Shame on you." "I'll wash your mouth out with soap." "You have sinned."

Were you shamed into doing what you didn't want to do, so you wouldn't disappoint or let someone down? "After all we did for you…"

Were you threatened by impending punishment? Were you put-down with gestures or words?

Let's say you accidentally broke a favorite piece of china; did you get the evil eye or a controlling sigh? Were you told that you were a "bad kid."

Guilt

Guilt and shame are unexpressed anger and fear directed inward. You feel guilt when you do something that goes against your conscience or against a trip laid on you by someone trying to control you. If you did something you shouldn't have done, and feared being found out, fear, turned inward, can become guilt. You may feel guilty for something you did or didn't do. Guilt may be based on rules, not necessarily your heart. Unexpressed guilt leads to sadness and depression.

Living In A Tornado

☆ *"Does your dog bite?"*

"*Nope.*"

The dog bites him.

"I thought you said your dog doesn't bite."

"It's not my dog."

Were you misled or given double messages? Did the rules change daily; what was acceptable one day wasn't the next? Did you never know what was going to happen? If so, you were stressed and emotionally abused. Chaos in childhood may train us to be compulsively chaotic or controlling.

The Continuum of Hurt

Irritation and rage are degrees of the same feeling: anger.

Displeasure, sadness and depression are degrees of the same feeling: sadness.

Remorse, repent and regret are the three ugly stepsisters of guilt.

The Shame Spiral

1. I punish myself by trying to destroy the love someone feels for me.

2. I hurt a loved one.

3. I feel ashamed because I hurt a loved one.

4. I punish myself by trying to destroy the love someone feels for me.

5. I hurt a loved one.

6. I'm ashamed because I hurt a loved one.

Disapproval

Were you "not good enough" according to family standards? Did your parents control and manipulate you with disapproval? If you got one A, "Why wasn't it two?" If you won a ribbon, "No biggie. We expected it of you." If you loved drama, "Actors are all bums."

If you were a "surprise" baby, unwanted or an attempted abortion, your very existence was greeted with disapproval. Did they *let you know* that your presence caused them undue difficulty? If so, you were power tripped by disapproval.

When this happens, we may continue to feel unworthy. You may choose rejecting partners, hoping that they will some day love you. Or, you may disapprove of others and reject them.

AFFIRM SUCCESS: Sensitivity Training

I apologize for any insensitivity I have shown toward others. If I hurt someone I ask for forgiveness. Then I return to living in the present, living honestly from my truth. I forgive myself.

I honestly and kindly express my feelings. "I'm angry at you" is a great guilt buster. I forgive those who have manipulated me with guilt and shame. I don't bite. God bless them, they did themselves perfectly. I avoid toxic people. Joy is my compass. I don't turn my joy over to hurtful people. I choose joy. Joy is my compass.

▲ Physical Abuse: Defile De Nile

☆ FRIGHTENED CHILD

Alone in his corner the frightened child cries tonight clutching his soft bear,
massaging the wounds that litter his side.
In this realm of toy and dream, behind the closed door, exists cruel reality;
the battle his parents are fighting.
Alone in the dark, a victim of Daddy's drunk hand,
the frightened child cries tonight
preparing for
the next time.

—Chris Aguilar, age 18

Photo by Carol Kozlovich

Camel-Flogged

Our culture is entertained by violence. Children laugh as characters pummel each other in cartoons and video games. Older children admire violent aggressive super heroes. Sadistic books and news enthrall us. Movies generally are a saga of violent acts strung together by pounding music and tactless dialog. Music lyrics are often hostile and abusive. In surveys, our presidents are most popular after they bomb another country. What's going on?

Were you taught to tolerate physical abuse by the examples of parents, neighbors or society? Police may turn a blind eye to domestic violence, yet the truth is; abuse hurts your life and can be terminal.

Battering comes in several varieties: verbal, physical, emotional and sexual. Battering can be done directly with fists or indirectly with humiliating words. Do these phrases sound familiar?

"This hurts me more than you."
"I'll get the belt if you don't do what I tell you.
"It was good enough for me, it's good enough for you."
"You'll sit there until you finish everything on your plate."
"Don't cry or I'll give you something to cry about."
"Bad boy."
"Be seen and not heard. Shut up!"
"It's your fault you're getting this lickin'."
"I'm going to wash your mouth out with soap."
"You spilled your milk, lap it up off the floor."
"I'll slap you silly."

AFFIRM SUCCESS: Self Respect
Read this and listen well to yourself.

I will not tolerate being hit or abused. I do not like it or want it and I will not take it. I am not to blame for being beaten and abused. I am not the cause of another's violent behavior. I draw the line. No more. I am an important human being. I am worthwhile. I deserve to be treated with respect. I am worth it. I deserve to be safe and happy. I change my life any way I choose. I have the power over my own life to take care of myself. I decide for myself what is best for me and for my children. I take full responsibility for my children's welfare. My children deserve to be safe and happy. I am not alone. I get help.

Silence Is Deadly

If your mother allowed herself to be beaten physically or verbally, you may identify with her and may unconsciously repeat her behavior, as a victim or an abuser. If you were taught to shut up and ignore violence, you may still be shutting up and your silence could be the death of you.

Have You Suffered Abuse in Silence, Afraid to Tell Someone?

If so, fear may cause you to stay isolated, with few friends.

Have You Lied, Pretended or Suffered for Years Without Getting Help?

Abuse victims very often shield the person who beats them, to "protect" themselves, their children or the family "honor."

Have You Blamed Yourself?

If you feel afraid, guilty or responsible for the violence, it is time you looked at the situation with fresh eyes. The more abuse you put up with, the less you like yourself. No one deserves to be beaten or physically threatened. No excuse can justify such behavior. It is a crime against nature to beat anyone, a child, a friend, a stranger, a mate or you.

Tolerance of family violence may have become a way of life. It may be your family's tradition, passed on from one de-generation to the next. It ends the day you stand up and say, "No more."

A TRUE STORY Tresa

My husband Bob hauled off to slug me as I was turning around and instead of hitting me, punched our four month old son Daniel, who was in my arms. I decided to leave him after that and asked my parents if we could stay with them 'til I got a job.

My dad, who has always beaten us, said: "There is no way. A wife's place is with her husband. Go home and patch it up. He didn't mean to hit the baby, he meant to hit you."

Busted: The Myth of the Stranger Bad Guy

☆ *"One-third of all women's injuries coming into our emergency rooms are no accident. Most are the result of premeditated acts of violence. Frequently, they occur over and over until the woman is killed. Family violence is one of America's most critical health issues. Yet society repeatedly sweeps it under the rug...Tragically, the victims return home to be beaten again."*
—Dr. Kevin Fullin, AMA advertisement

Someone of the same race kills more than 90% of homicide victims, and someone they know kills 50%.

One quarter of all murders take place within the family, according to the National Institute of Mental Health. Surveys of American couples show that twenty to fifty-percent suffer violence regularly in their marriage.

Between two and four million incidents of domestic violence occur yearly. Wife abuse occurs most commonly. Every twelve seconds, an American woman or child is beaten. Only seven percent of these abuses are reported to the police. Society repeatedly rationalizes domestic violence as a personal problem that people should settle for themselves.

A-Salt and Battery

Do you feel afraid, guilty and even responsible for the violence? Are you shielding the person who beat you, to "protect" yourself or your children?

There appears to be an energy pattern between couples who participate in the "wife-beating syndrome." I call this cycle of violence SOS...FU____

S tressed	the tension building phase
O utburst	the explosion and beating
S unshine	and roses, lovy dovy
FU ...neral	If this pattern is permitted to continue, if often ends in the final funeral phase

Once physical abuse begins, it will most likely happen again and again.

Child Abuse *by Attorney Kathy Popoff*

Picture a human being that is nine feet tall and weighs 800 pounds; a fantasy from science fiction? Maybe not.

Imagine this gigantic being attacking, beating, kicking, punching and slapping you. Pulling your hair, breaking your bones, blackening your eyes and knocking your teeth out. This creature is not something out of a horror story, but the very person you love and cherish most in this world. The person you look to for protection and nurturing. The person on whom you depend for your very life.

If you can, even in the very slightest way, imagine being in this situation, then you have a small inkling of what it is like for a first grader. A lad who weighs 50 pounds, is four feet tall, with a six feet tall, 200-pound parent, physically abusing him.

The incidence of physical and sexual abuse of children by adults is at an all-time high. We do not really know the magnitude of the increase, because child abuse traditionally has been ignored or covered up by parents.

In earlier centuries, and in some parts of the world even today, children were viewed as the property of their parents. They could do whatever they pleased with their children. Everyone else was to look the other way and mind their own business. Child abuse was not even defined as a problem. That's just the way things were.

Another reason societies did not—and perhaps still do not—have accurate figures about the true level of child abuse, is that it has been a "dirty little secret" that the abusive family usually does all it can to conceal. Even to the point that the children themselves are taught to protect their abusers from anyone else finding out what is going on.

This army of children and teenagers that survive physical and sexual abuse each year is more than four times the size of the army that came home from the Persian Gulf War in early 1992.

And, what about these children who do survive, at least physically? What happens to them over the long term? The statistics are just as grim: Three different research groups reported the following to a meeting of the American Association for the Advancement of Science. Children who are abused or neglected grow up with:

- Lower IQ's and lower reading scores.
- A greater likelihood of suffering from alcohol and drug abuse.
- More likely to be depressed or attempt suicide.
- More likely to be unemployed or arrested, both as juveniles and adults.
- More likely to become child abusers, acting out the only role model they experienced, thus passing this dreadful legacy on to future generations.

Studies not only confirm conventional wisdom about the disastrous effect of childhood abuse, they also indicate that the problem is much more severe than previously believed.

☆ *In My Mother's Pink Womb I Fell in Love*
In her baffled voice and her metronome heart I heard the angels.
When I met her face to face, Imagine my surprise:
My mother was perfection yet herself she despised.
Drugs made her ballistic. My father made her cry.
Her children made her crazy though I never knew just why.
People made her lonely. Animals brought disease.
Fear was her perception. She was very hard to please.
Control was her intention as she taught with guilt and shame.
Insults followed kindness. Victim was her game.
Breast cancer finally took her when she was seventy-three
and even in her passing she was beautiful to me.

—Shelley Stockwell

▲ Sexual Abuse: A Touchy Subject

Sexual abuse is an act against your person that feels instinctively wrong. If a child tells you that he or she has been abused, believe it. If you sense that you have been violated, believe it. No matter how we block out painful experiences, we always remember them subconsciously.

Incest and Child Abuse: The Strong Against the Weak

Incest is a crime committed by a related male, female, adult or child. It is estimated that incest happens to about one in three before the age of eighteen. Incestuous acts range from exhibitionism and voyeurism (watching someone naked) to masturbation, rape, sodomy, bestiality and ritualized torture.

Profile of a Child Abuser

Sexual child abusers are emotionally flat and frozen at a particular age, generally the age of their own victimization. They keep replaying that age, as if they are watching or acting in a stuck videotape.

Sexual abusers are angry con artists who have lost touch with their empathy, guilt, conscience and inner child. They lie to themselves and the world. Usually victims of dysfunctional families themselves, they usually have poor sexual relationships with those their own age.

Child molesters are often overly religious, compulsive and addictive. Their drug or trauma trance reenacts their own abuse and overrides their impulse control. An impulse that a healthy person would censor, a sexual abuser will act out.

It is estimated that one sex offender molests sixty to seventy-five children in his or her lifetime. According to one study, eighty-six percent of the offenders are known to the child. Some sixty-two percent are known as a father figure. And eighty-five percent of molested women have children that are molested. Chilling statistics!

The Set Up

Sexual abusers choose good boys and girls. If you were violated, your abuser probably chose you because you were needy and non-assertive and full of bright light. Abusers often set up, or "court" their victim by giving baths, tucking into bed, holding on their lap; or sharing little secrets. "Here's some candy; don't tell your mother." They may tell the child how "special" they are.

INNER•VIEW QUIZ

Have You Suffered Sexual Abuse?

Answer these questions impulsively, as quickly as possible, without thinking, analyzing or censoring. When you were younger, were you:

___ Touched on your privates.
___ Shown sexual movies or pictures.
___ Forced to listen to sexual talk.
___ Made to pose for sexual photographs or videos.
___ Raped or otherwise penetrated.
___ Coerced into performing oral sex with an adult or another child.
___ Given unnecessary enemas.
___ Fondled, kissed or held in ways that made you very uncomfortable.
___ Bathed in a way that felt intrusive.
___ Insulted about your body.
___ Forced into a ritual that was physically or sexually torturing.
___ Made to look at sexual parts or sexual acts.
___ Pressured into sex against your will.
___ Involved in prostitution or pornography.

"Yes" to any of these questions, means that you were sexually abused.
If so, you may cope in various ways:

Minimize it: "It really wasn't that bad."
Rationalize it: "He couldn't help it, he was drunk."
Deny it: "That couldn't have happened." It never happened." "He/she would never do that to me."
Forget it: "I totally forgot that it happened."
Leave your body: "I don't live here anymore. I am an observer."
Disown it: "That really wasn't me. I had a wonderful childhood."
Split from yourself: Takes on exaggerated multiple personalities that may or may not be aware of each other's existence. Their voice, posture, behaviors, allergies, and abilities can be distinct and separate..."I'm not myself today."

To be happy, GET REAL. Tell the truth. Express trapped emotions. Put that terrible experience in the past and start again by carving a new life for yourself in the here and now.

The Attack

The first violation often occurs when a child is asleep. Abusers threaten: "Don't tell," with a glare or a clear instruction, "If you tell your mother, it will be all your fault and she will send you away."

Abuse sometimes feels physically and emotionally good. These feelings conflict with guilt, pressure, confusion and the sense that something is terribly wrong here.

Children want to tell the truth, but may be too young to talk or too frightened to speak up. A little girl molested by daddy feels like she betrayed mommy and risks breaking their bond. "What if Mommy finds out and Daddy leaves? It will be my fault." "Maybe they'll want to kill me!" and the truth might just get her killed.

"Why didn't someone protect me?" ask the abused.

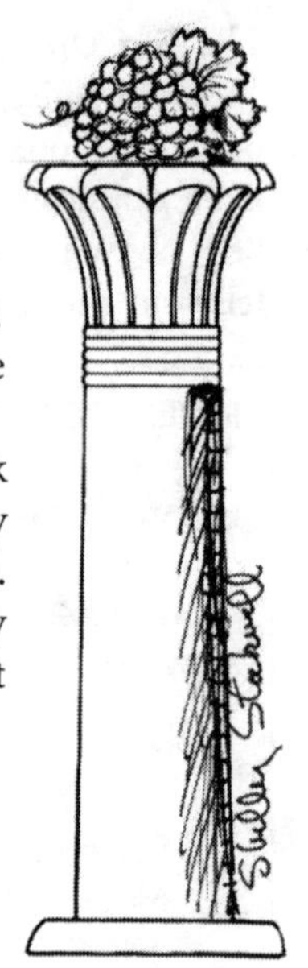

Statutory Grape

A TRUE STORY Jay

"After seeing the rape scene in the movie 'The Prince of Tides,' I felt furious. But I didn't know why. The movie upset me so much that I called my older sister. "Of course it made you uncomfortable," she said, "We were abused by mother."

I started to remember. From the time we were infants, mother gave us daily enemas "for health reasons." It was sexual abuse. If I swallowed a rock, she gave me a laxative and made me look for it in my potty.

Hypnosis helped me remember. During a hypnosis regression, I remembered when my sister was seven and I was five. We were playing in the basement with three teenage children. One boy brutally sodomized my sister and the other boy sodomized me. I went unconscious. I remember watching my sister and wanting to help, but I couldn't. The girl held my penis and the boy pushed his penis into me. I was screaming. My sister was screaming.

My mother came in. "What are you doing?" she demanded.

"Nothing," they said.

"It must be something." she said, "You kids get out of here and don't come back."

After they ran out, she cleaned us up in the basement sink. We were both bleeding. "It never happened," she said, looking us in the eye. "Your father is not to know. Do not go to confession and tell the priest." Then she gave us candy. I felt like a lie.

After the rape, mother always made an extra portion of dessert for me. At age six, I weighed 40 pounds. The nuns made an issue of my weight at school, so mother took me to a doctor. But instead of talking about my weight, she told him that she was "concerned" about the size of my penis. He gave me hormone shots.

EPILOG After telling my story, Shelley urged me to call my mother and tell her what I remembered. "I remembered what happened in the basement," I told her. "Well, if it did happen, forget it. You don't want to disrupt your sister's life, do you?" She said.

Three days later my sister called. Mother called her and said she was afraid that I would tell the neighbor lady (the aunt of our molesters) and if I did, that would hurt their friendship. I guess I know what's important to my mother.

Hypnosis really helped me. People tell me I look thinner and that I stand straighter. My voice is clearer and I am now comfortable speaking in public. Before, I feared that my secret would pop out. Now I can talk comfortably and stay calm with people. Just by telling my mother the truth, I changed. I can tell the truth and feel my rage. Sex is finally happening."

How Do You Know if You Were Sexually Abused?

After violations, some shut down physically or go hog wild. Do you mistrust men/women? Do you attract untrustworthy mates? Are you disconnected from your inner child? Dislike sex? Or turn off sex altogether? Vaginisma (tight or painful vagina) and impotency? Are you promiscuous or do you have a series of unhappy, unfulfilling relationships? If you numb yourself with drugs, compulsions or phobias, have a weight problem and are easily angered and rageful; suspect abuse.

Young children, who have been violated show changes in sleep, eating and weight patterns, don't want to be left alone and/or withdraw entirely. Preoccupation with any violation may affect schoolwork or cause troublemaker behavior. Some abuse victims attempt suicide.

If you are depressed, secretive and have a poor self-image, there is a good chance you were violated sexually or other wise. If your face in the mirror or in photos is "mask-like," that too is a tip-off. So is an above-average knowledge about sex, with exaggerated seductive behavior. It is estimated that ninety-five percent of all teenage prostitutes were sexually abused, the majority by a father figure.

If You Imagine You Were Abused, You're Probably Correct

If you were sexually, or any other way abused, denial is a way to cope with a painful problem. The most important thing to know is that if you imagine something happened, then it most likely did. Even if you cannot remember the details, if you suspect you were sexually abused, you are probably correct.

You may not have proof that you were abused. You may not get validation from your family. Your memories may be incomplete. Your family may insist that nothing happened. But, if your gut feeling says danger and upset, believe yourself; even if you think you've made it up. Abuse is not usually something a person makes up. The trick is to remember, *then* forgetting comes naturally. Blocking and denying painful memories is what sets the stage for disconnected behaviors. Remembering allows you to forgive yourself, release the past and get a brand new start.

Eve tells a tragic story of abuse;

A TRUE STORY Eve and The Yellow Blanket

"I've always felt a great sadness about my childhood. In hypnosis I remember why.

'I see a blanket, a yellow one; it's scratchy. I feel someone holding one of my hands. I'm hot. I have a little T-shirt on. I'm really, really little.

Now I'm very cold. I feel sick to my stomach. The yellow blanket is over my face. I can't see anything. I'm scared. It seems like mommy is by my hand and someone else is by my feet.

We play hide and seek with the yellow blanket; I feel sick to my stomach, crying and dizzy. I don't want to be under the yellow blanket. A lot of people put me under the blanket. It is a game, a bad game. First it was peek-a-boo. It was fun.

I'm on a table under the yellow blanket. No one holds me and loves me. There is nothing loving. My cousin is here, my dad is here, my mommy or some other lady is here, my grandmother maybe. I want to leave my body. They stare at me; analyzing me. They look and point at my body. I want to be held. Mommy doesn't like me. I love her and Daddy, but they treat me mean.

I see naked little girl parts. Her legs are apart. She is three or four. I get a strange feeling it's me. I see a black figure sitting with his knees up, sitting in a big black haze. He's got his finger down there. I'm wearing little socks. He might have taken my panties off. He's wearing a blue shirt and darker blue pants and tennis shoes. He's just sitting there. Mom is downstairs. I don't know where Daddy is.

There's a Volkswagen bug outside; it belongs to Grandpops. I guess my cousin Jim drove Grandpop's car. I didn't like it when we were in Oregon sitting in a wheel barrel and in the outhouse. He showed me a dog's penis, or his, or lipstick. They all look the same. They all said it was just lipstick. I'm confused. Maybe it was my brother who asked me to pull my skirt up and is rubbing me.

I remember a washcloth. Mom and Dad are holding it. They take turns washing parts of me. Mom washes me OK, but Dad has big hands and he is rough. He cleans me too much. He puts his fingers down there too much. He has big fingers. I am angry. I don't want him to do it. It hurts. Just leave me alone.

I remember being strapped or held down. My mother stick things inside my vagina. Sometimes father watches. I'm treated like I'm not a person.

They're covering up my head and telling me *peek-a-boo*. They do the same thing in the bathtub...

I visit my parents once a week and fall asleep immediately after dinner. After I remembered my past, I forced myself to stay awake. I pulled my father aside and told him, 'I've been remembering a lot of things from my past that I had forgotten. I'm disturbed to remember several occasions where you did not protect me.' My father looked sad and said, 'I'm sorry, I've been very self absorbed.'

Maybe my parents incorrectly assumed that since I was a baby I didn't know what they were doing or would not remember. But I do remember. I plan to start a center for victims of child abuse."

AFFIRM SUCCESS: Re-Member

I open my mind to remember. Remembering is the first step to my power and control. I easily remember every moment of my life. As I remember, I release pain and embrace joy. I am brave. With every memory, I learn to love myself. If patterns no longer serve me well, I change them into new, more positive patterns. Any memory, real or imagined, heals me. I am innocent. I am forgiven. I am whole. I am holy. I remember.

Today is my moment and now is my story. I laugh and I cry and I sing, today.

I feel terrific. There is no denial. My feelings are the key to peace. Now I see that acknowledging my feeling is the key to peace. Within my feelings live the passion for change. I am a growing and maturing personality. I feel great. I am grateful.

HEALING INCEST

It is time to release pain
with this sweet reframe:
The past is now a memory.
Tomorrow is a fantasy.
In this moment, I choose peace,
joy and love.

▲ Healing Actions

New tools make life work better.

Tell yourself the truth about your past and accept it. By accepting the truth, you may experience grief, rage and finally, self-forgiveness, resolution and much needed peace and relief.

You may need to re-experience underlying trauma to resolve it and reattach to your thoughts and body. Go back to the trauma, only to heal, release and make new choices.

There are six steps to healing:

1. Remember
2. Break the conspiracy of silence
3. Find new ways to love you and others
4. Forgive and be here now
5. Create your own world
6. Seek peace and joy

You can take these steps on your own or with the help of a good hypnotherapist.

1. Remember

Your mind is a computer that files every instant of your life. Every event, emotion, and perception is in your memory. During traumatic experiences, you may have tucked them into a hidden memory bank. Many people remember childhood violations only after they are forty years old. Some suppressed memories never surface.

If you have hurts or hang-ups and want to feel better, be outrageously brave and ask yourself to remember.

2. Break the Conspiracy of Silence

You break the conspiracy of silence by remembering and telling yourself the truth and putting responsibility where it belongs: totally on the offender.

You stop others dead in their tracks when you tell the world the truth. Don't look the other way when you recognize abuse—your own and others.

If you have been sexually abused, write a letter to all your friends and your abuser. Honestly tell as many of the details as possible. The truth sets all of us free. You don't have to mail the letters; but if you do, you'll heal any hidden pain. You might save hundreds of other innocent victims from pain. Mail it to your abuser, friends, everyone in the family, and to law enforcement people. Put it on the Internet.

Letter to a Sexual Abuser

Cousin Greg, son of my maternal aunt,

This letter is long overdue. I will no longer protect your sexual abusiveness toward me, and will take the necessary action to protect any future victim from your perverse behavior.

When you molested me, you caused me pain beyond belief. For years, I felt angry, violated and hurt. I even felt guilty, somehow thinking that I was "responsible" for what you did to me. That's how toxic your actions have been.

To refresh your memory, let me review exactly what you did to me.

When I was 11, you and your wife smoked marijuana in front of me and invited me to join in. After many invitations, I did.

When I was 12, I "babysat" your two children and you remained home. Why wasn't your wife there? You told me you were studying art and wanted to draw me nude. I felt very scared. You were my cousin, a grown, married man, 20 years older than I was, with children of your own. You coerced me, and, eventually I did what I was told. You were quite pushy about me removing my underpants. I refused. I knew something was terribly wrong with your behavior.

During other "babysitting" jobs at your house (from age 11 to 13), you often returned home, lit up a joint and encouraged me to smoke with you. You insisted that I spend the night, since it was "so late." On the few occasions when I did stay, I was startled awake by your lifting up my clothes. I pretended to be asleep and rolled over so you would leave me alone. I was terrified.

When I was 14, you moved to Hawaii. When I was 16, your wife invited me to visit for the summer. I was excited to go to Hawaii for the first time.

You picked me up at the airport in Kauai. The first night I slept on the daybed in the living room, and was awakened by your lifting up my nighty. I was panicked. Welcome to Hawaii, three thousand miles from family, safety and sanity.

The second week, I was told that your wife had to go to the mainland to buy a pound of marijuana. Oh no! We were going to be left alone. I was expected to take over her duties. I thought that meant babysitting the two boys. As soon as she left, you encouraged me to drink wine, take LSD and smoke pot. That night you had sex with a stoned-out 16-year-old minor. Those next two weeks were a blur of drugs (alcohol, hallucinogenics, pot) and sex.

When your wife returned, you ignored me entirely, saying you were disappointed that my Dad didn't pay you for your "hospitality," and that I was "a burden." You said you couldn't afford me at your house, so I was sent to stay with your friend Bill, his wife and their two daughters. Bill aggressively and repeatedly tried to have sex with me. I had nothing to do with him, but it was a nightmare fighting him off.

It's been seventeen years since that horrible and humiliating encounter with you. Greg, you need psychiatric help. You are sick. I pray that I am your only victim. I am sending a copy of this letter to all our relatives, and I have discussed this at great length with my father. I am also contacting the proper authorities to ensure that you receive the help you need to get well. (Copy sent to the state of Oregon bureau of child abuse.)

(Signed)

3. Find New Ways to Love Yourself and Others

Child rights activist Kathy Popoff says that you and all adults are responsible for the way children are treated. When people ask, "Do you have any children?" Say:

"Yes, I do."

If they ask, "How many?" Reply:

"Oh, about fifty-million."

Abusers

Abusers regain self-respect and respect for others when they vent rage through healthy exercise, telling the truth and staying conscious. Perhaps the biggest cause of abuse is the lack of impulse control caused by drugs, alcohol and sugar. Loving yourself means loving your body.

4. Forgive and Be Here Now

☆ Former Nazi concentration camp victim: *"I am consumed with hatred for them. I can't forgive."*
Friend: *"In that case they still have you in prison."*
—Victor Parachin

Unconditionally forgive yourself for what happened and begin afresh by living life in this moment. Telling your truth leaves the past where it belongs; in the past. In this moment, choose new patterns for joy and peace. Be stubborn about living joyously in the now. When you forgive, you give up hope for a better past.

Forgiveness allows you to reclaim parts of yourself that you've numbed or discarded. It restores your mental, emotional and physical wellness. To forgive, you don't have to forget, excuse or condone the one who hurt you. You don't have to have anything to do with your violator. You forgive for yourself to feel good.

AFFIRM SUCCESS: I Approve of Myself

I forgive myself and ask others I've hurt for forgiveness. Everyone is fallible. Old guilt changes to forgiveness. Old shame changes to pride. I am in control of well being. Forgiving is a priceless gift I give to myself. In my mind's eye, I imagine the one who hurt me. I say out loud, 'I forgive you. Go in peace. I am peaceful.'

I live honestly in the present. I look at myself in the mirror and find new ways to love the person I see looking back at me.

I am accountable to myself. I approve of my healthy behavior and actions. I approve of myself. I make amends if I have harmed another and I forgive myself. I am proud of myself. I learn from my mistakes. I am proud of all I have learned and continue to learn. I am proud and pleased with myself. I love me!

5. Create Your Own World

Where There's a Wheel There's a Way.

Become the hub of the wheel instead of bouncing along on the rim. The trick is to learn how to stay centered while spinning along. In your mind's eye, imagine yourself in a situation that in the past upset you. Pretend that you are reliving the upsetting situation, but this time be centered and relaxed, gliding through it with ease and grace.

Trigger Happy

Go to the moment or time frame just before you did or said that unfortunate thing. What triggered you to do that thing? What did you say to yourself before you took that action? What were you hoping to accomplish?

6. Seek Peace and Joy with a Soul Retrieval

Be as stubborn about being happy as you have been about anything in your life. Don't take 'no' for an answer. Make yes and positive behavior your style. If it is not fun don't do it. A soul retrieval often is a way of coming home again try it:

☆ Dead in the Water

A crackpot cruising 'cross the Nile, crashes into a crocodile.
"Croak well! Cries Croc. "You're just my style!"
"Croc don't be cruel. I taste quite vile."
Cracks the Croc, "What a crock!" Both smile.

—Leonhardt

Ancestors of all cultures: shamans, healers, hunas, medicine people and priests know that during painful rituals and traumas of life, we lose vitality and joy. Our language talks about lost souls or those who have had their spirit broken. Psychologists call such experiences dissociation caused by trauma or Post-Traumatic Stress Disorder. Trauma is held in your cells even if don't consciously notice them. Take back your soul. Stay conscious and you'll have healthy boundaries.

Hypnosis and Shamanic soul retrieval brings back disowned essences and heals the past. A nice way to do a soul retrieval is with a friend, sitter or specialist. Just like Hypnotherapy, the goal is integration.

INTO•GREAT POWER EXERCISE

How to do a Soul Retrieval:

Into-great yourself with this process.
See for yourself.

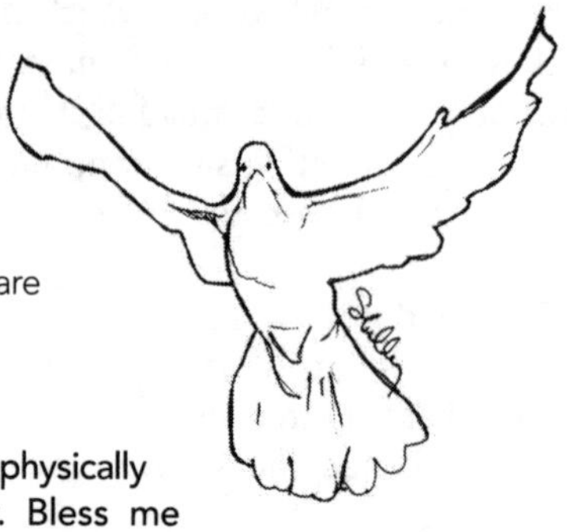

1. Play in•chanting music:
Drumming, the pounding surf or ohming are great.

2. Bless yourself:
"I bless myself on all levels. I bless myself physically with radiant health, energy and vitality. Bless me mentally with clear thinking, focus, and direction. Bless me emotionally with unconditional love, peace, joy, and harmony for myself and others. And bless me spiritually with guidance so that I may truly fulfill my life's purpose."

3. Breathe:
Take a deep breath, and let it out. You can shake a rattle, drum, chant and sing, hum or tone.

4. Affirm:
Think these words or say them out loud:
"I take back my soul, I am whole. I take back my soul, I am holy."

5. Take a shamanic journey:
Imagine yourself traveling in the void back to any time in life where your soul essence, vitality or energy separated from your being. It could be a little memory, such as skinning your knee, or a big memory, such as being beaten, molested or abandoned.

When you find that thought, image, memory, or uneasy feeling, invite that "little you" out of hiding. **"Come home, it's safe now. It's time to come home."**

Use whatever ploy is necessary to convince this frightened part of you to leave this parallel reality and come back home. Call upon allies, guides, angels, fantasies; anything you need to do the convincing.

When it is done, breathe fully to your heart, and let in that part of yourself, saying, **"Welcome home, it's safe now. I love you."**

INTO•GREAT POWER EXERCISE

You Are Pharaoh:

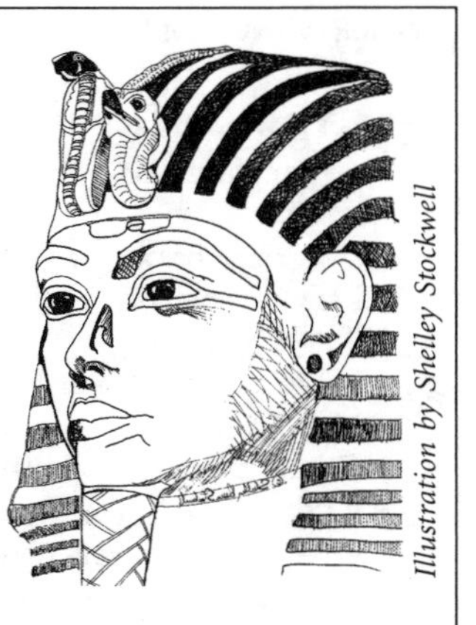
Illustration by Shelley Stockwell

Bad Memory

Recall a recent unpleasant situation and notice the details: What's happening. What happened just before? How did you react? "What is your payoff?"

I Am Pharaoh

Go back to the same memory, but this time, pretend and imagine that you are the Pharaoh of the Universe. It is true. You are the boss of yourself. Absolutely everything, everyone and every situation is your creation. Imagine:

YOU created your experience and everyone in it.
YOU are solely responsible for what you and others said and did.
YOU create it all.

Sweet Reframe

Go back into that unpleasant memory. This time, choose to feel great.

> *Example:*
>
> Bad Memory *I remember yelling at my son for not doing his homework. He grumbled under his breath. I sent him to his room. I felt self-righteous; indignant even. "That boy doesn't do what he is told."*
>
> I Am Pharaoh I realize that I created my son not doing his homework so that I would have the opportunity to feel big, powerful and vent rage. The payoff for my anger was that I got to go home again and feel bad just as I did when my mother yelled at me.
>
> Sweet Reframe This time, I remember the same situation, but I change my response. I choose distinct boundaries between my son and me. In creating those boundaries between us; I see him sitting there and me standing here. He is doing himself very well and I am doing myself very well. I give him information to use rather than trying to control him. He is learning his lessons, I am learning mine. My lesson is to give him loving guidance while I choose to feel joy, peace and health. I find constructive and positive ways to release my pent-up energy. Perhaps I beat up a tennis ball, sweep the front porch, or sing at high volume.

Given the same trigger in the same situation, what could you have done that would have made your actions more to your liking? Imagine yourself diffusing the trigger.

Imagine yourself in the same situation again, this time you take the action that suits you better.

INNER•VIEW QUIZ

Are You Co-Dependent?

Answer truthfully. Do you often think say and/or do:

___ I am responsible for what ___________ says and does.
___ I take everything ____________ says or does personally.
___ If it weren't for ____________, I'd ______________.
___ My relationships aren't fun.
___ Men (women) are all alike.
___ Others cause my problems. I blame and make others wrong.
___ It's hard to tell where others end and I begin.
___ When my child gets nauseous, I throw up.
___ My social circle is just you and me.
___ I'd die without my guru (church, minister, therapist, commune…).
___ I worry about what others think of me.
___ Without your approval I might as well be dead.
___ I'd do anything not to have you reject me or be angry with me.
___ My feelings about myself depend on your approval.
___ Only I know what's best for my significant others.
___ Having control over myself isn't as much fun as having control over you.
___ My job is to relieve your pain and solve your problems.
___ I always put others' feelings, problems and interests before mine.
___ My life is about rescuing, pleasing and protecting the needy.
___ I spend my time worrying about and solving others' problems.
___ I feel guilty about doing things for myself.
___ I am anxious and unable to sleep at night.
___ It is too scary to talk about my disappointment in relationships.
___ I have low self-esteem.
___ I blame myself for everything unless it's all your fault.
___ I'm depressed.
___ I'm just a girl who can't say "no."
___ I am a victim of sexual, physical, psychic or emotional abuse.
___ Good things never happen to me.
___ It's your fault that I drink.
___ If it weren't for you, I would have left your father long ago.
___ You make me blow my stack.
___ I manipulate, pout, threaten, ignore and/or intimidate others.
___ What did I do to deserve such horrible children?

If these statements apply to you, you make others responsible for your feelings or make yourself responsible for theirs. Victim, rescuer or persecutor roles are attempts to feel secure and smoke-screen your own issues.

Chapter 4
Co-Dependency

Deep•end

How can you make a relationship fun and nourishing? As you read this chapter you'll see the relationship traps we get into and how to avoid them.

▲ What Is Co-dependency?
▲ How Do You Catch Co-dependency?
▲ Bondage: Victim, Rescuer, Persecutor

☆ *Are the lights dimming or is it just me-*
My eternal soul blinded by capturing wings of others lives.
—Michelle Constantine

☆ Shelley: *"These pants someone gave me are too tight."*
Jon: *"You should have them lose weight."*

We all need someone to lean on occasionally. Healthy love allows you to have what you want and need and to support loved ones to have what they want and need. It lets you give and receive love within yourself and with others. It means that you have healthy boundaries between yourself and others.

The more self-intimacy you allow, the more whole people you attract to you and life is glorious. You don't need to marry someone to fill you up. To live happily ever after, become the person you want to marry and merry yourself.

▲ What Is Co-Dependency?

☆ *"That was wonderful for you. How was it for me?"*

☆ *"I'd join Co-dependency Anonymous if I could find someone to go with me."*
—I. Cant

Co-dependency makes you carry your own weight plus someone else's on your back. It is a cluster of unhealthy patterns, thoughts and actions that leave you feeling exhausted or depressed.

Co-dependency is a futile attempt to control situations and others and is founded on a belief that you and I are not separate individuals with our own path and purpose, but rather, that we merge in a designated "pecking order."

If you believe that someone or something outside of you controls you, or you must control others, you are working a lot harder than you need to.

Co-dependency keeps you from taking responsibility for yourself and taking charge of your life. This keeps you from joy. If you blame others for what happens to you, blame is the outward sign of an internal feeling of being helpless and powerless.

Every Person Does Themself Perfectly

Each arrives into life perfect in every way, with their own path, purpose and lessons. If your serving others serves you as well, generously support them. Encourage those you love to ask for what they need. This gives you freedom to ask for what you need. Never forget that you are responsible for your own joy, health and well being.

Healthy Family Ties: Caravan

☆ *Use a hug like a prescription, the cost is right.*
To see it works you don't have to be bright.
Hugs come with a money back guarantee
if you don't like it: Give it back to me.

—Bill Erwin

Seeds of your social style are planted in childhood. Infants are still partially fetal and therefore dependent on caretakers. Without support, they literally die. As we mature, we need caretakers to gradually give us freedom, so we learn to trust our perceptions and ourselves—and survive as independent individuals. Do you trust your own judgment? Self-sufficient caretakers teach children to be self-sufficient and stand on their own two feet while being thoughtful of others…a delicate balance.

Illustration by Shelley Stockwell

Dying to be Taken Care of

Dependence: I depend entirely upon you to take care of me, because I don't trust myself.

Co-dependence: I expect you to take care of me; you expect me to take care of you.

Inner•dependence: I trust myself to take care of me.

Independence: I take care of me; I expect you to take care of you.

Interdependence: I'm self-assured and so are you. When we combine our individual creativity, we enhance each other's lives.

▲ How Do You Catch Co-Dependency?: Swaddled

☆ *"How come people who drown their sorrows always look for someone to go swimming with them?"*

We learn most of our behavior and attitudes from long-ago caretakers. We unconsciously recreate them as adults to:

- Be close to home
- Re•solve old problems
- Cope

Families threatened by independence, train children to believe they can't make it on their own. They teach dependence. "Always be taken care of, or take care of others" is their message.

If you believe you are responsible for what others think or feel (or vice versa), you subconsciously attract others with the same mindset. That's how co-dependent relationships are born. Co-dependency is a never-ending control game.

Most likely you had a special role to play in your family drama, and a designated position in the family pecking order.

Were you Mommy's mommy or Daddy's daddy? Or were you allowed to be a child?

Were your ideas put down or ignored? Or were they honored?

Were you asked to "stay little" forever? Or were you encouraged to gradually mature into self-sufficiency?

Is your childhood conditioning serving you well now?

Trauma vs. Drama

Co-dependency often attempts to recreate and re•solve past trauma in a present-day drama. The situation that triggers a trauma/drama may be unconscious. The performance is done like a well-rehearsed scene in a long-running play.

For example, if you were a victim in your childhood (and most children are), you may "hire" someone to play the role of persecutor in your current drama. You would do this hoping, in some bizarre way, that you can work it out this time. That's why some marry the "same" person again and again. Trauma/dramas are always a tragedy.

In a trauma/drama, you may "stand in" as any of the "actors." You might "act" out the "you" from the past. Or you may be "the one who traumatized you." Or you may play the "one who didn't protect you." Or the "one you hoped would save you." Regardless of the role you chose, if you get "on stage," the scene never re•solves under•lying anguish. You never meet a new person or have a truly new experience. You just reinforce painful patterns.

Dominance and Submission

☆ SISTERS

Women bonded with powerful might
Together achieving more than one can.
We as sisters unite,
except when we want the same man.

—Amber Costello

Another reason for co-dependency is an exaggerated pattern of natural dominance and submission. All animals have a pecking order. Maturity over youth, male over female, brains over brawn, muscle over flab, blondes over brunettes. Children fight for their parents' attention. Men compete for the best women. Women compete for the best men. Men and women worry about how they "measure up" in acquaintances, accomplishments, admiration and appendages. Competitive sports are a global addiction where we cheer the top dog and jeer the bottom dog.

Illustration by Shelley Stockwell

Intimidation

☆ *"Any brothers and sisters?"*
"One big brother."
"Any problems?"
"I can't tell you."
"Why not?"
"He's sitting in the audience.
—Art Linkletter, *Kids Say the Darndest Things*

Did your family intimidate, threaten or imply impending punishment? Were you put down with gestures or language? If your family was out-of-control and you felt weak and powerless, you may be exuberantly dominant or powerful. Or you may take on a passive role and submit to another. Your parents' patterns of dominance and submission may become yours as well. Such competitive tomfoolery is possibly the main source of violent acts in our society.

Power-tripped children feel weak and often grow up to be control freaks themselves. They may adopt an overly (underly) submissive role. "Top dog" or "bottom dog" postures make life a bitch.

> To thwart off an aggressive dog, don't make eye contact, lower your head, lower your hand, make a limp wrist and whimper.
>
> To stop an attacking goose, lift your arm above your head and tip you hand down above the flapping one. He'll run away thinking you are a bigger bird.

A TRUE STORY Tiara

"My stepmother is a rude lady who regularly puts me down and insults my son. I call her and my passive father once a week. I guess I call them because kids are supposed to call their parents. If I don't, they make me feel guilty, because I don't 'fulfill my obligation' to them. I want to feel like a good person. But after I hang up the phone, I feel terrible.

Shelley, my Hypnotherapist, asked me, 'What is a good person?'

'A good person doesn't hurt others and is kind and thoughtful,' I answered.

How strange that to feel like a 'good person' I phone 'nasty people' and hurt myself. I also get to make them wrong. In some way, I'm as angry as they are, or I wouldn't call them. My guilt is anger turned inward.

When I discovered this sick game of dominance and submission, I didn't want to play any more. I no longer give them permission to make me feel guilty. I only call once a year and am short and sweet.

If I were to put my limiting life script in a few words, it would be "helpless, hopeless, powerless and passive." I replaced this familiar old pattern with a new life script. I call it personal power and control, joy and peace. I feel better.

Inner•Dependence

If you learned inner•dependence, you honor your feelings, thoughts and body. You are self-confident; have high self-esteem.

If you weren't taught inner•dependence, now is your time to learn it! Then you will attract others who are self-assured. Together you form beautiful inter•dependent relationships.

AFFIRM SUCCESS: Interdependency
Read the following aloud, or to yourself and affirm healthy interdependency.

I am 100% response•able for everything in my life—my health, my behaviors, my relationships, my success and my peace of mind. I cherish myself.

I allow others to run their own life. I regard them with positive neutrality and I honor their right to make their own choices and learn their own lessons. I take full responsibility for my life and am keenly aware of any games I play. I control what I say, do, think and learn. I am in charge of the work I do, the people I associate with, and how I spend my time.

I maintain clear and well-defined boundaries between myself and others. I am in charge.

Illustration by Shelley Stockwell

A Loving Relationship

In all situations, I ask myself, "Whose problem is this, anyway?" If I played victim, I now lovingly reclaim my power, and the game stops. If I played rescuer, I now give others their space to grow. If I played persecutor, I now find healthy ways to release rage as energy without hurting others or myself. I control my emotions and express them in appropriate ways, time and place.

If I choose to assist others, I do it with love. I am not attached to the outcome.

I take responsibility for my self and my life. I am the captain of my ship. I am the master of my soul.

Breaking Free: Unshackled

Teenagers rebel in an attempt to "cut the apron strings" and break co-dependency; only to recreate the same co-dependent patterns later in life. The company you keep can lift you up or bring you down. Limiting patterns often keep us immature and unable to create intimate, loving and grown-up relationships. The trick to achieving a healthy relationship is to notice and consciously choose better patterns.

▲ Victim, Rescuer, Persecutor: Bondage

☆ *"A person can move throughout the victim triangle without needing other players. For example, let's say you feel out-of-control with food (victim). You decide to rescue yourself by going on a crash diet (rescuer). When it does not work, you become angry with yourself by feeling guilty and putting yourself down (persecutor), making yourself more of a victim, feeling more helpless and out-of-control."*

—Diane Zimberoff

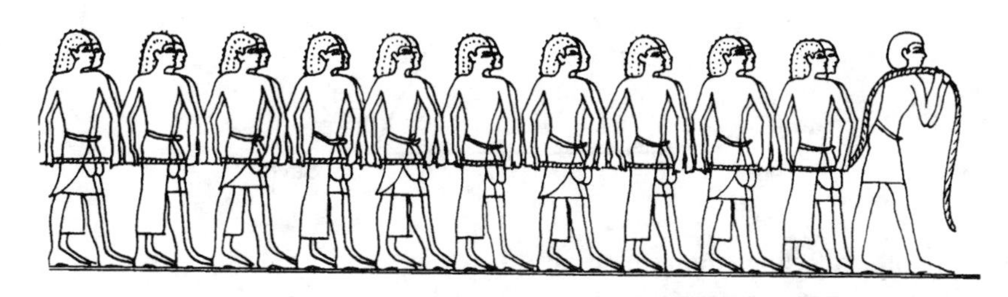

Limiting relationships keep us immature and unable to make intimate, loving contact. Victim, rescuer and persecutor are co-dependent games or postures.

Each make us feel little, helpless, hopeless, angry, guilty, shamed, and depressed. Each attempts to resolve past patterns, but actually keep us spun out in past patterns.

The more these behaviors are reinforced, the more challenging it is to recognize and release them. Notice how you act, then choose new behaviors that are more fun.

The interesting thing about the victim, rescuer and persecutor game is that people often play various ones at various times. Do you play victim, rescuer or persecutor?

A TRUE STORY Kim

"My boyfriend and I were constantly 'leaving.' After a 'farewell' address, I would cry and he'd come back 'all peaches and cream,' and we'd pretend it never happened—until the next time.

Over time, I got headaches, constipation and felt rotten. In conversation, I was cheerful beyond belief. However, our relationship had gone flat.

I told a friend how difficult my mate was.

'Sounds like a victim story to me,' she said.

That bowled me over. Victim. Just like my childhood. 'No more,' I said. I told my boyfriend I wanted to feel good. I said to myself, 'He's doing himself perfectly. I don't have to engage in crazy conversation.'

The next time he left, I dragged myself from bed and took a walk. I got work done, drank water, called a friend and got a grip. I now honestly tell him what I observe and that I choose joy. He seems to hear, and things are much better."

The Problem: Co-dependent Triangle

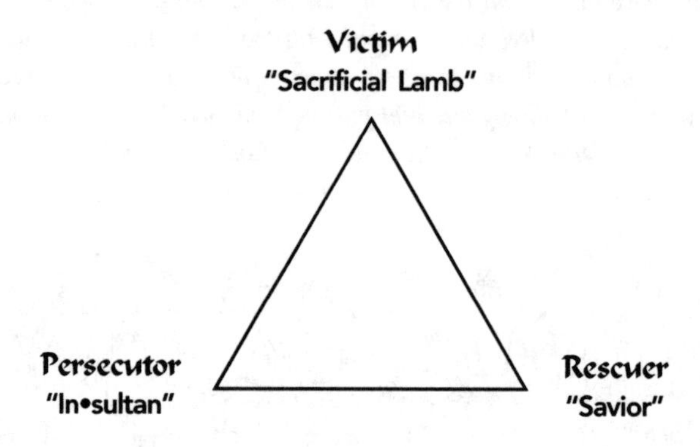

Are others feelings more important than you?
Do you ignore or deny your feelings, to take care of another?
Do you think you are selfish if you think of your feelings first?
If so, you are playing rescuer.
Make someone happy today; mind your own business.

Do you take your hurt, rage and frustration out on another?
If so, you play the persecutor role.

Do you feel weak, debilitated, stuck, hurt and abused with no way out?
Helpless and hopeless is the victim game.

Each are boring, repetitive patterns. Enough! It's time to create new, fun and dynamic relationships. Here is the solution:

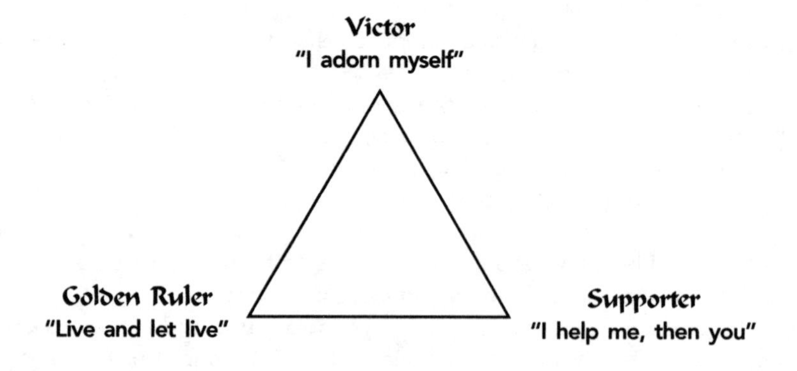

The Solution: Interdependent Triangle

One dividing line between compulsive and healthy behavior is the word "appropriate."

Picking up another golfer's golf ball is not the most appropriate way to meet new people.

Downing a six pack is not the most appropriate way to relax for an exam.

Getting stoned is not the most appropriate way to go to work or drive home.

Starving yourself to death is not the most appropriate way to live a beautiful life.

Spending more money than you have for things that you don't really need is not the appropriate way to relax.

If you want to know if your behavior is appropriate, take a deep breath, close your eyes and ask yourself, "Is my behavior appropriate?" If you feel uneasy, confused or unhappy, it's probably not. If you feel joyous or good, it probably is. Here's what happened to my client Darla:

Darla's father showed her pornography when he sexually molested her (victim). When she grew up, she devoted her life to publicly stamping out pornography in America (rescuer), while secretly complying with her husband's demands for her to pose nude for photographs (victim). She was furious at her husband and herself (persecutor), yet she did it anyway (victim).

When she acknowledged her pattern, she stopped making her life about her childhood. She told her husband, "no more photos." Her husband was startled. "I thought you enjoyed the picture taking" he said. Together they had a fine bonfire of toasted photos.

She confronted her father. He asked for forgiveness. He was no longer drinking. She forgave him.

She still is an advocate of no pornography, and it is no longer her obsession.

Magnetic Attraction That Repels

Co-dependents find each other in the world. Victims find "professional" rescuers or persecutors to play with. Then later resent them saying, "You never let me think for myself." "You never trust my judgment." The rescuer attacks (becoming a persecutor), "How dare you talk to me like that, after all I've done for you." The victim takes back the victim job and cries or withdraws. The rescuer returns, "Don't cry, I'm sorry."

Victims: Sacrificial Lamb

Stanislavski, the inventor of method acting said, "To suffer is to live," and taught performers to funnel victim games into high drama. Are your relationships high dramas?

Victims were usually neglected or abused as children. Victims subconsciously want to be saved from their underlying pain, anger, confusion or disappointment.

Do You Play Victim?

I often think, say or act as if

___ Why suffer in silence when I can moan, whimper and complain.
___ No one appreciates me.
___ I'm embarrassed to say, 'I've been terribly mistreated.
___ Poor me and after all I do.
___ Poor me. Life is so difficult.
___ Poor me.
___ I'm shattered, I'm devastated.
___ I have the worst luck.
___ Woe is me.
___ I live in poverty city. Lots of lack.
___ I feel helpless and hopeless.
___ If self pity won't get you, I nag.
___ Partners who argue are more exciting.
___ It's my fault they hit, yell or insult.
___ I tick people off.
___ I say or do bad things to myself.
___ People always let me down.
___ I am weak and helpless. Help me.
___ Nothing ever seems to work out.
___ I am ugly, stupid and disgusting.
___ My glass is half empty.
___ Why don't you just leave me alone?

Sacrificial Lamb

If any of these sound like you, you play victim—a role you may have learned long ago. Victim is an unsuccessful attempt to resolve the past by re-creating it in the present. Victims feel weak, hopeless; blame others; are sorry for themselves; control with guilt; hold others responsible for their welfare.

No one is an island. Of course, we all feel weak and need a helping hand at times. When you cross the line from moderation to overriding helplessness, you play the victim game.

Zelda is a great victim story:

A TRUE STORY Zelda

"I had the ten zillionth fight with my insensitive husband. He stormed out and slammed the door. 'Don't come back. I hate you,' I said under my breath.

Suddenly, Sister Ignacio from my second grade school popped into my mind. She whapped me with a ruler because I laughed and was disruptive.

Then I noticed what I was doing. I was, at that moment, lying on my back on the floor. One foot was on top of the other, and my arms were outstretched. Somehow, I almost felt a wreath of thorns upon my brow. Martyr was my game. That was a turning point for me. I got off my cross."

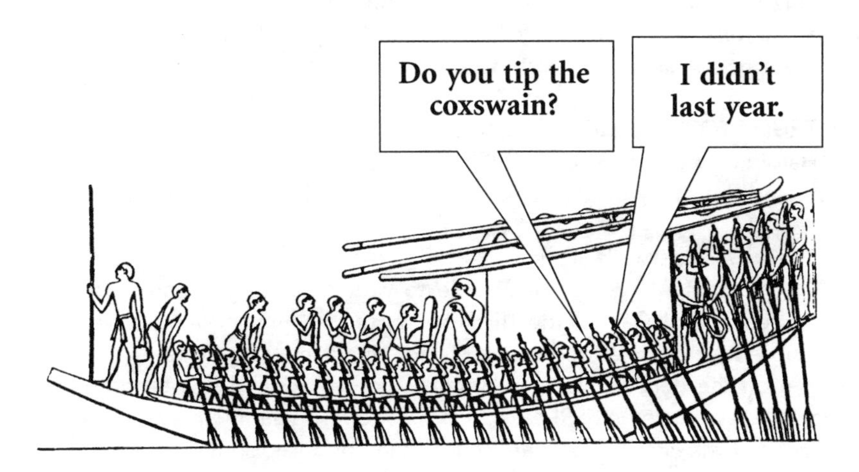

If you drown your sorrows and look for someone to go swimming with, look out! Relationships built on rescue missions usually sink. You may have adopted an "active" or a "passive" victim style.

Active Victims

"Oh, life is so difficult."
"Everything always goes wrong."
"My mate beats me."
"My kids insult me."
"My boss is terrible to me."
"My health is so poor."

The perils of Pauline. Sufferin' succotash. Ain't it awful? Active victims go public with suffering. Some are opportunists who enjoy suing people, and take full advantage of the welfare and disability system.

Passive Victims

☆ *"I used to be indecisive, now I'm not sure."*

"Take care of me."
"You know I can't take drafts."
"Remember, I can't climb stairs?"
"Could you please bring me that?"
"I'm so depressed; I'll just curl up over here and die."

Passive victims are walking open wounds. They know how to bring the house down with a sigh, or control others in subtle ways—discounting your problems and requiring you to focus upon their problems or needs. Agoraphobia, fear of leaving the house, is a popular passive victim pattern.

Some folks don't want help, they just want to play the victim game in four part harmony. Harold is a perfect example:

A TRUE STORY Harold

Harold is twenty two-years-old. In the three phone calls I had with him, he repeated this litany of problems. To underscore them he wrote this note:

"Dear Dr. Stockwell;

I regret that I have not been able to write back to you earlier to order your Peace and Calm Tape. [Editor's note: He never did] I have been diagnosed with bipolar depressive disorder. I am in a stage where I am trying to get off the Benzodiezapines (Xanex/Clonopin) which I was taking for five years and switch to an SSRI called Paxil. To refresh your memory, I have been diagnosed with Panic Disorder. I have many phobias; some major ones like mild agoraphobia and severe fear of driving alone and some minor phobias like fear of spiders and certain food anxieties.

I am sorry that I did not answer the phone when you called. I have a fear of answering the phone...

Sincerely,
Harold"

Excuse Me for Living

"Victims" who chronically apologize and repeat the hollow echo of "I'm sorry" or "I don't know" are unconsciously showing the outward sign of inward misery.

Cries For Help

Babies can't talk in words, yet communicate well with a cry that says, "Come pick me up." "Feed me." "Hold me." "Change me." If the cry is wasted, and no one comes, baby escalates the volume, for cryin' out loud. People who cry a lot as grown-ups, are victims crying for help.

When we grow up and need something, we often cry out in more "refined" ways. When not heard, we escalate by hurting ourselves, hoping someone will notice us and hear our cry, "Come pick me up." Feed me." "Hold me." "Change me." "Love me." Use the following affirmation and stop playing the Sacrificial Lamb Game.

AFFIRM SUCCESS: Victor: "I Adorn Myself"

☆ *"I decided long ago, never to walk in anyone's shadow. If I fail, or I succeed, at least I live as I believe."*

—Whitney Houston,

I forgive myself for the past and at this moment, I adopt a new attitude. I am 100% responsible for my life. Others are just folks I encounter. I choose to be happy; therefore, I take action to be happy. I claim my body, emotions, behaviors and my life. I am brave. I value the truth above all else. Each day, I learn new ways to unconditionally love and express myself. I deserve happiness and peace of mind.

Rescuer: Savior

Do You Play Rescuer?

☆ *"I've come to collect my dead friend's belongings."*
"Why doesn't he pick them up himself?"

____ I lead the casserole brigade.
____ I save every stray dog and/or every poor pathetic soul?
____ I am always the white knight in shining armor.
____ I am willing to make a mistake if someone else will learn from it.
____ I'm surrounded by weak people who can't get by without me.
____ I'm attracted to people who have bad luck. It makes me feel useful.
____ I 'help' victims because I secretly want someone to help me.

If this sounds like you, you may secretly want to be rescued. Perhaps you personify one whom you wish had rescued you when you were a child.

A rescuer is responsible for every one but themself. A rescuer often becomes "super-mom" or "super-dad," a health professional, nurse, psychologist, psychiatrist, hypnotherapist, flight attendant, neighborhood do-gooder, "activist," minister or "professional" volunteer.

Chronic rescuing comes from a subconscious desire to be rescued. Being a rescuer is the flip side of being a victim. Rescuers silently suffer as used or misunderstood martyrs.

Rescuers are fatally attracted to victims. Victims give them the opportunity to take charge of someone else's life or take the heat off themselves. Do you attempt to control others by "doing for" them?

Passive Rescuers

Worry, worry and worry.

Active Rescuers

Blatant rescuers are often at the forefront of church and service organizations and are responsible for everyone else. If you do this, read the following affirmation and give up being a Savior; it's too much work.

AFFIRM SUCCESS: Supporter: "Lemon•aid"
Read the following out loud or to yourself and affirm success.

I honor others' innate ability to run their own life. I trust that every human being is endowed with profound inner wisdom. I take responsibility for babies. I teach children to think for themselves so that they can learn to fill their own needs when they are grown.

I teach myself to tap and trust my inner wisdom. I allow others to be new each day. I assist others in ways that empower them. I enjoy empowering myself.

I trust the innate ability that (insert name) has to tap their own wisdom. I unconditionally love and I honor (insert name) ability to fulfill their own needs.

When I help others, I hold the mirror so they may 'reflect.' I only offer 'tools' for empowerment not co-dependency. I support others to solve their own problems.

Worrying makes problems worse. I now release tension—I let go. I let God. I am optimistic.

Persecutor: In•Sultan

☆ Two cannibals eating a clown: *"Does he taste funny to you?"*
—Jim Vogl

Persecutor styles resemble rage directed at them in childhood or the way they internalized or acted out their rage long ago.

Tantrums or quiet passive-aggressive people "don't get mad, they get even." This veils rage. So can put-down humor, snipes or "just kidding!"

Most persecutors express anger while slipping into denial in an out-of-control "trauma trance." After an "outburst" or "gotcha," they feel remorseful and numb.

Angry folks tend to develop their own style that resembles rage directed at them in childhood, or the way they expressed rage when small. Rage can be blatant or subtle, running the gamut from full-fledged tantrums to complete withdrawal. However it shows, rage feels ugly to all parties.

Do You Play Persecutor?

☆ Victim: *"Hit me, hurt me."*
Persecutor: *"Maybe I will and maybe I won't."*

____ People tick me off.
____ I have a bad temper.
____ I'm a grouchy, old bear.
____ I laugh at the ridiculous things you do.
____ I put myself down.
____ I overreact with anger.
____ A good scapegoat solves my problems.
____ The sweetest words: "I told you so."
____ People who fight, attract and excite me.
____ I'm mad at myself for things I say and do.
____ I hit, confront or put others in their place.
____ Recognizing my flaws leads me to the next step, blaming my parents.

Illustration by Shelley Stockwell

If you answered true to any of these questions, you play persecutor. You probably act out the role of the person who victimized you. Persecutors usually vent buried rage from the past. Ingested substances, such as drugs, alcohol, excessive sugar or caffeine can cause you to blow your stack.

A TRUE STORY Julie

"I used to pride myself in 'getting people' who hurt me. They never knew I had set it all up. It was a sick art form. I would plan and scheme revenge for months. Then, when they were 'got' (hurt), they never knew how it happened. I guess I was manipulative but, quite frankly, it felt great to out-fox those nasty dopes.

I don't do it any more, because it was too much work and took too much time. And somehow, I'm not as angry as I used to be. I guess I was just mad at my mom. Now I've forgiven her and don't want to hurt anyone.

Active Persecutors

From verbal slams to physical violence, active persecutors let us know who's boss. "I'll show you." "Do it my way or you'll be sorry."

Passive Persecutors: Digs

Passive persecutors take silent revenge. "I'll reject, withhold, or punish you for this." "You won't get the best of me, 'cause I won't give you the best of me."

For passive persecutors, put-down humor is all the rage. Snipes, though funny, hurt. Passive persecutors often grind their teeth and hurt themselves. Passive-aggressives don't get mad, they get even. If you are the victim of a persecutor, you most likely are numb and feel beaten up emotionally.

A TRUE STORY Shelley

"Before I had children, I vowed I would never yell at my kids like my mother, Irma, screamed at me. And I didn't. Instead, I put myself down with humor, at my own expense. When I had my son, Bryce, I was well controlled, unless stressed. One tense day, I heard myself yelling in my mother's voice about some trivial messy room. It was sickening.

I didn't bring Bryce into the world to absorb my rage. I never wanted him to feel like I did when my mother screamed. I changed my pattern. Now, I tell him what bugs me with a calm voice. I take charge of my behavior and I avoid stress by eating well, getting exercise, telling my truth and, if need be, I call a friend or have a good cry."

AFFIRM SUCCESS: Δ Golden Ruler: Live and Let Live

☆ *Real gold does not fear even the hottest fire.*

Read the following affirmation and take charge of your joy:

I release anger as energy in positive, non-destructive ways. I have no right or permission to attack or insult anyone—including myself. I get a grip.

I am consciously aware of my behavior and words. I express my thoughts and feelings in controlled and pleasant ways. It is not so much what I say but how I say it. I am keenly aware of my thoughts, attitudes and behavior. I listen from the heart. I am kind and give others the benefit of the doubt. I stop judging others and myself. I am caring. I ask for what I want, and I take responsibility only for myself by asking, 'Whose problem is this?' I get a grip. I respect the seasons of life. I honor children and I respect their age and process of learning.

Freedom

☆ *"Nobody can make you feel inferior without your consent."*

—Eleanor Roosevelt

To return to joy, you need to notice how you act. Then choose new behaviors that are more fun. Exaggerated roles of victim, rescuer and persecutor are mental blocks that keep us little, depressed and unconscious. Get and stay conscious.

No Mummy, I Ain't Takin' This Wrap No More

☆ *"I had a second birth when my soul and body loved one another and were married."*

—Kahlil Gabran

Imagine yourself in a gorgeous sarcophagus (coffin) inside the Great Pyramid. Your name is inscribed in hieroglyphics on a cartouche on the side of the coffin. You are tightly wrapped in bandages—pressed for time.

This is it!

Take a deep breath and unwrap yourself. As you remove each bandage one by one, depression, limiting attitudes, disappointments and anxiety peel off.

I'm free!

Stand up, climb out and stretch. You return to your true self, a magnificent body, full of energy and movement.

Pharaoh thee well.

A portal opens. Follow the light and leave this sacred tomb. Your eyes adjust easily to the light. You walk tall. You are the kind and loving ruler of yourself.

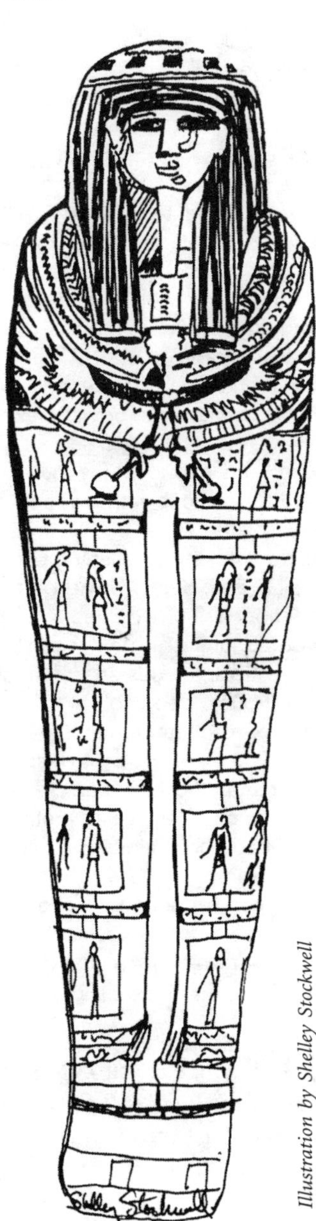

Illustration by Shelley Stockwell

Good-bye my mummy,
Good-bye my daddy.
Good-bye the helpless waif.
Hello me, grown up and free.
I'm perfect, strong, and safe.

INNER•VIEW QUIZ

Are You Depressed?

Rate the following. Dare to be honest. I think, act or feel:

	Often	Sometimes	Rarely
My life is dull and flat.	____	____	____
I'm depressed.	____	____	____
I have negative thoughts and attitudes.	____	____	____
I feel rotten, sad and/or empty a lot.	____	____	____
I pick on myself/beat myself up.	____	____	____
I hate myself.	____	____	____
I have no appetite or I eat 'til I "burst."	____	____	____
I have constipation/diarrhea.	____	____	____
If I get my feelings hurt, I go into high drama.	____	____	____
My energy is low or I never stop moving.	____	____	____
I am numb and/or immobilized.	____	____	____
I hurt physically.	____	____	____
I hurt mentally	____	____	____
I'm overly emotional or withdrawn.	____	____	____
I often cry or feel like crying.	____	____	____
I have no control over my moods.	____	____	____
I hate to be alone with my thoughts.	____	____	____
I feel isolated.	____	____	____
I hold my breath or hardly breathe.	____	____	____
If I kill myself; others would be better off.	____	____	____
I feel hopeless or worthless.	____	____	____
I have no interest in sex or can't get satisfaction.	____	____	____
I am restless, anxious and/or irritable.	____	____	____
I have trouble sleeping.	____	____	____
I can't concentrate, remember or make decisions.	____	____	____
I can't "snap out of" past disappointment or loss.	____	____	____
I am spiritually constipated.	____	____	____
I suffer from: ulcers, colitis, irritable bowel, headaches, migraines, asthma, arthritis, fibromylgia and/or chronic fatigue.	____	____	____
I have friends I don't like, books I don't read, shoes I don't wear and do things I don't enjoy, projects I don't complete.	____	____	____

Any one of these disabling symptoms can keep you from feeling great.

☆ Question: *Are you Depressed?*
Answer: *If life isn't fun and you're numb or glum:*
You've got some.

—Shelley Stockwell

Chapter 5
Depression
Gloom and Dune

The Denial Triangle begins if you feel sad, awful, stressed and frustrated with no place to go. The trick is to learn how to cope with depression while standing in it. Reading this chapter will show you how to recognize depression so you can take yourself from the pit to the peak.

▲ How You Dune?
▲ Signs of Depression: Wreck-We-Am
▲ What Causes Depression?
▲ How Do You Get To Camel-Lot?

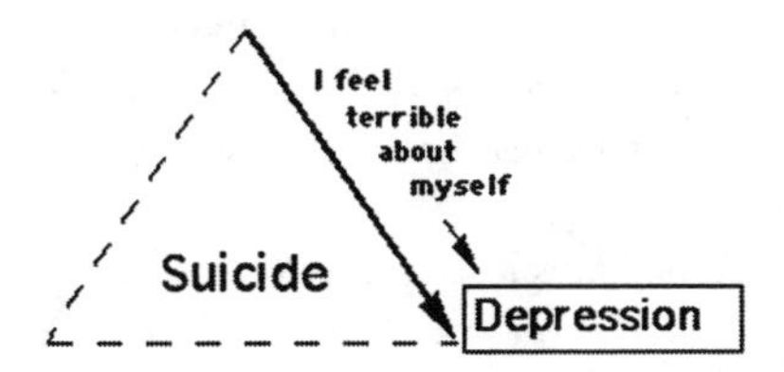

Depression An area sunk below its surroundings—moroseness, mood, brood, gloom, doom, blues, grief, mourning, sad, overwhelmed, helpless, hopeless, conflicted. Usually includes self-blame and pessimism.

Doldrums A part of the ocean near the equator where winds are mild.

The Great Depression *"When the Republican congress passed the Smoot-Hartley Tariff on imported products, all other nations retaliated and world commerce froze. Then the federal reserve abruptly contracted credit for the banking system, which collapsed the stock market bubble that was built on credit. It was called a 'panic' until (then president) Herbert Hoover said, 'This is not a panic. The business men are just depressed'. And that is how the Great Depression got its name."*

—Tom Cobb

Photo by Jon Nicholas

☆ *"Depression is a physical biochemical disorder that affects your entire body, mind, and soul. It affects your personality, who you are, the way you think, the way you feel about yourself, and ultimately, the perceived failure or success of your entire life."*

—Robert Smith

☆ DEPRESSION

What is it of your disposition
That puts you in this glum condition?
Take some time. Put on the light
And stay at home for one whole night
To view the movie that is your life.
And decide if that movie feels real true; for you
And if it doesn't, here's what you do:

Gather the strength, put yourself on the line
And take a risk; this really works fine.
And say, "Just what I want for me?"
That's what it takes to break you free.
For it's harder to stew in depressing old juices
Convincing yourself and making excuses
Than moving ahead with the excitement of change
For movement is living and stagnation is strange.

Your life is a sculpture to mold as you will.
You're not a victim of mom, your mate or your pills
Your life's a pattern of thinking that's your own design.
Take a chance, move ahead, now is the time.

—Shelley Stockwell

All of us get depressed. I'm not talking about someone else. I'm talking about you.

Some people believe they should never feel bad. But a variety of moods are normal. We all experience joy and harmony and on occasion, upset, sadness, anxiety or anger. Depression can manifest in numbing ways or in wild hysteria.

Some people experience short-term depression because of a problem that never recurs; a trauma or loss and "abra•cadaver," in one "swell foop," they spiral down into depression.

For others, depression lingers and life loses luster.

If your life is flat, this kind of flattery gets you nowhere but upset. A depressed mind is fatigued, negative, pained, numb, anxious and restless. Numb or hyperactive, depressing symptoms can last for weeks, months or years. Not everyone experiences every symptom. Yet, if you experience any one of them, they keep you from optimum joy and radiant health.

Depression is discomfort with no place to go. Depression feels terrible. It's not living, it's stagnation: like going down the sewer in a slow glass-bottom boat. It feels terrible and worse than that; it's boring!

▲ How You Dune? Overviews of the Blues

☆ *"Storms come and go. The winds become a whisper."*
—The Storm Within (movie)

☆ Question: *"How did Cleopatra know she was depressed?"*
Answer: *"She asped."*

ASP yourself: "Are you depressed?"
Answer honestly.

Stag-Nation

Illustration by Shelley Stockwell

Put downs, stress, chronic illness, personal loss, financial loss and radical changes in life style can set off depression. The resulting deep sense of sadness may cause more stress, chronic illness, personal and financial loss and radical changes in life style. It's a down hill spiral.

The more depressed you feel, the more depressed you feel and the less likely you are to get help. And, if you accept mood swings, negativity, health problems and anti-social behavior as normal, you might not even notice that you are depressed.

Spin the Barrel, Pull the Trigger and Take Your Chances

☆ *"All antidepressants may create the following side effects: headaches, nausea, nervousness, insomnia and agitation."*
—U.S. Institute of Mental Health

People try to solve a problem with things that caused the problem in the first place. So it is with depression. Drugs, peculiar eating, tobacco, alcohol, sugar, caffeine, self-destructive behavior and negative thinking: dehydrate, fatigue, frazzle and depress.

Although a blues bout may be a temporary one-time sinker, health care practitioners often prescribe anti-depressants. Read the small print and you'll discover that many of these drugs *cause* anxiety.

Chemicals don't resolve underlying problems; they cause more depression. If you resist drugs and change your mindset, in the words of Ross Perot, "problem solved."

A shocking solution is electro-convulsive or "shock therapy" for depression. For this, a cattle prod is used and brain cells are shocked to death. Now that's depressing!

Beware! Drugs Can Depress

If you are depressed you might consider drugs as a cause. (For more information on the ill effects of prescription drugs, see Chapter 9: *Addictions.*)

Depression may be created or made worse by many prescription medications including:

Antidepression Medications: Xanax, Valium and other sedatives. Prozac, Paxil, Zoloft and Luvox
High Blood Pressure and Hypertension Meds: anti-arrhythmics, prednisone & other corticosteroids
Glaucoma Medication
Oral Contraceptives
Antihistamines
Pain Pills
Ulcer Medication
Arthritis Medication
Appetite Suppressants

☆ *"Even if you've been taking medication for six months to a year and then begin to experience the blues, it could be your medication."*
—Dr. Arthur Jacknowitz
W. Virginia University School of Pharmacy

▲ Signs of Depression: Wreck•we•am

☆ TICKLISH SITUATION
A hammock's dandy for repose"
Until a horsefly finds your nose.
—Dick Wheeler

Illustration by Jeff Bucchino

Someone who's depressed looks like a walking open wound. Their outward signs are obvious: flatness of face and voice, shallow breathing, lack of vitality and movement. A droopy body, shoulders rolled forward and head hung down, makes depression look like a kind of physical compression. Radical up-and-down mood swings and wild hysteria are also depression tip offs.

The inward signs of sadness, loneliness, lack of energy, numbness, anxiety, hurt, upset and negative thinking are obvious too—when you stop denying. Depression may appear in babies as "colic" and eating and sleeping disturbances; in toddlers as chronic nightmares and strong separation anxiety and in early childhood as learning and sleep disorders or hyperactivity. Withdrawn, hard-to-manage and accident-prone children may be depressed.

Mummified Life.

☆ Question: *"Is it true that ignorance and apathy are ruling the world?"*
Answer: *"I don't know and I don't care."*

—Joe Brown

☆ Disturbing Patterns
There was a young man of the Clyde,
Who went to a funeral and cried.
When asked who was dead,
he stammered and said,
"I don't know, I just came for the ride."

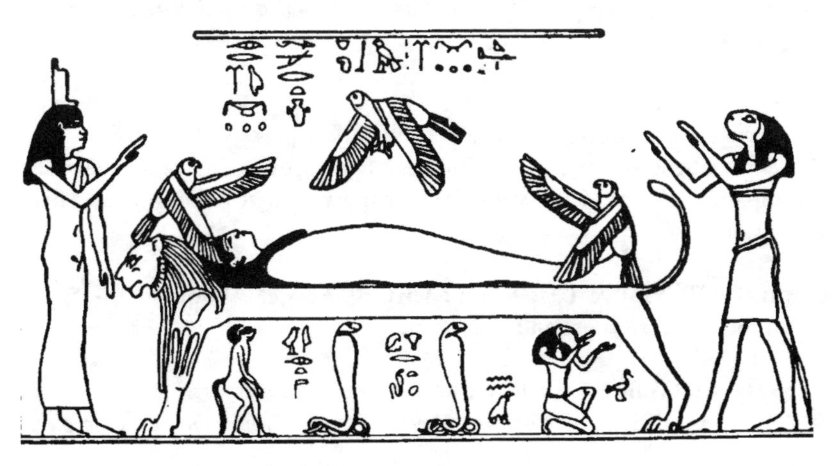

Do you wake up tired saying:
"I never get enough sleep" or
"I sleep all the time, and never want to get out of bed?"
If you are fatigued, can't sleep, and yet want to sleep all the time, suspect depression.

"I go numb when I eat; I eat to go numb."
Changes in appetite—obsessive hunger and/or no appetite—and rapid yo-yoing weight up and down, also signal depression.

Panic attacks, sadness, worry, disturbing thoughts or dreams, and unremitting irritability can also signal depression. So can being suddenly and chronically accident-prone.

Down Attitude

"I don't know what I want." "I'm a failure." "I never do things right."

It's not fun to play army when you're always the enemy.

If life is bad news; you've got the blues. Unhappy, dissatisfied, restless, helpless, hopeless, sad, empty and overwhelmed feelings are a tip-off of depression. "What's the use? I might as well just quit." "I wish I were dead" really translates into "I really want to stop the pain."

"I really want to stop the pain."

Mental Fatigue and Pain

☆ *"Lack of decisiveness is probably a bad trait... on the other hand, maybe it's not."*

—Shelley Stockwell

"It's difficult to keep up any more."

"I have trouble concentrating and making decisions."

Mental fatigue in the form of dullness, hyperactivity and restlessness often accompanies gloom. Over-stress saps vitality and joy from you. This is depression.

Confusion: If You've Lost Your Memory, Forget About It

"I procrastinate, forget and space-out."

Sadness and Guilt, Ain't It a Shame

☆ *"Sometimes, I think it's a shame; I get feelin' better when I'm feelin' no pain."*

Sadness is a straightforward reaction to loss. Self-blame and pessimism increase depression. Was guilt and shame a manipulation used to got you to do things you didn't want to do or didn't feel right about doing? Manipulative parents, who control with guilt trips, teach guilt. Guilt and shame can really get you down; give it up. Guilt is anger turned inward. Guilt robs you of self-confidence and self-esteem. For God's sake, forgive yourself.

Anger and Rage: Lamb-basted

☆ *"Resentment is like taking poison and waiting for the other person to die."*
—Malachy McCourt

Unrelenting irritability may signal depression vulnerability.

It takes a healthy person only fifteen seconds to release anger. Then it's over. Yet, society tells us not to express anger. "Stuff it." "Be good little boys and girls."

Attack•y Act

If we follow this advice, suppressed anger continually surfaces toward others or ourselves. Put down humor, aggressive behavior, and rages are outward signs. Hostile self-talk, self-abuse, and depression are inner signs.

Physical Discomfort

If you're depressed, you feel physically rotten, physically sensitive to pain, or feel nothing. Such discomfort rarely responds to "treatment." Persistent aches, heart palpitations, difficult breathing, dizziness, headaches, digestive problems, constipation, diarrhea, and arthritis-like symptoms commonly cause or are caused by depression.

Illness: Lost in the Malady

☆ *"How is Mabel anyway?"*
"She is, as we say, enjoying ill health."
—Shelley Stockwell

Depression can cause illness and illness can cause depression. Chronic illness, like gastric ulcers, irritable bowel syndrome, colitis, headaches, migraines, sinus problems, asthma, arthritis, fibromyalgia, upper respiratory and chronic fatigue may contribute to or activate depressing changes in brain chemistry.

Sexual Letdown

Can't keep it up? Maybe you're down. An apathetic libido could be the blues incognito. Decreased energy makes us lose interest in pleasurable activities, including sex. Antidepressant drugs commonly cause even more sexual dysfunction and depression.

Anxiety High

When negative thoughts or fears control behavior, your brain chemistry responds with depression. Fear, worry, nervousness, anxiety, difficulty handling stress and irritability may mean a depression cork is popping.

Europe, You're Down, You're All Over the Place

☆ Patient: *"I'm manic depressive."*
Doctor: *"Calm down. Cheer up. Calm down. Cheer up."*

Are you sometimes on top of the world and at other times, the world is on top of you? An emotional roller coaster ride, out of control, with strong mood swings, is what psychologists label "manic depressive." Such depression may not be obvious at first. After all, sometimes you feel terrific. A manic high can go for days with little or no sleep. You're not just happy YOU ARE ECSTATIC! Then, the roller coaster dips, and down you go into the pits of pain and YOU ARE IN AGONY.

"Mania" is the up side of medically categorized "manic depression" or "bipolar depression." According to the National Institute of Mental Health, it may include inappropriate elation, irritability, severe insomnia, grandiose notions, increased talking, disconnected and racing thoughts, increased sexual desire, markedly increased energy, poor judgment and inappropriate social behavior.

The Silent Scream or How to Stay Depressed

☆ *We cough to clear our throats*
We sigh to clear our hearts

Poor diet. Poor air. Poor me.
Booze, sugar, negativity.
Breathing air from an exhaust pipe
Hanging around with people I don't like.
Snorting drugs, puffing leaves
Calling myself a slug or sleaze.
Not expressing true emotion,
Being invisible or making a commotion.
Living the past and not my dream.
Makes me want to cry and scream…
I'm a wreck, I'm a mess
in simple terms: I'm depressed.

—Shelley Stockwell

The Silent Scream

▲ What Causes Depression?

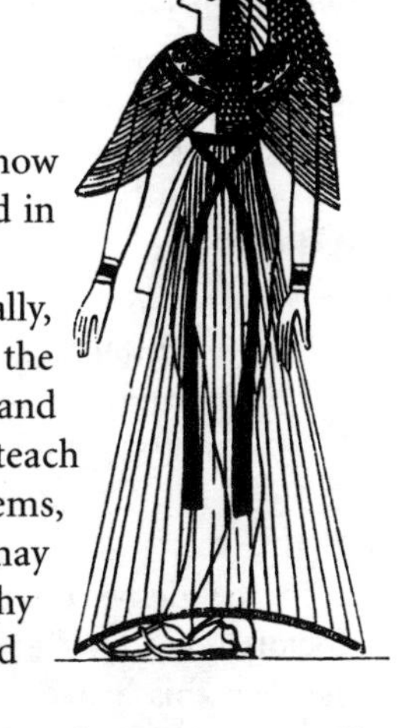

☆ *"Women in ancient Egypt wore corsets."*
—Bertha DaBlues

Depression results from internal and external stress, now and in the past. Hurtful happenings in utero, at birth and in life can cause depression. So can a shock.

If you were abandoned, neglected or abused—verbally, emotionally, physically or sexually—and have not cleared the pain or conflict, you may be depressed. Family secrets and traditions of depression, self-abuse and self-neglect teach depression. A difficult relationship, financial problems, ingested chemicals or any dramatic change in life may activate depression. A person can appear perfectly healthy one moment, take cocaine, eat chocolate or sugar and suddenly become severely depressed.

Low self-esteem, stress, chronic illness, loss and abrupt change can set off depression. Conversely, depression can create low self-esteem, stress, chronic illness, loss and radical change. Without healthy ways to express hurt, disappointment, terror and confusion, depression results.

The More Negative You Are, The More Negative You Become

If your parents were depressed, you may be too. Depressed parents are sad role models. They can't be positive and self-abusive at the same time, even if they try.

Studies show that we're positively or negatively influenced by those around us. The more negative the people around us, the more negative we become. Conversely, the more positive the people around us, the more positive we become.

Pre-Disposition?

☆ *"Most people are as happy as they make up their minds to be."*
—Abe Lincoln

Womb Gloom

There is some evidence that some people are born depressed.

Your mother was born with you, the egg, inside her. You shared your mother's chemical experiences throughout her/your entire egg life. When you became joined to dad's sperm, you took on his chemistry, too. As a fetus, whatever Mommy put into her body went directly into your body. If you were exposed to caffeine, drugs, nicotine, sugar, salt or alcohol, you took substances early.

Were you born stressed by drugs? As Conn and Silverman note, an American born in 1990 had a one-in-ten chance of being exposed to illegal drugs in utero.

Did Mom or Dad have drugs or alcohol in their system when you were conceived? Did Mom smoke? Drink? Or use drugs during "our" pregnancy? Did she take prescription medicine? Was your birth a drugged birth? Were you marinated in toxicity?

No one knows the long-term effects of drugs on a developing fetus.

Baby Blues

☆ *"As soon as you're born they make you feel small*
by giving you no love instead of it all
'til the pain is so big you feel nothing at all."

—John Lennon
"Working Class Hero"

In the delivery room, your parents and the doctor didn't look at you and ask, "How can we mess up this baby?" Grown-ups usually want the best for babies.

Birth trauma alone places enormous stress on a baby. Drugs and emotional upset compound this (a fact borne out by my thousands of rebirthing hypnosis regressions). Forceps, being pushed back in, laid upon a cold table or greeted by, "Oh, God, not another baby" can ruin a newborns whole day...and many days that follow.

Did Mom want you?

Did she try to abort you?

Babies are given shots or drugs to "protect" them from childhood disease. However, experts say that drugs given in infancy may not leave the spinal column for as long as three years! The long-term effects of most drugs are unknown.

Drugs "condition" children to future drug taking.

What shots were you given in childhood, and could they be related to any problems you have today?

Some neglected babies literally die if they are not held and loved. Infants and children, who are berated, hit, ignored, violated or insulted, feel terrible. When bad things happen, with no way to express hurt, depression begins and sets the groundwork for coping patterns you may use to this day. Imagine living an entire life from decisions you made as an infant!

Did you have sugar in your formula? Both sugar and caffeine depress.

The Adolescent Depressant

Being a teenager is depressing. Depressed teens and young adults may have radical mood swings, defiance, volatility and crying spells. No wonder some teenagers identify with bands with names like the Grateful Dead.

A TRUE STORY Stella

"I was so ashamed. As an actress, I had to keep an image in the world, but underneath, my life was a chaos of sneaking, stuffing and regurgitating. I was so depressed. My teeth were starting to loosen and I hadn't had a period for three years—and no one knew.

I was a depressed teen the first time I purged. I was at boarding school and we ordered pizza. One of the girls said, 'I know the best diet in the world. You can eat as much as you want, as long as you throw up afterwards.' We all thought it was a great idea, so we threw up together. The problem was, I continued this pattern for years.

During hypnotherapy with Shelley, I had a remarkable rebirthing experience. I recalled my mother trying to abort me.

When I was small, I remember hearing her throw up in the bathroom.

I've toughed out six months of Overeaters Anonymous, hypnosis and hungry news reporters. I feel good for the first time. It was the combination of remembering, being around others with the same problem, and my determination to stop being like Mom that made me well. My relief is immeasurable."

Dooms Bury

☆ *Mother, you had me, but I never had you.*
I wanted you, but you didn't want me...
Father, you left me, but I never left you.
I needed you, but you didn't need me."

—John Lennon, "Mother"

Were your parents emotionally available?

Hormonal shifts from birth, birth control pills and other drugs, may trigger post-partum depression or "the baby blues." If mom has the blues, baby may too.

If no one protected you or allowed you to express feelings, you are probably depressed. Caretakers, who don't know how to love themselves, can't teach love very well. How can they fill a child's needs if they can't fill their own?

If "stifle thyself" was a family dictum, this too is a bummer. You can't stifle your needs, talents and gifts without feeling pain.

Part•um Me, Mom

☆ *"...post-partum depression is a transient phenomenon...with a biological cause."*
—George Chrousos

At the National Institutes of Health, endocrinologist George Chrousos has studied hormone secretions in mothers. He found that new mothers have lower-than-normal stress-fighting hormones, sometimes as low as depressed patients. The lower the level, the more depressed the women. Chrousos speculates that these low levels of CRH (corticotropin-releasing hormone) occur because the placenta, which raised this level during pregnancy to support the additional stress of birthing, is no longer there. It takes a while for the hypothalamus to get the signal that it needs to make more CRH.
—Discover Magazine

Depressing Drama

☆ *A guy answers a knock on the door and finds a snail standing there.*
He picks up the snail and throws it out the window.
Two years later, he answers a knock at the door and there is the snail who says: "What was that all about?"

Children are usually bit players in the family drama. Depressed caretakers don't know how to encourage kids to be perfectly themselves and model depressing life skills. Did you have a depressed parent? What part did you play in the family drama? Are you still playing it today?

Lower•glyphics

A lot of depression comes from painful experiences that happened to us when we're not supported, protected or honored and then coerced to not express truth.

For example, let's say that at age 4, Uncle Bentley (or a priest, teacher, or neighbor) violated you sexually. Maybe you didn't go to Mommy and Daddy because of fear, shame and guilt." If you did, you're told, "I don't want to hear that kind of talk. It never happened. Don't you dare tell anyone. Now stop crying and go to your room."

Higher•glyphics.

A healthy child's world has grown-ups to protect and honor your truth; and trauma is easily over-ridden.

I•deal Communication

Mommy and Daddy, in a perfect world, would say:

"Why sweetheart, that's terrible. They should not do such a thing to you. Let's call in Uncle Bentley and all the neighbors, relatives, the authorities, and friends. Let it be known Uncle Bentley violated this precious one. 'Uncle Bentley stop your inappropriate behavior, immediately'. You need help. Until you behave properly, all children will avoid you."

The result: No family secrets. No saving face. No abuse compounding abuse. Depression was easily processed, healed and released because you are supported in full, honest and complete communication.

Shut Up and Shut Down

Silence "like a cancer grows." Did you shut up and shut down by punishing yourself for crimes you believed you committed? Did you protect those who trespassed against you? If so, you could be depressed.

For you to be emotionally healthy, you need healthy expression. Accept the fact that our past won't get any better and go from now into the future.

Photo by Gerry Lumian

Precious Little Jewels

American Indian babies are thought of as pieces of precious jade, fresh from Mother Earth. Each separate and unique piece is flawless. The job of the parents is to not interfere with the integrity of this wonderful stone, only to polish a rough edge here and there.

It's Stifling in Here

Trauma triggers fear, hurt, rage, confusion, excitement and/or anxiety. If abuse or neglect traumatized you, you may still feel terrible. Witness another being abused or neglected, and you still experience trauma. TV or movie violence is also traumatic, because subconscious minds, especially young ones, often can't discern between reality and fiction.

Trauma brings up powerful feelings that need expression. If these emotions are stifled, they don't go away but turn into depression. Unexpressed negative feelings create energy that stays in the body and needs release. Drugs, fear and numbing behaviors meant to suppress hurt actually intensify depression and waste valuable energy as well—energy that could be spent having fun, being productive and loving. Numbing isn't living. It's slow-motion suicide.

A TRUE STORY Abby

Abby always chose rejecting men. She clung desperately to her abusive husband who put her down, demanded perfection, choked and beat her. During a hypnotic regression she found out why:

Shelley: "What's going on?"

Abby: (little voice and crying) "I'm inside my Mommy's belly."

Shelley: "Why are you crying?"

Abby: "My Mommy doesn't want me here. She is trying to kill me."

Shelley: "What are you going to do about it baby?"

Abby: "I'm going to prove to her that I am loveable. Then she'll be glad she had me..."

GENETIC DEPRESSION: Chip Off the Old Block

☆ *"Substance abuse and depression are often inherited together."*

—The US National Institute of Mental Health

To determine if you are genetically depressed, look in your genes. Genetic depression is referred to as "sugar imbalance," by biochemists. Do your relatives have suspicious symptoms? Maybe they "taught" you unhealthy ways biochemically. But don't worry, all depression can be overridden with a healthy life style and positive thinking.

Illustration by Shelley Stockwell

Science is proving that environment controls and activates genes, not the other way around. Make a positive world for yourself, and you pull down downer genes.

Pull-Downer Genes Research

☆ *"Depression is the result of a mysterious link between genes and environmental factors. There is an alarming generational trend that suggests that some environmental factors increase the incident of mood disorders in people who are genetically susceptible to such disorders."*

—Elliot Gershon
National Institute of Mental Health
—Ronald Rieder, Director of Research
Columbia University Scientific American

In a study of the differences between biology and environment, Loring Ingraham and Paul Wender studied 67 adults who had been adopted as children. Those with depressed biological parents were twice as likely to develop depression or substance abuse (usually alcoholism) than those whose parents were not depressed.

Growing Pains

The onset of depression has been linked to hormonal shifts that take place during life passages. Perhaps the following case study of Gloria was exacerbated by the hormones of puberty:

Photo By Bryce Stockwell

A TRUE STORY Gloria

"My ugliness started in the sixth grade when I got eyeglasses. I had bronchitis and I stayed home for half the year. I felt ugly inside and out. I had ugly glasses and an ugly permanent in my hair. When I went to the dance with Michael, my blouse would not stay tucked in. My friend Mary was fat. We looked like Mutt and Jeff. Cute boys would not even look at me. I was supposed to be a boy; that's what my parents really wanted. I tried to be one of the boys. I did boy things, not girl things. I was afraid that if I was beautiful, I would have to go to bed with boys. People would then talk about me behind my back and say I was a slut. If I was beautiful, I would have to live up to other peoples' adoration.

With the help of hypnosis, I now have a different focus on the past. The truth is, that if I had let myself feel pretty, I would have had a wonderful time. I would have been in the center of attention. I would have loved myself.

I screwed myself up by feeling ugly. I punished myself by making myself ugly. I survived junior high and high school by withdrawing and not being in the forefront. I am not going to screw myself up anymore. I am beautiful."

Mood Lighting

Environment affects your mood. Limited sunlight and poor air, diet, water and sleep can "bad vibe" us into depression. So can foods with pesticides, hormones and drugs (in any combination). All these stressors create negative chemical reactions in the central nervous system.

SAD

INNER•VIEW QUIZ

Are You SAD?

1. I experience fatigue in winter but not in summer.
2. Work and family life are more difficult to cope with in the winter.
3. I eat more starch and sugar in the winter.
4. When it's dark and cold, I get the blues.
5. I feel fine in the spring and summer.
6. I suffer from PMS.

If these describe you, expose yourself to early morning light for thirty minutes a day for two weeks and you'll feel perky as a daisy.

Some folks experience a winter-season funk that grows worse as the days grow shorter. Brought on by winter's darker grip, seasonal depression, or seasonal affective disorder (SAD), is caused by lack of full-spectrum lighting. For some, this triggers chemical changes in the body that translates into depression.

Dark rooms make people more depressed than bright rooms. If you wear dark sunglasses in the winter, you get a double dose of darkness. A decrease in light can lower seratonin levels. Open the curtains, trim obstructing shrubs and use full-spectrum Chroma 50-watt light bulbs and rods. Expose yourself to light by going outdoors or sitting by a window.

Sunlight is a fuel for humans. Jaundiced babies exposed to sunlight pink right up. If you are susceptible to depression, let there be light!

INTO•GREAT POWER EXERCISE

Color Me HAPPY!

The colors you wear affect mood. Wear the colors that make you cheery and leave black clothes in the closet. Wear whites, pastels or brights—anything that is cheery. And stand up straight! Good posture gets you out of a slump. The more you uplift your immediate environment, the more energized you become.

Swallow the Rainbow

☆ *Close your eyes.*
Breathe in and out three times and see yourself swallowing a rainbow.
Sense and feel the uplift this gives you.
Stay with the feeling for a minute, then open your eyes.

—Gerald Epstein, M.D.
Healing Visualizations

Add color and light to your environment and you'll be more energized.

▲ How Do You Get To Camel•lot?

For Crying Out Loud: Good Grief

☆ TEARS
Tears are from islands salty with sea
washing my pain to the outside of me.

—Bryce Stockwell (Age 4)

Loss may trigger depression. Losing a relationship, pet, job, home, country or possessions can cause extreme pain. Your emotions are not static. Energy in

Illustration by Shelley Stockwell

Camel Lot

motion = e-motion. E-motion constantly moves from one emotion to another.

If you suffer a loss, you need to express grief. Grief is a natural and healthy response. A loved one dying or divorce, makes us feel abandoned and shocked. This may evoke overwhelming emotional outbursts that comes close to pleasure. Allow yourself to have a good old-fashioned cry. It's a great release.

If allowed full expression, grief can heal. If grief becomes a re•creation•all activity, it creates more grief.

Mourn enough, but not too much. A good way to do this is to set an alarm for 15 minutes. Tell yourself: "I give myself 15 minutes for a pity party. Then I'll do something like take a walk, groom the dog or soak in the bath.

Your rendition of any story is based to some degree on your mood at the time of that experience. As you get happier, the story becomes less tragic.

Your body chemistry responds to emotions. Stress and prolonged activation of the hypothalamus, cause a chain reaction of imbalances. Depression is an upset in the delicate chemistry of neuro-transmitters; that part of your brain that sends electrical signals.

The hypothalamus secretes cortotropin-releasing chemicals, which in turn stimulates the pituitary gland to produce adrenocorticotropin, which then stimulates the release of cortisol. Natural seratonin levels drop. When cortisol is excessive and seratonin is low, we feel depressed.

Women cry more easily than men because their lachrymal glands are different. Also, they have fifty to sixty percent higher prolactin hormone levels than a man. Prolactin effects your tearing threshold. A women is more likely to get teary before her

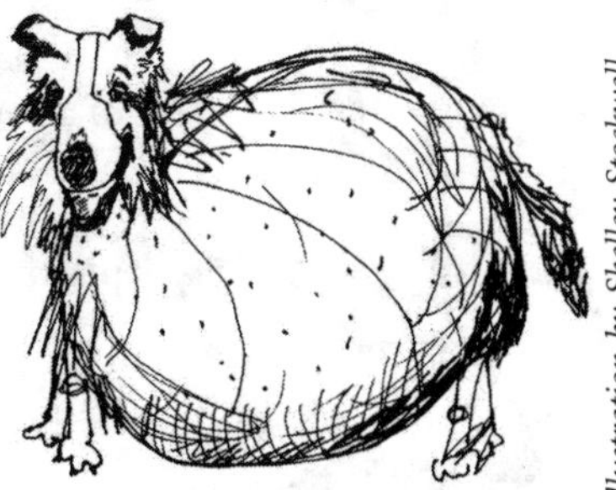

Illustration by Shelley Stockwell

Melon-collie

period because of these hormones.

When in good health, your brain monitors your cortisol level and keeps it in balance. But when you're depressed, your cortisol level is excessive. You can instantly raise your seratonin level with positive thinking, laughing and proper nutrition.

INTO•GREAT POWER EXERCISE

Good Mourning

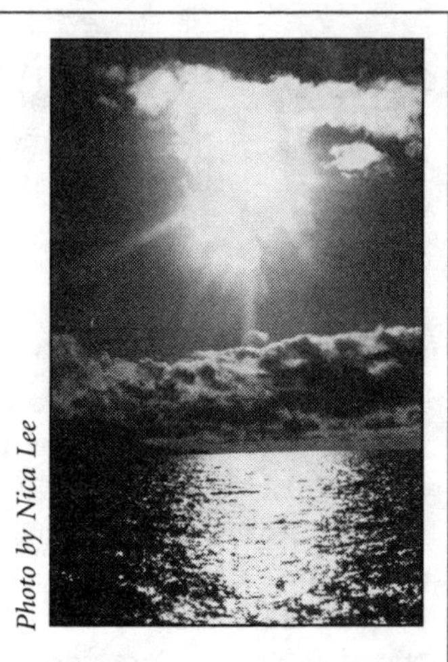
Photo by Nica Lee

▲ Imagine a wise and loving presence on the other side (i.e., Moses, Mary, Buddha, Jesus, Quan Yin, a totem animal, a departed loved one—any image that means something for you).

▲ Imagine your lost beloved taken into the loving arms of this wise one.

▲ Send them (or it) light saying, "I release you with love."

▲ Take a deep breath, and let them go. Affirm:

"I refuse to die with the dead. Each day, I honor them with a blessing or prayer, a good word or two, and I consciously bring myself back to the land of the living. I choose to shine my light enhanced by having known them."

Get into Action: S.M. O. K.

☆ *Experts agree, nearly all cases of depression can be reversed, even the most serious ones.*
—The Doctor's Book of Home Remedies

What can you do if you are a few french-fries short of a happy meal? There are many ways to help yourself become un-depressed. Do them—they work!

Above all else, do something positive. Anything positive. Step toward feeling great. Do it now.

Take One Bite at a Time.

☆ *"The main thing is to keep the main thing the main thing."*

—Jewel Diamond Taylor

How do you eat an elephant?

One bite at a time!

Set little goals for yourself. You don't have to feel perfectly well in one day's time. Little by little, every day, allow yourself to feel better and better. Break down monumental tasks into small ones. And then do only as much as you can. Lower your expectations to fit reality.

Sad Ain't Bad

Don't get sadder because you're sad. It's your job as a human to have a few downs. Downers aren't drowners. A mother may have strong emotional reactions while pregnant and giving birth. It's nature's way. Babies cry to communicate: hunger, dirty diapers, a need to be held and to make sure that you don't forget about them. For a baby, crying is their main form of exercise; it generates warmth, increases lung capacity, burns off energy, tension and increases alertness. Crying eases stress; it may allow you to absorb endorphins through the nose. Perhaps that is why you feel better after a good cry. If you have a down day; say, "Oh, well, tomorrow will birth a higher high."

Think it Out

Sometimes, just understanding a problem makes you feel better. Ask yourself: What's really bugging me?" If what's bugging you is an unfulfilled or unrealistic expectation, give it up or check it out. If you think someone is lying to you, ask him or her.

INTO•GREAT POWER EXERCISE

Breaking Free

- **Get Funky** Right now feel/think your misery: _______ (stuck, dejected, immobilized, angry, miserable, anxious, worthless, guilty, helpless, hopeless, lost, numb, sad).
- **Rather** How would you rather feel/think? _______________ (free, happy, energized, peaceful, joyous, relaxed, valuable, forgiving, in control, hopeful, vital, proud, loving, loved).
- **Solution** What could you do right now to feel or think the way you'd rather feel or think? ______________________________.
- **Action** Do something in this moment that allows you to feel or think the way you'd rather feel or think (smile, move, think a pleasant or happy thought, take a bath, take a walk, laugh…).

Eat Happy Foods

Garbage in, garbage out. Feed yourself healthy food and drink. Make sure you eat regular, healthy meals and avoid foods that depress: sugar, caffeine, alcohol, aged cheeses and meats (and for some wheat and dairy).

B vitamin complex and 1000-3000 milligrams of the amino acid L-tyrosine is reported to cheer up many.

Women who lower their cholesterol levels through diet feel more positive about life, according to a study at the State University of New York at Stony Brook.

Be Gentle with Yourself and Others

It's time to stop picking on yourself. Lower your expectations to fit reality. Do not permit yourself to snipe at others, because they will snipe back, and that's the last thing you need.

Avoid Big Decisions

Postpone monumental decisions until you feel better. The person you divorce, the job you quit or decisions you make, could be distorted by pain.

Move

☆ *"After all is said and done, do more and say less."*

—Shelley Stockwell

Moping around the house makes you more depressed. If you do something active, anything active, you elevate your attitude. Pushing the button on the remote control doesn't qualify as activity. Volunteer, take a class or complete a project.

Studies show that an hour a day of brisk walking helps severely depressed people as well as psychotherapy. If you are too spun out to move, get a friend or family member to walk with you. One step at a time, take a walk.

Light activity, gardening, strolling through an art museum, shopping, doing the laundry, being active in any way releases happy chemicals into your being. This strengthens body wellness and combats osteoporosis. Studies show that every hour of activity may add one and one-half hours to your life. Play cards. Go to a movie—a funny movie. Read a book. Do volunteer work. Visit someone. Choose to be around people in social situations. Find pleasurable diversions and company.

Let Pain Go

☆ *"I woke up feeling great today."*
"Where did you go right?"

Do a symbolic act, like writing down a list of everything that bothers you...then burn it.

Seek Joyous Challenges

☆ *"Sit down before fact, like a little child, and be prepared to give up every preconceived notion. Follow humbly to wherever and to whatever abyss nature leads and you shall learn."*

—T. H. Huxley

Positive action makes you feel challenged, not beaten. Be of service. Volunteer. Find healthy ways. Learn something new.

Talk to Someone

Help yourself by getting help. See Chapters 16 and 30 for help getting help.

Take Time To Be with Yourself

☆ *"Throughout history, our ancestors have had enlightenment experiences on their own. We arrive alone, grow alone and leave alone. Even though mother is present at birth and loved ones may be there at death, your life is your own singular enlightenment experience"*

—Shelley Stockwell, *Time Travel*

AFFIRM SUCCESS: Yes! Reverse The Curse of Depression

Read this affirmation to yourself and lighten up

Dear God, please assist me to fill my emotional needs.

Make my life one of love, peace, passion and play. Make joy my compass. Teach me to love myself unconditionally and to be more compassionate with myself. Assist me to pursue my many hobbies, interests and talents. Amen. Awomen. Ah life.

I take care of number one. I listen to my inner wisdom. I decide what I want. I take charge of my life and get what I want. I choose right work.

I forgive the past, make amends and tell the truth.

I laugh. I love. I say the word "yes."
I spend time in nature. I become friends with God or spirit.
I eat nourishing food and drink plenty of water.
I avoid the downer substances or behavior. I am disgusted by poisonous caffeine, alcohol, sugar, salt, drugs and negative thinking. I am conscious of my choices and choose to be happy, healthy, peaceful and feel great. I live 100% in joy.

I am emotionally balanced. I listen to myself make positive strategies that make me feel better.

I sleep easily and have a healthy, normal appetite. I eat when I need fuel and I stop eating when physically full. My digestive system and bowels work perfectly. My metabolism rate is excellent. I stand tall and proud. My posture is excellent.

The alchemist inside my body now produces balanced bio-chemical responses. I have positive thoughts and behaviors and produce positive bio-chemical responses. My endocrine system functions perfectly just as God intended it to. I activate the joy center of my brain. I focus my attention 2 1/2 inches from the front of my nose to my subgenual prefrontal cortex and it swells with joy. My body reinvents healthy neurological responses, and positive thought and action.

I'm talking now to my hypothalamus. 'Hypothalamus secrete Cortotropin. Release Hormones. Let them easily cascade Cortisol into my blood.' These wonderful positive brain chemicals help my natural blood sugar level and blood pressure calm me in all situations.

My emotions are stable and appropriate. I bless each rich emotion. I take each emotion as it comes and goes. I am in charge of my flow of emotion. Just as wind carves beautiful canyons, my feelings mold a portrait of character across my face. The windstorms of life polish me into a precious jewel.

I have plenty of energy to pursue my many interests and hobbies. I am well balanced. My body and mind feel wonderful. I love being alone with my thoughts. I concentrate whenever I want to; my mind is sharp. I make decisions easily. I am a growing, learning and maturing personality. I love myself.

I enjoy the company of others. I am a person of action and in control of my actions. I am pro-active. I congratulate myself for reading this affirmation.

My life is full. I like to try new things; I have many interests; I enjoy new projects and hobbies. I enjoy being with people and I enjoy my own company. Life is exciting. I am exciting and in full energy.

I like new days. Mornings are terrific. I dwell on good things that are going to happen; and I discover them happening.

I am a worthy, hopeful, satisfied person. I'm always in good spirits.

Uplifting Assignments

☆ *"I can live for two months on a good compliment."*
—Mark Twain

A TRUE STORY: Dayna

Three letters from Dayna:

A Letter From Dayna

"It angers me that I am not doing things to get out of my current slump. I don't have any interests. I find it difficult to motivate myself when I am not interested in anything. I get more and more clouded by anger—and more tired.

I feel useless and worthless. Many people try to guide and support me but I don't know how to change. I don't want to bother people. I feel flat, helpless, and obnoxious. I'm always in everyone else's way.

After years of therapy, a psychiatrist admitted me into an institution because I was "suicidal." The hospital was a nightmare. When I got myself out of there I became more silent and sullen."

Another Letter from Dayna

"Feeling as if I can't do anything. Don't understand the changes in my moods, feelings, thoughts and perspective. One day, one mood, the next, another.

No clear remembering, just being stuck. Can't even get myself to move.

Sitting. Waiting? Wondering. When will this end? When will I be 'normal'? Angry. I cannot do anything. I can't even help myself. So incompetent. I can't (won't) function.

The easiest way to be me is to learn how to do something, to be of use to myself. If only I could learn how to paint spots on giraffes. No shock treatments. No anti-psychotic drugs, no anti-depressants, no ice cream and no lollipops. It's everyone else's answers. I am a ladybug. If I only could learn to share my spots with the giraffe. So stuck. I think elephants should have had spots. Giraffes should have had stripes. Zebras should have had diamonds. And a ladybug should have a heart.

I am disconnected from myself and I have pushed everyone away, putting a wall around me. The thought of loving saddens me, because I'm not worthy. I won't let anyone love me."

A Thank You Note From Dayna

This is the letter Dayna wrote after her hypnosis visit:

"Thank you for allowing me to share. I was in the process of shutting down, closing out, deleting. I was sad, hurt, lonely and angry. How different today is. How different from yesterday. How different from the morning. How differently things look when sunlight is allowed to pierce the clouds—the shattered pain glass. The healing rays reveal the beauty that is always shadowed by the clouds—the shattered pain glass window.

I feel good. I feel alert. My physical body feels good. I am not in pain. There is hope."

INTO•GREAT POWER EXERCISE

Whatcha Dune? Action Steps

☆ *"Do Be Do Be Do"* — Frank Sinatra

Sing.
Take a walk.
Look out a window.
Dig in the garden.
Say the word "yes."
Read a book.
Paint a picture.
Growl or scream.
Pound a pillow.
Write a grateful list.
Clean up anything.
Take a shower.
Cook something marvelous.
Drink some water.
Relive a time when I felt loved.
Watch a funny movie.
Pleasantly surprise someone.
Tell someone you love them.
Give something away.
Sit up straight, walk tall.
Compliment yourself or someone else.
Listen to your inner wisdom.
Enjoy silence.
Become a friend with God or spirit.
Avoid negative religion and people.

Make up a song.
Work out.
Spend time in nature.
Arrange some flowers.
Plan a vacation.
Write a poem.
Do a craft project.
Go to the library or a bookstore.
Pound your chest.
Clean out a drawer.
Wash your face.
Get a massage.
Get organized.
If tired, rest.
Take care of #1.
Stop being a victim.
Hug someone.
Love an animal, play with a pet.
Decide what you want.
Sniff peppermint and lavender oil.
Listen to soothing and uplifting music.
Chant a mantra.
Pray to a happy God.
Laugh out loud.

Go to the card store and buy a card for someone.
Make a list of five healthy distractions and do them.
Think of someone who has been kind to you and call them.
Think of something you want and make a plan to get it.
Apologize to someone you hurt, and then forgive yourself.
Learn from someone else how they got what they wanted.
Do a symbolic act, like writing a list of all that bothers you—and then burn it.
Soak in a bath (the Greek mathematician Archimedes discovered his famous principle while in the tub).

Tell the truth.
Laugh.
Love.

Choose right work
Hypnotize yourself or listen to the "Peace and Calm" Tape.
Avoid substances or behaviors that make you depressed, (i.e. caffeine, alcohol, sugar, salt, drugs, negative thinking and toxic behaviors).
Forgive yourself.

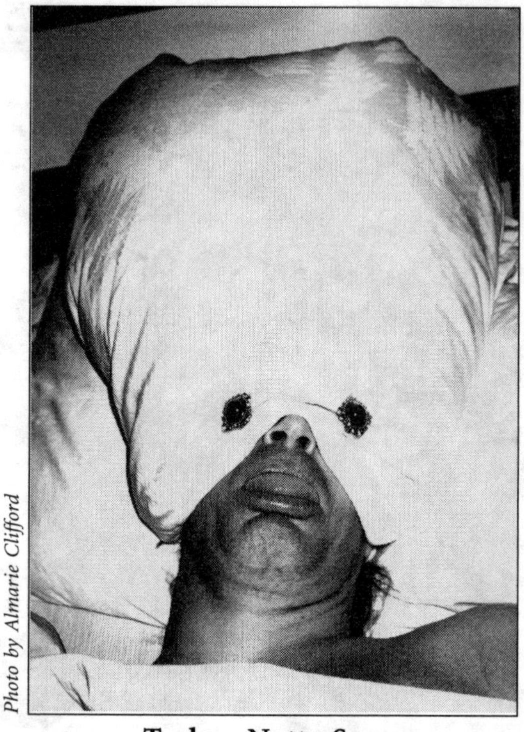

Photo by Almarie Clifford

Turban-Nutto Sugar

INNER•VIEW QUIZ

Am I Out Of It?

___I override challenges and stress with behavior that numbs.
___I am always busy organizing or disorganizing.
___I am absorbed and obsessed by my work, sports or hobbies.
___ I go hysterical.
___I throw tantrums.
___I try to control others.
___I live in fear.
___I have anxiety attacks.
___I'm out of control with some of my habits.

If any of these are true, you smoke screen real-life issues and complicate your life with even more issues. Repetitive thoughts and compulsive behavior are futile attempts to heal or displace underlying pain.

Chapter 6
Crazed Ways

☺ Zombie Jamboree

Attempting to feel well and forget problems, we numb with self-destructive behavior.

This chapter helps you wake up and examine crazy thinking. It's fun to rise above self-deception and take charge.

▲ Mentally Hooked: Grave Sight
▲ Cross Addicted: It Adze Up
▲ Habituated: Ancient Ruin

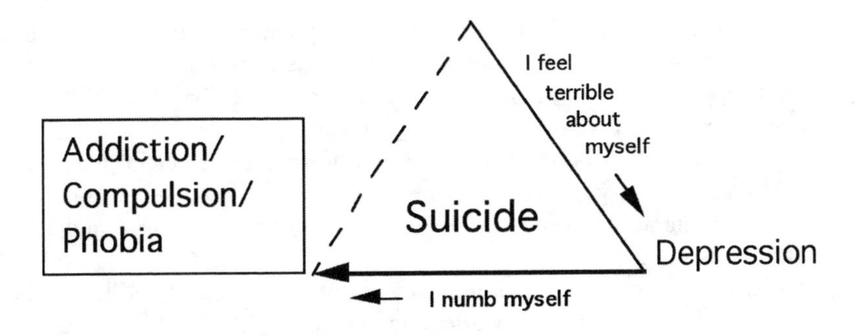

☆ All At Sea

Order; let my fractured mind find order.
Peace, let my discordant heart find peace.
Trust, so lands long lost, return.

—Solomon Blue Waters

▲ Mentally Hooked: Grave Sight

☆ HOW TO STAY DEPRESSED

Poor posture, poor diet, poor air, poor me.
Booze, sugar, negativity.
Breathing air from an exhaust pipe
Hanging around with people you don't like.

Snorting drugs, puffing leaves.
Rudely calling yourself a sleaze.
Not expressing what you feel.
Going unconscious with every meal.

Fear and worry stick and last
And keep you living in the past.
You can't become your heartfelt dreams
when you embrace depressing themes.

—Shelley Stockwell

Everyone has impulses and feelings—some good and appropriate, some inappropriate and perverse. All feelings and impulses are human. In a healthy mind state, you censor and don't act upon inappropriate, crazy ones. If you do, you get in trouble. A wise man is not a wise guy.

There is a difference between the *experience* of a negative thought or emotion and the *release* of a negative thought or emotion. Loss of impulse control results in inappropriate action. Later, you regret your behavior. Tantrums, and stress embarrass us.

A BIG reaction gets your attention so you can play detective and learn what inner conflict needs healing. Pay attention.

Fixing attention on fear and obsession depletes and saps energy.

Hurting Yourself, Hurts Yourself.

The pharmacist that lives in your brain holds the key to all your pain and pleasure. Your brain searches out brilliant and creative ways to make you feel high. Your pharmacist offers up its own prescriptions. Every thought and substance effects the delicate chemical interplay of brain and resulting behaviors. If you give your brain healthy resources, it makes you feel terrific.

In the early stages, compulsive behavior brings pleasure, stimulation, excitement, numbness or release. Over time, this will make you sick, sad and destroyed.

Self-destruction isn't fun. The high you get off gambling gets stale when you lose your money, family and self respect. The high you get smoking marijuana flattens out when you can't get things done and you screw up work and relationships.

Sexual Chemistry

☆ *"The cat, having sat upon a hot stove lid, will not sit upon a hot stove lid again. Nor upon a cold stove lid."*

—Samuel Clemens (Mark Twain)

☆ *"An hour sitting with a pretty girl on a park bench passes like a minute, but a minute sitting on a hot stove passes like an hour. That's relativity."*

—Albert Einstein

Your brain is your most highly developed sex organ. Think about the rush you get when you are sexually attracted to someone? Your phenylethylamine, norepinephrine and dopamine stimulate, excite, raise your pulse, make you shake, perspire and be more aggressive so you overcome shyness. Pheromones, the trace "odors" that trigger attraction in plants, butterflies and mammals could result.

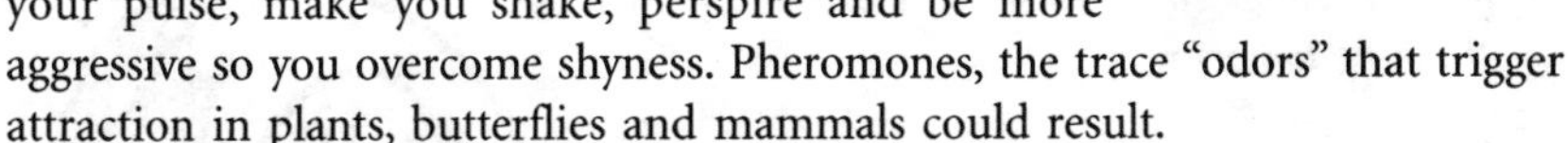

Strangely, fear and passion evoke the brain to release the exact same chemicals. Maybe that's why insecurity and anxiety colors sexual attraction.

Bored Stiff: Papa Ooh Mao Mao

Chemicals that your brain creates stimulate highs and lows and are called natural opiates, androgynous opiates or MAO's (mono-amine-oxydase). These catalyze pleasure by stimulating every molecule in your body. Dopamine, epinephrine and seratonin are some well-known MAO's.

PET scans (Positron Emission Tomography) show that bored or depressed folks have low neuron activity and presence of MAO. This sparked the notion that we should ingest MAO inhibitors (a category of antidepressants) to get happy.

No one knows the long-term effects of chemicals on the human body. But we do know the short-term effects of antidepressants, and it's not a pretty picture. For many, antidepressants make depression worse and when mixed with other drugs like Prozac or alcohol, can and do, cause seizures and death.

Mind-Your Behavior

Brain functions cause all behaviors. If you have a low metabolic rate, or idle neurons not being opened, your cells choose excitement anywhere they can get it.

The dictionary defines obsessive behavior as "besieged" or "taken over," which implies that obsessions take place outside of the brain: not so. Obsession, addiction and compulsion take place inside the brain where, on a cellular level, each cell desires stimulation and opening. Drugs and crazy patterns do not contain highs. They trigger your brain's natural ability to be high and low.

Like a mind burglar with an aptly named skeleton key, toxic patterns trigger the brain's natural high. This so excites the brain that laboratory animals and some of us choose drugs over food and water. In a stunning study of brain cell activity, Dr. Belluzzi determined that single brain cells exhibit addictive behavior. A healthy brain cell will chose a diet of heroin over glucose.

Addiction and compulsion stimulate the emotional and motivational centers of the brain by creating brain opiates like dopamine, which in turn causes psychoactive effects and drug dependency. All drugs do one of three things. They depress, stimulate or alter perception via the central nervous system. This in turn motivates us to take more drugs.

Stubborn or Tenacious?

☆ *If you're stubborn; at least you know what you'll be thinking tomorrow.*

Do you stubbornly cling to old ways saying, "I'm not stubborn? That's final. I won't budge one inch on that one!"

Repeating old hurtful trauma/drama is a neurotic stubborn ritual. It is so boring! Albert Einstein said that insanity is doing the same thing over and over and expecting a different outcome.

Change is gonna do you good.

▲ Cross Addicted: It Adze Up

☆ *" I used to be f____d up on drugs. Then I found the Lord and now I'm all f____d up on the Lord."*

—Cheech and Chong

Photo by Shelley Stockwell

Jon, Restoring the Sphinx

Many people exchange, mix and/or match addictions, compulsions, phobias and fear. That's why at some Alcoholics Anonymous meetings, members chug down coffee and cola, make a volcano in the ashtray and eat candy like there's no tomorrow.

Have you met someone who quit

smoking and then went on an eating, drinking or gambling binge? One over-the-wall addiction or compulsion was replaced with another.

Pain Precipitates Progressive Patterns

On her TV show, Oprah Winfrey revealed sexual abuse and personal battles with weight. In January 1995, during her program featuring female drug users, she cried and confessed that she had used cocaine in the '70's and had overcome an addiction to it. "That is my life's great big secret that has been held over my head... I understand the shame, I understand the guilt." Like many, Oprah has suffered from sequential addictions and compulsions.

Yes! Instant Joy

▲ On a scale of 1 to 10 evaluate how happy you are at this moment.
1 = not very happy, 10 = ecstatic.

▲ Put your arms over your head, with palms wide open, say "Yes!"

▲ Keeping your hands up, continue saying "yes" silently in your head. You might even smile as you do: **"Yes, yes, yes."**

▲ Close your eyes and evaluate on a scale of 1 to 10 how you feel at this very moment.

I choose joy, think positively and move my body in positive ways.

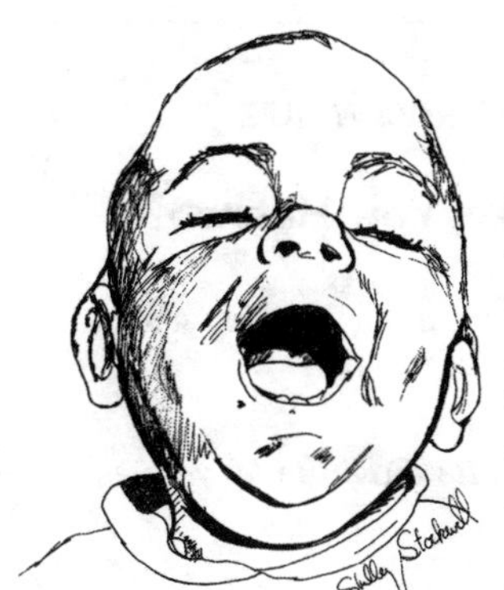

Illustration by Shelley Stockwell

To Your Brain it's All the Same

Your body cannot determine whether chemicals enter your brain though your mouth, nostrils, internal glands or from itself.

The word endorphin comes from endogenous (produced from within the body) + morphine. Endorphins are the drugs you give to yourself when you internally "switch on" your brain chemistry. They reduce tension, tranquilize and make you high. This is a natural high.

Substances and thoughts stimulate the same neuro-chemical circuits of the brain. For example, caffeine and gambling both stimulate the brain the same way. Both evoke the same endorphins.

TV watching, overeating and video games activate similar neuro-chemical circuits. Horse betting, cliff hanging, shooting heroin and shoplifting stimulate the brain chemistry in a similar manner.

Crazy or stinkin' thinking distorts your ability to mentally map behavior.

This Swell Ganglia of Mine

Doctors speculate that self-destructive behavior is a result of stress and a swollen basal ganglia in the brain. Swelling affects thinking. Drugs to reduce this swelling cause additional stress, and don't address the underlying cause of pain: your swell brain.

Crazy, negative thinking chemically makes you up tight. Negative thinking and behavior are only antiquated patterns that aren't serving you well. The challenge is to step outside limits so you see what's really going on and then make positive and clear decisions.

INNER•VIEW QUIZ

Are You Hooked?

☆ *"...a loud sucking sound..."*

—Ross Perot

☆ *"It's alright to let yourself go, as long as you can get yourself back."*

—Mick Jagger

__ Hurtful behavior takes priority in my mind.
__ I obsess about my next cigarette, my next drink or my next donut.
__ I choose bingeing over a walk in the park.
__ When it comes to java, I just gotta hava.
__ I use crazy behavior to remove me from my true feelings.
__ I feel bad, think I'll eat something (light up, have a drink…).
__ I experience withdrawal when I stop.
__ Craving makes me jittery and I just can't go without "it."

If any of these are true for you, it's a tip off that you're "hooked" or addicted to a substance or behavior.

▲ Habituated: Ancient Ruin

We don't think about limiting behavior consciously. Nor does society. We ignore caffeine, sugar, prescription drugs and workaholism because they are socially acceptable. And, in certain crowds, so is alcohol, cocaine and dope. Yet, even with sanctions and denial, if you hurt yourself, you know it. Take a reality break: What behavior hurts you and robs you of true joy? You know the truth.

Withdrawal Is Real

A TRUE STORY Shelley

The first time I tried to quit sugar, I hallucinated with little cakes and candies dancing in tap shoes before my eyes. I just couldn't seem to quit on my own. That's when I discovered hypnosis. Hypnosis made quitting possible. After I was hypnotized, I stopped the sweets. It was easy and the tap dance was over.

AFFIRM SUCCESS: **Healthy with Conviction!**
Healthy ways that pleasure me are more fun. The first step is to be honest and honestly commit to change. I choose to take charge of my life! I quit any negative behavior once and for good. My actions are positive. I am joyously healthy. I begin a wholesome, happy life-NOW."

Woe → Wow

I'm driven to fill a void.	→	I am full•filled.
I don't know who I am.	→	I rediscover myself each day.
I give up control quickly.	→	I stay response•able.
I am tightly structured.	→	Open minded.
I have a negative outlook.	→	Positive outlook.
I feel insignificant.	→	I love myself, I am enough.
I lack direction.	→	I wisely follow heart-felt desires.
I live in fear.	→	I in•courage myself.
My growth is stunted.	→	I blossom.

☆ *"The mind, once expanded to larger ideas, never returns to its original size."*
—Oliver Wendell Holmes

Gary's story is a perfect example of sequential self destruction and hope:

A TRUE STORY Gary

"**All my life I felt like I never fit in.** Dad was a workaholic. He never took time out for us. When he wasn't delivering bread, he worked in the garage. He never told me that he loved me—no hugs. When I was 7, I tore apart a gasoline motor. He saw it and called me names. He told me I was stupid. Even when I put the motor back together and started it up, I believed him. I thought, no one will hang out with 'Gary Dumb.' He told me I would never amount to anything unless I finished college. I quit school in tenth grade.

Drinking made me feel like I fit in. When I was 13, I started smoking and drinking. The other kids were doing it, why shouldn't I? I never liked the taste but I remember the warmth when the first drink went down. I felt it from the minute it touched my lips all the way to my stomach. Everything was suddenly OK. It was as if alcohol was a lubricant that let me slip into a chair that was too small to hold me. It made me fit in. I could talk to girls. After that I got my wine from winos at the shopping center where I had my paper route. They would buy me a case and I would give them a bottle.

Almost immediately I was a blackout drinker. People would say to me, 'Did you know what you did?' I didn't.

I was always looking for recognition. With money I got from selling papers, I bought go-carts and doodlebugs to get attention. I raced cars with my go-cart down the main street of San Pedro. At 15, I got a letter from the California DMV saying that since I had 18 tickets and 3 drunk driving citations and I wasn't old enough to drive, my privilege to apply for a license was revoked. I was proud of that letter; I showed it to everyone. The DMV recognized me.

During the next year, I got 2l more drunken drivings and drove without a license.

I slammed shut my emotional door. At 14, I met Lona. At 16, she had my daughter.

Lona and I broke up when our daughter was 11 months old. 'I have never loved you,' Lona said to me. I vowed, 'never let anyone get close again.' I went out and got drunk.

I was in jail for 100 days for drunk driving. She visited with our 14-month-old daughter. It was a nice visit. I was released from jail because it was overcrowded. I called a high school buddy to pick me up. When we were at his house, the phone rang with terrible news: Lona's male friend had abused our baby to death.

I went nuts. The three times I saw the murderer after that, I blacked out emotionally—just like an alcoholic blacks out. People had to hold me back.

Being an addict is a full-time job. I smoked marijuana, but the first joint made me feel dizzy and sick to my stomach. After that, I found the magic of barbiturates. Someone gave me five red devils (Seconal barbital). They said, 'Take one or two and get mellow.' I didn't want to get mellow, so I took all five. I was falling against the walls. It was like falling apart. I liked that feeling.

After my daughter's death, booze and pills did not kill the pain. Heroin addicts, who lived in my building, asked what was wrong. They gave me a shot of heroin and I found utopia. It was an immediate escape. I felt relaxed and nodded out.

I used to drink a fifth of Jack Daniel's a day just to cope. Now, I needed $300 a day for heroin, just to stay well. Without it, my nose ran and my bones ached. Being an addict is a full-time job.

I stole to get attention. I got my money from working and stealing. I first stole about $20 a day from my Dad to buy my friends things from Rudy's Five and Dime. I knew stealing was wrong, yet I felt that it was something I had to do to have friends. Dad would find different hiding places for his wallet.

When I started drugs, I needed more money. I knew Dad hid his wallet under the refrigerator. One night, while I was on the kitchen floor pulling out a $20 bill from his wallet, he turned on the light and caught me. I told him I lost something, and dropped the $20. He reached under the refrigerator, recovered it, grabbed me by the arm and, still in his pajamas, took me down to the police station.

He told the police, 'I caught my son stealing.' They put me on my first probation. I did not get off probation until I was over 30 years old. Probation is like doing life on the installment plan, three years of probation equals 90 days in jail. I kept getting into trouble, so probations kept being added on.

I stole to feed my habit. To get money for heroin, I'd go to the supermarket, steal meat, and sell it in a shopping center parking lot. I'd sell it at half price. It was easy to sell.

I got bolder. I'd follow a cigarette deliveryman into the store with a dolly. When he left his boxes of merchandise in the market to return to his truck to get more, I slid my dolly under the cigarettes and walked out. I never got caught.

I learned to steal from watching TV's Dragnet. I picked up the mistakes others made, so I wouldn't. 'She told the woman.' 'They hocked the computer.' 'He left fingerprints.'

A friend was having a party because his parents were out of town, I went and unlocked a window. When the party ended, I left, went to a pay phone, and called him. 'Hello, this is Dr. Ross at the Bay Hospital emergency ward,' I said, 'your parents have been in an accident and we need you down here right away.' When the lights in the house went out, and the fellow left in panic, I casually drove my trailer up to the house, climbed in the window, put the music back on, and loaded up my trailer. The police caught me, but they didn't have sufficient proof to prosecute.

I stole from my drug suppliers. A supplier would sell me thirty $10 bags for $200. Ten bags were mine, and when I sold the other twenty, I was to pay the $200. But I would do 15 bags, so I would come up short on the money. They would not stand for that. So I used it all and moved to a new connection and lied, 'Can you front me 30 bags?' I had been fronted 30 bags from four people; I ripped them all off and they were looking for me.

I knew stealing was wrong, but I had to have heroin to 'stay well.' I didn't get a break. I would rob a house, and even before I had hocked the stuff, I would think, 'Where is my next job?'

There was a thrill in stealing. I would buy $150 in groceries and steal a book of matches or a nasal spray. 'I can do it and get away with it.' It is just a sick ego.

At twenty-eight I went to my first rehabilitation program. I had accumulated a seven and one-half page arrest record: drunk driving, burglary, suspicion of drug sales, and the sale of drugs. Felony after felony was dropped to a misdemeanor. If it were not for our corrupt judicial system, I would have gone to the penitentiary. Even the man who killed my daughter pleaded involuntary manslaughter and spent less than a year in jail.

What was there to live for? One day, I threw more into the spoon to cook up; secretly hoping that this would be the shot that I wouldn't wake up from. As I got the needle registered and was pushing it in; the police kicked in my front door. With the needle still in my arm, a cop came over to me with a cocked 357 magnum pointed at my head and said, 'Stop, or I'll shoot.' I continued to push the plunger. Afterward, the cop said, 'Didn't you realize I could have killed you?' I thought, 'Why didn't you?'

I was finally arrested and sentenced to one year, for possession and sale of heroin. In jail, I went to church every Sunday and prayed a lot. They let me out after eight months for good behavior.

When I got out, I knew drugs weren't the answer and decided just to drink. After two weeks, a buddy drove us to Venice. We went to a bar poured down a few, danced and decided to go to another club.

The fatal turn. In the car, he asked, 'How did you stay away from drugs?' I said, 'I went to church and prayed.' He said, 'There is no God.'

We made a left turn, and I saw the car accident before it happened. After our car was hit, it spun backwards three houses down the street and parked perfectly in a driveway between two hedges. My drinking buddy was dead and I was barely alive.

I was 'John Doe.' I had no ID. I was rushed to Marina Mercy Hospital, where a miracle occurred. A terrific neurosurgeon saw me being wheeled into the hospital, and performed emergency brain surgery to remove a subdermal hematoma. As I was being wheeled to intensive care, a friend of my sister walked by and yelled my name, and the hospital learned who I was.

I remained in a coma and underwent a second brain surgery. Two weeks later, I awoke. I was twenty-five years old and my entire left side was paralyzed. The doctor said I would remain paralyzed. I pictured myself in a wheelchair using drugs.

My brother-in-law brought Mormon elders to heal me. They laid their hands on me, and ended with 'Thy will be done.' They asked me to join them in a prayer of thanks. I could barely mouth the words, 'Thy will be done.' The eldest elder stared at me and said, 'Gary, be not afraid, just believe.'

Four nights later, I awoke with a cold chill, my left leg was up, and my hand was across my chest. I screamed. The nurse said I was a miracle. The doctors arrived with electrodes. 'We can't explain it. You have a friend upstairs. You brain shows normal function.' After all the bad things I had done, God brought me back with love.

In spite of this, I went back to addiction one more time and was arrested. The judge who had sentenced me before had said, 'This is your last chance. Next time, you go to the state penitentiary.' He was my judge again.

In the past, my prayer was, 'Please get me out of this, I won't do it again.' This time, my prayer was, 'God show me a way.'

The public defender gave me three choice: 'One, go to the penitentiary; two, go to the California Rehabilitation Center (and if you mess up, you'll do 10 years to life in the penitentiary), or three, go to Impact House in Pasadena (and if you mess up, you will do 15 to life.)'

I picked Impact House because it was co-ed. I expected to get laid. But, ex-alcoholics and addicts ran the house; they knew all the cons. I went to 19 AA meetings a week, ate three square meals a day, and changed. We were required to sit down for dinner at 5:30 p.m. It was the first time in 20 years I had a sit-down dinner. I looked forward to it: grace, eating and chatting. It was wonderful. The whole drug culture is so sorry because people just want to be in a family.

I was given the gift of working at Impact House. I became part of the staff and worked with the addicts. It gave me a feeling I never got from a syringe, bottle, or money. I didn't expect anything in return except that feeling.

Now I can help others. After sixty-four arrests, this was the first time I was offered a program that really helped me with my drugs and stealing. Courts do not recognize alcoholism, yet 80% of the people incarcerated are there because they are addicted to drugs and/or alcohol.

Life is too short to hate anyone, especially myself. The most important thing I have learned is to forgive. After I sobered up, and trained as a paraprofessional, I still wanted to kill the man who killed my daughter. My spiritual counselor said I must pray for him instead, because he is a very sick man. For two weeks, I say this prayer twice a day:

'My Father, who art it heaven, give (name) your healing spirit, health, material and spiritual prosperity, a grateful heart, sadness and forgiveness for whatever (name) has done wrong. Amen.'

After two weeks people told me I looked better. After a year, I stopped my truck at a crosswalk and the man who killed my daughter walked right in front of me. In the past, I would not have thought twice about stepping on the gas pedal and killing him. But this time, I thought, 'What a sick human being he must be. He must live in hell each time he sees a little girl. What a punishment that is.' Then an overwhelming feeling came over me: God took my daughter from me to keep her out of the pain of an abusive life.

My cup had been filled with self-loathing, hate and anger from drinking and drugs. But now that cup has been emptied and filled with love, joy and happiness. Life is too short to hate anybody."

Gary's poem

Every moment that passes by
Speeds the day that you and I
Will walk together once again.
Hopeful, happy, and confident.

With a sober love
Content and true
An honest heart I give to you
That changes not with joy nor pain
Always your friend I shall remain.

▲

Yes
Joy
Free
Play
Love
Open
Calm
Move
Dream
Magic
Giggle
Laugh
Dive In
Believe
Imagine
Celebrate
Stay Loose
Moonbaths

Step Two ˙•.•

Book of the Dead:

Veil of Illusion

How and Why You Go Numb

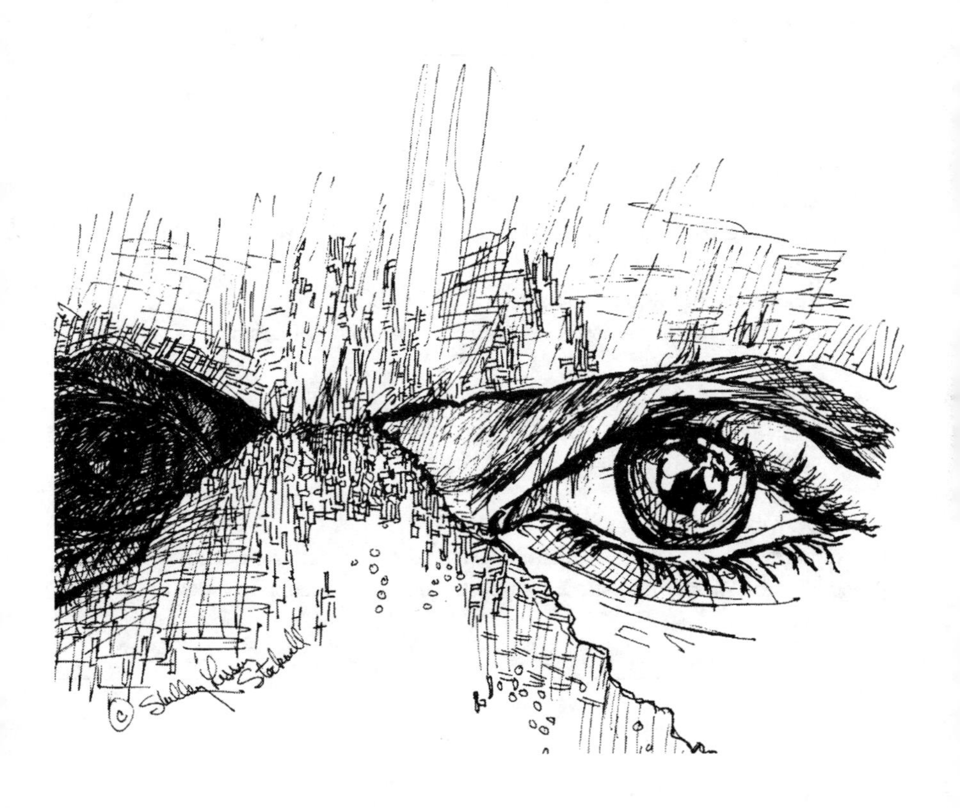

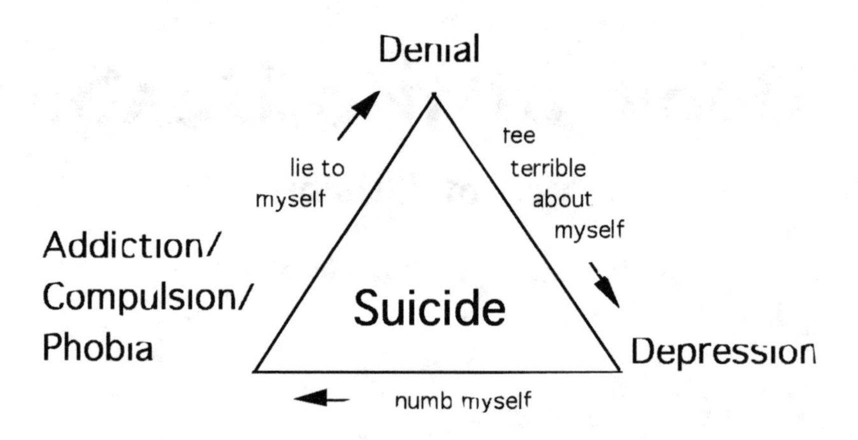

▲ Depression
Denial begins when sad and frustrated, with no place to go.

▲ Addiction/Compulsion/Phobia
To feel better and forget problems, we numb out with self-destructive behaviors.

▲ Denial
The very pain we avoid exaggerates and intensifies. Inner wisdom cries, "Stop hurting me!" We shout back, "Shut up."

▲ Slow-Motion Suicide
The more we lie to ourselves, the more depressed we get. Life becomes a never-ending saga of sadness, stress, self-destruction and deception. We break our own hearts.

Step Two

Book of the Dead:

Veil of Illusion

How and Why You Go Numb

INNER•VIEW QUIZ

Are Your Behaviors Overboard?

☆ Question: *"When did you get paranoid?"*
Answer: *"When they were all out to get me."*

Be brave enough to answer honestly:
___ I am anxious and afraid.
___ I'm ashamed of my senseless actions.
___ I fear something bad will happen if I don't perform my "routine."
___ I lost my health getting wealthy and lost my wealth getting healthy.
___ I grind my teeth.
___ I wring my hands.
___ I grasp the arms of a chair and/or lock my ankles rigid.
___ I feel like I'm playing a violin at the Hollywood Bowl and learning as I go.
___ I wake up "worn out."
___ I find it difficult to look someone in the eye.
___ I hide out a lot.
___ I postpone going to the bathroom when I need to.
___ I'm stressed to the max.
___ Certain things make me freak out.

During a panic attack, I have had the following experiences:
___ Heart palpitations and/or chest pain.
___ Dizziness.
___ Shortness of breath.
___ Numbness or tingling.
___ Nausea or indigestion.
___ Choking.
___ Hot flashes, perspiration or chills.
___ Nothing is real (things are distorted).
___ Irrational feelings that something terrible will happen.
___ Fear of losing control, dying or going crazy.
___ Fear of having another panic attack.
___ I must urinate/ move my bowels.

If you checked these symptoms, you may be suffering from an over taxed central nervous system. Don't panic. Eat good healthy foods and avoid stressful drugs, sugar, chocolate, alcohol, caffeine and irritants. Use the relaxation techniques in this chapter. Mellow out...and you'll mellow in.

Chapter 7
Compulsion & Obsession:
Entombed

I was compulsive about finishing this chapter for you. It is bound to make you chuckle at our human foibles. It also has some terrific affirmations and exercises that are transformational.

▲ Handy-Dandy List Of Compulsive Behavior
▲ What Are Compulsions and Obsessions
▲ Specialized Compulsions
  - Drama Junkie
  - Surgery addicts
  - Vidiots
  - Health Freaks
  - Workaholics
  - Money Madness
  - Hooked on Beliefs
  - Rageaholics

It's A Shoe Thing!

☆ *"I finally got my son to stop biting his nails."*
"How did you do that?"
"I bought him some shoes."

☆ *There was an old man from Edfu*
Who dreamed he was eating his shoe.
He woke in a fright,
In the middle of the night
And found it was perfectly true.

Feet•ish
The average man and woman in the US owns 5 pairs of tennis shoes!

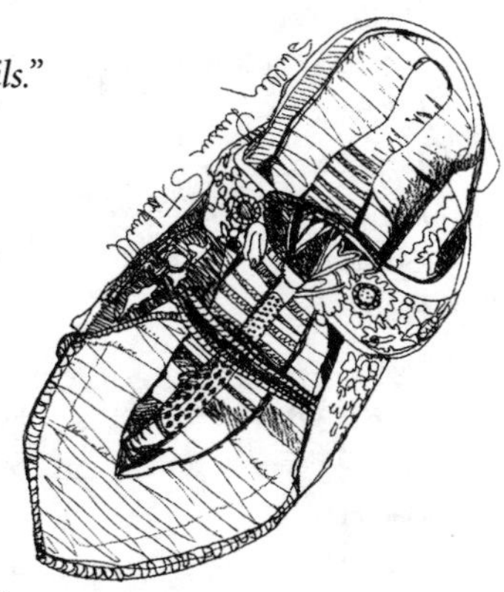

Illustration by Shelley Stockwell

▲ Handy-Dandy List of Compulsive Behaviors:

___ Addiction
___ Adrenaline Junkie
_Dare devil
_Emotional freaks
_Thrill seeker
___ Busy Body
_Foot tapping
_Leg bouncing
_Lip biting
_Ticks
___ Chaos Junkie
___ Co-dependent
___ Control Freak
___ Cosmetic Surgery
___ Counting
___ Cleaning
___ Do Gooder
___ Eating Disorders
_Eating fabric
_Eating objects
_Overeating
_Starving
_Purging
___ Eyebrow Plucking
___ Exhibitionism
___ Fanaticism
___ Genealogy Freak
___ Gossiping
___ Hate
___ Hair Combing
(Cata•comb•comb•comb)
___ Hair Twirler
___ Hair Puller
(trichotillomania)
___ Hermit
___ Hypochondria
___ Hurting Yourself

___ Hysteria
___ Inhibitions
___ Love Obsessed
___ Lying
___ Money $$$
_Gambling-lottery
_Miser-y
_Scamming
_Shopaholic
_Shoplifting
___ Nail Biting
(calcium deficiency)
___ Neatnik/Perfectionist
___ Nose Picking/Eating
(sodium deficiency)
___ Pack rat
_Collection freak
_Garage sale hound
___ Philosophy
___ Picking
___ Politics
___ Rageaholic
___ Reading
___ Rage
_Aggressive
_Anger
_Arguing
_Passive Aggressive
_Resentment
_Temper Tantrums
___ Religious Rites
___ Seminar Junkie
___ Sleepaholic
___ Sex
_Addict
_Exhibitionist
_Hit me, hurt me
_Masochism
_Masturbation
_900 numbers
_Nymphomania
_Pornography
(phallus/see)
_Promiscuity
_Prostitution
(Hor-us)
_Sadism
___ Songs-in-the-head
___ Super Jock/Jockette
_Boating
_Exercise
_Fishing
_Football
_Hockey
_Golf/Tennis
_Jogging/Biking
___ Sports Addict
_Voyeur
___ Superman/Woman
_Workaholic
_Competition
___ Surgery Junkie
___ Videots
_TV
_Video Gamer
_Computers
_E-mail Chat Rooms
_Movies
___ Washing
("Out, out damn spot.")
___ Worry Wart
___ Name Your Own

▲ What are Obsessions and Compulsions?

☆ *"Hypochondria is the only illness I don't have."*

☆ *"Repeated thoughts, urges or images that distress, are tip-offs that you obsess."*
—Shelley Stockwell

If you are obsessive, you've got to do "it." If you are compulsive, you've got to do "it" again and again. Compulsions are repeated acts performed to relieve anxiety from an obsession.

Obsessive-compulsive behavior may happen briefly, chronically and/or in varying degrees.

Obsessions and compulsions run from slight peculiarities (I must eat my dinner from the left side of my plate to the right) to massive obsessions (I must eat my plate). Comedienne Lilly Tomlin's character "Lucille" explains it this way:

"I'm a rubber freak...I started small with rubber bands. I didn't swallow them, at first. Then moved on to pencil erasers, art gum, spatulas, garden hoses and children's raincoats...I bottomed out in a Playtex girdle factory. The court psychiatrist said, 'She's not a criminal, she's just twisted.' In gratitude, I kissed his feet and ate the crepe soles off his shoes. I've overcome my addiction but I keep a Good year tire in the closet as a reminder. Thank God, I'm no longer a woman obsessed with an unnatural craving. I'm just another normal, socially acceptable alcoholic."
—Lily Tomlin

We begin compulsions to feel good or better. It gives us a sense of being in control of something. We choose what we do with our thoughts and actions. We do it our way. It can also be a great escape and smoke screen something else. Sometimes we become compulsive to punish ourselves.

Where's The Beef?

Exaggerated thoughts make everything worse.
Exaggerated actions are a burden and curse.
Secret routines shame and isolate.
Anxiety makes you not relate.
If you're out of control repeated
You'll be exhausted and depleted.
Compulsive eating makes you fat.
Starvation makes you whither
Compulsive gambling makes you broke.
Fears leave you a quiver.
Self-recriminations make you verbally abused.
in a rigid mental prison, full of nasty news.
—Shelley Stockwell

The problem is "Where's the peace." Obsessive thought and compulsive activity leave you feeling upset.

It is considered culturally cute to be out-of-control. One perfume ad says: "I can't get you out of my mind." But, out-of-control behavior, ritualistic thoughts, and "have-to" responses mire the mind. If you are preoccupied with unnecessary concerns and convincing yourself with lies, the spontaneity of life is lost.

Obsessions

Obsessive thoughts run you. You don't run them.

Obsession is defined as being besieged, taken over or possessed. Taken over by what? Obsession is not possession, demon or otherwise. It does not happen outside your brain. It is simply "overboard" preoccupations of thought inside of you.

Behavior takes place within your brain. Each brain cell desires stimulation and opening. If you obsess, it is you who "turned yourself on" with crazy thinking. Healthy balanced thought and behavior turns your mind on and uplifts.

So why would you obsess about things? Well, it's a terrific diversion from dealing with problems. Unfortunately, it diverts your attention so much that you have no time for much else and therefor creates more stress and issues than any problem you avoided in the first place. Obsession masks depression.

Compulsions

A compulsion is an irresistible impulse to perform an irrational act. When the irresistible meets the irrational; compulsions run behavior and attitude. If you have a compulsion you'll find yourself doing senseless repetitive actions or behavior. Usually these out-of-control actions are accompanied by a feeling that something bad will happen if you stop. Compulsive behavior is repetitive, restrictive, rigid and not any fun. What would life be like if you weren't chronically busy doing or thinking that obsessive thing?

A TRUE STORY Jim

Jim, a popular radio announcer in his early 40s, was in an automobile accident with his family. It was a major cruncher that totaled his vehicle. Fortunately, he wasn't hurt. He thought he had handled the situation well, yet several hours later, he washed his hair in the shower eight times in a row. When he ran out of shampoo, he asked his wife to run out and buy some more. She took Jim to a psychotherapist. The therapist explained that he was experiencing an imbalance of seratonin (nature's natural mood elevator) caused by his recent trauma.

Jim refused antidepressant medication and instead visited a Hypnotherapist (smart fellow). In one session, he released the trauma and resulting behavior. Interestingly, his accident triggered a childhood trauma of his mother scrubbing his hair before leaving him at an orphanage at age six.

What a relief! Jim stopped his compulsive behavior, forgave his mother and father and now feels terrific.

A TRUE STORY Gloria

"My husband left me for another woman. I had a deep pain in my heart, difficulty concentrating and I couldn't sleep. I drove by his house. I felt like I couldn't breathe and I continually relived the day he left.

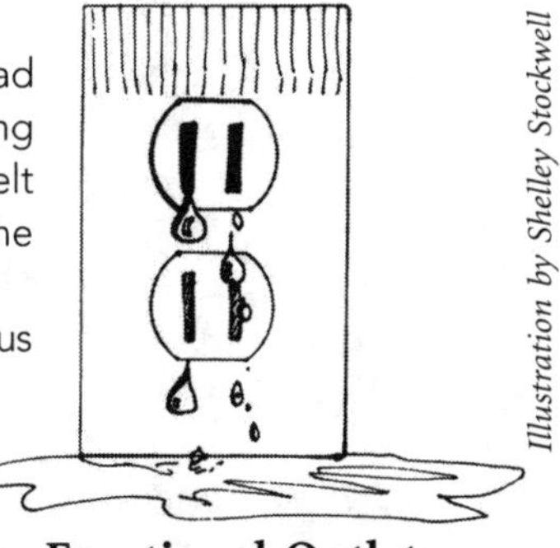

Illustration by Shelley Stockwell

Emotional Outlet

During a rebirthing, I saw my mother sick, nervous and upset when I was born. Dad was away at war and mom was left alone and crying. When my father came home, he had a disease. So he too left me alone. As a baby, I felt I couldn't breath. I got the message that I made mom and dad sick. It was my fault. My husband's leaving me must have been mixed up with my baby memory. After my rebirthing, I stopped chasing my ex-husband. I guess I stopped equating his leaving to mom and dad's actions. Anyway, I feel a lot better. Thank goodness for hypnosis.

AFFIRM SUCCESS: Inner Peace

I take control of my actions in small ways every day. I take charge of my behavior. Choosing to say yes or no is my right and responsibility.

I do kind, considerate, nurturing things for myself. I seek balance in all I do. I control my thoughts and actions. I enjoy the adventure of my life. I mature, grow and learn new ways to bring to myself peace, harmony and fun. Joy is my compass. If it's not fun, I don't do it. I enjoy necessary tasks that make life balanced and rewarding. I am proud to be a good citizen.

I handle my life in a sane and joyful way. I am in charge of my life. I shed past hurts, real or imagined. If, in the past, I deliberately made myself miserable, I stop that behavior right now. I deliberately make myself ecstatic. I love myself. I forgive myself.

I have enough time in my day to work, rest and play. I choose how to spend my time. I'm focused on today and all the opportunities today brings me. I'm open to adventures in my life.

I am responsible for my lifestyle. I am ME. I am not my work, the people in my life or my home. My work, the people in my life and my home are simply opportunities to enrich the life I choose.

▲ Specialized Compulsions: Aren't We Hysterical

Overboard hysteria manifests as novelty thrill-seeking, high drama and impulsive, fickle patterns. We follow these with denial, saying things like,

"That wasn't such a big deal, next time I need more...challenge, high drama, confusion."

"Where does all the money go? I hardly buy anything."

"How could I gain weight, I hardly eat anything?"

Love and Sexual Addicts

☆ Moe: *"Don't cry, Joe. Your wife died today, but in six months you'll find another woman."*
Joe: *"Six months, six months! What am I gonna do tonight?"*

☆*Running wide open*
into an airplane propeller
yelling, "Here I come,"
and, "What was that?"
when it was done.
—Shelley Stockwell

☆*As I was letting down my hair,*
I met a guy who didn't care;
he didn't care again today—
I love 'em when they get that way!
—Hughes Mearns

INNER•VIEW QUIZ

Might As Well Face It, You're Addicted to Love

☆ *Sex is terrific.*
Without it, you'd be non-specific.
—Shelley Stockwell

___ My sweetheart's behavior always bugs me and spoils good feelings.
___ I stay sad, mad or obsess over small things he/she does.
___ They are the reason for my unhappiness.
___ I spend a lot of time fretting over my relationship.
___ I am always suspicious of my partner.
___ I suffer when my darling doesn't do what I want.
___ I was in last, but it didn't lust.
___ Phone sex gave me an ear infection.

If you answered yes to any of these, suspect a love addiction.

When Ann Landers told a writer that her boyfriend's fascination with pornography was "immaturity," not addiction, she received thousands of complaints. "My response was one of my worst," she later concluded.

Good sex provides pleasure, releases tension and leaves you feeling happy, peaceful and full of self-respect. Healthy sexual expression honors your gut reaction.

Eroticamania takes the fun out of sex. Constantly thinking about sex, masturbating, pornographic magazines, movies, peep shows, strippers, inhibitions, promiscuity, phone and cyber sex creates tension, boredom, loneliness and self-hatred.

So do sexual fears and impotence.

As with any compulsion, if sex runs you, you feel out-of-control, have low self-esteem and trouble relating in real relationships. The more you use outside stimulation to numb underlying pain, the more stimulation it takes the next time.

A TRUE STORY Tony

"I felt I had to sexually perform for someone else. I was afraid that my partner would get pregnant or that she won't enjoy the experience or that I would come too fast. I was afraid of oral sex.

I went to Vietnam and had successful sex with local prostitutes who were supposed to be the enemy. I felt guilty.

In hypnotherapy, I traced my guilt back to my mother's attitude that sex was dirty and to the priests who told us sex was evil. I had great sex with my high school sweetheart and she got pregnant and insisted on an abortion. When I identified where my fears came from, I made some new decisions about loving a woman. I forgave myself, my mother, the priests and my high school sweetheart.

Since then, I have been able to pleasure my woman and myself.

If you are sexually compulsive, most likely your mate feels inadequate and/or responsible. Sexual compulsions imbalance a satisfying, interactive relationship. In healthy relationships, partners lead balanced lives, including a mutually satisfying sex life together.

Your Mind is your Biggest Erogenous Zone

☆ Psychiatrist: *"I can't cure your premature ejaculation, but I can put you in touch with a woman with a very short attention span."*

Sexual response arouses adrenaline, which causes the heart to beat faster, blood pressure to rise, and activates the autonomic nervous system, causing you to perspire. Your sexual drive and expression lives in the outer layer (cortex) of the brain. Pornography relies on visual or sound stimulation to tap this part of the brain. Fetishes or objects used repetitively can become a substitute for real contact.

A TRUE STORY Ataco

"My father was a strict man who never talked. When he died, my mother sold our house for 150 million yen (approximately $1,500,000 U.S.) and she and I split the money. It' s now three years later and I don't have one yen to my name. I threw all that money away on a pay-as-you-talk phone number; talking to girls. [Like a 900 number in America]. I talked to girls all day long for over a year. The only time I didn't talk was when I was sleeping, eating or going to the bathroom. When I had spent all my money, I had to borrow money from my mother to pay my rent."

"Did you have any fun spending that money?"

"No. It wasn't any fun at all."

Rotten Reasons for Having Sex

☆ *"I'm just a girl who can't say no.*
I'm in a terrible fix.
I always say, 'Come on, let's go,'
just when I oughta say 'nix.'"

—Rogers and Hammerstein, Oklahoma

☆ Question: *"What do you call a camel without a hump?"*
Answer: *"Humphrey."*

Everyone else is doing it.
I'll show them (whomever you're rebelling against).
I'm getting pressured into it.
I'll be ostracized and laughed at if I don't.
I'm a great conqueror (conquerette), come count the notches on my bedpost.
I'm afraid to say no.
I do it because it's dangerous.
I do it because I hate myself.
I do it because I'm drunk or stoned.
The only time I feel alive is when I'm doing it.
There's nothing else going on, and it's better than a sharp stick in the eye.
I want to hurt myself or I want to hurt someone else.
I want to trap some one into marrying me.
Because of sex, I secretly call myself names and am in constant anxiety.
I'll show mom and dad that I'm grown up.

Good sex enhances learning and/or pleasure. It is a beautiful expression of heart, soul and body. There are no "wrong" reasons to enjoy your sexuality, as long as you are at peace with your choice and accept the consequences and responsibility of your decision.

AFFIRM SUCCESS

If life were a pie, sex would be only one of many delicious slices. My life is in balance. I am the master of my body and mind. I choose healthy right thinking. I do not go off into the wild blue yonder of crazy thinking or overboard behavior. I avoid triggers of thought that make me self-destruct. I am in control of my mind, thoughts, reactions and behavior. I am self-nurturing. Sex is a healthy part of my well-balanced life.

Surgery Addicts

There are two participants in surgery compulsions: surgeons and those in search of surgery. Motivation for going under the knife varies from "fixing" yourself to needing attention and care-taking. Jen, the cosmetic surgery addict, like many other surgery junkies, may be attempting to re-member her true self by literally remaking herself. Here is her story:

A TRUE STORY Jen

"By the time I was thirty, I had turned myself into a real life Barbie Doll. I was hoping to find my Ken. I had so many surgeries, I needed cosmetic surgery to smile. Now it's hard to smile, my mouth looks like a stretched balloon. I've been completely made over from head to toe. I advertised for my Ken in the newspaper and the perfect guy showed up. After 3 months we got married in the wedding I had planned since I was a little girl. We had a horse drawn carriage and I looked like Cinderella. We released white doves and church bells chimed. A month later the marriage was annulled. We just weren't compatible. I wish I could just relax and accept myself."

Vidiots

☆ *"I cannot continue, my life's on hold*
Since I lost the remote control."
—Virginia Shaw

☆ *DISK-GRUNTLED*
The software ads have done their job
They've made me a computer snob.
My ego is at serious risk
If I don't own the latest disk
—S. Minanel

We are children of an electronics age. Computers, computer games, television and movies often add a new program to our compulsion menu. Tyler a 43-year-old computer programmer tells his story this way:

A TRUE STORY Tyler

"My ability to enjoy others is like being undercooked in a microwave oven—full of cold spots. I keep my mouth closed because I don't want to be thought of as weird. I learned a long time ago not to make waves. For the past seven years, I've lived in patterns. I sit all day in front of my computer screen. At night, I drink a six pack of beer, eat a bag of potato chips and watch television. Sixty pounds later, I cut out the six pack. Now I spend my evenings acquiring and watching X-rated videos. I have some 200 in my collection. Three times a week, I go to the movies by myself. I got out of control with credit cards. I got one, then another, then another. Pretty soon I had dozens. I charged on all of them. Two years ago, I declared bankruptcy. What a relief to get rid of all those debts. It's as if I'm numb. I'm tired of it. I want to come back to the land of the living.

When I went to Shelley, I regressed to the source of my compulsiveness. I recalled being four years old and standing on the front lawn with my mother's upright vacuum cleaner. I was entertaining three neighborhood girls pretending I was Elvis. The vacuum handle was my microphone. My mother screamed "How could you be so stupid?" I went off and watched television. That's where I got the "don't make waves" message. I don't make waves when I watch my computer.

Hypnosis helped me change this pattern.

Health Freaks

☆ *"Be careful about reading health books. You may die of a misprint."*

—Mark Twain

If you are preoccupied with your health to the point that vitamins, diets and exercise occupy the majority of your thoughts, suspect a health obsession.

Vitamin Mania

You can overdose with too many vitamins and minerals.

The best sources of vitamins and minerals are organically grown fruits and vegetables. It's much harder to overdose on fruits and vegetables.

The most dangerous vitamins to overdo are fat-soluble ones. A, D and E are stored in body fat. Too much vitamin A (more than 25,000 IUs a day) might damage your liver and cause hair loss, blurred vision and headaches. Megadoses of vitamin D can cause calcium deposits that interfere with your muscles, including your heart. Overdoses of Vitamin E can cause irregular heartbeat. A neighbor of mine took megadoses of vitamin E for over a year to "keep his cholesterol down." His doctor recommended it. Chest pains put him into intensive care. The doctor was going to operate and insert a pacemaker when my neighbor figured out that it was the vitamin E. He checked himself out of the hospital. Ten years later, without vitamin E, his heart is still fine.

Megadoses of anything should only be taken only under guidance of a health care professional.

Too much niacin can cause jaundice and liver damage. Excessive B6 can cause numbness in the mouth, hands and difficulty walking. Megadoses of vitamin C causes diarrhea and stomach aches. Iron megadoses (more than 100 milligrams) interferes with zinc absorption, needed for healing and immunity. Yeast-based fillers and gelatin capsules (made from animal hooves) taken along with vitamins can cause allergic reactions.

Exercise Mania: Aswan, As Two, As Three

INNER•VIEW QUIZ

Are You A Fitness Addict?

Answer true or false for each question

___ I'm compulsive about exercise.
___ My exercise has gotten out of control.
___ A healthy weight for me is different from standard weight charts.
___ I focus on one particular body flaw, demanding perfection.
___ I continue to work out in spite of injuries.
___ If I don't exercise, I feel anxious and distressed.
___ If I don't exercise, I get depressed and have trouble sleeping.
___ I've tried to stop exercising, but it didn't work.
___ I occasionally increase my exercising to maintain a "high."
___ I must maintain a rigid training schedule.
___ I constantly worry about getting enough exercise.
___ I feel guilty or shameful about exercising or not exercising.
___ I feel empty inside.
___ I obsessively keep records of my exercise.
___ I work out even when it's inconvenient, or interferes with work or relationships.

If you answered true to any of these perhaps you are out of balance in your life. Exercise mania is like being a runner with your foot nailed to the ground; you can get a fast start, but you'll never get very far.

If your self-esteem wrapped around exercise, you know how stressed and guilty you feel if you slack off. A fitness compulsion leaves no room for friends, fun and relaxation.

Exercise becomes addictive when you use it exclusively to relieve intense anxiety, improve your mood or heighten self esteem.

Frank, an All-American runner put himself through college by performing jazz music, painting and running competitively. Here is his story:

A TRUE STORY Frank

"I am the youngest of three children. When I was 11, my father lost his medical license, his practice and our house. We moved to a low-rent apartment in Lomita while my father went to a rehabilitation program for alcohol abuse.

Shortly after his release, he hit my mother, so I hit him back. He picked up a knife, and I ran as fast as my legs could carry me, out the front door and three miles down the road. It was at that moment that I took up running.

In my sophomore year, I began running with a vengeance. I was the star of our cross country team. When I won, I told myself, 'Well, that's one down; maybe I'm an athlete like Dad.' When I lost, I heard my father say, 'You won't amount to anything.' I would leave the track and sneak a few beers. My grades were low, and in spite of an ankle injury, I became a ranked cross-country runner.

By now, I smoked marijuana every weekend. I got it from a college friend whose parents had beer on tap. I started smoking cigarettes and had my first bout with asthma. After I lost several races, I decided to stop drinking and smoking, and I finished first on my team.

When school began, it was varsity running. One day, in the middle of running, I realized I was rewarding my father and not myself. I quit the team.

Finally, I stopped drinking. I have not had pot in a year. I have a steady job and I am putting my life back in order by keeping busy. I let out energy by playing in a small band and I am writing. One day I might start running again, but just for fun."

Workaholics

If life a list of must-dos with not enough time to do them, slow down. If a workaholic takes a time management course they only rearrange the tread on their treadmill. To get off the clock, look behind mad activity. What is really going on? What brings you the most fulfillment? If you didn't have to work for a living, what would you do with your time?

INNER•VIEW QUIZ

Are You Overworking Work?

☆ *"I'm late, I'm late, for a very important date."*

—The White Rabbit, *Alice in Wonderland*

Answer true if these apply to you:

___ I try to make a killing, not a living.
___ I hide from life by working.
___ I'm driven on the road to success.
___ My work is dedicated to avoiding not just providing.
___ I work day and night to buy toys I don't have time to play with.
___ I leave little time for the people I love.
___ My family only values me for what I do.
___ I say "I'm an accountant" not "I do accounting."
___ Life disappears in an increasing blur of work.
___ A big deal is always just around the next push.
___ I cut my nose on the grindstone.
___ I keep on going on and go numb-er and numb-er.
___ I'm so busy I can't remember what I did last month, let alone last year.
___ I am bombarded with world knowledge and thousands of messages . through the media.

If you answered true to these questions, watch out! Your life needs more balancing. There is a thin line between passion and a lopsided life. Workaholics often get a permanent vacation, well urned.

AFFIRM SUCCESS: A Great Trip For Workaholics
Close your eyes and imagine a cloud taking you to a favorite place. Feel yourself in that place and let the earth cradle you, blessing you with smell, sound and peace. Enjoy! And read these affirmations:

Δ What I choose to do with my time is up to me.
Δ I take responsibility for how I live my life.
Δ I achieve my goals and dreams.
Δ I develop my many hobbies and interests.
Δ I allow time each day for a blissful vacation or holiday.
Δ I create and honor time to love my family and friends.
Δ I inject magic into my life.
Δ I earn more than I spend.
Δ I love my work; my work is my play.
Δ My work helps me be in control my money flow, time and intelligence.
Δ I know I can get another job if and when I want.
Δ I stay in this job from a place of personal power.
Δ My job enhances my joy.
Δ My work has enough challenge to be interesting.
Δ My work has enough leisure to feel refreshed.
Δ My work has quiet time for productivity.
Δ My work has enough money to live comfortably, plus some.
Δ My work has enough companionship to be nourishing.
Δ My work has enough time to get the job done.
Δ My work has enough value to be personally rewarding.
Δ My work is creative enough to satisfy me.

Return to your room awareness refreshed and invigorated.

Mind Your Busy•ness

What motivates you to be chronically busy? Put a T by statements that apply to you and discover any hidden agendas...

___ 1. I work because I'm afraid of being alone.
(If so, you substitute work for intimacy).

___ 2. I work hard to feel valued.
(If so, you feel unworthy except in work and accomplishments).

___ 3. I work constantly to satisfy other people's needs.
(If so, you satisfy other's needs before your own. People-pleasing to the extreme is exhausting).

___ 4. I'm not happy but change scares me.
(Yes means as a creature of habit, you would rather stay painfully safe in routines than take the energy to change and feel better).

___ 5. I've got to have better things then other people.
(Yes says that super-achievement makes you feel victoriously competitive and perhaps resentful that others "have a life").

___ 6. I'm scared to death of success.
(Yes here means that you do anything and everything instead of being successful) .

___ 7. I don't know how to say "no."
(This one means that you please others so you won't be rejected.

Money Madness

☆ Question: *"When is high finance mentioned in the Bible?"*
Answer: *"Pharaoh's daughter took a little prophet (profit) from the bulrushes."*

☆ Question: *"Where do Egyptians save their money?"*
Answer: *"The Banks of the Nile."*

☆ *"By the time the meek have inherited the earth, your inheritance will have been squandered."*

☆ *"It's not a problem if you have money. It's a problem if money has you."*
—Lee Grimes, Tulsa Cab Driver

Money isn't everything but it's way ahead of whatever is in second place! Money is a 4000 years old socially admired and applauded addiction.

If you're addicted, your attraction is so intense that you believe that money is the essence of happiness: more important than good health or intimate relationships. If just money and stuff brings you fulfillment, it won't work. Money is just one delicious slice of the pie of life.

INNER•VIEW QUIZ

Are You Mad about Money?

Answer T for true and true for T.

___ I think about money constantly.
___ Money is an end unto itself?
___ My credit cards are maxed out.
___ Easy come, easy go.
___ I'm out-of-control with spending.
___ Money is more important to me than relationships.
___ I carry budgeting and saving to the extreme.
___ I keep a strict control on spending. I can live on nothing.
___ I never spend money, even if I have it.
___ I'd rather sleep on a lumpy mattress than spend money for a firm one.
___ When it comes to money, I divide and conk her.
___ When I have money, I have to spend it.
___ If I don't have money, I have to spend it.
___ I say, "Everyone spends like me. I'm just like them."
___ I'm over billed and under-cashed because of my buying.
___ My bills add up faster than I can pay them.
___ I instantly blow my paycheck and have nothing until the next paycheck.
___ I have had to declare bankruptcy because I overspent.
___ Spending money makes me feel connected and less lonely.
___ I feel better when I buy something.
___ I am sneaky about what I spend (I throw away/ hide receipts).
___ Hay big spender, spend a little time with me.
___ The thought of not having enough money fills me with panic.
___ I hide new purchases before mt mate sees them.

If any of these apply to you, you spend too much energy around spending or not spending money.

Shopaholic: Hem Locked

☆ CONSUMING PASSION

Massive buying by the masses. Gotta give us credit.
Gimme, buy me, take me, send me. Please Mom, can I get it?
To buy, buy, buy makes me so high;
If I can't have it I'll just die.
Boutique, department store, catalogue,
Swap meets, home sales, on the job,
Television marketing, unsolicited call,
Bury me near the shopping mall.
Wave some plastic near my head.
If I don't move, you'll know I'm dead.

—Shelley Stockwell

INNER•VIEW QUIZ

Are You A Shopaholic?

☆ *"How do you keep a rhino from charging?"*
"Take away his credit cards"

—Jon Nicholas

___ I shop 'til I drop.
___ As a kid I could never have enough Barbie dolls, GI Joes or games.
___ I can't resist extras at the cash register, catalogs and phone solicitations.
___ I spend money, whether I have it to spend or not?
___ Garage sales have my name on them.
___ My car automatically turns into the parking lot of the mall.
___ The Home Shopping Network hosts know me by name.
___ I find excuses to buy new clothes.
___ Clothes in my closet still have price tags on them.
___ I forget presents I already bought and buy them again.
___ There's a big difference in how I feel when shopping and not shopping.
___ I buy clothes, jewelry or cosmetics even though I don't need them.
___ I buy books I don't read, tools I don't use.
___ I discard so I can replace them with more things.
___ Money is no object when it comes to my hobby.
___ Shopping is my recreation.
___ I shop when I'm bored. Buying makes me high.
___ I spend time I can't afford to waste shopping.
___ Shopping consoles me.
___ I have to have the newest "thing."
___ I can't resist a bargain. I buy it even if I don't need it.
___ I crave more shopping excitement and feel lower than a snake's belly after.
___ My bumper stickers reads, "I came, I saw, I shopped." or
"Whoever dies with the most toys wins" or " Born to Shop."
___ I worry and fret about NOT spending money.
___ Money causes me distress, worry, humiliation and disagreement.
___ I hide my latest purchases so others won't know how much I buy.
___ If my friends buy it, I must get one too.

Shopping is fun. We use shopping for socializing and as a way to spend time. In moderation it seems to work well.

But, what if your self-worth and status is centered around spending or not spending money and the stuff you buy or don't buy? What if shopping boosts your self-esteem more than anything else? What if you use spending to get high or tranquilize? What if you shop to look good to others and don't look good to yourself? Well, then you go from dalliance to disaster. It is not about money; it's an attempt to satisfy inner poverty. All the spending or not spending in the world can't fill emptiness.

Materialism is a belief that externals offer you inner peace—a baby bottle, a blanket, a bicycle, a BA, a BMW and eventually a bong and a booze bottle.

If you are addicted to shopping or spending money it only brings upset. If you pretend you are made of money, everything costs an arm and a leg.

A shopping obsession is agonizing. And, as with all addictions, a spending high is temporary and requires that you dole out more and more to get the same effects. No matter how much bigger or better, excitement dwindles and the letdown gets worse and worse.

TV, radio, print and display advertisers excite children and ensnarl grown-ups with ads, point-of-purchase items entice at the cash register. Catalogs in the mail and phone solicitations make us lick our chops for more and more stuff.

Shopping malls and muzak lull and seduce.

Credit card companies assist you down the garden path...to their credit. It is no longer a matter of living within your income: it's all we can do to live within your credit.

Sixty-five percent of new credit card recipients are college age and have their card "maxed to the limit" in two and one-half months from the date it was issued. The credit limit is usually $500. Jennie is a perfect example:

A TRUE STORY Jenine

"I went on a shopping spree when I got to college. No Mom around to throw a fit over my taste or extravagance. Before I knew it, I owed $4000 on my credit cards, and my roommate $600. I felt like I was in quicksand. To make matters worse, I didn't tell anyone for a long time. Fortunately for me, my Dad bailed me out. But I've never heard the end of it. What a lesson."

U.S. teens spend per year:
- Δ $72.4 million: shirts
- Δ $88.1 million: sweaters
- Δ $110.1 million: dresses
- Δ $118.1 million: jeans
- Δ $217.1 million: athletic clothes
- Δ $1.3 BILLION: shoes

$$ Trouble Right Here In River City

If fashion magazines are your bible, you won't have a prayer in the mall.

If mom took you shopping and that's the only time you felt close to her, find something better to do when you need attention. Here is Carole's story. I call it "mother may I?"

A TRUE STORY Carole

"I sneaked purchases into the house so my husband Tom wouldn't see them. He knows I'm hopeless with money and keeps a grip on the checkbook. Growing up, Mom never paid attention to me except to pay for my school clothes or lunch ticket. I think I made Tom my parent so I could act out my part as child.

When Tom and I understood this pattern, we were able to tell each other the truth. He shows me love in so many other ways. Now I accept it more. I feel much closer to him and act more rationally about spending."

Illustration by Shelley Stockwell

Ump•teen Dollars on Clothes

☆ *"To make money last, you have to make it first."*
—The Complete Toastmaster

Grocery store owners know that 53% of all purchases are made at the spur of the moment. And hardware store owners know that 47% of their products are grabbed on impulse. In a survey of over 3400 mall shoppers, only 25% said they came in pursuit of a specific item. 70% of all adults in the US visit a shopping mall weekly. There are more shopping malls than high schools. In 1957 there were 2000 shopping malls, now there are well over 30,000.

Bust the Splurge Urge

The first step to breaking free of crazed shopping patterns is to notice them.

C heck in at Checkout: Why am I buying this? Is it for attention? Love? Security?
A sk: Will buying this really fill that need?
S elect: If the answer is yes, buy it and enjoy it. If not, put it back.
H appiness: Laugh out loud.

AFFIRM SUCCESS: Ha•R•Money

Close your eyes and breathe in and out slowly three times. As you read this script imagine yourself descending into a beautiful valley or garden of relaxation. With each thought and idea you go deeper and deeper into trance. Let these ideas make a deep and permanent impression on your mind and behavior.

Bye, Bye; Buy Buy.
Money takes its rightful place in my life. I am practical with money. I am in control of my behavior. I am worthy. I am keenly aware of my behavior. I shop when I need something. I think before I spend, "do I really need it?" "Can I get it at a better price somewhere else?" "Can I afford it?" "Am I buying this only to give myself a lift?" "Am I depriving myself of something I really need?"

I'm in charge of my behavior. I only spend money when relaxed. If I feel rushed, I pass on it and say "I can live without it." I cut up credit cards; pitch catalogs. I avoid impulse buying. I am in control when I buy something. I take a mental time out and evaluate, "Do I really, really, really need this?" I purchase with a logical attitude. I avoid peer pressure. I'm in control. I go grocery shopping when I'm full. I shop when I'm happy. If I'm bummed out I get exercise, take a bath or call a friend. I get a grip. If I really need something, I go and buy it. If not, I find many more interesting things to occupy my time and thoughts. I get pleasure out of my many interests. I learn new and exciting ways to occupy my mind and time.

Gambling: Delta Crummy Hand

☆ *"Do you gamble?"*
"No."
"I'll bet you do."
"How much!"

☆ CASINO

The luscious fittings and decor so grand
Makes me clearly understand
To maintain this wealthy lavish spot
It's unlikely that one wins a lot.
Game, wage, bet, stake
Venture, risk, speculate
Take the plunge. Take a flyer
To win the lottery you aspire?
Take a gamble, spin the wheel
Any day you'll close a deal.
Borrow, sweet talk, pie in the sky
If you live like this, your life's a lie.

—Shelley Stockwell

Gambling stimulates, excites and arouses. Not everyone who gambles, gambles compulsively. Overboard excitement transports a person from social gambler to out-of-control gambler.

The thrill of the chase! Compulsive gamblers try to fill a need to control something or prove their self worth. Seeds of addictive gambling are rooted in initial large wins, the opportunity to gamble and watching others gamble.

It is often a family disease. In the denial phase, no one sees it as a problem, and believes they're going to bring in the bucks. There is a lot of excitement, high energy and ego. The high roller is a high experience. When you're winning, everyone in the family gets emotionally high together. Big wins bring big presents to the kiddies.

As the passion for gambling intensifies and the losses start, generosity wanes. Compulsive gamblers begin to take money from home, family and children to feed their habit. Co-dependent families pray that the gambler's luck will turn. The greater the losses, the stronger the compulsion, and the more pain the family experiences. Some children even go out and gamble to rescue the family.

A TRUE STORY Jeremy

"I've always been the black sheep of the family. Gambling gave me a charge that made me feel like I was somebody important. My family didn't appreciate it. We were so heavily in debt. My wife and children did not have enough of anything. I woke up and noticed my family suffering. I was stealing from my own family. I was lying to everybody. It's funny, I always thought of myself as an honest, upstanding man. I joined Gamblers Anonymous and went into remission. But it wasn't until I used hypnosis that I could actually say I was in my integrity. Now, I am respectful of telling and living the truth. I am creeping out of debt."

Shoplifting: Thebes

Children learn that taking something that "doesn't belong to you" is wrong. Have you stolen in your life? If you did and were outrageously lucky, you were caught, punished and never stole again. Or, if you felt guilty or afraid, you may never have done it again. People who continue to steal never learn to control the "gimme" game. Poverty stricken, drug addicts, bored teens and even the successful and glamorous may steal.

The object is more than something for nothing or what is stolen. The theft itself is most significant. The adrenaline charge or sexual rush of getting away with something and proving prowess is the real payoff for some. Others steal because, on some level, they want to get caught for attention, punishment or to override boredom. Some justify it because they are poorer than others.

Whether the payoff is guilt, excitement, control, self-destruction, self-esteem or anger, stealing feels terrible inside no matter how you rationalize it.

Illustration by Shelley Stockwell

Crook

A TRUE STORY Ginger

"The more I got away with it, the more invincible I felt and the easier it got. I had a moral code, I only stole from expensive department stores. For them it was a drop in the bucket.

I was a good shoplifter because I was blasé. Double D is the secret; deadpan and daring. Because I look respectable, no one would believe that I was stealing.

When I got in my car with my prize, my blood ran hot and cold like just before an orgasm. I liked casing the store, outsmarting the staff and security.

If you get a tag that squirts dye, put them in the freezer. The ink freezes and they just snap off. Now they are getting smarter and putting antifreeze in some and it's a mess.

I finally got caught stealing vitamins from the drug store. The camera saw me and the next thing I knew, a warm hand was on my shoulder. They played back the video of me stealing. My sicky feeling was stronger than the first time I stole something. I cried and said that I had never stolen before. But they searched my bag and found the jewelry and perfume I took earlier.

My legs shook uncontrollably when they put me in a police car. I was treated like a criminal. I was in the police station three hours and it seemed like three weeks. When I left the cell, I knew that I'd never steal again.

I was charged, convicted and fined. I now have a record.

AFFIRM SUCCESS: Honest Kicks

I get my kicks in healthy, honest ways. If I take something that is not mine, I hurt many people, particularly myself. I pay by laying off innocent workers, higher prices and my personal self respect.

I choose to be kind to people. I respect myself and my actions. I enjoy making an honest wage. I get my thrills learning new expanding ideas and hobbies. I get turned on being a good citizen. The past is just a memory; I leave it where it belongs…in the past. I live, think and behave in healthy, positive ways.

Misers: Cheap Chiselers

☆ Robber: *"Your money or your life?"*
Victim: *"Take my life, I'm saving my money for my old age."*

Ebenezer Scrooge in "A Christmas Carol" is a wonderful allegory for transformation.

The first ghost of the past, allows Scrooge to show compassion toward his inner child. Scrooge is forced to regress to his feelings of abandonment in boarding school. The Ghost of the future, is the grim reaper, reminds him that he reaps what he sows. If you are compulsively hoard money, you work too hard and miss joy in your life. Step back and ask yourself "Where did these patterns originate?" and "What will happen if I continue?"

Scammers: Foul•con

☆ Bank Manager firing his accountant:
"Where were you educated?"
Accountant: "*Yale.*"
Bank Manager: *Such a fine university; what is your name?"*
Accountant: "*Yim Yohansen.*"

You get nothing for free. Scamming compulsions turn "buyology" into "criminology."

True Believers: Hooked on Religion, Beliefs and/or Rhetoric

INNER•VIEW QUIZ

Are You A True Believer?

Honestly answer true to those that sound like you.
___ I'm obsessed by my beliefs.
___ My viewpoint is the only correct one.
___ I rigidly follow my beliefs. I am 100% locked on my viewpoint.
___ I truly believed in philosophy, I must have been crazy.
___ Things are black and white.
___ I hate people with different beliefs from mine.
___ I do what my Guru/ Minister/ Teacher says. They know better than I do.
___ If I don't pray/ meditate/ go to services/meetings. every day, I get depressed.
___ I have attempted to stop being so gung ho, but it didn't work.
___ I occasionally increase my devotional routine to maintain a "high."
___ I must maintain a strict and rigid devotional schedule.
___ I feel guilt or shame about my belief practices and secretly resent them.
___ I'm empty inside.
___ I continue devotional practices even if inconvenient. or interfere.
___ I wish I were dead. Life isn't any fun.
___ Life would be drastically better if I could just be more diligent in my beliefs.
___ I believe that love is based only on performance.
___ I have only superficial relationships with other people.
___ All I ever want to do is practice my devotion.
___ I lie about my behavior.
___ I think committing suicide is to punish someone else.
___ Thank God I'm an atheist.

☆ THE RELIGION
"We are right," they shout
While the silent "You are wrong."
Is the flip side of their song.
In their clusters large and small,
It makes them feel so tall.
So they shout out with their might,
"We are right! We are right!"
By pitying the others
They betray them as their brothers.
Building walls up as they "Spread the word."
Perhaps God should be felt, not heard

—Shelley Stockwell

☆ *"Fanaticism redoubles your efforts when you have forgotten your aim."*

—George Santayana

☆ *"I don't want to be saved, I want to be spent.*

—Fritz Pearls

I'm Not Judgmental: I'm Not Like You Bigots

A religion or belief structure is an obsession/compulsion if it runs you; you don't run it. Fanatics are hysterical and lie to themselves. If a true believer weren't obsessive, they would have stopped the inner hurt, fear, and rage long ago. One client blamed the loss of every job on not being allowed to practice his religion. In reality, he was lazy. His religion ploy worked so he didn't work. He was so heavenly bound, he was of no earthly good.

The Common Cult

☆ Tony, the puffed-up pious one: *"Steve, you want to go to heaven, don't you?"*
Steve: *"I'm not sure."*
Tony his hands in the prayer position: *"You must be sure."*
Steve: *Are you sure that you will to go to heaven?"*
Tony: *"Oh yes. Absolutely sure."*
Steve: *"Then, Tony, I don't want to go to heaven."*

Are you addicted to a guru or charismatic leader?

Cults attract people who are alienated, going through tough times or have low self-esteem. They also attract co-dependents that like to play "mother may I" and would rather not bother taking responsibility for life's decisions.

Cults usually seduce a newcomer with love, inclusion and information. Moonies sugar dose initiates with Kool-Aid and never leave their side. Someone who doesn't feel great about themself suddenly feels special and honored. These "chosen ones" are then trained to feel humble and unworthy before the great muck-a-muck at the top. The chief guru generally controls the flow of information to his groupies, analyzing and explaining the true meaning of news, behaviors and books. They prohibit input from other philosophies by threats of punishment, excommunication, abandonment or worse. Sleep patterns are often purposefully disrupted. Such brainwashing is calculated to have devotees submit unquestioningly.

If you are a fanatic, you work overtime to be right or to do "it" right. Your inner feelings fluctuate from elated to empty, to hateful and numb. If anyone questions your beliefs, you get threatened and upset. To keep believing, you exercise "selective" listening skills.

To blindly follow a leader, regardless of his wrappings and trapping, is the ultimate co-dependent game. Embittered ex-scientologists claim that they were put in solitary confinement when they said they wanted to quit the group. Later when they did quit, they say, they were unabatedly harassed. Jim Jones dragged hundreds of people to Guyana who truly believed he was the path to enlightenment and love. They left Guyana in body bags.

What is God's religion?

Does your God love my God?

Does your God/Guru love your individual thought?

Rageaholics: Hit 'em in the Cheops

☆ IF YOU WANT TO BE LITTLE

Be little.

—Shelley Stockwell

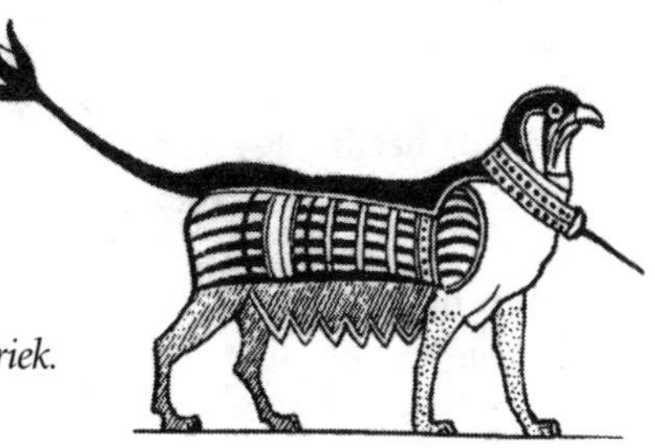

☆ YOU NEVER LISTEN

You never listen (perhaps your ears are weak)
You never take the time to acknowledge what I shriek.
You never understand anything I say,
I can tell by your wrong answers and the ignorance you display.
Stop interrupting, swearing that you do.
Define your terms, shut up right now. Listen, I'm talking to you!
You never listen, (perhaps your ears are weak)
You never take the time to acknowledge what I shriek.

—Shelley Stockwell

Rageaholics regularly hit others and themselves with words, sarcasm and violence. Anger is a healthy, lusty emotion that need healthy release.

Frustration, disappointment and heartache may show up as anger.

Irritation, animosity and fury are three degrees of the same feeling: anger.

Anger may be expressed as guilt (anger turned inward), snipes (passive punching) and rage (out•rageous tantrums). Victims of angry people suffer from "post traumatic stress syndrome." Being around anger can stress you to the max.

Anger turned inward makes us self-abusive, self-destructive and depressed. Pummeling yourself is deadly. Banging your head against the wall hurts! Held in anger takes control over feelings. Repressed rage can make you sick, and/or make you explode in the wrong places.

It's fine to be angry. It's not fine to take it out on others. It messes up relationships and you. How can you trust a loose cannon? Pummeling another hurts you inside.

Some angry folks choose a life partner to express rage for them. Some get even in covert ways. Passive aggressive folks use sneak attacks to keep rage under wraps. Here's a true story I'm not proud of:

A TRUE STORY Shelley

"When I was 16, I decided I hated a girl I'll call Penny. I suspect It was because she reminded me of my mother and it was safer to vent my rage on her than my mom.

Penny and I were going to be camp counselors for the summer. I heard she liked a lifeguard there, named Bill. Sight unseen, I decided to steal him from her. When we arrived, I did everything to catch his eye and win his affections. It worked! A month later, after camp, he came to visit me googly-eyed. I was repulsed. Guess I showed her."

Underneath all anger is a level of truth that says, "About me I feel..." and those feelings are not good.

All In the Family

☆ *Dad was like that, Mom was too*
What else did they expect me to do?

—Shelley Stockwell

The *intimidator* has a loud voice, slams doors and threatens to leave. The *brooder* withdraws into stony silence, the *sniper* takes pot shots. All anger, whether blatant or subtle is learned behavior. Children learn by watching grown-ups.

If your parents had unrealistic expectations of you, were out-of-control, and hit you with fists or words, you might do the same. Rageaholics usually come from families where the person who is "right" yells the loudest or the longest. Children of rageful role models, imitate with rage of their own. Some scream to irritate or get attention.

Did you go to your parents for protection, and they protected by entering the fray, making the fight worse? For example, brother slugs sister, she tells father, and father rages and punishes sister for being a snitch. If so, rageful punishment builds resentment and anger.

INNER•VIEW QUIZ

Are You A Rageaholic?

☆ *"I keep picking fights with people."*
"How long have you had this problem?"
"Who wants to know?"

Answer T if a statement applies to you.

____ I'm a rageaholic.
____ I'm all stressed up with no one to choke.
____ I awake surly in the morning.
____ I get ticked off easily. I have a short fuse. I lash out.
____ I discipline kids with threats, verbal attacks and/or hitting.
____ I expect more self-control from my children/mate than from myself.
____ I teach my kids not to hit by hitting them, not to yell by yelling at them.
____ I flip out if the waitress takes too long with my order?
____ I often threaten, curse and/or nag. It's your fault.
____ I yell at people in front of others. I shout insults or accusations.
____ I call people names, insult with sarcasm and/or bring up past anger.
____ I snip and snipe at others.
____ I am condescending.
____ If someone does me wrong I think of ways to get even.
____ Anger runs me, I don't run it.
____ I relive slights over and over.
____ Others are out to get me.
____ When I have a problem with a product or service, I call up and shout.
____ If someone performs a task too slowly or I have to wait, I get mad.
____ I feel guilt, upset, regret and remorse after I fly off the handle.
____ I often bite, scream, thrash on the floor and/or hold my breath.
____ I jump to the worst conclusions.
____ I have the same reaction to major problems as I do to minor ones.
____ "No" is my favorite word.
____ My anger is influenced by sugar, alcohol, caffeine, drugs and/or PMS.
____ I feel like punching someone.
____ I kick the dog or cat.
____ I beat others or myself.
____ I get ticked off a lot when driving a car.

If any of these sounds like you, wake up and simmer down. You are out of control. You can channel rage into positive action, accept the things you cannot change and deal constructively with things you can.

Old Yeller, the Outrageous Surgeon

The English surgeon, John Hunter's, research showed that anger and anxiety brought on chest pains. He died after he got furious with two other doctors during a staff meeting.

Here are three case studies that show the ripple effect of rage:

A TRUE STORY Carlos

"I lived in foster homes four times. I was the youngest of seven kids and my parents were always drunk. My stepfather often beat Mom. And then my older brother would beat up my stepfather. My older brother and I are both alcoholics. My life's purpose is to grow bigger than my parents and I have."

A TRUE STORY Jan

Lou lived in my apartment building. I stalked him. When he said, 'Go away,' I persisted pursuing. Finally, Lou gave in and moved in. If he was 15 minutes late, I'd call everywhere in a panic and run to his hangouts. I was furious. When he came home I'd throw things at him. Our fights were horrendous. Once, he pushed me and I called the police.

He would not find a job. While I worked, he sat on the beach. When I told him to move out, he drove to the motel where we went on our first night together and shot himself to death. His family said it was my fault.

I was the third of five children, raised in a strict Catholic family and attended Catholic school. Under hypnosis, I recalled my first grade teacher, Sister Mary Josephine, telling me that I required discipline because I talked too much and had too much energy. She said I would never go far because of my 'pathetic family background.' Sister Mary Josephine wrote a note to my parents and said that I was not living within the church's boundaries and that my conduct was unsatisfactory. My father beat me. A devout alcoholic, he beat my mother, too. When he was sober, he was a lamb and begged to be warmly welcomed home.

Thanks to hypnotherapy, I understand how my rage came from my childhood. I tried to control Lou to feel OK about myself. I chose to be emotionally out of control. Now I choose to be in control. I am responsible for my behavior. It is not correct to hit another person. I listen to my hypnosis tapes, do aerobic exercise and I quit smoking.

My father is not all men and Lou was not my father. I am under construction. I'm learning to feel OK about myself.

A TRUE STORY Shelley (Hypnotized Violently)

Several years ago, a friend and I were walking down a street in downtown Boston. As we turned the corner, two ambulance attendants ran from a Radio Shack store carrying a stretcher holding a young man in his 20s. He was bleeding from the chest. We silently watched the litter slide into the ambulance and drive away.

"That guy just got shot in the chest."

"That's too bad," my friend Christina said, with equal lackluster.

As if in a stupor, without another word, we walked two more blocks. Then it hit us. That was a real human shot in the chest. We had seen thousands of people shot in the chest on television and in movies. We had read about this scene ad nauseam in newspapers and magazines. To us, a man shot in the chest had become commonplace.

"Oh my God," we said, "we just saw a human being shot in the chest! But look at us, we stopped being human." We cried and held each other and promised to be conscious of our fellow human beings. Then we said a prayer for the poor victim.

> In a UCLA study, Dr. McGuire and his students found that dominant male monkeys have twice as much seratonin as non-dominant ones. Within two weeks after a dominant male monkey is removed from a situation where he must dominate, his brain returns to a normal amount of seratonin.

Angry Myths

☆ *"The cause of this accident was a little guy in a small car with a big mouth."*

—Insurance claim

Myth #1: Winning Is All

It's OK to fight dirty as long as you win. Children told this often grow up to be politicians and lawyers. The news reports an athlete, cool in the championship game, who flips out and pummels someone later in the bar.

Myth #2: I Am Superior

Some of us are trained to believe that we are superior to others. Superior perceived status gives them license to bash and insult the lowly.

"If you don't do what you're told, I'll slap you down."

Boys trained to believe that they are superior to girls, may grow up to batter wives. Some think it's OK for prison guards to beat criminals, soldiers to torture captured enemies and parents to beat children.

This top dog/bottom dog posture makes the top dog feel safe to growl and bite until a bigger dog comes along.

Myth #3: Just Kidding, Can't You Take a Joke?

Is someone making jokes at your expense? Do you make fun of others, laugh at their foibles and demand perfectionism or you'll blow? Suspect veiled rage.

Myth #4: One Up Yours

There are several styles of this game. The public offender is sugar and spice in private but snipe in public. The put-down artist enjoys the public slam dunk.

Myth #5: All's Fair in Love and War

☆ WAR GAME: IT'S THE RAGE

Fat cat, smiling bureaucrat,
Strategic planning diplomat,
Run chess games played by smooth faced pawns
On deserts, oceans, manicured lawns,
Jungles, islands, airways, bars,
Local turf or distant shores.

The young pawns die to do it right,
For home or glory or the thrill of the fight:
To take a castle, or a king;
Be knighted for the suffering.

Behind his desk the gamesman grins,
Carefully sips a glass of gin,
Counts his money and
Plans his win.

No elder statesman can berate
This conscientious diplomat.
CHECKMATE!
Slowly, mankind has learned the score:
Fodder can't father anymore;
Widows and cripples sift the rubble
And wonder if life's worth the trouble.

The grim truth hurts humanity.
Change begins with you and me.
We know the game.
We know the score.
Let's not fight war anymore.

—Shelley Stockwell

Some make marriage the War of the Roses: an all-out, in-your-face fight.

Myth #6: Brutally Honest

Honestly, this person enjoys the brutality more than the honesty.

A TRUE STORY Julia

"Mom threw tea cups at Dad. Once, when he was teaching her to throw darts, she threw a dart at his foot. She would throw shoes. He was quick; he rarely got hit.

When I married, my husband would hit me and I retaliated by throwing his dinner on his head. Throwing things was part of every TV and movie in my day, "You beast," they would exclaim as the victimized housewife chased her husband with a frying pan. I only dumped food, but I figured out early on that this is more of a mess than it was worth and I was the one who had to clean it up. So, I gave it up."

What To Do If You Are Abused

1. Report any rageful games that you observe. If you are doing them, stop it immediately.

2. If someone is abusing you, tell them that you want it to stop, right now, then run like hell. If it is not safe to tell them, just run like hell.

3. If someone is bellowing, stand quietly firm and don't budge. If you can't be bullied, they'll have to talk.

4. If an aggressor is a brooder, with sulking, stony silence; let them sulk until they become adult again.

5. If your abuser is a put-down artist who calls you dumb, a bad parent or worse; know your own worth and refuse to let them undermine it.

6. Most importantly, use laughter to smooth ruffled feathers.

If none of these work "turn in the key Lee and set yourself free"...move out.

Myth #7 What I Do in My Car, Doesn't Count

Is your anger appropriate to the situation? Do you over-react? Is it worth it? Ask those who have been paralyzed, gone to court or been shot.

Rage and roads don't mix. Driving is not a contest. It is not a race against the clock. And, it is definitely not a place to throw a fit. The solution for road rage is to be alert, courteous and patient behind the wheel or turn in your driver's license.

INNER•VIEW QUIZ

Are You Road Rageous: Ramses

☆ Grown up: *"How do you drive, Ollie?"*
Four-year old Ollie: *"You put the key in the ignition and stick your head out the window and yell 'God damn son-of-a-bitch.'"*

Do the following sound like you?

___ I over react to situations when driving a car.
___ Driving in the car, if someone reads the map wrong, I get furious.
___ Late for an appointment, I get angry with the other drivers in my way.
___ If a car cuts me off I get even.
___ I have tried to run someone off the road.
___ I have driven very slowly to get even.
___ I select certain people to yell at and insult (female drivers, young people, the elderly, an ethnic group, truck drivers).
___ Zig-zaggers or tailgaters put me in a stew.
___ When road conditions aren't to my liking, I swear.
___ I yell at myself.
___ I am ready to kill when someone gets my parking spot.
___ I justify anger with sentences like "It was her fault, she wouldn't let me pass."

If you answered yes to any of these questions it's time you got a grip.

Traffic Do's

Calm Down Allow time to drive leisurely. Instead of making good time; make time good.
Control You cannot control traffic or others. Control your reaction.
Courtesy Commit to being courteous even if others aren't.
Avoid Conflict If another driver threatens, avoid conflict, take a deep breath, pull over and get out of their way.
Avoid Confrontation If another driver is hostile, ask yourself "is it worth it to get involved?" Avoid eye contact and distance yourself from the rude one. Give them lots of room.
Avoid Gestures If you make a mistake, apologize with an appropriate gesture.

Traffic Dont's

- Don't honk your horn.
- Don't box car someone in.
- Don't tailgate.
- Don't block the passing lane.
- Don't switch lanes without signaling.
- Don't take more than 1 parking spot.
- Don't hit parked cars with your door.
- Don't blind others with high beams.
- Don't blast loud music on nearby cars.
- Don't engage in rage.
- Don't give the finger or any other negative hand gesture.

☆ MAD
When I'm pissed off, I do things faster.
Muffling complaints under slitted eyes that see nothing.
When I'm mad, it's always your fault. "What's wrong with you anyway?"
When I'm angry, my tizzies are energy spun out on a dusty burning racetrack.
When I'm ticked, I don't feel well. I don't hear the little child within,
frightened and alone, desperate for a friend.
When I'm pissed off,
I forget to love.

—Shelley Stockwell

So What's The Solution?
Fight Aggression: Temper Your Temper

☆ *No man can think clearly when his fists are clenched.*

—George Jean Nathan

☆ *No one can shake hands if their fists are clenched.*

—Indira Gandhi

☆ *No one can laugh if their teeth are clenched*

—Shelley Stockwell

☆ *"Express your needs and hurts to your beloved and you get cooperation and affection. Vent rage and for sure you'll receive rage, withdrawal, and finally, they'll stop loving you."*

—Dr. Alex Lessin

☆TANTRUM
The demons are dancing in and out
Tight rubber bands snapping tension with their taunting.
"Don't use me. Don't abuse me. Don't tell me. Don't hurt me."
You snit in sniping glares and criticism.
The demons laugh with glee at what you will not see.
You take your aggression seriously
When it's only naughty energy breaking free.
Take a deep breath. Surrender. Be.

—Shelley Stockwell

The way to manage anger is to:

1. Identify What Triggers Your Anger.

When you discover what sets you off, you discover what you need to know about your self-esteem and self-control. Some have buttons pushed because of a cycle of aggression from parent to child. Some rage is unleashed because of drugs or poor diet. Some tizzies are defensive smoke screens to hide depression, hurt and disappointment.

2. Accept and Love Yourself More.

Positive thoughts about yourself positively stimulate your brain's limbic system and frontal lobes; the place that regulates aggression.

3. Use Cool Down Strategies.

When you detach, go into neutral, clear your thoughts or leave a situation, you diminish tension. Use these cool-down strategies:

Three Breath Strategy

BREATH ONE

Take slow, deep breaths. Oxygen to the brain relaxes your body and melts rage. Breathe to the bottom of your feet. Take in all that your lungs can take. Hold the breath as long as you can and let it go. Think to yourself **"I'm blowing it off. I'm letting it go."**

When you let the breath go, release tension in the body. People who keep their cool have lower blood pressure.

BREATH TWO

Take a deep breath to your mind. Hold it in for as long as you are comfortable. When you let it out, release any tension that you hold in your mind.

BREATH THREE

Now take a third deep breath and hold it in. When you let it out, release all tension from your body and mind.

Now focus your attention on whatever troubles you. Take a deep breath and BLOW IT OFF. Say, **"I am in control of my emotions. I express emotions in positive and productive ways. I am 100% responsible for my behavior."**

Counting Strategy

Slowly count backwards from ten to one. Chant a mantra, such as **"Mellow out. Calm. Peaceful."** Clear minded. Kick back. These divert attention so that you chill out.

Mind Strategy

Consciously choose positive thought. Forgive, get a grip, and dedicate yourself to joy. Meditation, biofeedback and hypnosis are excellent ways to positively train your thoughts. Read this affirmation script every day until it becomes your reality:

AFFIRM SUCCESS: Tame Your Anger

I honestly get a grip on my emotions. It is not permissible to power trip another. Rage directed toward others, regardless of my excuse, is unacceptable. I know my own worth and refuse to let myself or anyone else undermine it. I honor the self worth of others. I manage all my feelings. First I say, 'Cool down.' Then I identify the true underlying cause of my reaction. I ask myself; "What is really bothering me?"

If I decide that I want to confront another, I wait. I give myself time to cool down. While I wait, I exercise, laugh or recite the serenity prayer, 'Grant me the serenity to accept the things I cannot change, the courage to change the things I can, and the wisdom to know the difference.' This gives me time to be more constructive and collected. I gather my thoughts. I think about how I can improve the situation.

I am compassionate to myself. Rage directed toward myself is unacceptable. I am keenly aware of the relationship of what I eat and drink to my emotions. I avoid anything that takes me from peace and joy. Soft drinks, sugar, coffee, alcohol and drugs are all the rage. I eat and drink healthy foods.

If I can't be kind, I wait. I take a walk. I feel my deeper feelings. I release pent-up emotions from the past. I talk rationally and from the heart about how I feel. I am kind to myself and others.

4. Use Bio-Chemistry for Relief.

Physical exercise and the resulting relaxation takes down the heat. Anger is simply naughty energy needing release. If someone hurts you with insensitivity or abuse, expressing energy releases indignation. If you don't release it, anger pops out in inappropriate, destructive and potentially deadly ways. Your challenge is to release energy in non-destructive ways. Expressed appropriately and in a timely manner, clears frustration.

Instead of hitting yourself or another, count to ten and then:

Hit a punching bag.
Smash a tennis ball.
Pound the sidewalk with your feet.
Pummel a pillow.
Write swear words on a piece of paper.
Scream at the sea.
Sing loudly.
Become drug free.
Talk about what makes you mad and then immediately talk about what makes you glad.

INTO•GREAT POWER EXERCISE

Chill Out

This simple biofeedback exercise helps you transform rage into peace.

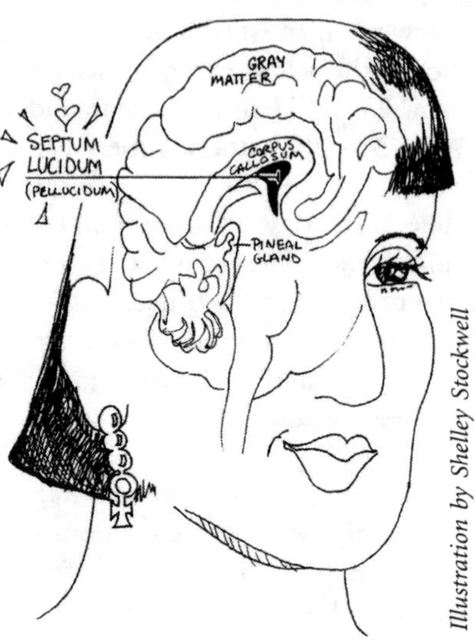

Illustration by Shelley Stockwell

1. Take a deep breath, relax the jaw and close your eyes.

2. In your mind's eye, imagine a place about one-and-one-half inches above your eyebrows in the center of your skull.

3. Hold your attention there by picturing a beam of energy caressing and stroking the pleasure center of the brain (your septum pellucidum) as if it were a furry pet.

4. Make your attention light and relaxed. You'll feel a gentle "AHHH" when you reach the septum pellucidum.

5. Continue to stimulate your sweet septum and imagine an anger-provoking situation or person. Take these thoughts to this part of your brain. You'll notice it just melts away.

6. Use this technique instead of doing anything that harms you.

—based on Pete Sanders, Jr.'s Joy Touch Technique

INNER•VIEW QUIZ

Anxiety High?

Answer true to the statements that fit you:
___ My life IS the fast lane; otherwise I'm bored.
___ If it's too quiet, I get uncomfortable or go through withdrawal.
___ I am a never-ending hub of activity.
___ I go for the quick boost.
___ I am passionate about sports that push my limits.
___ Sporting events get me "wired."
___ High speed chases excite me.
___ I enjoy real-life dramas.
___ I am hyperactive.
___ I have a high pain threshold.
___ My music is loud and jumpy.
___ Coffee, tea, soft drinks, sugar or uppers regularly stimulate me.
___ Pushing my limit runs me, I don't run it.
___ When things are too calm, I wait for the other shoe to drop.
___ I'm my best during a crisis.
___ Secretly, I feel fearful.
___ I'm a nervous wreck.
___ I worry a lot.
___ My immobilizing fears are only limited by my lack of imagination.
___ Life is dangerous.
___ I'm always stamping out fires.
___ I suffer from ulcers, headaches and/or gastric distress.
___ I often awaken heavy-headed or nauseated.
___ I wish I lived in a more frenzied time in history.
___ I enjoy teasing.
___ I have panic attacks.
___ My life is one crisis after another.

For every answer that applies to you: take a deep breath, hold it in and as you release it, say to yourself, "I am relaxing more with each breath I take."

Chapter 8
Fear and Phobia:
Scarabed to Death

You wouldn't believe what scares some people, and they probably won't believe what scares you. Fear is a biochemical response that is easily rewired. You'll love this chapter; I sure do. When you've read it, you'll know how to bust a phobia in less than three minutes!

▲ How People Get Scared
▲ Panic Styles: Stars of the Silent Scream
▲ A Laundry List of Little Fears: Unlock Dreadlocks:

- Activities
- Animal or Person
- Appearing Foolish
- A Place
- Danger
- Death
- Disease
- Failure
- Flying
- Freaking Out
- Mistakes
- Natural Phenomenon
- Public Speaking
- Situations
- Success
- Things

▲ Stockwell's Ten Strategies for Success: Cozy Fire

Up Your Egypt

Scarabs

In ancient Egypt, wearing a scarab charmed you with good luck, eternal life and resourcefulness. Beetles, in fact, survive in the most challenging circumstances and are one of earth's longest living residents.

A special heart scarab, with magic spells written in hieroglyphs, was often placed within a mummy's wrappings. Its spell cleansed sins and allowed the departed entrance into the afterlife.

Real life scarabs or cockroaches can run three miles per hour.

INNER•VIEW QUIZ

I Fear There Are Many Phobias

Do you feel like a turtle with claustrophobia phobia? A phobia, or exaggerated fear can happen to anyone. It can be in response to any situation, person, place, substance or thing. Are you able to change a thought that hurts into a reality that hurts even more? Have any of these fears grabbed you by the throat or any other part of your anatomy?

General Phobias

Tombstones (Placeophobia)
Alone in the house (Domo•silly•phobia)
Being idle (Thaasophobia)
Blushing (Erythrophobia)
Childbirth (Tocophobia)
Coitus (Coitophobia)
Crossing bridges (Gephyrophobia)
Crossing the street (Agyrophobia)
Crying (Sobophobia)
Death (Thalassophobia)
Eating (Phagophobia)
Falling or high places (Acrophobia)
Falling Acrobats (Acrobatophobia)
Falling in love (Philophobia)
Flying (Fly-in-the-ointment phobia)
Gaiety (Cheery•phobia)
Going to bed (Clinophobia)
Learning (Sophophobia)
Long waits (Macrophobia)
Movement (Kinesophobia)
Passing high buildings (Hi-Risa•phobia)
Peeing in pants (Tinkle•phobia)
Public speaking: (Fool•a•phobia)
Ridicule (Katagelophobia)

Activities (Doaphobia)

Riding in a car (Amaxophobia)
Sin (Peccatiphobia)
Sitting (Cathisophobia)
Sleep (Hypnophobia)
Smothering (Pnigophobia)
Soiling (Rypophobia)
Speaking (Laliophobia)
Speed (Tachophobia)
Spelling errors (Typochondria)
Spending money (Dis•purse•phobia)
Standing (Stasibasiphobia)
Stealing (Cleptophobia, Kleptomania)
Swallowing (Phagophobia)
Swimming or water (Hydrophobia)
Talking (Phonophobia)
Too many birthday candles (Waxophobia)
Tickling (Pteronophobia)
Touch (Thixophobia)
Traveling (Trip•a•phobia)
Trembling (Tremophobia)
Work (Ergophobia, Ergasiophobia)
Writing (Graphophobia)

Animals (Zoophobia)

Bees (Apiophobia)
Birds (Ornithophobia)
Bulls (Taurophobia)
Cats (Aelurophobia) (like Napoleon)
Dogs (Cynophobia)
Fish (Ichthyophobia) (dread lox)
Frogs (Batrachophobia)
Germs (Spermophobia)
Horses (Hippophobia)
Insects (Entomophobia)
Mice (Musophobia)
Microbes (Microbiophobia)
Mites (Acarophobia)
Monsters (Teratophobia)
Reptiles (Herpetophobia)
Snakes (Snakophobia)
Spiders (Arachnephobia)
Worms (Vermiphobia)

Disease (Bletchophobia or Pathophobia)

Anemia (Anemophobia)
Cancer (Cancerphobia)
Cholera (Cholerophobia)
Constipation (Coprostasophobia)
Diabetes (Diabetophobia)
Heart disease (Cardiophobia)
Insanity (Maniaphobia)
Insect stings (Cnidophobia)
Rabies (Hydrophobophobia)
VD (Venereophobia)
Vomiting (Emetophobia)
Wounds (Traumatophobia)

Natural Phenomenon (Ohshitophobia)

Bad breath (Cacoerophobia)
Body Odor (U•reeka•phobia)
Cold (Psychrophobia)
Comets (Cometophobia)
Decaying matter (Septophobia)
Snow (Chionophobia)
Drafts (Aerophobia)
Electricity (Electrophobia)
Flames or fire (Pyrophobia)
Floods (Antlophobia)
Fog (Nebulaphobia)
Heat (Thermophobia)
Heaven (Uranophobia)
Hell (Stygiophobia)
Lightning (Astraphobia)
Night or darkness (Nyctophobia)
Shadows (Sciophobia)
Sound (Acousticaphobia)
Stars (Astrophobia)
Sun (Heliophobia)
Thunder (Brontophobia)
Tornadoes (Lilapsophobia)
Wind (Ancraophobia)
High Winds (Anemophobia)

People (Themophobia)

Children (Pedophobia)
Crowds (Demophoibia)
Demons (Demonophobia)
Foreigners or strangers (Zenophobia)
Ghosts (Phasmophobia)
God (Theophobia)
Infants or children (Pedophobia)
Men (Androphobia)
Mobs (Ochlophobia)
Oneself (Autophobia)
Parents-in-law (Soceraphobia)
Politicians (Poloticophobia)
Pope (Papaphobia)
Robbers (Harpaxophobia)
Satan (Satanophobia)
Women
(Gynophobia, Harem•Scare•Em)
Young girls (Parthenophobia)

Places (Theraphobia)

Certain places (Topophobia)
Church (Ecclesiphobia)
Cities (Metropophobia)
Heights (Acrophobia, Vertigo)
Home (Echophobia)
Narrowconfined spaces (Claustrophobia)
Open spaces (Agoraphobia)

Situations (Isaphobia)

Being alone with oneself (Autophobia)
Being dirty (Offa•my•sopha•phobia)
Dampness (Hygrophobia)
Depth (Bathophobia)
Failure (Kakorraphiaphobia)
Fear itself (Phobophobia)
Freedom (Eleutherophobia)
Pain (Algophobia)
Pleasure (Hedenophobiao)
Poverty (Penniless•phobia)
Punishment (Poinephobia)
Remaining single (Anuptaphobia)
Responsibility (Hypegiaphobia)
Sex (Erotophobia)

Imperfection (Atelophobia)
Jealousy (Zelophobia)
Marriage (Gamophobia)
Nudity (Nud•o•phobia)
Void (Kenophobia)
Weakness (Asthemophobia)
Rap Music (Yo-phobia)
Uncleanliness (Mysophobia)

Things (Stuffaphobia)

Beards (Paganophobia)
Blood (Hemophobia)
Color red (Erythrophobia)
Dead bodies (Necrophobia)
Dirt (Mysophobia)
Drugs and poison (Tocicophobian)
Dust (Amathophobia)
Elevators (Lift•a•phobia)
Things stuck in teeth (Flosstrophobia)
Magic (Rhabdophobia)
Mirrors (Eisoptrophobia)
Money (Chrometophobia)
Needles (Belonephobia)
New things (Neophobia)
Number 13 (Triskaidekaphobia)
Poetry (Metrophobia)
Poison (Toxophobia)

Everything (Pantophobia)

Feathers (Pteronophobia)
Flowers (Near•roses)
Flutes (Aulophobia)
Food (Sitophobia)
Fur (Doraphobia)
Gold (Aurophobia)
Hair (Chaetophobia)
Innoculations (Vaccino•phobia)
Large things (Megalophobia)
Machinery (Mechanophobia)
Slime (Blennophobia)
Small things (Tapinophobia)
String (Linonophobia)
Teeth (Odontophobia)
Telephone (Telephonophobia)
Unknown fear (Apeirophobia)
Vehicles (Ochophobia)
Wooden things (Xylophobia)
Words (Logophobia)
Wrinkles (Rhytiphobia)

Triskaidekaphobia

Of all bad luck, superstitions, triskaidekaphobia (fear of the number 13) is the most popular. Some skyscrapers do not have a 13th floor, some airplanes do not have a 13th row, and the Italian national lottery omits the number 13. Folklorists have reinforced this hysteria. If you believe bad things happen with the number 13, I've got your number.

Think of it this way; in numerology, one and three (from thirteen) add up to four, which stands for stability and home.

Ancient Egyptians said your soul must climb the 13th rung of the ladder to reach eternity.

Besides the incomplete pyramid, the US dollar bill has 13 steps, the bald eagle grasps an olive branch with 13 leaves and 13 berries in one claw and 13 arrows in another. There are 13 stars above the eagle's head. Bless your lucky stars!

Scaredy Cat

☆ *"Of what are you afraid, my child?"* asked the kindly teacher.
"Oh Sir, the flowers they are wild." replied the timid creature.

F riendly	F alse	F _____
E nergy	E vidence	E vacuate
A nnouncing	A ppearing	A nd
R isk	R eal	R un!

Do you sometimes feel like you are diving off a high diving board and halfway down you discover that you have on your non-water proof watch?

Babies are born with two basic fears:

1) The fear of falling
2) The fear of the dark

After that, we invent fear to protect ourselves from danger, hurt or abandonment. The three most common adult fears are:

1) Fear of falling
2) Public speaking
3) Fear of dying

Apparently, many of us would rather die than speak in public.

Fear is a useful emotion. It makes us cautious. It tells us to drive carefully on icy roads, avoid dark alleys and show respect for an open fire.

Fear protects. When fear is irrational or out of proportion to the situation, it becomes a ploy to get you "high," or to numb and divert your attention from under-lying issues. Fears and phobias are unsuccessful attempts to heal old hurts. Hidden or repressed pain builds up as anxiety with no place to go. The kitchens on fire and the plants won't grow. No, no, no, no.

Caretakers teach fear-driven habits that we then practice as rituals; rituals we repeat to feel close to them or use when we want to escape or don't want to take charge. If Dad freaked out over rutabaga, you might do the same.

Fear For Profit

Fear fascinates and hypnotizes.

Merchandisers present fearful scenarios to convince you to buy a home security system, a car phone and estrogen. If you are not living in a city at war, you can watch it on television, read about it in the newspaper, or listen to it on your car radio. Bloody gloves can become your life and translate into top market shares for advertisers. Dismemberment movie thrillers, horror shows and hair-raising books sell.

Ambulance chasers rush to an emergency.

Insurance is sold on the "probability" that disaster will strike or you will get sued. Fear gives insurance and pharmaceutical CEO's make the highest salaries in the world.

Some, hypnotized by fear of an angry ghost, god, or ministerial reprisal, join religious groups or go to an exorcist.

Roller-coaster-ride thrill-seekers frighten and stimulate an adrenaline rush followed by a cool aftermath.

We scare ourselves in much the same way we touch a sore tooth with our tongue again and again. When terrorists attack the World Trade Center, a British department store or and Israeli business, we repeatedly look at pictures, frightened and heartbroken.

▲ How do People Get Scared?

☆ *"Fear is a dark room where negatives develop."*

—Robert Otto & Winifred Morice

☆ *"Imagination is more powerful than knowledge."*

—Albert Einstein

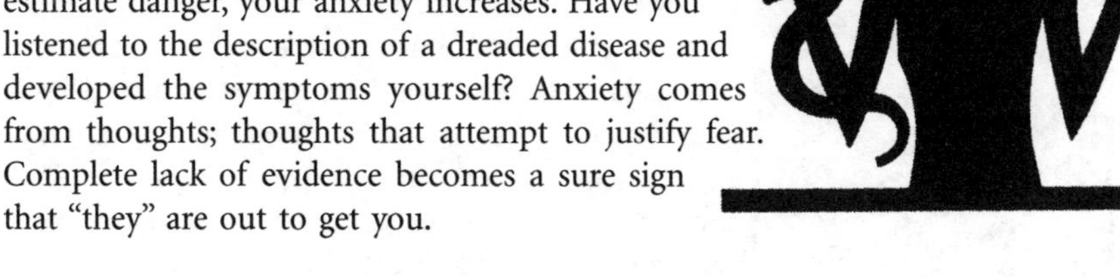

Have you ever heard a ghost story and every shadow seems haunted? If you predict or overestimate danger, your anxiety increases. Have you listened to the description of a dreaded disease and developed the symptoms yourself? Anxiety comes from thoughts; thoughts that attempt to justify fear. Complete lack of evidence becomes a sure sign that "they" are out to get you.

Repressed Stress Expressed

Outwardly we say, "I'm afraid" when something jars or threatens. Inwardly, we are anxious, panicked and stressed. *Thoughts of real or imagined danger stimulate your nervous system in exactly the same way.* All fear evokes the same chemical changes in your body.

Logically, fear makes little sense. That's because it is an instinctive subconscious reaction. You may think that burying or denying fear brings peace. But real peace comes when you confront fear head-on, move past it, and "rewire" your subconscious responses to frightening stimuli.

Experience is a great teacher. A powerful single experience can make deep impressions that may later imprison or liberate. A traumatic, dangerous or seemingly dangerous experience, all cause your heart to race, adrenaline to rush, breath to speed, muscles to tighten and the hair on your arms to stand on end.

Long after the cause is pushed aside and consciously forgotten, you may trigger the same seemingly unsolicited response. You might not be aware of its original cause, then something strikes a familiar chord and revivifies the memory and you play that old familiar tomb.

Oy Phase Mere

Stress from out-of-control behavior, coupled with underlying tension, intensifies out-of-control behavior. "I am more anxious; I panic more." Here's how this down hill spiral works:

Phase 1. Behavior Becomes A Crutch
"I freak out to be close to Mom."
"I freak out to get attention from others."
"I freak out to give myself attention."
"I freak out to scare myself for a rush."
"I freak out so I don't have to go to work."
Phase 2. You Increase Your Tolerance
"I freak out more often so I pay attention to my needs."
Phase 3. Your Upset Behavior Creates Bigger Problems
"My behavior makes me sick."
"I lose my job."
"No one wants to hang out with me."
Phase 4. You Stay In Fear Because You Fear Change
"At least my habits are safe and comforting."

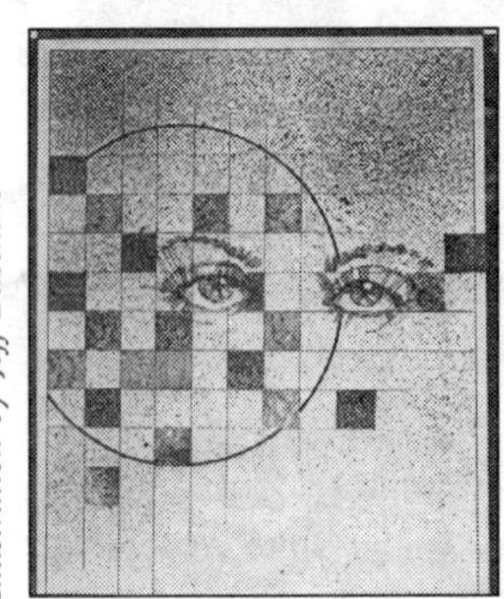
Illustration by Jeff Bucchino

General-Eyes Emotions

Your emotional circuits are centered in your amygdala, a little almond shaped structure deep in your brain. It scans incoming sights, sounds and experiences for emotional content and responds chemically. Your brain uses the same pathways to generate or respond to emotion.

If a sight, sound or experience is positive, you wire your brain's "calm down" response and you sooth stress. Negative sights, sounds, experiences and threats wire your brain's fear response. Let's say, when you were a kid, dad came home drunk and beat you up. Your amygdala flooded your circuits with neurochemicals before more rational parts of your brain knew what happened. Circuits can stay in high alert for days.

The more often fearful pathways are activated, the more easily they are triggered. In this case, the mere memory of dad may frighten you. Or a subtle reminder—a facial expression, an angry voice tone, the kind of shirt he wore can each activate the same excited, fearful response. When you repeat fearful rituals, fear is as addictive as any drug. It leaves you feeling and acting equally out-of-control.

Here is how Myrna solved her panic attacks:

A TRUE STORY Myrna

"I had several episodes I call 'my anxiety attacks.' With hypnosis, I discovered that they were the results of when I was seventeen and worked in a drug store. My boss, a creepy old guy, fondled my breasts. That same day, my boyfriend committed suicide.

The anxiety attacks were my hidden solution to the unfinished business of that traumatic day.

I took control of my life. Things are much better when I exercise and take life one day at a time. Eating well is extremely important. Chocolate makes me tense. As for my anxiety at work, I quit my job and am now self-employed. I'm falling in love with the boss."

Adrenaline Fatigue

The endocrine system controls your hormones and your fight, flight, fright or excite reaction. It is separate from and in constant communication with your brain. When you overuse your fear response, adrenal glands and endocrine system, you eventually suffer from "hypoadrenia." Hyperadrenia causes the nervous system to change, nodes to shrink, severe body weakness and weight loss. Blood pressure makes the heart pound and temperature rise or drop.

Stressful thoughts, environmental stress, food allergies, drugs, alcohol, sugar, caffeine, nicotine, salt, hormones, glucose and dyes also contribute to fear. Each may throw you into crazy thinking and behavior. Each changes the production of noradrenaline, the chemical that triggers your body's arousal mechanism.

If you lived in the wild and were in real danger, your instinctive fight or flight mechanism would make you turn and run like mad or stand and bare your teeth. Your body would go into eager response. Blood would move swiftly from brain into muscles and legs, making them strong. At the same time, the lessening of blood in the brain may distort thoughts.

In our culture, when we have the same instinctive response; to run like mad or bear our teeth, we often force ourselves to stand still and be "nice." Good little boys and girls translate frustration into stress and fear.

A TRUE STORY Blanca

"I checked the lock on my front door three times before leaving my house. Driving to work, I worried that I may have inadvertently hurt someone by causing an accident. I checked my rear view mirror, and occasionally stopped my car to look back and check.

I've always been fearful. When I was a little girl, I was always afraid something terrible would happen to my family. Maybe Dad would not come home from work. I thought that keeping my room clean and orderly would keep my family and me safe from harm.

I know I'm crazy when I wash my hands and do the laundry, washing a load again and again. But things somehow never seem to be clean.

With hypnosis, I finally left my childhood family systems in the past, I was able to change my behavior. I'm still a little 'neurotic,' but at least I'm not driving myself nuts any more."

▲ Panic Styles: Stars of the Silent Scream

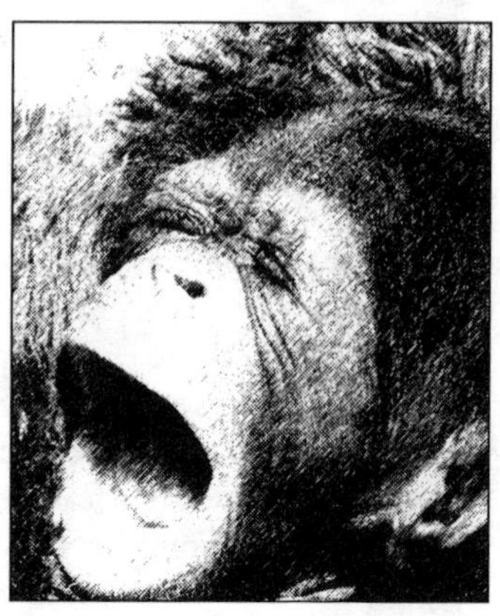

Panic is no picnic, no matter what style it takes; worry wart, panic attack, thrill seeker or crisis junky. Each approach is hysterical.

Red Alert A constant state of alarm. Nerves are trigger ready.

Yellow Alert You anticipate a panic attack and you want to avoid it at all costs. Now you no longer just dread fear, but you also fear dread.

Pink Alert You're super-aware of symptoms of approaching panic, emotion, reaction or trigger that reminds you of panic.

Green Alert You avoid any person, place, thing or situation that even vaguely resembles your panic or reaction to panic.

Up Your Egypt

Wigged Out

In the old Kingdom (2700-2200 BC) men and women wore fanlike shaped wigs. Later they wore longer, skinnier wigs with short hair under the wigs. The well to do had many wigs for all occasions. One female was entombed with seventeen wigs.

Full tapered braids around the face were popular. The length of the hair of the wigs varied. Sometimes men wore short hair and women long hair and vice-versa. Ancient Egyptians wore wigs and hair extensions to simplify hairstyling and to fend off head lice. The oldest head lice and wigs so far date back to 3500 B.C. Hairpieces were treated with vegetable oil and animal fat and then perfumed with flower petals and cinnamon wood chips.

Phobia

☆ *"We have nothing to phobia but phobiaphobia."*

—Winston Ecumenical-Molehill

A phobia is an intense, gripping, unreasonable and overblown fear reaction that seems to come from nowhere. Signs of phobic reaction are rapid pulse and breath, sweaty palms, raised blood pressure and increased muscle tension. You may believe you're having a heart attack or going crazy. You are not. Phobic response is simply your central nervous system misfiring.

A TRUE STORY June

"I was terribly afraid of spiders (arachnophobia). If I just thought about one, I'd break into a cold sweat and tremble uncontrollably. During hypnosis, I recalled spiders in grandma's attic, but could not figure out the correlation.

Dr. Stockwell had me "cage" my fear and it worked!" (See The Cagey Cure below), Now spiders catch mosquitoes in my garden. I live and let live."

No Fear: The Cagey Cure

Here is the exercise that worked for June:

Center Yourself Take a deep breathe, close your eyes and imagine yourself calm and relaxed.

En-caging Fear Imagine putting a very tiny cage around the object, person or situation you have feared in the past. Put white light around the tiny cage.

Angel to Angel Invite your higher self to visit the higher self of the caged person, object or situation. Let your higher self admire the captured one's creativity, diligence and pursuit of happiness. It is safe for you to let your soul touch their soul. AND AFFIRM:

"I'm the ocean, you're the shore, I'm protected from you, ever more. We are both God's creatures. I forgive myself for harsh judgement. I forgive you for your mistakes. We live together in peace."

Light Up Now put white light around you; like you are in a spotlight. It is safe in your world; you have boundaries. Protective light makes you invincible. Congratulate yourself. Nothing and no one can permeate your white light. You live and let live.

Stockwell's Simple Steps to Relaxation

☆ *"If you don't stand for something, you'll fall for anything."*

—Bonnie Dean

☆ *"What? Me worry?"*

—Alfred E. New Man

Use my simple steps and you will relax at will.

•• Set Goals

Set clear goals. Start with big goals. You can break them into steppingstone, short-term goals to build confidence. This makes bigger goals easier.

•• Make Peace Your Main Goal

Decide and commit to calm down and mellow out.

•-•-• Say Kind and Nourishing Things to Yourself

Kindness boosts self-confidence.

•-•-•-• Heed Your Hot Button

Be aware of how you turn on your hot button so you can figure out how to turn it off. Acknowledge fear and it will go away.

•-•-•-•-• Avoid Toxic Stressors

To overcome upset, avoid sugar, caffeine, alcohol or drugs; they always exaggerate your biochemical responses. When we feel inadequate to deal with life, we may turn over control to external substances, habits, groups or individuals to get us through. This is why addictions and compulsions are called dependencies. The cure for dependency is responsibility.

Have A Real Talk with Yourself

☆ *"If we all worked on the assumption that what is accepted as true is really true, there would be little hope of advance."*

—Orville Wright

Ask yourself:

"What are you really afraid of?"

"What is the worst thing that could happen?"

"Why do you go off center?"

"Why would you choose to hurt yourself?"

"What crazy payoffs keep you out of control?"

Make your answers as specific as possible.

Let's say you answer, "I am afraid of dying." Tell yourself exactly what about death scares you. Are you afraid of the pain of dying? What the doctors might do to you? That no one will be there to take care of you? Are you freaking out about what you'll look like? How your loved ones will cope? Or are you concerned about missing out on doing a specific thing?

After you get down to the details of exactly what's bothering you, create a metaphor that resolves it. If you are visual, picture your fear as a little crying baby and then pick up the baby. "Dear Little Fear, I love you so." Notice what happens. Creating metaphors helps you separate from a problem and take control of it.

It is essential that you choose to live in the moment and choose to feel good. In this moment ask yourself, "What do you want to do?" Your true desires move you out of "robot mode" (denial) and enter back into the adventure of life.

A great way to eliminate pain and stress is to redefine it. Pain is like labor pains; each contraction is one less you'll need to birth your true peaceful self. The pain of divorce can lead to the happiness of being a single person. Redefine each door closing as a door opening, each glass as half full. Count blessings and stay positive. Finally, let yourself out of prison. If you have imprisoned yourself with illness, physical or emotional pain, negative thinking or limiting belief, open the door now. Haven't you suffered enough?

Voodoo Trepidation A shaman simply repeats again and again: "It never happened. It never happened. It is safe in my world."

The trick to make panic go away is to stay awake and acknowledge it. What triggers it? Diffuse the trigger. "Hi. No Trigger! Away!" Don't go down fearful roads; take another route. Become conscious of your reactions and make other choices.

▲ A Laundry List of Dirty Little Fears: Dread Locks

☆ THE GHOST

Listen—there it goes again! Hear it?
Should I investigate, or not go near it?
The bumps, the knocks, the squeaks
What's the source?
My imagination's running wild, of course.
Under covers, I'm shaking
Eyes closed, but faking.
But I lay frozen
'Til early light creeps in my window
Then cautiously I go, to confront my foe
Hanging in the air, I watch it disappear
The only "spirit" there—my fear.

—Charmaine Bice

Voyager Tarot Card James Wanless

Tarot Death Card

Here is a handy-dandy list of out-of-control concerns and solutions that relieve:

Fear of Activities

☆ *You can excel at anything you repel. You're swell.*

—Shelley Stockwell

If an activity frightens you, think of a place that is soothing; that brings you peace of mind. Image this beautiful place. Picture and imagine yourself there.

You are learning to enjoy __________ (name the feared activity.) Experience the activity, remembering to breathe and calmly take it into this most soothing place.

Fear of an Animal or Person

Feel yourself calm and relaxed as you imagine the presence of ______________ (Name the animal or person). Look into his or her eyes. Admire his or her structure, movements and sounds. Put white light around them and know that you are safe in their presence. And affirm:

AFFIRM SUCCESS #1: Feeling Safe with Animals and People
"My white light protects me. I take a deep breath, and cut any cords that connect to this being. I release them to their own white light. I take a deep breath and send a rainbow bridge from my heart to theirs as they leave. Good-bye. Fare Thee Well."

AFFIRM SUCCESS #2: Animal Plan It
Imagine observing a(n) ______ (name the animal). Look directly into its eyes; take a deep breath and feel calm and relaxed. Pretend to see the animal's soul.

The animal touches my soul.

Admire the animal's texture and structure; it's movements and sounds.

I am calm as I reach out and touch it. The animal, in return responds with love and introduces me to his family and friends. I am wise when I deal with animals. I respect that they act like animals.

Face Fear with a Smile

Select a Specific Fear
Write down the specifics about it. For example, if you are afraid of enclosed spaces write, *"I am afraid of riding in a car/riding in an elevator/being trapped in a closet..."*
Reverse the Fear Gear
Imagine yourself in the identical situation enjoying being there. Enjoy yourself being in the car. Seeing the sights whizzing by is fun. (e.g.: *"Elevators are fun, though they have their ups and downs."* See yourself laughing with the other passengers on the elevator).
Associate
Associate the emotionally charged experience with a happy moment in your life. (e.g. *"I picture myself stepping into a closet, which turns into a picture of myself making love with my mate"*).
Imagine Control
Imagine yourself in control of all thoughts and emotions. *"I always choose joy, peace and fun. I maintain control at will. All I have to do is stop, take a deep, easy and full breath and relax."*
See, feel and imagine white light all around you—the white light shields and protects you. Only positive light comes through your shield of light.
Anything in the past that made you feel uneasy just melts away.

Fear of Appearing Foolish

If you are afraid of what other people think, your real fear is probably that they'll reject you. Give it up. Most people don't even notice you because they are too involved in themselves.

AFFIRM SUCCESS: Not Foolish, Just Human!
If I was always hung up on how I looked, I would have never have learned to walk, eat with a spoon or make love.

Fear of a Place

AFFIRM SUCCESS: Safe in Places

Imagine yourself in the place that in the past caused you discomfort. Take a deep breath and think about a place you love to go. These two thoughts are now superimposed.

I feel peaceful and easy in this imagining. I am in control and enjoying myself. I can leave any time I like. I take a deep breath and find myself thoroughly enjoying this moment. I am safe. I am confident. I am serene.

Fear of Danger

Danger in the mind is often much larger than real danger. Fear makes you tense and on guard. Do you imagine that at any moment someone will attack or some disaster will occur? Do you fear for your safety or the safety of loved ones? Is the world fraught with danger at every turn? Do you fear things that are beyond your control? Such "mind loops" are exhausting.

AFFIRM SUCCESS: Safe Sensational News
Fears are just beliefs that cause anxiety. I choose new beliefs. I am optimistic and positive in my beliefs. I stop reading newspapers, watching television or listening to the radio if they depict violence. I enjoy soothing music instead. I make conscious choices to receive information that is relaxing and calming.

Fear of Death: Crypt Trip

☆ *"You're going to die," he yelled shaking his finger. Then he turned to me and winked. "We're all going to die."*

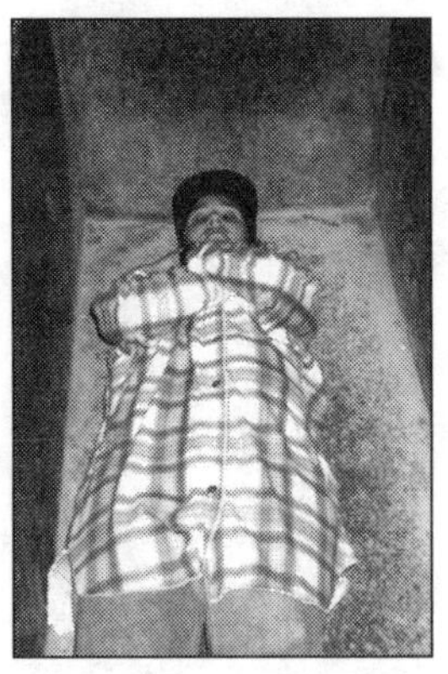

We save the most dreaded worst for last. Death is like that. Death is an inevitable part of your cycle of life. Perhaps no single human experience has been more mystified or glorified as the passage from your physical earth-bound body. If you make death too big, you miss out on living.

In the hilarious movie, *What About Bob*, Bob overcomes his fear by counting his blessings, taking baby steps and finally facing death soundly in the eye. He experiences it with a kind of cosmic glee. As wise as you become, as many books as you read, as many gurus as you visit, and as spiritual as you are, you can never solve the puzzle of death while living. Might as well just live.

A TRUE STORY

"In life, you have two choices. You can choose to take care of yourself, or not take care of yourself. If you choose to take care of yourself, everything will work out fine. If you don't take good care of yourself, you'll get sick. If you get sick, you have two choices. You can choose to get well, or you can choose to die. If you choose to get well, everything will be OK. If you choose to die, you have two choices. You can choose to go to heaven, or go to the other place. If you choose to go to heaven, everything will be OK. If you choose to go to the other place, everything will be OK, too, because all your friends will be there waiting for you."

Fear of Failure

INNER•VIEW QUIZ

Do You Go PP? *(Perfectionism, Procrastination and Paralysis)*

☆ *"What happened to the third P?"*
"It ran down my leg"

☆ *"What a pity! He died before I answered his letter, which he sent five years ago."*
—Manuel de Falla

☆ *"Lack of decisiveness is probably a bad trait...on the other hand, maybe it's not."*
—Shelley Stockwell

I often think or say:
___ What if I make a mistake? What if...
___ I spend hours on tasks that should only take minutes.
___ I agonize over which clothes to wear.
___ If you can't do it right; don't do it at all.
___ If you want it done right; do it yourself.
___ I'm so overwhelmed I don't know where to start; so I don't.
___ If I start writing now, I'll be too tired. If I wait 'til tomorrow, I can use the computer. If I have a good dinner I might be too sleepy...
___ I'll get married when the relationship is perfect (when the time is right).
___ I'm waiting for the perfect time to have kids when the money is right.
___ I can't start 'til all the ducks are in a row.
___ I'm waiting 'til the planets are perfectly aligned.
___ I'll workout when I look perfect in workout clothes.
___ You must be your best or you are nothing.
___ I'm too over committed to succeed, so I won't do it.
___ My work performance fails to meet my standards.
___ I piddle away time with trivialities like sharpening pencils, picking lint balls.
___ I say, "I can't" when I feel incapable or I want to do something else.
___ I say, "I can't" when I'm afraid of failure or disapproval.

Fear of failure can paralyze.

Doing things right is important. But pushed to excess, self-perfectionism destroys spontaneity, wastes time and is perfectly boring.

So called failures are simply situations that don't live up to your own expectations.

The three P's in the PPP game stand for perfectionism, procrastination and paralysis. The PPP dance begins: "I must do it perfectly." "I won't tolerate mistakes." And "Rather than fail, if I can't do it perfectly, I'll put it off until I can." Then finally: "If I can't do it perfectly, might as well not do it at all."

Perfectionists judge their worth, potential or ability as superior and will not settle for less. They focus on what has *not* been done. Instead of praise, they criticize.

Perfectionism causes social problems if:

1. Your demands of others or yourself are not realistic.
2. You expect others to do things you would not do yourself in the same circumstances.
3. You expect others to reach your unrealized goals.
4. You are not any fun to be around because you are too intense or don't follow through.

Here are some helpful hints to get you moving:

1. Ask yourself, "What's the worst thing that could happen?" Things that terrified you most, probably were not based on truth.
2. Get someone who cares about your goal to hold you accountable for getting started.
3. Write a list of priorities and concentrate on the ones with the most positive rewards.
4. Take it one small step at a time. Devote 30 minutes to a small goal; you will feel a sense of completion.
5. Recognize that procrastination hurts you and others. Lack of completion holds up others in their goals and dreams.
6. Clean off your desk and put things that you don't need in a box or drawer. Eliminating visual distractions makes focusing easier.
7. Reward yourself for taking charge of action.

Perfect Demands for Others

Perfectionists demand perfection in others and expect the world to conform to their (often-unrealistic) standards. A perfectionist usually wants others to reach their unattained goals. Perfectionistic parents usually get the opposite result. Instead of Junior trying harder, he often quits. Demanding neatniks yield sloppy kids, straight "A" pressure results in "D's and F's."

AFFIRM SUCCESS: Overcome Perfectionism
If I don't try, I fail before I begin. Either I win the race or I don't. Either I make the deadline or I don't. Either I get the job or I don't. Either I lick this thing or I don't. Either way, I can handle it. I'm just experiencing life.

I like completing tasks. I do them step-by-step until they are complete. I'm terrific at doing things well. I grow and learn with each task. I open myself to each new challenge. I do my best. I develop and learn as I do.

Best is better than perfect. I am my journey. My destination is a glorious gift that presents itself when I enjoy this moment—and this moment. I am beautiful because I "am." I realistically accept myself as a human, coming to balance. "Mistakes" become opportunities to learn. I am realistic. I am in action.

I move my body and thoughts in positive ways. I move my face to a smile. When I'm in action I feel terrific. I break tasks into small action steps. I do the part I want to do least and get it out of the way. I do something every day for at least ten minutes. As I progress, I reward myself with a walk, a sip of tea or a glass of water.

I enjoy beginnings, middles and endings. Life is an adventure. I love to move my body and mind. I reach my own goals. I enjoy the journey to my goals. I do what I want to do. I do what you request only if I want to.

Other's goals are their business. I support others when they request my help if I want to. I make sure that my children have guidance and REALISTIC expectations from me.

If I demand that others conform to my rules and standards, I get into hassles. I allow others to do it their way. I honor other's rhythms and style. If something must be done perfectly for realistic reasons, I make sure that I am diligent and accurate. I honor each person's right to live their own life, learn their own lessons and choose or not choose their own goals. I focus my attention on learning, growing and, I lighten up. I have all the resources to meet all of life's challenges. I value myself. I believe in my self. I can. I will. I am.

Fear of Success

Many are terrified of "making it." Usually these fears are based on co-dependent conditioning "If I am on my own…I die." You may have a life script that says "No matter what, I can't make more money than my dad." Or "Because of some crime I committed, I don't deserve success." When you pinpoint the limiting script, reverse it into a positive affirmation.

AFFIRM SUCCESS: Safe To Succeed
"I love being on my own. I get to have everything my way. It's fun."
"I make as much money as I want. My Dad, bless him, makes as much as he wants. We are proud of each other."
"The past is forgiven. I deserve success. I have learned from my mistakes. I am a winner."

Fear of Disease

AFFIRM SUCCESS: Healthy Me!
My body is healthy, radiant and energetic. I imagine I look into a mirror, right into my beautiful eyes, and say the words *"I love you. You are forgiven."* In my mind's eye, I see my eyes sparkle, I am vital and feel energetic. I release any physical discomfort to the light. I feel great!

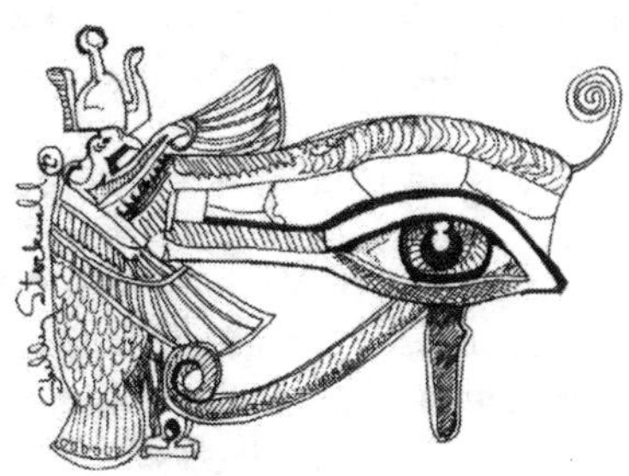

An Eye for an Eye

Illustration by Shelley Stockwell

Fear of Flying

☆ Shelley: *"More people die in pleasure boating accidents in one year than ever perished in plane crashes for the whole history of aviation."*
Nervous Passenger: *"That may be true but if I crash in a boat I might learn how to swim, but if I crash in a plane, I ain't never gonna learn to fly."*

Flying encompasses other fears—fear of heights (or falling), fear of being closed in, fear of giving up control (losing control), fear of dying, fear of the unknown and fears generated from recent terrorism. Flying is 100 times safer than driving. Your chance of being killed by a plane falling out of the sky today is 1 in 7 trillion. But fears and phobias are not based on statistics. Use the following procedure and have a great trip.

AFFIRM SUCCESS: Safe To Fly
I make a mental note of my comfort level as I take a deep breath. Good. On a scale of 1-10 (10 great, 1 not so great) how relaxed am I? I imagine myself in a beautiful place in nature; doing something I thoroughly enjoy. Take a deep breath and repeat, 'I am calm and relaxed.' On a scale of 1-10 how good do I feel now?

Still noticing my scale of feelings, I think about flying. This is called a mental rehearsal. If at any time my tension rises, I take a deep breathe and go back to the pleasant scene and bring the gauge down again. I now rehearse my journey from beginning to end; bringing my number to a comfortable level with each thought. If my number goes above a six I bring it down easily. I imagine myself packing, leaving the house, getting to the airport, getting on

the plane. The ground staff, the captain's voice, the flight attendants and all the other passengers help me relax. They are like soothing muzak.

I touch my thumb to my forefinger to serve as an anchor for my good feelings. I change the word "fear" to "excitement." I am excited to fly. When it is time for my real life adventure, I touch my thumb to forefinger and say, "Calm and relaxed." I love to fly. It's fun.

Get a good night's sleep before you travel. An airplane has little humidity. To make your flight more enjoyable, drink lots of water and fruit juice and avoid coffee, tea or alcohol which dehydrates you. Put moisturizer on your skin and wear glasses instead of contact lenses.

Eat lightly and move around if you have the opportunity, it boosts your circulation.

And remember to, "Sit back, relax and enjoy your flight.'

Photo by Nica Lee

Fear of Freaking Out

Do you fear that you will go nuts, lose control and/or embarrass yourself beyond belief?

A vulnerable child inside usually generates such catastrophic thinking for good reasons. Did Mom and Dad have panic attacks? Did they experience a trauma? If so, you may freak out to be like them or close to them. If your parents were overprotective, and you came to believe that you are fragile or incompetent, this too could be the basis for fear. Seeds of vulnerability can come from being unprotected, or experiencing a traumatic event or illness.

AFFIRM SUCCESS: Panic Perfect

The craziest thing about fearing that I am crazy, or dying, or losing control, is that every time I think it, I create panic. Reality check! I am safe and mellow. I am in charge.

Fear of Making a Mistake

OK, so you blew it. Do you wallow in the aftermath with self-loathing? Do you lie awake hashing it out again and again? In the long run, will it matter? Every experience has a positive message. Answer two questions:

1. What did I learn?
2. If it ever comes up again, what will I do differently?

Then forgive yourself and put it aside. This gives your mind time to regenerate.

Fear of Natural Phenomenon

☆ Professor: *"I predict that the planet earth will disintegrate in 10 billion years."*
Student: *"How many years did you say?"*
Professor: *"Ten billion."*
Student: *"Oh, thank God, I thought you said ten million."*

Image yourself in the situation of ______________(name the phenomenon) and being calm and relaxed. Suddenly, think of three very funny things about the situation. Laugh.

Affirm: I am safe, confident and strong. Life is an adventure. I enjoy being in the elements of life.

Fear of Public Speaking

☆ *"I don't call it nervousness, I call it concentration."*
—Carol Channing

Fear or nervousness of public speaking is called lalophobia or tpophobia. Some popular lalophobics have excelled in spite of their stage fright: George Burns, George C. Scott, Sidney Poitier, Joan Baez, Liza Minelli, Sally Struthers, Maureen Stapleton, Barbara Streisand, Anthony Quinn, Erica Jong, Joan Rivers and Garrison Keillor, have done fine. So can YOU.

AFFIRM SUCCESS: I Love To Speak
I express myself clearly and easily. I release any tight thoughts before I speak by using an emotional diversion. I can touch my thumb to my forefinger, shake my hands, meditate, practice self-hypnosis or whistle. Sammy Davis Jr. put on his rings and jewelry.

When I speak, I enjoy the sound of my voice and the wonderful feeling of being with people. I like people and they like me. Somebody needs to hear what I have to say. If I reach that one person, I have made a big difference. I like to make a difference. I enjoy talking to one person at a time.

Everyone gets a rush when they speak in front of others. I'm here for a very important reason. The energy of what I convey is strong. I always appear confident no matter what I feel. The folks listening to me, like me. They want me to do well. I accept my body and its expression with love and release any tightness. I am loose like a goose.
I think about what I am saying.
Practice makes perfect.

Fear of Situations

☆ *"Yea, though I walk through the valley of the shadow of death, I shall fear no evil, for thou art with me; thy rod and thy staff they comfort me...my cup runneth over."*

—Twenty-third Psalm

Imagine yourself quiet and peaceful in a beautiful place. Give yourself complete permission to do anything you like.

AFFIRM SUCCESS: I Deal Situations
I'm peaceful and easy. I now realize I am capable of dealing with any situation easily, perfectly. I give myself permission to do all the things I love to do. I take a deep breath and smile.

Fear of Things

Imagine yourself near the ____ (name the object). Imagine looking at ____ being calm and relaxed. Imagine admiring the object's structure, form. Imagine yourself touching that thing, as you remain calm.

AFFIRM SUCCESS: This Thing is Now Safe
The object seems to smile in my presence. As I touch it now with assuredness. I now associate that object with a pleasant scene from my imagination.

▲ Stockwell's Ten Strategies for Success: Cozy Fire

STOCKWELL STRATEGY #1: HYPNOTIZE YOURSELF

Shift Your Fear Gear

Hypnotic tools for change include re-framing, behavior modification and mental rehearsal. Reframing takes you back to the scene of the crime. It's a little like getting back on the horse after being bucked off. Do that and fear loses its charge. Subconscious patterns are best changed in the subconscious mind. That's where self-hypnosis comes in. Use fear as a positive energy...energy you can recycle into productive pursuits.

Get into center and read the following affirmation. Read this affirmation three times:

AFFIRM SUCCESS: Activate Your Distress Eliminator
I imagine myself comfortable and clear minded.
When centered, I imagine a situation that in the past frightened me. I make it a worst case scenario and put myself in the memory 100%. Now I call in the part of my mind that knows how to help. 'Distress Eliminator, Angel of Joy, Higher Self, gently quiet the high voltage in my brain's cortex.'

'Distress Eliminator, Mother, Father, God, gently quiet the high voltage in my brain's cortex.'

Distress Eliminator, Great Calming Force, gently quiet the high voltage in my brain's cortex.'

Now take a deep breath. I am now activated. Disruptive emotions are replaced by my favorite emotions, colors, vibrations, smells, tastes and places. It is safe in my world. Thank you. I am grateful for joy and peace.

STOCKWELL STRATEGY #2: HYPNOTIZE YOURSELF

The Three Minute Time-Out

Positively reposition responses and read the following affirmation out loud or to yourself:

I am safe. Panic passes in less than three minutes. All feelings are temporary, coming and going like breath, like waves. I go with the flow and easily return to harmony. I am peaceful. I breathe easily and fully.

A three-minute time-out returns me to balance. If my heart pounds fast, I know that it will slow down within three minutes. I lovingly congratulate myself for coping easily. I honor my feelings. 'I love you. You're doing a great job, heart. Safe and relaxed.'

I confidently accept my emotions. I develop new coping skills. I am a growing and maturing personality. I feel terrific and am proud of myself. I relax, smell delicious, taste yummy and look good! I am in charge of my life. Any tightness loosens and easily changes to relaxation. Yes. Yes. Yes.

'I am balanced.'

I get a grip and loosen my mind and body. Gently and persistently, I stretch my limits and move toward joy. I am flexible. I am my true joyous self. The happy positive me, the real me, is ready, willing and able to take over.

I stubbornly devote myself to doing what I truly want. If I get in my way, I feel the fear and do it any way. I get a grip. Overstressed sub-personalities get well-deserved vacations and a golden handshake. I am relaxed. My sub-personalities play together to bring me joy. I celebrate the daily surprises in my life.

Fear is just naughty, protective energy breaking free. I take time to evaluate how I feel and what decision I want to make. I rename fear "excitement" and proceed. I feel excitement and do what is in my best interest.

"Bolt and jolt" is the parasympathetic flip side of "stay and play." I condition myself to open my parasympathetic parachute. I stay and play. I'm in control of my emotions. I'm strong and self-confident.

I am keenly aware of my thoughts and reactions. I choose thoughts that make me feel good. It's fun to think positively. I transform every thought and action to positive thought and positive action.

Whatever happens I say 'I'll handle it' and I do. Whatever comes my way I deal with in the here and now. I accept and grow from life's challenges. Freedom of mind gives me is a friendly space to accomplish all my dreams.

Creative mind, assist me to make a new plan, idea or strategy. Allow me to be unlimited. My creative mind now gives me five new positive ways to move forward. (Pause)

I carefully review these five safe, healthy, pleasant solutions. (Pause)

Each solution is now safe and acceptable and is now my reality. (Pause)

All parts of me now fully accept each of these solutions. They are now my natural response in thought and action.

I go to happy times. I feel secure and good. I take positive action. I gather the facts and stubbornly use positive energy. I am successful and victorious. I win. Joy prevails.

STOCKWELL STRATEGY 3: HYPNOTIZE YOURSELF

A Breath Away

If your heart pounds, say, **"I love you. You're doing a great job, heart. I am safe. Relax."** All panic results from adrenaline, which is released by adrenal glands during real or imagined danger. Adrenal glands create and reabsorb adrenaline in less than three minutes. Learn how to breathe and reframe your reaction.

I am safe. I breathe easily and fully; my legs are strong beneath me. I see myself standing tall, looking in a mirror and smiling. I feel myself calm and relaxed and I take a deep cleansing breath. I am in charge of my life. I am balanced. I breathe fully and deeply and my diaphragm relaxes:
Inspiration…Cleansing
Calm…Relax
Slow…Easy

STOCKWELL STRATEGY 4: MOVING MEDITATION

Put the Pharaoh of God Into You.

This simple "walk-about" really works. Try it; you'll like it.

Begin Start by standing still in a place where you have some room to move. It can be indoors or out. Focus on a point of attention in front of you; a tree, a leaf, a rock, a book, or a chair. Now relax.

Focus on your Breath Move your attention to the bottom half of your body. Feel your connection to Mother Earth below you. Breathe through your feet into the earth.

Think of a Deep Desire It can be internal or external, emotional, physical or spiritual. Maybe you want a situation resolved. You can choose a little or a big thing. What do you really want? What does your physical comfort want? What does your soul want? Take your time and choose a true desire.

Fulfill Your Desire Close your eyes and imagine that you already have what you deeply desire. It has already happened! What does it look like? Feel like? What is it like to have this dream fulfilled? What proves to you that you have your dream?

Create a Place where your Desire is Fulfilled Open your eyes and visually pick a spot in front of you. Focus on this place. Imagine that this place is the physical manifestation of your true desire. Hold an image of your desire to be fulfilled in this spot.

Slowly walk toward the Place Be aware of your weight as it shifts from foot to foot, muscles to bones, foot to earth. Notice each muscle, nerve, ligament and bone that moves you step by step forward to The Spot. Move slowly, there is no rush. Keep the awareness of your feelings and emotions as you move to where your desire is fulfilled.

Notice any Presence or Absence of Fear Neither search for it nor push it away. If there is fear, feel it, taste it, smell it, hear it, see it or intuit it and stay present with it. Continue to move forward. If fear stops you; pause. Feel any fear and let your desire to reach your spot grow larger than it. How easy or difficult is it for desire to find you again? Do you try not to override fear move quickly? Just notice. Notice how fear creates numbness. Notice how fear, allowed to express itself, shape-shifts.

Repeat this Meditation Several Times Each time will be different as you learn to feel fear and move forward to what you want for you.

STOCKWELL STRATEGY 5: IMAGINE

Panic Panacea

Conscious Recall Imagine yourself in the past panicked by ________________ (name it). As you imagine yourself there, become aware of your thoughts. Notice what you tell yourself about the situation and your reactions. What do you tell yourself? How do you react? Did you get overly dramatic? Did you create the worst scenario possible?

Map your Body Notice where in your body you put thoughts and feelings. Where do you feel these feelings? Ask that part of your body for a word or phrase to describe that feeling.

Regress Bring yourself back to the very first time you had this same feeling and observe, smell, taste, hear and see the situation as if you were watching a movie. Add amusing nuances and clips to the movie.

Rerun the Scene Watch or experience the movie that originally upset you. Notice amusing nuances or subplots. Rerun the scene with a happier conclusion. Rewrite the scenes, as you would like to see them, with a win-win solution.

Return Come back to the now and a new beginning.

STOCKWELL STRATEGY 6: RELEASEMENT

High No Trigger…Away

Focus On Fear Focus your attention on a recent freak out or a time you were out of control. Be there.

Map it in the Body Take a deep breath and notice where in your body you feel the fear or upset.

Give it a Word What word, phrase or sound best describes this feeling in your body.

Go Back Go back to the very first time you had that same feeling or reaction to a word or phrase. What was your initial traumatic experience or upset? Be there.

Detach Face your trauma with new power and strength. View this past scene on a movie screen. Imagine it performed on a stage far away. Watch it through the back end of binoculars, so it is very small. Smile. You no longer need it; you no longer want it.

Play it Safe Pretend that you are a spectator viewing the past and gaining more understanding as you do. Remember to breathe, easy and relaxed, releasing any unpleasant emotions. Each time you breathe, release a web of memories. Imagine that you change your brain wiring with each breath.

Disconnect Breath by breath, cord by cord, release the past. When complete: Return each time to this moment of healing breath. Say: "I am free from the past. I am free. I feel great."

Photo by Bryce Stockwell

STOCKWELL STRATEGY 7: NLP SCRIPT

The Fast Movie Cure

☆ *"Diminishing your fear and finding your courage is an adventure in self esteem. The only thing you have to lose is the heavy yoke that fear imposes."*

—Captain T.W. Cummings
Help for the Fearful Flyer

NLP (Neurolinguistic Programming) can set you free by re-training your neuro responses to stimuli. Logic and reason usually do not override a phobia. Reprogramming and physical responses do.

How rapidly your brain learns! Most phobias are learned in a single, dangerous (or seemed dangerous) experience and unlearned as rapidly. An imprinted phobia can be easily eliminated in one re-learning experience.

A traumatic event brings up vivid internal images, sounds or statements within us. These are sometimes exaggerated or distorted by imagination. At this time, a trigger is created. Usually a trigger is a fragment of the original trauma or thought to be part of the original stimulus. We often don't consciously remember the trauma or the trigger.

Use this exercise to instantly change limiting behavior.

Pretend Assume that you are sitting in a seat in a movie theater with your eyes open or closed. Look at a black-and-white picture of YOU projected on the screen.

Projection Room Take a deep breath. Imagine yourself in the projection booth.

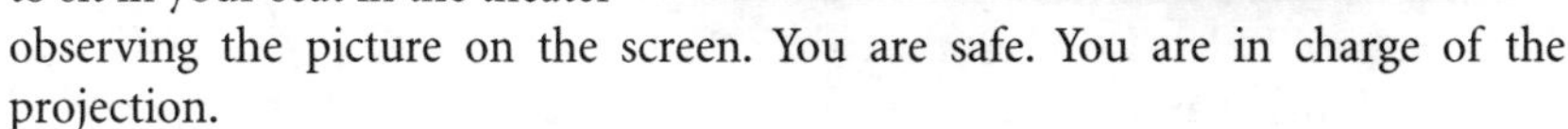

At the same time continue to sit in your seat in the theater observing the picture on the screen. You are safe. You are in charge of the projection.

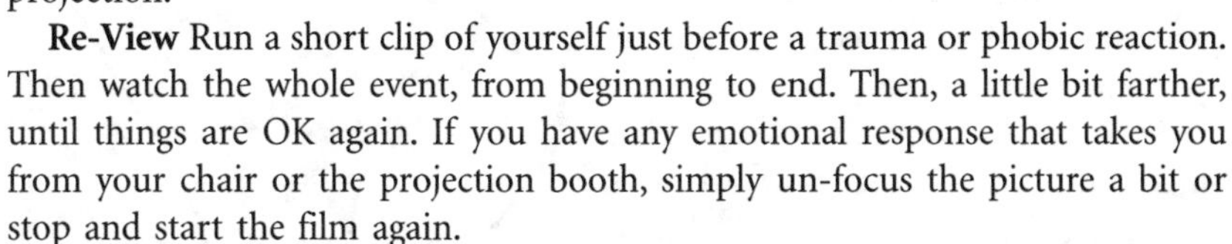

Re-View Run a short clip of yourself just before a trauma or phobic reaction. Then watch the whole event, from beginning to end. Then, a little bit farther, until things are OK again. If you have any emotional response that takes you from your chair or the projection booth, simply un-focus the picture a bit or stop and start the film again.

Happy to be Me Project on the screen a photo of yourself feeling great.

Repeat 'til Complete Repeat this imagery until you really do feel great.

STOCKWELL STRATEGY 8: MSIRR

Move, Sniff, Inspire, Rub and Remember

These steps are terrific to eliminate panic attacks. Use them if one happens. The worst thing you can do when having a panic attack is to sit and try to relax. For, at that moment, your body is releasing adrenaline. Moving your body burns off adrenaline:

Move Take a walk, stretch, release sound, move your body and diffuse anxiety.

Sniff Smell often brings back happy memory. Baby powder works well for a lot of people. Flowers for others. Fresh or salt air, farm animals and barbecued meat mellow some people out.

Inspire Take five deep diaphragm breaths, slowly contracting and expanding your stomach.

Rub Rub your neck, one side at a time, while breathing deeply from the diaphragm.

Remember Remember that, "this too will pass." It is only temporary.

STOCKWELL STRATEGY 9: PALM PRESS

The One Minute Palm Phobia Cure

This amazing system, popularized as *palm therapy* by hypnotist, Dr. Moshe Zwang, eliminates unwanted behavior. You press on two specific points of the hand; the *heart line* and *head line.* Use the left hand because it's cross-wired to the right or emotional brain. Perhaps it is this wiring that makes this system work so well.

If you are helping someone overcome a phobia ask yourself (or the person that you are helping) if they really want to get rid of the phobia. If they say "no," stop. If they say "yes," proceed.

1. Look at the palm of the left hand. Around the thumb you'll see the *life line*, above that the *head line* and finally closest to the fingers, the *heart line.*

2. Go down from the index finger, near the middle finger and locate the spot where it intersects the *head line.* (See Diagram).

If the *head line* connects with the *life line*, press a little closer to the inside of the hand to avoid pressing the life line. This is the first spot, that you will press.

3. Go down from the little and ring finger and locate the spot where it intersects with the *heart line.* When you press on that spot they may feel a slight ache or pain.

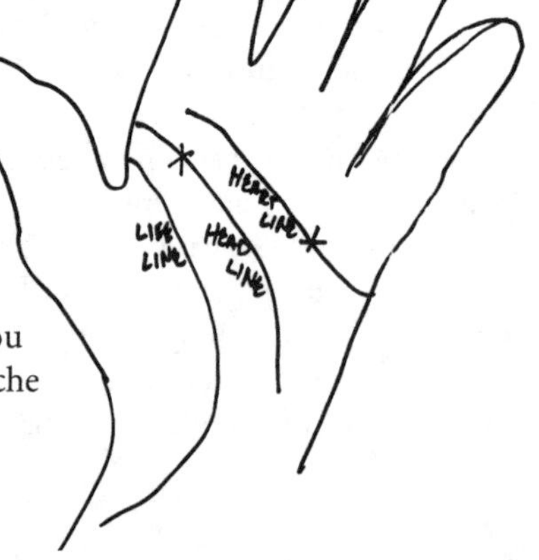

4. Position yourself so that you will press on both of these spots at the same time. Have your friend close their eyes and imagine the frightening situation. And ask, "On a scale of one to ten (one being weak and ten being intense), how strong is that feeling now?"

5. Ask "Where in the body is the tension?"

6. Have the subject close their eyes as you press firmly for ten seconds on the *heart line* and *head line* pressure spots.

7. Then with eyes open, while continually pressing for an additional two minutes, ask a pleasant diverting question like:

"Where do you like to go on vacation?"

"Do you have any pets?"

"What do you do for fun?"

8. Have them again close their eyes and imagine the situation that was the problem and notice their reaction this time. The phobia will have completely vanished. Or, be greatly reduced. If ever a fear comes up, use this technique again. It works!

A TRUE STORY Georgina

"I am fiercely independent, but claustrophobic and deathly afraid of anesthesia. I smoke one to two packs of cigarettes a day and take uppers and downers. I sometimes go on sweet binges.

I'm a neglect survivor Hypnosis has helped me remember my painful and frightening birth. I was heavily drugged and pulled out with forceps. I was born with a hiatal hernia that required surgery. When I was six, I was sent away to a boarding school run by French nuns. I was so shy. The nuns were cold and expected me to take care of myself.

Mother died when I was 16. When I was 35, I came to America. At 40, I gave birth to a child. That's when my anxieties began. I felt fenced in. I did not know how to take care of a child. I did not have a husband or mother to help me. I was all-alone. I started getting migraine headaches.

I understand myself better now I began the tender process of re-nurturing, loving and supporting the child within me. I acknowledge myself for creating a $120,000-a-year business and my strength. Hypnosis helped me reset my mind. I'm still not thrilled with tight places, but I can do anything: ride in an elevator, sit in a car. It's not such a big deal after all. I understand my fear of anesthesia, too. My daughter is grown up and I am married to a very good man. The more I understand myself, the more my husband seems to understand me."

STOCKWELL STRATEGY 10: TAPPING

Emotional Freedom Tapping Technique (EFT)

This system uses a repeated negative phrase as you tap on special body spots. It is based on acupressure, acupuncture and meridians. EFT aficionados claim that it busts fears in minutes and that the results are long lasting or permanent. This technique has been used very successfully with people with post traumatic stress disorder and addictive cravings as well. It is popularly used as an adjunct to hypnotherapy. See what you think.

1. Focus on one aspect or emotion at a time. Some fears have many emotions attached to them. If so, use one tapping sequence for each aspect.

2. Tell your subconscious mind what you would like the result to be from tapping. "**Subconscious Mind, help me. I want to be free to** ________ (e.g. walk past a dog). **I am open to any and all changes that occur**."

3. As you tap each of the "spots" say, "**Even though I have this fear (problem, issue, challenge),** (e.g. even though I'm afraid of dogs) **I deeply and completely accept and love myself.**"

4. When complete, **"I now permanently release this issue and any related issues."**

5. Permanently install your desired outcome. (e.g. I feel fine walking past a dog).

Here are the Spots you Tap. Tap each spot 7–10 times.

1. The OUTSIDE OF THE HAND

Tap the tender place on the side of your hand, above your wrist and below your little finger. Rub or karate chop this place seven to ten times and say with feeling: "Even though I ___________ I deeply and completely accept myself."

2. TOP OF HEAD (TH)

Seven to ten taps on what was your soft spot of fontanel top and slightly back.

3. EYEBROW (EB)

4. SIDE OF EYE (SE)

5. UNDER EYE (UE)

6. CHIN (CH)

7. COLLAR BONE (CB)

8. UNDER YOUR ARM (UA)

Tap four inches down from your armpit or in the middle of the bra for women and for men in line with your nipple.

9. WRIST (W)

10. TOP OF ANKLE (TA)

Tap both inside and outside about four inches above the anklebone.

11. Take a deep breath and notice on a scale of one to ten how much better you feel. It will most likely be gone! When this is so, tap all the points again saying; **"I am completely at ease."**

If you still have some charge on the initial problem, repeat the process again this time saying; **"Even though I still have SOME remaining ________ (fear), I deeply and completely accept myself."**

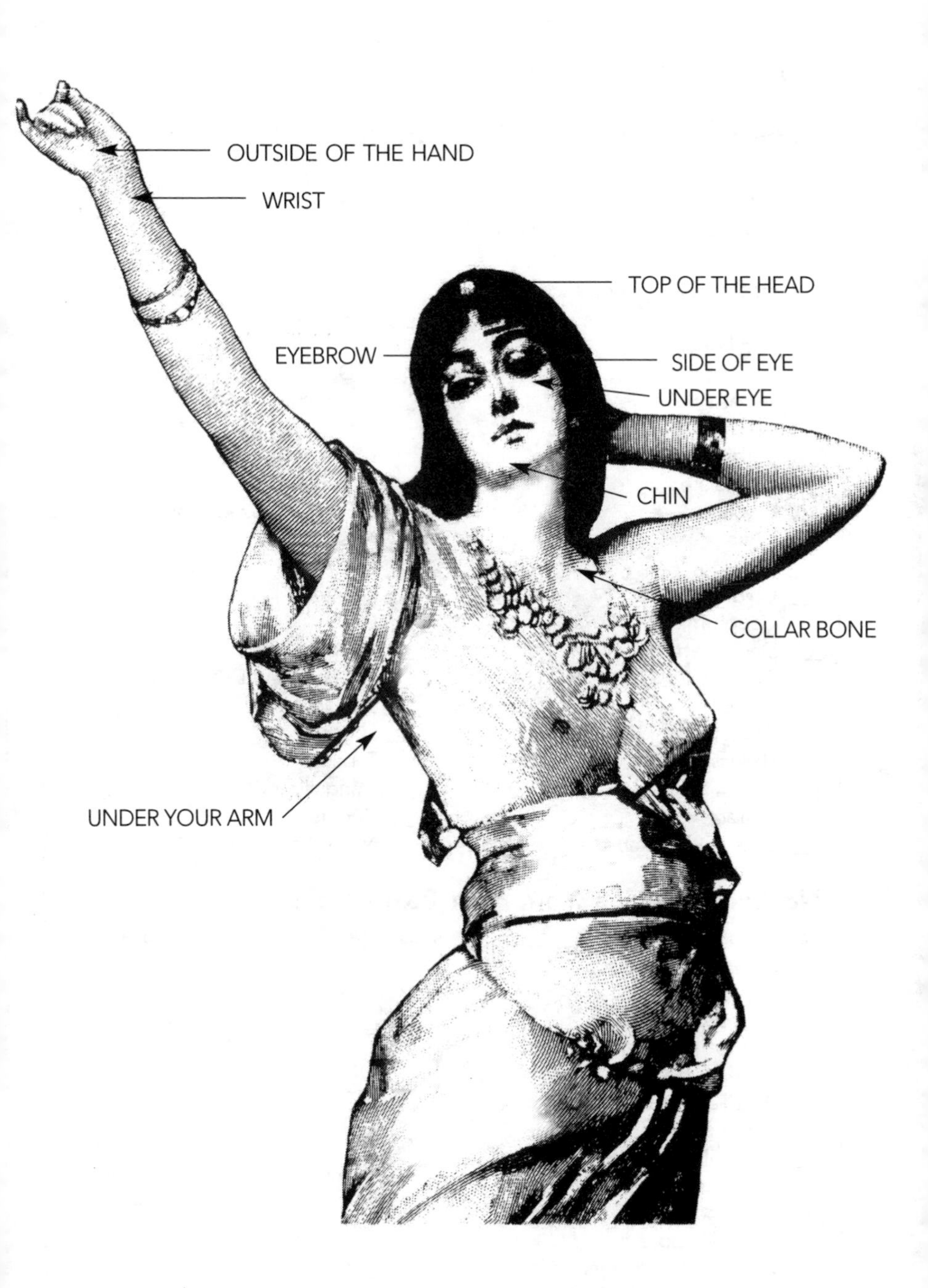
OUTSIDE OF THE HAND
WRIST
TOP OF THE HEAD
EYEBROW
SIDE OF EYE
UNDER EYE
CHIN
COLLAR BONE
UNDER YOUR ARM
TOP OF ANKLE

INNER•VIEW QUIZ

Substances That Hurt Your Body

☆ *"Why did you take up the piano?"*
"My beer kept sliding off my violin."

I use the following substances:

___ Aerosol sprays
___ Alcohol
___ Antidepressants
___ Aspartame
___ Aspirin/pain killers
___ Barbiturates
___ Chocolate
___ Cocaine
___ Coffee
___ Cola
___ Cold remedies
___ Cough medicine
___ Decongestants
___ Downers
___ Drugs
___ Ecstasy
___ Hallucinogens
___ Heroin
___ Inhalants
___ Over the counter/ Designer/Street
___ Prescription
___ Preservatives
___ LSD
___ Marijuana
___ Mescaline
___ Methadone
___ Morphine
___ MSG/Hydrolyzed Protein
___ Nose Sprays
___ Pesticides
___ Peyote
___ Salt
___ Sleeping pills
___ Solvents/Hair Dye/Nail Polish
___ Steroids
___ Sugar
___ Tobacco
___ Tranquilizers
___ Uppers
___ Name Your own

No Excusals: It's You, You Bamboozles

I bamboozle myself with ___________ (substance of preference) because:

___ Everyone uses it.
___ It's glamorous.
___ I feel grown up.
___ It's what partying is all about.
___ It makes me a big shot.
___ I handle it better than anyone else does.
___ I need to relax.
___ I need it to get going.
___ Things go better with it.
___ My friends do it.
___ My family does it.
___ Movie and rock stars do it.
___ I won't get hooked.
___ I didn't notice what I was doing.

Chapter 9
Addiction

Enslaved

Many of us spend a lifetime consciously or inadvertently taking drugs that we ignore by breathing, eating, drinking, absorbing and shooting them it into our body.

This chapter explains how addiction works and the sometimes insidious effects of household chemicals and remedies like antacids, pain relievers, antihistamine, hormone replacement drugs and the current world favorite; antidepressants.

The Down and Dirty Section, chapters 21 through chapter 28, are in-depth explorations of Eating Disorders, Alcohol, Tobacco, Antidepressants, Marijuana, Uppers, Downers, Hallucinogens and Inhalants.

Freedom awaits.

▲ The Substance of Addiction
▲ Hormones and Additives: Food or Drug
▲ Pesticides
▲ Sugar and Sweeteners: Lost in My Dessert
▲ The Blood Sugar See/Saw: Insulin to Injury
▲ Artificial Sweetener
▲ Food As A Drug: Crumby Addictions
▲ Salt: The Dead Sea
▲ Caffeine: Jump Like An Egyptian
▲ MSG: Conspiracy
▲ Drug Store Seduction

▲ The Substance of Addiction

☆ *"Addictive behavior is a mood-altering event, experience, relationship or substance which initially gives you a euphoric feeling and later leaves you feeling dependent, out of control, helpless. The purpose of it is to avoid feelings."*

—John Bradshaw
Healing the Shame that Binds You

The word *addiction* comes from the ancient Latin "addicene" meaning *someone captured and enslaved.* Addiction is a craving that seems to run you; you don't run it.

Addictions stimulate your brain's emotional and motivational centers by creating dopamine. Dopamine, in turn causes psychoactive effects and motivates more of the same addictive behavior. Nicotine and other chemicals makes a smoker, while smoking, want to smoke more.

A person can get hooked on one substance, sequentially substitute, one substance for another or take multiple substances.

All drugs do one of three things to your central nervous system. They depress, stimulate or alter perception.

Drugs that depress, increase the release of brain chemicals.

Drugs that stimulate, block or destroy brain chemicals.

Drugs that alter perception both stimulate and depress. Drugs that open the mind may also slam it shut.

DEPRESSANTS	STIMULANTS	MIND ALTERING
Increase brain chemicals	**Stimulates, blocks or destroys brain chemicals**	**Stimulates then depresses brain**
Alcohol	Amphetamines	**Narcotics:**
Sleeping pills	Antihistamines	Heroin, opiates, analgesics
Barbiturates	Antidepressants	**Hallucinogens:**
Quaaludes	Caffeine	Acid (LSD)
Anti-psychotics	Diet pills	Angel dust (PCP)
Anti-anxiety	Nicotine	Peyote (mescaline)
Skeletal, muscle relaxants		Mushrooms (psilocybin)
Sedatives		Marijuana
		Designer drugs like MDA, ecstasy (MDMA) and DMT
		Inhalants:
		Spray paint
		Liquid Paper
		Aerosol Deodorants

Up Your Egypt

Gall, Soma and Kohl

☆ *"When they came to Golgotha, they offered him (Jesus) wine mixed with gall and he would not take it"*

—Bible

"Gall" referred to in the bible is opium. Ancient Egyptians and Jews used wine with opium added for pain. In 1500 BC, the Aryans from the north invaded India. The Aryans brought with them ancient writings or Vedas. These writings contain numerous references to a sacred drink called soma. "The wild drink lifts me. Have I not drunk soma?" Soma was "squeezed from a plant." Soma went from a ceremonial drink to a recreational elixir. What do you reckon soma is?

In 4th century Greece, Eleusis rituals of initiation used hallucinogenic wine made from the barley fungus elgot. It was later outlawed.

10,000-year-old clay jars for wine and beer sport names like "heavenly" and "joy bringer." In ancient Mesopotamia 30% of the annual grain harvest was mandated to go to the production of beer. The distillation of spirits, invented in Europe, was given the name alcohol because it used the distillation process used by ancient Egyptians to make perfume and eye make-up called kohl.

Christopher Columbus reported that the natives of San Salvador "drink and smoke." He was fascinated with the Indians who carried three-foot long cigars in long tubes, propped them up on a little wooden support before lighting, smoking and "sending prayers to heaven."

We usually don't know what we take in; after all, we're not chemists.

What's in your food, mouthwash, face cream, makeup, hair spray, hair dye, deodorant, household cleaners and bug sprays? What do they do to you when you absorb it into your skin or it goes up your nose?

Take your shampoo and toothpaste, for example. Does it contain Sodium Laureth Sulfate, or SLS? Manufacturers use this chemical to produce bubbles. It is highly suspect as a cause of cancer.

We drink caffeine-laden soft drinks like it's water and toast the bride and groom 'til we're toasted. Hung over the next day we say, "Boy, that was a heck of a party."

Does your crowd get high? Recreational drink and drug feels good, lets us fit in, forget problems and/or keep us from being bored. Getting stoned, drunk, or bingeing becomes a way to go home again. If you associate addictive substances with a loved one, you may use it in a subconscious attempt to be close to them.

We use drugs for seemingly good reasons; to get healthy, to be socially acceptable, to get high, to stay young or go numb, or because your mother, mate, friend, doctor, pharmacist, health food store owner or the media suggested it.

Not too long ago, drugs meant orange flavored aspirin. Now it means cough medicine with codeine, antibiotics, Ritalin, laxatives, antidepressants, hormones and antihistamines.

A doctor's prescription is socially acceptable. We trust. We don't ask or question. We rarely read the small print on advertisements or packages.

Is something you take hurting you?

Even if you pretend, you know on some level if something is messing you up.

"Better living through chemistry" is changed to "better living without chemistry" when negative side effects like death, illness, sweating, jaw grinding, nausea, vomiting, headache, bruising, bleeding, sores, paranoia, anxiety, social disdain, clashes with the law; coming down effects, depression and the risk of becoming a junkie, confront us.

A TRUE STORY Shelley

In 1953, when I was a kid, I often went to the James and Williams Shoe Store in downtown Los Angeles and spent long periods "looking through my feet" on the X-ray machine in the middle of the store!

▲ Hormones and Additives: Food or Drug?

☆ *How doth the little crocodile improve his shining tail*
And pour the water of the Nile on every golden scale.
How carefully he seems to grin, how neatly spreads his claws
And welcomes little fishes in with gently smiling jaws.

—Lewis Carroll

Hormones come to us in our food chain; poultry and beef are fed steerroids. Processed food is loaded with additives, artificial sweeteners and MSG. Soft drinks and decaffeinated coffee are lethal chemical nightmares. Table salt contains iodine. Iodine is used in making commercial bread and processing milk. Large doses of iodine is known to aggravate acne. What else does it do?

You Ate What?

- Nutritive Dextrose, calcium saccharin, cream of tartar, calcium silicate = **Sweet and Low**
- Monoglycerides, diglycerides, cellulose gel, polysorbate 80, sodium acid pyrophosphate = **Frosting**
- Xantham gum, soy lecithin, polysorbate 60, potassium sorbate, calcium disodium, EDTA =**"Butter" spray**
- Corn syrup, modified food starch, dextrose, artificial color, tetrasodium pyrophosphate = **Marshmallows**
- Partially hydrogenated soybean oil, modified food starch, cocoa (processed with alkali), sodium stearoyl, lactylate = **Chocolate pudding**

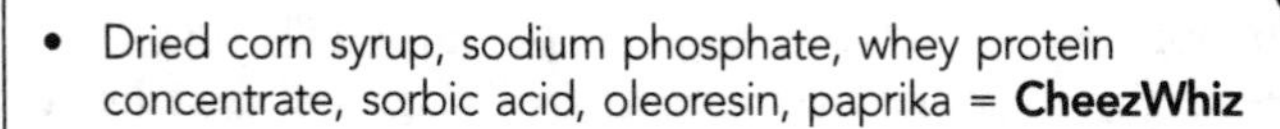

- Dried corn syrup, sodium phosphate, whey protein concentrate, sorbic acid, oleoresin, paprika = **CheezWhiz**

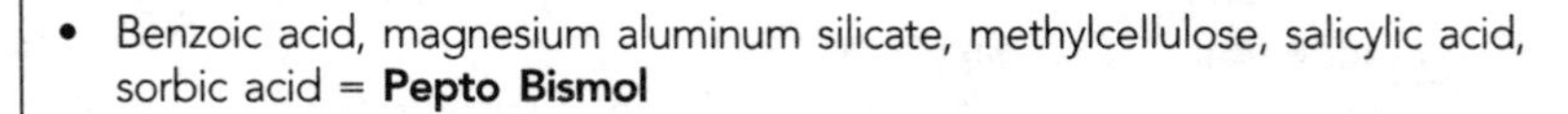

- Benzoic acid, magnesium aluminum silicate, methylcellulose, salicylic acid, sorbic acid = **Pepto Bismol**

▲ Pesticides

☆ *"We can state with certainty that many pesticides are developmental neurotoxins that can have lasting effects on the brain."*
—Philip Landrigan, M.D.
Mt. Sinai School of Medicine

We sniff or eat bug sprays, preservatives, cleaning solvents, gasoline, copy machine toners, paint fumes and nail polish.

Food is sprayed with toxic spray to keep it fresh, colorful and to repel bugs. The Consumers Union reports that apples, grapes, green beans, peaches, pears, spinach and winter squash contain pesticides at levels hundreds of times higher other foods. A friend of mine who studied husbandry at a university won't touch artichokes because he say they pour enough pesticides into a choke to make him choke.

Apples and zucchini are often coated with pesticide laced wax.

Salad greens are often freshened up with water and chemicals like formaldehyde.

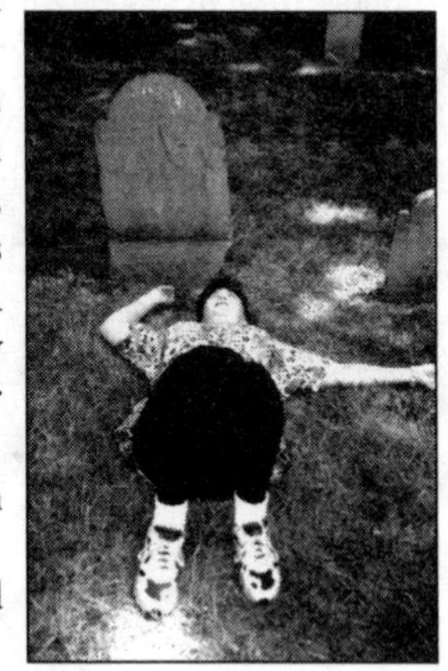

Photo by Jon Nicholas

Last year the Environmental Protection Agency (EPA) finally banned the use of methyl parathion and azinphos methyl that were regularly sprayed on apples, peaches, wheat, rice, sugar beets and cotton.

The Consumers Union and Consumer Reports say that only a single daily serving of some food delivers pesticide levels unsafe for children. Pesticides may cause developmental problems, hyper activity and aggression in youngsters.

Some of the same pesticides used on produce are dusted on pets, sprayed on lawns to control weeds, and used by exterminators to kill pests. Pesticides like chlorpyrifos are used to kill fleas outdoors. Their toxicity is supposedly rendered "harmless" when exposed to sunlight. But what happens when your pet brings them indoors to your floors or you spray them indoors? What happens when you or your toddlers are exposed?

Pesticides from farms filter into groundwater and contaminate wells. What's in your water?

Pesticides disrupt the normal functioning of a bug's nervous system and they act the same way on humans, even though doses are proportionally smaller and effects hard to detect. The FDA approves six hundred agricultural pesticides. Seventy-three of them have strong evidence that they cause cancer and genetic and/or immune response damage.

Speaking of pesticides, if you want to kill ants, try dumping a couple of NutraSweet (aspartame) packages where they congregate. Within 24 hours ants are reported to disappear.

RIDDLE•CULOUS: What Kind of Drug Am I?

Pacifiers are dunked in me. Formulas are too.
Baby food is laced with me. Oh, what goo!
Mommy spoons me in and makes the medicine go down,
Bribe, reward, or potty train, "Erase that grumpy frown."
Grapevines are shot up with me 'cause I'm a little sweetie.
136 pounds a year make you plump and meaty.

French fries are sprayed and coated.
Processed foods are loaded.
If you're feeling bloated,
Your demand for me exploded.

What am I?

Answer: Sugar!

▲ Sugar and Sweeteners: Lost In The Dessert

☆ Question: *"What does a ghost have in his morning coffee?"*
Answer: *"Scream and sugar."*

The word sugar can be confusing. It may mean the sugar in the blood "glucose" or simple carbohydrate sugars like sucrose and dextrose or the complex carbohydrate sugars and starches like potatoes, cereals, fruits and vegetables.

Your brain depends on glucose to survive, thrive, remember, concentrate and be happy. How you think and feel is a direct result of blood glucose. Your brain is only 2 percent of your body weight, yet it consumes 30 percent of your glucose.

Constant levels of the right kind of glucose makes you healthy and happy.

When you eat a carbohydrate, it is converted into the single sugar molecule, glucose, that is absorbed into your blood. If blood sugar rises gradually, this goes smoothly. But if you eat too many of the wrong types of carbohydrates, sweets and starches, you spike blood glucose and insulin. These in turn causes unbelievable short and long term problems.

"Desserts" is "Stressed" Spelled Backwards

☆ *"I've always been a hypocondriac. As a child, I'd eat my M&M's one-by-one with a glass of water."*

Sweets stimulate the pleasure center in the brain, tastes good, makes you high and reminds you of Mom and apple pie. It even relieves depression, for awhile. Then, it lets you down and you crave more.

A sugar rush is usually followed by fatigue, nervousness, headaches, depression, craving for sweets, low tolerance for alcohol, allergies, difficulty concentrating, or low blood pressure. All are signs of sugar's destructive journey.

Sweet Tooth

Imagine eating over six hundred cherry pies a year! If you are typical, you consume that equivalent in refined sugar.

We need less than fifty pounds of natural sugar from natural sources like milk and fruits a year. Today, we consume on average 100 to 185 pounds of refined sugar per person per year. We consume some eleven pounds of cookies, fifteen to twenty-three quarts of ice cream and eleven pounds of chocolate and candy a year. Refined sugars make up one-fifth of an adult's caloric intake and one-fourth of a child's.

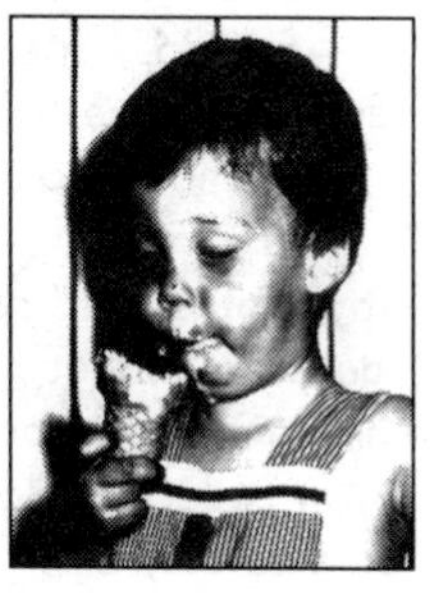

Photo by Jon Nicholas

When Americans in the 1800s, started manufacturing processed sugar, consumption rose to about ten pounds per year and tooth decay became rampant.

The biggest sugar customers are food processors, the tobacco and alcohol industry. Sugar is added to most products in supermarkets. You'll find it hidden in baby formula, baby food, cereals, granola bars, catsup, bread, ice cream, pastry, peanut butter, bacon, meats, soups, sauces, nuts, colas, wine, beer and cigarettes. Table salt often has sugar added. Fruit drinks list their main ingredient, sugar, as corn syrup.

Fast food chains lace everything with it, including the french fries. According to Donald Smith, President of Burger King, fries are sprayed with a sugar solution shortly before being packaged. The sugar caramelizes in the cooking fat, giving them their golden color. Without it, fries would be nearly the same color inside and out.

A grape grower told me that he injected sugar into the grapevines before harvest to assure sweet fruit. Sweetened breakfast cereal contains upwards of four teaspoons of sugar per serving.

Mary Poppins was right, a spoonful of sugar does make the medicine go down, that's why vitamins and medicines give heavy doses. The tobacco industry knows this well. They spray tobacco leaves with sugar before drying it in hot houses.

Alcohol breaks down chemically in the body much like sugar.

Candy Ain't Dandy

A 4-ounce bite-size Butterfinger has 76 grams of sugar—the highest in sugar and calories of a dozen candy bars studied. It also contains 20 grams of fat, and 532 calories.

Even the smallest candy in the study contained 14 grams of saturated fat. The highest in saturated fat was a 3.4-ounce Kit-Kat bar; it contains 18 grams of saturated fat, 26 grams of unsaturated fat and 40 grams of sugar.

CASE STUDY Shelley

As a kid, I spent my allowance on penny candy. I ate so much I felt sick and would crash into a dead sleep.

My Dad loved candy; his favorite was coffee candy. My mother was intimate with ice cream. When I was 11, Mom and Dad went on a vacation and left my brother and me with a cranky babysitter. The Helm's Bakery truck came down the street playing his "buy sweets" music. I bought six glazed donuts and ate every one.

In college, following frustrating "make-out" sessions with my boyfriend (I had to stay a virgin to marry a professional man), I returned to the dorm, bought three or four candy bars, and ate them all in one sitting.

One day in college, I read a health food article about sugar being poison. "What bunk," I said. But I never forgot the article. By now, I avoided food just to eat sweets.

I used candy bars as sleeping medicine. I knew which ones would conk me out the fastest.

"I want to stop eating sugar," I said to myself. "I have will power." For two weeks, I diligently tried to stop. I went through withdrawal; I hallucinated, and saw little cakes, cookies and candies dancing by in tap shoes. I dreamed about hot fudge sundaes. My hands shook uncontrollably.

I thought drugs were things like marijuana, cocaine or heroin. It never occurred to me that medicine, alcohol or sugars were drugs. I ate sugar to feel better, get high or sleep. After sugar, I'd get very tired, tense or "crash."

One day I met a flight attendant who quit smoking through hypnosis. I made an appointment with her hypnotist. After my session, I didn't eat a bit of sugar. However, when I drove by See's Candies, I salivated profusely. So I went back to see the hypnotist a second time. After another hour, I stopped eating sugar for one entire year. And, I had no withdrawal symptoms. This is why I became a hypnotist.

☆ *SICKY SWEET*
Sugar is poison,
Sugar is blame.
Sugar keeps me juvenile,
Sugar masks my pain.
When life is bitter, I crave sweet,
But sweet doesn't come from what I eat.
Best bite an apple, best chew a pear
Best drink some water and show that I care
for the joy that wellness brings me and with mind that contemplates
the gifts that life gives to me is so much more than what I ate.
—Shelley Stockwell

What's Wrong with Sugar, Anyway?

☆ Man with a Twinkie in his ear: *"what's the matter with me?"*
Doctor: *"You're not eating properly."*

Processed sugar is refined but not genteel.

An anti-nutritive, it robs the body of stored resources, weakens the immune response and over-stimulates your brain, adrenal glands, liver and causes sluggish digestion.

Pure protein, fresh vegetables or fruit, fuel your body. Protein with added sweetener putrefies into ptomaines and leucomaines (poisons) that forms a sluggish mass that clogs internal plumbing. The results, over time, are ulcers, gas, colitis, hemorrhoids and foul, loose, impacted, pebbly or bleeding stools.

Let's say you eat a nice, healthy fresh apple. You derive health-giving nutrients, fiber, pectin, vitamins and natural sucrose; just what your body needs. Your stomach easily secretes the necessary digestive enzymes. You receive life-giving water, vitamins and minerals. What remains, travels out the intestines, cleansing you.

Eat that same apple, laced with sugar (applesauce) or laced with starch and sugar (apple pie) and a terrible thing happens. The sweetener stops your stomach from secreting its necessary gastric juices for digestion. The food just sits there and doesn't pass on through. It literally rots in your stomach. Bacteria forms, causing fermentation. Carbon dioxide, acetic acid, alcohol and water are formed. All, except the water, are known poisons.

Too much processed sugar contributes to or causes insomnia, bad breath, tooth decay, bleeding gums, ulcers, hemorrhoids, high blood pressure, stiffened arteries, restricted blood to the brain, stroke, heart disease, kidney disease, hypoglycemia, migraines and, of course, diabetes. It is now suspected that sweets also contribute to near-sightedness, menstrual cramps, asthma, cancer and mental illness.

INNER•VIEW QUIZ

Are You A Sugar Junkie?

Put T for true and true for T.

____I have a sweet tooth.

____I skip meals to get to dessert.

____With sweets, "I can't believe I ate the whole thing."

____I suffer from chronic fatigue syndrome, diabetes, or hypoglycemia.

____At every meal, I have to have dessert.

____I sneak-eat sweets.

____I drink my sweets in soft drinks, juice, and/or alcohol.

____I have an intimate relationship with vending machine sweets.

____I use sugar to numb, sleep, or elevate my energy.

____My health would improve if I stopped eating sugar.

____Sweets make me high.

____It's trendy to be a sugar junkie.

If you answered true to any of these questions, there is an excellent chance that you are a sugar junkie.

41 Ways Excess Sugar Ruins Your Health

I have debated some of these with doctors and dentists, but my research says that each one of these can result from excess sugar. If you have these symptoms, why not cut out refined sugar for six months and see if your symptoms just go away. You have nothing to lose but maybe ten pounds or more.

1. Suppresses and weakens body strength.
2. Steals minerals and interferes with of calcium and magnesium absorption.
3. Hyperactivity, anxiety, difficulty concentrating and crankiness.
4. Significantly raises triglyceride levels.
5. Reduces the body's defenses against bacterial infection.
6. Can cause kidney damage.
7. Reduces the high-density lipoproteins in the body.
8. Leads to chromium and copper deficiency.
9. Leads to cancer of the breast, ovaries, intestines, prostate and rectum.
10. Spikes blood sugar levels. Increases fasting levels of glucose and insulin.
11. Oral contraceptives plus sugar elevates glucose and insulin levels.
12. Causes drowsiness and decrease activity.
13. Can cause hypoglycemia and contribute to diabetes.
14. Interacts with bacteria producing acids that cause cavities.
15. Increases the risk of Crohn's Disease and ulcerative colitis.
16. Causes the same changes as found with gastric or duodenal ulcers.
17. Contributes to candida albicans (yeast infections).
18. Contributes to obesity.
19. Can make saliva and stomach acidic.
20. Raises adrenaline.
21. Can age you.
22. Often leads to alcoholism.
23. Can cause arthritis.
24. Can cause asthma.
25. Gallstones.
26. Heart disease.
27. Appendicitis.
28. Multiple sclerosis.
29. Hemorrhoids.
30. Varicose veins.
31. Periodontal disease.
32. Osteoporosis.
33. Insulin sensitivity.
34. Decreases growth hormone.
35. Weakens eyesight.
36. Increases cholesterol.
37. Increases systolic blood pressure.
38. Causes migraine headaches.
39. Interferes with absorption of protein.
40. Causes food allergies.
41. If pregnant, it can cause toxemia.

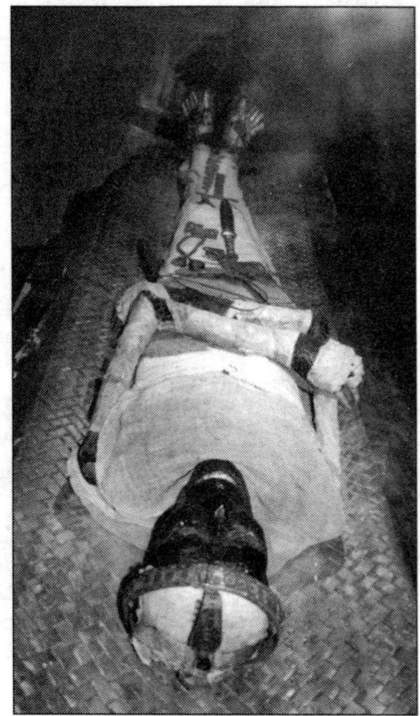

Photo by Jon Nicholas

▲ The Blood Sugar Seesaw: Adding Insulin to Injury

The most devastating problem that sugar and stressful chemicals cause is to your blood sugar levels. Often, diabetes and hypoglycemia result.

A chemical chain reaction over-stimulates the pancreas, adrenals, liver, and may overload your stomach with acidic digestive enzymes. You ride the blood sugar seesaw as soon as five minutes after ingesting refined sugar, caffeine, alcohol, tobacco, some medicines and/or marijuana.

If your pancreas (that produces insulin) is healthy, it produces enough insulin to balance your body's internal sugar level. This is radiant health:

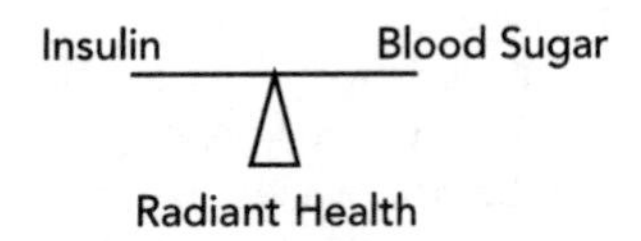

Refined sugar, alcohol and some drugs raise your blood sugar level and throw your body out of balance:

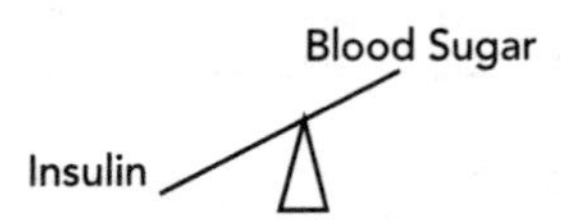

To create homeostasis, your pancreas pumps out more insulin. But, if it becomes trigger-happy due to overuse, it ends up being thrown off the balance in the other direction. When it produces too much insulin (the hypoglycemic hormone), blood sugar levels drop and you feel hungry, irritable, over-reactive, fatigued, faint.

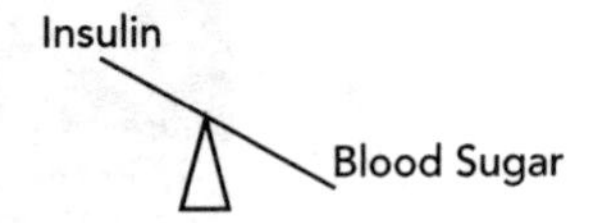

When blood sugar is down, you may reach for more "hair of the dog" (probably more sugar or alcohol) as a pick-me-up. Often, this raises blood sugar into a panic mode and causes the pancreas to dump more insulin into your system, trying to balance things out, but failing. Diabetes occurs when your exhausted pancreas stops producing enough insulin or stops working altogether.

When the pancreas is continually overworked, it calls upon your adrenals to help. They respond by releasing adrenaline, which makes you jumpy and nervous.

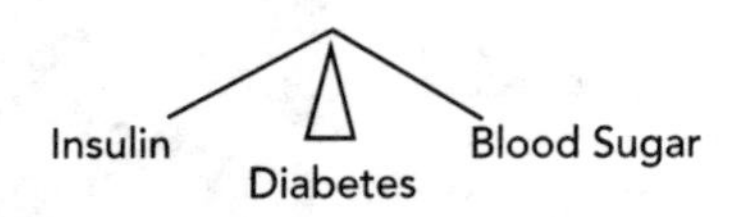

Your liver is your body's refuse bin; it absorbs and processes toxins and chemicals. It also plays a role in balancing your blood sugar level. When your blood sugar level is low, it releases stored glycogen (the hyperglycemic hormone), which mobilizes glucose in the blood. If your liver over-reacts, your pancreas comes in to provide more insulin to balance the blood sugar level. This sends a signal to your liver to stop producing more glycogen. This stresses your overworked liver. That's why many alcoholics suffer liver damage.

Sugar Harms Children

Photo by Jon Nicholas

Have you observed children at a birthday party or after Halloween, and how they act after they consume candy, punch, soft drinks, cake and ice cream? Frazzled, jet propelled, and crying for more "treats"?

Advertisers entice children to beg for high-sugar cereals, snacks and treats, conveniently shelved at children's eye level in grocery stores.

Sugar overtaxes small nervous systems, lowers immunity and are gateway drugs to Ritalin and antidepressants.

Many studies correlate hyperactivity in children to sugar consumption. The sugar whacks kids out. More than one million children are now diagnosed with "attention deficit hyperactivity disorder" (ADHD) and "attention deficit disorder" (ADD), and prescribed Ritalin, Dexedrine, Cylert, Tofranil, Norpramine and Elavil.

How many of these children eliminated caffeine, sugar and additives from their diet before being given such drastic drugs?

A TRUE STORY Meg

"My 12-year-old son is having serious troubles. He has a superactive disorder. He's impossible. I'm going to put him on Lithium (or Ritalin)."

"Meg, why not eliminate sugar from his diet first? That could be the cause." (This child was raised on candy, cookies, ice cream, soft drinks, french fries and hamburgers).

"No, that's too difficult. That would mean I'd have to change my diet too. It's just too much of a hassle."

Two years later: "How's your son?"

"His grades are better since he's been on 'Bennies.' But he's smoking cigarettes, and flunked out of school because he's doing drugs with his friends."

Sugar Makes You Sluggish

Sugar interferes with the brain's ability to think, feel and do. It stimulates the release of insulin into blood, and the insulin binds certain amino acids to cell tissue, thus reducing the availability of amino acids that the brain can convert to neuro transmitters. Good, healthy food aids digestion and lets you assimilate energizing nutrients into your blood stream and brain. Every physical, mental and emotional function of your body needs the right "fuel" to do its work.

> **Does Sugar Affect Your Energy?**
>
> Touch your little finger to your thumb and try to keep them touching as a friend tries to pull them apart. Notice your strength as you resist.
>
> Now, drop a glop of sugar on your tongue and swallow it and repeat the resistance tests you just did.
>
> Notice the difference? Where did your strength go?

Sugar Disturbs Sleep

Ever notice how candy and refined sugars make you crash, and then hours later, jack you awake? If you have difficulty sleeping, do not eat or drink anything with sugar (or alcohol) after 4:00 p.m. You will sleep like a baby.

Sugar Dehydrates

You need water and nutrients for new cell growth to keep yourself healthy. Things that contain sugar, alcohol and caffeine pull water, vitamins and minerals from your cells.

Sugar junkies are dehydrated. What they interpret as a craving for sweets is actually thirst. When sugar in the mouth makes you salivate, it affects your brain's hormone balance. This tricks you into thinking that your body is receiving life-giving water. But the opposite is true. Sugar is actually a diuretic, stealing water from cells, and taking with it reserves of vitamins, minerals and salts that you need to fight infection.

Sugar Makes You Fat

☆*Sparkle, sparkle, twinkle cake.*
I have got a bellyache
From candy, pie and frosty flakes
Instead of food, for goodness' sake.

—Shelley Stockwell

There's a hole in a sweet tooth that goes directly to fat cells. Refined sugar provides calories but no vitamins, minerals, dietary fiber or protein. These empty calories replace more nutritious food. As your body attempts to process and store a glut of sweetness, you deplete the stored vitamins and minerals that you need to be healthy and fight illness.

Sugar and artificial sweeteners stimulate the appetite and the production of insulin, which encourages the body to store calories as fat instead of burning it as energy. Ironically, most "liquid diet plans" are 17-30% sugar.

Six hundred calories a day in refined sugar (forty-two hundred calories a week) can translate into thirty-one pounds of body fat a year.

The Twinkie Defense

In 1979, Dan White murdered two important politicians, San Francisco Mayor George Moscone and Supervisor Harvey Milk. In the ensuing trial, White's attorney, Douglas Schmidt, blamed his client's behavior on Twinkies. Psychiatrist Martin Blinder testified that the high sugar content of the many Twinkies White ate resulted in "diminished mental capacity." The jury bought this explanation, and convicted White of voluntary manslaughter instead of murder.

Lean infants reject sweet solutions. Chubby infants, on the other hand, suck harder and show great activity when offered sweets.

INNER•VIEW QUIZ

Do You Have Diabetes?

Do you experience?

___ 1. Extreme thirst
___ 2. Blurred vision
___ 3. Numbness in fingers and toes
___ 4. Itchy skin
___ 5. Intense hunger
___ 6. Frequent urination
___ 7. Sudden weight loss
___ 8. Weakness and fatigue
___ 9. Skin infections
___ 10. Achy body
___ 11. Irritability
___ 12. Nausea and vomiting
___ 13. Cuts that heal slowly

These are all symptoms of diabetes.

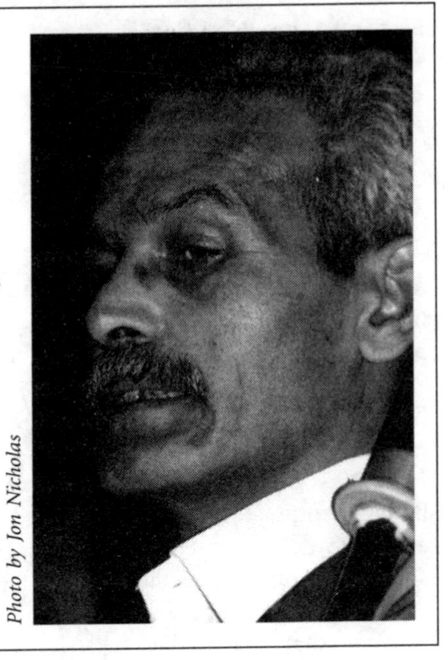

Photo by Jon Nicholas

Diabetes

Diabetes is an epidemic, affecting some 5 million Americans and killing some 300,000 each year. It affects people of all ages with symptoms like loss of limbs, heart and kidney failure. Diabetes is the leading cause of blindness.

Early detection and changing poor eating habits can cure adult onset diabetes. Diabetes can be avoided by eating fresh fruits and vegetables and avoiding processed sugars and other toxins.

Overweight people are two hundred times more likely to get adult onset diabetes.

A five year study in Japan of 1,266 middle aged men showed that those who smoked more than 31 cigarettes a day were four times as likely to develop diabetes.

AFFIRM SUCCESS: Bust the Sugar Blues

Here's a terrific affirmation to bust the sugar blues. (Or you can order the tape, No More Sugar Junkie, at the back of this book.) As you read these words, let them become your reality:

At this moment, I begin life anew. I have an uncontrollable desire to be radiantly healthy. I take control of my mind, body, energy and life. Since I take command, my potentials are unlimited.

Personal strength and power let me move toward my goals and dreams. I tell the truth to myself and others. I am honest, awake and assertive.
I conquer addictions. Nothing holds me back. I do it now. I make a pact with myself, to take charge. I do whatever is necessary to take control of my body and my life. I am honest with myself and others. I am healthy and free of toxins.

Processed sweets, icky, gross, good-bye. Cane, beet, turbonado, raw/brown or white sugar are drugs that damage organs, mind and perception.

Fresh whole food is good for me. I love fresh organic fruit: like an apple or orange. A fresh apple gives me health-giving nutrients, fiber, pectin, vitamins and natural sugar that work perfectly for me. A fresh apple helps me breathe and digest. Fresh foods help my stomach easily secrete the necessary digestive enzymes. I receive life-giving water, vitamins and minerals. What remains, travels out my intestines, cleansing me. I love fresh whole food. Yum.

Every cell in my body speaks loudly to me saying, "Thank you for healthy nourishing food."

There is no holding me back. My brain returns to perfect balance and clear thinking.

I drink lots and lots of water. I don't put anything poisonous into my perfect body. I am no longer ruled by one small orifice, my mouth. My whole body and mind now have a vote. I listen fully to my natural body wisdom.

I eat for fuel, so that I have energy to pursue my many talents and interests. I only eat good healthy fresh fruits, vegetables, whole grains, fish, chicken and lean meats. I drink lots and lots of water, get exercise and take vitamins. Nature blesses whole foods to protect human health. Whole food is holy.

I listen well to my inner wisdom, for it knows exactly what I need to do to enjoy my life in a full, healthy, energetic, clear minded. Each of these ideas has made a deep, permanent and lasting impression on all levels of my mind

I read the labels. Poisonous sugars are hidden with sneaky "ose" at the end, such as sucrose, dextrose, glucose, fructose, levulose, maltose, lactose. Yuck. Disgusting corn syrup, sorbitol, mannitol, moltitol, xylitol and especially aspartame harm me. I eat for fuel. I eat healthy food. I am active and happy and vital. I choose to live.

▲ Artificial Sweeteners

(Based on an article by Nancy Markle)

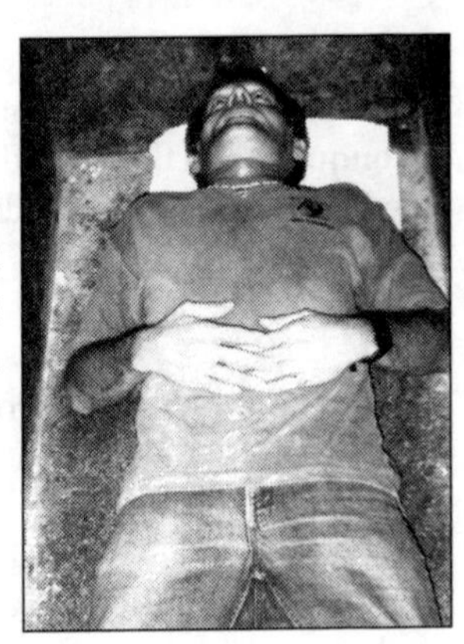

Chemical concoctions called artificial sweeteners taste like sugar. They "lower calories and will not promote tooth decay," their promoters sing. But artificial sweeteners may be deadly poison. Return or throw away anything that contains aspartame or artificial sweeteners.

IF IT SAYS "SUGAR FREE" ON THE LABEL—
DON'T EVEN THINK ABOUT IT!

Drop Deadly Diet Drinks and Sweeteners or Drop Dead

The Center for the Science of Public Interest in Washington, DC (30,000 members strong) reported that saccharin slightly increased the risk of cancer. The FDA tried to ban it, but Congress decided to post cancer warning labels instead.

So what has that got to do with you?

Have you read your toothpaste and mouthwash ingredients lately? It most likely has saccharin in it. The lining of your mouth and your skin absorbs chemicals. Do these harm you?

In 1970, Cyclamates were banned because large amounts were said to cause testicular injury and increased risk of cancer and birth defects. Do you use cyclamates now? Read your labels.

Enter aspartame (phenylketonurics) sold as 'NutraSweet', 'Equal' and 'Spoonful," produced by Monsanto® and added to over 5,000 different products in over ninety countries worldwide. The Ambassador of Uganda testified to the US Congress that his country's sugar manufacturers add aspartame to sugar!

Two congressional hearings attempted to warn the public about aspartame. Senator Howard Metzenbaum's congressional bill proposed:

1) Pregnant mothers, infants and children be warned of aspartame's dangers.

2) Independent studies about aspartame's influence on seizures, brain chemistry and neurological and behavioral changes be conducted.

Powerful manufacturers and chemical lobbies were said to have killed the bill.

So What's The Problem With Aspartame?

There are ninety-two documented dangerous symptoms of aspartame from nausea to death.

Poison Break Down

Aspartame = Aspartic acid, phenylalanine, formic acid and methanol.

These poisonous chemicals in turn cause metabolic acidosis and methanol toxicity.

Heat liberates methanol from the aspartame at 86 degrees Fahrenheit. When that happens, and you ingest it, 10% of the methanol by weight is metabolized and converted to formaldehyde. Formaldehyde is grouped in the same class of drugs as Cyanide and Arsenic: DEADLY POISONS!

The formaldehyde then changes to formic acid. Formic acid is the poison found in the sting of fire ants.

Aspartame could be one factor of US Dessert Storm troops' health problems. Over 60 Desert Storm attendees reported burning tongue and other symptoms identical to aspartame poisoning. Service men and women reportedly drank diet drinks that sat in the 120-degree F. Arabian sun for weeks. Several babies born to these vets had severe birth defects.

If the methanol converts to formaldehyde in the retina of the eye, it can cause blindness. Physicians may mistakenly believe this is retinopathy (the cause of blindness in diabetes).

Do You Have Aspartame Poisoning?

Do you use artificial sweeteners and suffer from:

___ Anxiety Attacks
___ Birth Defects
___ Bloody Diarrhea
___ Blurred Decreased Vision
___ Blindness
___ Burning Tongue
___ Depression
___ Exhaustion/Fatigue
___ Fibromyalgia Symptoms
___ Insomnia
___ Joint pain
___ Lupus Symptoms
___ Memory Loss/Confusion
___ Multiple Sclerosis Symptoms
___ Nausea
___ Numbness in your Legs
___ Rashes/Hives, Itching
___ Seizures
___ Severe Headaches
___ Shooting Pains/Cramps
___ Slurred Speech
___ Spasms/Abdominal Pain
___ Tinnitus (ringing in the ears)
___ Vertigo/Dizziness

If so, suspect ASPARTAME POISONING! Stop soft drinks and artificial sweeteners immediately! Advanced methanol toxicity is serious and deadly. The best hope is to get off aspartame immediately. If you do, most symptoms disappear. Vision, and even hearing, have returned and tinnitus (ringing in the ears) stops.

Brain Drain

☆ *"The ingredients of Aspartame stimulates the neurons of the brain to death, causing brain damage of varying degrees."*

—Dr. Russell Blaylock, Neurosurgeon

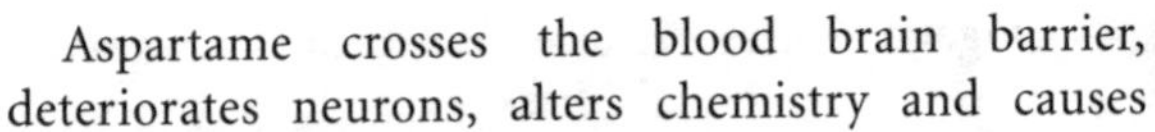

Aspartame crosses the blood brain barrier, deteriorates neurons, alters chemistry and causes neurological damage. It's resultant formaldehyde is stored primarily in fat cells of the brain, sex organs, hips and thighs.

It depletes seratonin, which can then cause mood swings, depression, panic attacks, rage and violence.

Aspartame changes the dopamine level in the brain. How does that effect those with Parkinson's Disease?

Lab tests report animals given aspartame, develop brain tumors. The phenylalanine reputedly breaks down into DKP, a brain tumor agent.

Aspartame sensitizes reactions to MSG and other chemicals. Phenylalanine breaks down the seizure threshold.

Three or more 12oz. glasses of artificially sweetened diet drinks, coffee or a candy bar a day, changes your brain's chemistry and may destroy neurological functioning. Results vary from memory loss to seizures.

Aspartame can be addictive. H. D. Roberts, MD says a large percentage of his patients, suffer severe withdrawal symptoms when aspartame was removed from their intake.

How Much Aspartame Is In This Drink?

Diet Coke	125mg
Caffeine free Diet Coke	125mg
Diet Cherry Coke	125mg
Diet Sprite	118mg
Tab	19mg and 63mg of saccharin
Barq's Diet Root Beer	170mg
Barq's Diet Red Cream Soda	170mg
Barq's Diet French Vanilla Cream	160mg
Diet Minute Maid Orange	150mg
Diet Mello Yello	126mg
Fresca	118mg
Diet Mr. Pibb	125mg

Fountain versions of Diet Sprite, Diet Coke, Diet Minute Maid Orange and Fresca are sweetened with a blend of aspartame and Saccharin.

List Given by Coca-Cola Bottling Company 3/99

Big Fat Myth

Aspartame is not a diet product. It actually makes you crave carbohydrates that makes you fat. Dr. Roberts observed that when obese patients stopped aspartame, they lost an average of 19 pounds!

The wood alcohol in aspartame is especially deadly for diabetics. Confusion, memory and severe vision loss may be caused by aspartame, not diabetes. Aspartame may keep blood sugar levels out of control.

PKU Warning

People, with the genetic disease PKU (Phenylketonuria), are said to be at great risk if they use aspartame.

MS, Lupus or Aspartame Disease?

Artificial sweeteners may cause our "epidemic" diagnosis of multiple sclerosis and systemic lupus. Diet cola drinker's methanol toxicity mimics MS and lupus. The victim and most physicians don't know that aspartame may be the problem.

Oh Baby

☆ *"Consuming aspartame at the time of conception can cause birth defects."*

—Dr. H.J. Roberts

☆ *"Aspartame Diseases can cause Birth Defects. The phenylalanine concentrates in the placenta, causing mental retardation."*

—Dr. Louis Elsas, Professor
of Genetics Emory University
In testimony before Congress.

This letter was sent to me on the Internet:

I tried to get a mother who had a child using Nutra Sweet to get the child off the product. The child was having grand mal seizures every day. The mother called her physician, who called the ADA, who told the doctor not to take the child off the Nutra Sweet. We are still trying to convince the mother that the aspartame is causing the seizures. Every time we get someone off of aspartame, the seizures stop. If the baby dies, whose fault is it?

WARNING
Aspartame is hazardous to your health.
Regular use can kill. Don't use it.

▲ Food as a Drug: Crumby Addictions

Have you crossed the line from nourishment to fixation? Does your eating behavior run you? Do you eat the whole thing, vomit, starve and take enemas? If so, out-of-control behavior is a futile attempt to control life, numb underlying depression and bring back the past. Using food to deal with old hurts causes more hurt. Chapter 21 gives a more in depth approach to healthy eating.

Do You Carrot All?

A-beta carotene found in carrots has been established to prevent night blindness and possibly reduce the risk of breast, lung, colon, prostate, cervical cancer, heart disease, and stroke. Twenty-five mg or more a day may be necessary.

Siwwy Wabbits

Dr. Lawrence Price, a psychiatrist at Yale University says that carrot abuses he has treated were anorexic people who chose carrots instead of high-calorie food.

According to the Associated Press, two Czechoslovakian psychiatrists reported that three patients ate so many carrots that their palms, soles, and the whites of their eyes turned orange. When they tried to quit eating carrots cold turkey, they suffered withdrawal symptoms, including carrot hallucinations and deep yearnings. The patients reportedly consumed as many as five bunches of carrots a day.

Other researchers claim that the orange skin color caused from carrot consumption is the result of the liver cleansing or beta carotene.

A TRUE STORY Marty

"In our family, no one knew how to deal with problems. And, I guess I didn't either. Starving myself kept me away from eating with my family at the table. There was always a hassle at dinner. I ate so little that, after a while, I just couldn't think straight. I believed that weighing 87 pounds wasn't a problem. After all, I was studying to be a professional dancer.

I'm not sure when I crossed the border into crazy thinking, but I remember saying to myself, 'It's easier to die than change my eating habits.' I guess I wasn't kidding. One morning when I woke up with ballooning swollen ankles and legs, I freaked out. In an attempt to be thin, I'd blimped. (Note: Swelling may be caused by a lack of protein in the blood and from too few calories. It's called hypoproteinemia.).

I went to a therapist who gave me a no-nonsense diet. I had to count each bite, each grain of rice and I did it as automatically as my dance routines.

When I got some food in me, everything in my life improved. Even my ballet. I crossed the border of my brain again, and said, 'Now I see where I've been. Now I can make clear choices on where I'm going.

▲ Salt: The Dead Sea

☆ OH BUOY

The Dead Sea is so salty that it is impossible to drown in it unless you are held under the water, or are face down.

☆ *"If you throw salt on a slippery sidewalk, it dissolves the ice; if you sprinkle it on your food, it can dissolve your bones."*

—Dr. Neal Bernard, MD
Eat Right, Live Longer

We have 8 ounces of salt inside us to regulate the pressure in our veins, retain water, and help transport nerve impulses to our brain. We get that minimum amount naturally in grains, beans, fresh fruit and vegetables.

Historical: A Salt And Battery

☆ *"Being kissed by a man who doesn't wax his moustache was like eating an egg without salt."*

—Rudyard Kipling
The Gatsby

Salt (NaCl) is sodium and chloride joined in a chemical bond. Salt is the only rock that we eat. Salt has been bartered, used as money and fought over. A common method of suicide in China used to be eating a pound of salt. Actually, if you eat more than 4 ounces at once, it will kill you.

Throughout history, taxing salt often brought violent protest. In Greece, salt was literally worth its weight in gold, and traded ounce for ounce. Ethiopia used salt disks as currency until early in this century.

Arab traders went by caravan from oasis to oasis along the Sahara desert to southern forests and traded salt for gold dust, ivory, goatskins and slaves.

In biblical times, salt was rubbed on newborn babies' feet to ward off evil spirits. Lot's wife became

Photo By Jon Nicholas

Sea Salt Farmer

a pillar of the society. Roman Catholics put salt in holy water and a baptized child's mouth to symbolize purity. However, newborn babes grimace if you give them something salty. Salt is an acquired taste.

At a king's table, the most important guests were seated "above the salt."

In the 1800's salt was used to dehydrate and preserve meat and the dead. Today salt has over 14,000 uses from making soap, paper, detergent, plastic and rubber.

Salt comes from two sources, the dehydration of salty water or the mining of rock. There are variations in the color, size and texture of salt crystals. The Celts were mining salt on the Durnberg 3,000 years ago with wooden and bronze tools. In Bali, Indonesia, salt is still harvested by dehydrating sea water. Modern technology makes salt plentiful.

Today, salt has become trendy and aficionados tout the subtle taste differences influenced by trace elements that come along for the ride.

If You Salt Your Food Before You Taste It, It Could Be Your Last Supper.

Sodium is a vital part of your body. Body tissue swims in a salty sea, a remnant perhaps, of our aquatic evolution. Your cells contain potassium, with just a little bit of sodium. But the solution around your cells is mainly sodium, with a little potassium. There is continual osmosis between the two. Liquid continually flows through each semipermeable cell membrane, moving from lower density to higher density.

If you have too much salt, your cells contain too much sodium, you draw in and retain fluid and lose potassium. Extreme potassium deficiency can kill.

Perspiration depletes water, increasing salt concentration in your blood.

Your kidneys keep normal levels of sodium in your fluid. If you have too much sodium, you excrete it. If you need sodium, your kidneys reabsorb it from your urine and put it back into the blood. If you eat excess sodium for years, your kidneys fail to operate properly. They cannot get rid of all the sodium you consume.

Eating something salty makes you thirsty because the body needs extra water to dilute it. Your thirst keeps salt concentration within a narrow range. The trick is to maintain a proper dilution or concentration, of sodium and water. Bartenders offer salty nuts and pretzels because thirst is good for business.

Large amounts of salt undermine your main means of support, your bones, by stealing much needed calcium. Salt can literally eat through bone.

Salt has been linked to high blood pressure and its consequences, stroke, heart and kidney disease.

The FDA warns that five to ten percent of Americans are sodium sensitive, which means that their blood pressure responds directly to any change in salt intake. In her nutrition book, Jane Brady says that fifteen to twenty percent of Americans are genetically prone to develop high blood pressure if their diet is rich in sodium.

Hypertension

Hypertension afflicts some 60 million Americans. Though hotly debated, the sodium in salt and a person's sensitivity to it is the main suspected cause. Sodium constitutes 40% of the salt molecule, by weight.

Hypertension generally produces no symptoms until permanent organ damage appears as illness or death. In Japan, where sodium is consumed in excess, hypertension is the leading cause of death and disability. Places like New Guinea and the Kalahari Desert, where they use little or no salt, have no hypertension.

PMS

The primary cause of PMS (pre-menstrual syndrome) is the retention of sodium just before the start of a period, causing bloating, headaches and irritability. Women, who crave salt and eat more, compound the problem. Birth control pills increase the appetite for salt, which explains why some women gain weight while taking birth control pills.

Addiction to Salt

Taste buds are desensitized by salt. The more salt you eat, the more you require to taste it. Salt appetite is principally determined by early diet patterns.

A TRUE STORY Fred

"Added Salt for me was a matter of fact. I salted everything before I even tasted it; vegetables, meat, salad, tomato juice...I could go through a box of salt a month. I don't like sweets. One hypnosis session with Shelley got me to get rid of this habit. I am healthier and feel much better."

Swell, He's Worth His Weight in Salt

High salt intake contributes to extra weight because your body retains more fluid. For each three-quarters teaspoon of salt, you gain one pound. The sodium in salt causes swelling (or edema) in and around body tissue. If the swelling is around your heart, it can cause congestive heart failure. In the legs, difficulty walking and potential blood clots. In the pelvic region, painful menstruation. In the brain, depression and irritability.

Salt pulls stored vitamins and minerals from the cells. If you sprinkle salt on a cucumber, it wilts because water is drawn out of the cells by the salt. The same thing happens in your body. When salt pulls fluid from muscles, they cannot contract normally. Your body needs an extra pint of liquid to flush out each extra one-forth teaspoon of salt you consume. The purpose of thirst is to keep a healthy balance between salt and water.

From Salty Sea to the Dead Sea

The FDA recommends five hundred milligrams of sodium a day (one-forth teaspoon) and no more than two thousand milligrams (one teaspoon or forty-eight pinches) a day. Unfortunately, the average American consumes a whopping ten to fifteen thousand milligrams a day (5 to 7.5 teaspoons or 240 to 360 pinches)! That adds up to about fifteen pounds of salt a year. The actual physiological requirement for sodium is 1/10 teaspoon of salt a day and can easily be obtained from natural food and water.

According to a US Food and Drug Administration survey, infants consume enough sodium to equal four teaspoons a day. Human breast milk is the perfect food for a growing human baby. Babies receive forty milligrams (mgs) of salt in breast milk and a whopping one hundred milligrams of salt in cow's milk. Cow's milk is produced for baby cows not baby humans.

The average toddler receives almost five teaspoons a day. Infants and toddlers receive this unbelievably high intake in baby food and foods prepared by adults, seasoned to their taste.

How Do We Get So Much Salt?

A standard breakfasts of orange juice, two eggs, ham, toast and margarine/ butter equals 1/2 teaspoon of salt or—double the FDA's recommended total daily intake.

You get salt from cooking, the salt shaker and processed food. Processed foods give us 55% of our salt intake. Salt is used in baked goods to control the action of the yeast, strengthen the gluten, reduce water absorption, and to improve the color of the crust.

Processed meats, uses one to two percent of salt by weight as a preservative.

Food already comes with salt, from the earth or from the animal. Spinach, celery, beets, turnips, kale and artichokes are very high in salt content. Some drinking water is too. In the South, one cup of tap water can have as much as 400 milligrams of salt.

Canning increases the sodium while it decreases the potassium in the food. This is a shame, because potassium wards off high blood pressure. Six canned asparagus spears have about 410 milligrams of sodium!

Added salt and sodium are hidden under the names: seasonings, sodium nitrate, sodium phosphate, sodium ascorbate, monosodium glutamate (MSG), soy sauce, sodium saccharin, leavening agents, baking powder and baking soda, dry skim milks, whey solids and butter.

Another hidden source of sodium is drugs, especially antacids. A single dose of pop-pop-fizz-fizz has 567 to 1000 milligrams of sodium. Antacids, cough preparations and laxatives are salt loaded. So is vitamin C labeled as sodium ascorbate.

Pet foods are loaded in salt. Perhaps that's why congestive heart disease is now a common problem in middle-age pets.

Canned, pickled, deli and smoked foods, dry cereal, baked goods, catsup, mustard, sauces and gravies, fried and breaded foods; herring, tuna, anchovies, sauerkraut, cheese, crackers, pretzels, chips and dips, salad dressings, vegetable juices, nuts, and pizza, are all worth their weight in salt.

Product	Tsp. salt	Mgs sodium
Alka-Seltzer (1 tablet)	1/4	560
Big Mac w/ cheese or Reuben sandwich	1/2	962-1,000
Bromo Seltzer	1/2	1,000
Baked beans (1 cup)		810
Campbell's red/white label soup (1 cup)	1/2	1,100
Canned green beans (One serving)	1/6+	360
Canned shrimp (3 oz)	1	2,000
Canned Salted Peanuts (1 ounce)		132
Dill Pickle (1 large)		1137
Egg McMuffin		914
Instant chocolate pudding (1/2 cup)	1/5+	480
Catsup (1 tablespoon)		154
Mustard (1 tablespoon)		21
Manhattan clam chowder (1 cup)	1	2,000
Miso soup (1/2 cup)	2 1/2	5,000
Nissin Cup Noodles/shrimp	1/2+	1,070
Pancake Mix (3 four inch pancakes)		1,050
Peanut butter (2 tablespoons)		167
Potato chips (14)	1/6	230
Pretzels (thin)		735
Rice-a-Roni Chicken & Vegetables (1 cup)		1,320
Saltine crackers (4)	1/8	184
Sauerkraut (1 cup)	3/4+	1,800
Soy sauce (1 T.)	1/2	1,000
The Colonel's chicken (3 pieces)	1 1/6	2,300
Whopper		909

Half a cup of cottage cheese has as much sodium as 32 potato chips
One bowl of Wheaties has twice as much sodium as a bowl of potato chips
Corn flakes has twice as much sodium as the same amount of cocktail peanuts.

Sodium Steps to Stopping

1. **Taste** Use the salt-shaker only after you have tasted your food.

2. **Read** Look for the amount of salt (sodium) on the labels.

3. **Substitute** Use lemon, pepper, garlic and other seasonings instead of salt or skip it all together.

4. **Use Less** Remember that a teaspoon of salt has near to 2,000 milligrams of sodium. Cut it down.

Here's an affirmation that sets you free from salt. Take a deep breath and read it slowly to yourself:

AFFIRM SUCCESS: So Long Salt
I enjoy the natural goodness of fresh fruits and vegetables. I really taste the luscious flavor of natural food. Processed foods gross me out. My sense of taste is sharper and keener. I crave water.

I read the labels of the food I eat. Even those labeled "low sodium" may be a trick. I don't like the taste of salty things. Because I use salt sparingly, my bones grow stronger and stronger. My hypothalamus, at the base of my brain, accurately balances and adjusts my water/sodium balance.

I enjoy fresh fruits, vegetables, whole grains and protein. If I eat butter, I choose unsalted. I season my food with lemon, lime, garlic, oregano, pepper and fresh herbs. I avoid canned vegetables and if I have to use them, I drain and rinse them first. I love the natural flavor of fresh food. Nature offers terrific flavors. I am healthy and happy with fresh food.

▲ Caffeine: Jump like an Egyptian

The coffee plant is pollinated by flies. Caffeine is found in over sixty species of plants and trees. Large amounts of caffeine are in coffee, soft drinks (dark and light, diet and regular), tea, cocoa, chocolate, cold medications, diet pills, antihistamines, stimulants and drugs prescribed for migraine headaches and menstrual relief.

Bean Around for Years

Caffeinated beverages have been used socially and ceremonially, from coffee klatches to tea ceremonies to warm the body and perk the senses. It smells delicious and seductively forestalls depression by uplifting and stimulating your brain. It increases circulation and reaction time and relieves drowsiness, fatigue, and takes away stress…for a while.

Photo by Jon Nicholas

Coffee Grower

Tea: Nefer-Tea-Tea

Since prehistoric times, tea has been a favorite beverage. The ancient Chinese cultivated it; "Strong tea quenches the thirst but lessens the desire to sleep," wrote Chinese Emperor Shenung in 2737 BC.

In the 1400s, Venetian traders introduced tea to Europe where it became very popular, particularly among the British. "Tea time" and "coffees" were a social event for homebound women to sit down and relax with each other.

INNER•VIEW QUIZ

Are You Hooked On Caffeine?

___ I have more than a cup of coffee, tea or cola daily.
___ My body runs on caffeine.
___ I regularly reward myself with chocolate milk, hot cocoa, chocolate chip cookies, cake, candy, tea, soft drinks and flavored tea drinks.
___ I use soft drinks, coffee, chocolate, black or green tea, guarana root, or yerba maté to get myself started, move my bowels or jolt me over a slump.
___ If I feel let down, I take caffeine (with or without sugar), chocolate, soft drinks, flavored water or tea.
___ I often use Midol, Premens, Aqua-Ban or Cope for menstrual pain relief.
___ I regularly use the cold remedies Dristan and Sinarest.
___ I regularly use NoDoz, Vivarin, Refresh'n, Dexatrim, Diatec, Excedrin, Anacin, Vanquish or Empirin.
___ If I go on caffeine my eyes itch, I sneeze and my nose runs.
___ If I go off caffeine I crave it.
___ Off or on caffeine, throbs at my temples, head & eyes.
___ I stay on coffee to avoid a withdrawal headache or breaking a tradition.
___ If I go off or on caffeine I am irritable, constipated, shaky, nauseous, depressed and exhausted.
___ If I go off or on caffeine my nose runs, heart beats irregularly, I feel hot & cold and can't concentrate.
___ Once in a while I just gotta hava java.

If so, there is a strong chance you may be hooked on a caffeine high. Caffeine is our "stimulation" society's number one drug problem

Coffee

☆ Customer: "*Waiter, there's a fly in my soup.*"
Waiter: "*Wait 'til you see the coffee.*"

☆ Question: "*What do you drink on a sinking ship?*"
Answer: "*Sanka*"

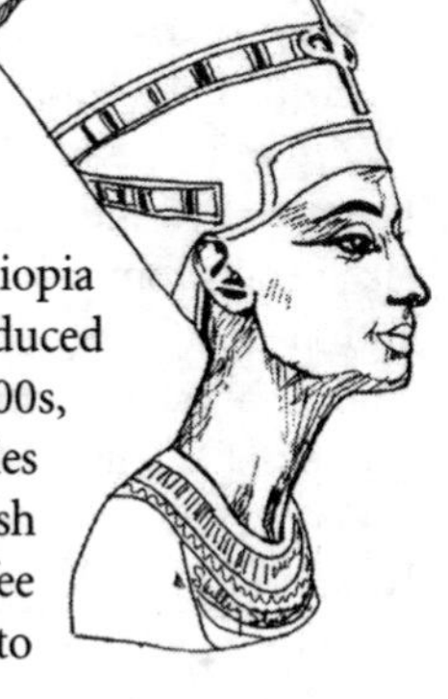

Coffee beans were first made into a hot beverage in Ethiopia around 1000 AD and spread to the Arab world. It was introduced to the Europeans in the late 1500s. By the late 1600s, coffeehouses were the rage of Europe. The American colonies drank coffee too, but it really became popular after the British imposed the tea tax; the reason for the Boston Tea Party. Coffee was originally introduced into the American workplace to increase productivity among factory workers. Give them a coffee break, jolt up their central nervous system, and get more work done.

Today, caffeine is for many a daily wake-up ritual. Coffeehouses dot every corner. Coffee connoisseurs percolate with exotic names for beans and blends. In the United States, over ten pounds of coffee per person is consumed yearly.

Chemicals used in growing and processing coffee are often toxic. Decaffeination uses bleach (methylene chloride and trichlorethylene TCE) to remove the caffeine from the coffee, leaving toxic residue. Occasionally, a less toxic steam decaf process is used.

Tombstone in New Hampshire

Chocolate

Cocoa trees have grown wild in the Orinoco and Amazon jungles for over 4000 years. The Toltecs, Mayans and Aztecs claimed it was a gift from the gods. Cocoa beans were used as food and currency. Ten beans could buy a rabbit; (Today we spend $10 for a chocolate rabbit). Twelve beans bought the services of a woman.

"Chocolatl" was a cold, bitter, grainy brew of roasted and ground beans mixed with spices like red pepper and fermented corn mash. The Aztec emperor Montezuma II drank over 50 tankards of chocolatl a day. When Hernan Cortes arrived in 1519, a drunken Montezuma thought he was the "Second Coming" of the God Quetzacoatl and showered him with gold jewels, and of course, cocoa beans and chocolatl. Cortes wrote to Charles I of Spain that chocolatl "builds up resistance and fights fatigue. A cup of this precious drink permits a man to walk for a whole day without food." After they drank their chocolatl, the golden goblets were discarded. The grateful Cortez, plundered and pillaged.

In later years, Mexican nuns mixed the cocoa with milk and sugar. The Vatican banned the use of chocolate because the nuns went overboard making and using it. The ban didn't work. Spanish monks began adding sugar and vanilla to the bean concoction. By 1615, when the daughter of the Spanish monarch (Anne of Austria) married Louis XIV, "hot" chocolate was the rage of Versailles.

In 1828, the Dutch chemist, Coenraad Van Houten invented the cocoa press and alkalizing process to filter out 2/3rds of the cocoa butter. It left a cake that could be pulverized into fine cocoa powder. This alkalizing (or "dutching") process uses alkali (salt from wood ashes or hydroxide) to "smooth out" the taste and texture and to change the color to a reddened hue. In 1875 Daniel Peter of Swiss General Chocolate, along with Henri Nestle added condensed milk and the "conching" process of stirring. This laborious task took a week to make one batch.

As a child, did you salivate over hot chocolate, chocolate cereal, chocolate bars, chocolate ice cream, chocolate cake and chocolate chip cookies? Many

Recipe to Make Chocolate: Ashes. Ashes. We All Fall Down

1. **Get some cocoa beans.** The bean (or nib) comes from Venezuela, Trinidad, Jamaica, Ghana and New Guinea, and may by heavily laced with pesticides like DDT that is banned in the US but sold to these third world growers.
2. **"We're painting the chocolate red."** To bring out an aesthetic red color from the beans, soak them in a solution of any of the following: alkali, limestone, sodium carbonate, hydroxide, calcium hydroxide, ammonia or carbonate.
   - **Alkali** Burn thistle from the salt wort plant into ashes. The resulting sodium salt bleach can also be used to make soap, glass, household cleansers, bleach and photo processing solvents. I recently saw a cocoa powder that used "fermented beans" in lieu of the alkali.
   - **Limestone** any remaining can be used to make porcelain cement and antacid tablets and calcium supplements.
   - **Sodium Carbonate**, found in soda lakes, formed from volcanic ash and water. Be careful this can be highly toxic to animals.
   - **Hydroxide**
   - **Aluminum Hydroxide** Alzheimer's victims often have aluminum in the brain.
   - **Calcium Hydroxide** can also be used in powdered bleach.
   - **Ammonia**
   - **Ammonia Carbonate** this is also used for smelling salts.
3. **When the cocoa bean absorbs 1/2 its weight of this solution, dry roast.**
4. **Add sugar or artificial sweeteners to kill the resulting bitter taste.**
5. **Cocoa oil and cocoa butter are the fatty acids in chocolate.** This fat is enhanced by adding more saturated butterfat in the form of lecithin or condensed milk to smooth out texture. Hershey's uses one million pounds (250,000 gallons) of milk a day to make chocolate, which keeps some fifty thousand cows "employed." Some chocolate products, like cocoa mixes and candy bar coatings, add more saturated fat like tropical oils of coconut and palm.
6. **Stir repeatedly.**
7. **Dry into cakes, powders and/or molds.**
8. **Package attractively.**
9. **Advertise heavily.**

American children ingest as much as a quarter of a pound of chocolate a day. That's some ninety-one pounds of chocolate a year. If you eat 4 ounces of bittersweet chocolate, you receive as much as 140 milligrams of caffeine!

Researchers, hired and quoted by chocolate companies, say that chocolate (dark, specifically) will not boost cholesterol levels. Their research omits the effects chocolate has on your adrenal glands and your fight or flight response.

How Much Caffeine is in Chocolate?

1oz. bittersweet = 5–35mg
1oz. milk chocolate = 6–10mg
8oz. chocolate milk = 2–7mg

Soft Drinks as Drugs: Carbon•dated Drinks

In 1860, Europeans extracted cocaine from the coca leaf. In May of 1886, Dr. John Styth Pemberton cooked up "coke syrup," a combination of cocaine and the caffeine-laden cola nut, in a three-legged brass pot in his back yard in Atlanta.

Coca-Cola® was originally green. Dr. Pemberton shipped his syrup in twenty-five gallon red wooden kegs and red has been the color associated with the brand ever since. Coca-Cola was a medicine sold in drug stores. If you had a headache, you'd belly up to the bar and say "Give me a shot in the arm."

The coca in soft drinks is extracted from the coca leaf, the same plant that yields cocaine.

In 1903, Coca-Cola switched from pure coca extract to "decocanized" coca leaf extract. According to William Poundstone's intriguing book *Big Secrets*, this decocanization process is similar to the decaffeination process. A solvent (California wine or alcohol) is passed through the leaves, leaching away cocaine. No coffee producer claims that decaffeinated coffee is totally free of caffeine. In fact, a cup of decaffeinated coffee has about 6 milligrams of caffeine! But what about the decocanization process? How much cocaine is in soft drinks? A Coca-Cola representative read me "the company's statement on cocaine" which said that the cocaine was extracted from the coca leaves under the guidance of the US government, but no cocaine is added to Coca-Cola.

Cola is extracted from the kola nut or African "hell seed" and adds 5–10% caffeine. Additional caffeine is added for more kick. This caffeine is leached from decaffeinated coffee cocoa beans, cola nuts, yerba mate, guarana root and hell seeds with chemical solvents or carbon dioxide. The strong bitter taste of pure caffeine is covered up by huge amounts of sugar, artificial sweeteners and flavorings.

In 1912, Coca-Cola considered removing the caffeine from Coke. But, after their study revealed that caffeine taken at one p.m. was detectable in the body at nine a.m. the next morning, (twenty hours later), they decided to leave it in.

A True Story: A Call to Coca-Cola®

Recently I called the Coca-Cola Company and asked:

"How much caffeine is added to Coke Classic?"

"An 8 ounce can contains 31 milligrams of caffeine," the customer service representative replied and quickly added; "That's half the amount of caffeine in an 8 ounce cup of coffee."

"What is the main source of the caffeine?" I asked

"We get our caffeine primarily from decaffeinated coffee." He said.

"How much decocanized cocaine is used in Coke?" was my next question.

"The natural flavorings used in our products is proprietary information and is in accordance with the legal guidelines of the American Food and Drug Administration." He replied.

Recipe for Half-Life Cola Coca
The Real Thing In The Back Of Your Mind?

Cola drinks are made from coca and cola extract, caffeine, sugar or artificial sweeteners, citrus and spice flavorings (often containing MSG), glycerin as a preservatives and carbonated water. Six hundred and one million Coca-Colas are sold throughout the world each day and in 170 countries and territories. International operations account for 68% of the syrup sold worldwide and 80% of the operating income. It costs them more to make the can than the cola inside. In Chinese, the word "Coca-Cola®" means, "bite the wax tadpole."

Here's the recipe for cola drinks that could make even a tadpole croak:

1. Soak coca leaves and cola nuts in 20% alcohol (California white wine or other). Discard leaves and nuts. Retain liquid.
2. Dilute citrus and spice oils in 95% alcohol.
3. Combine coca/cola syrup with citrus/spice liquid.
4. Add vegetable glycerin as a preservative.
5. Add caffeine.
6. Add ten teaspoons of sugar (disguised as "high-fructose corn syrup") per 12 ounce can or artificial sweetener to cover the bitter taste.
7. Add carbonated water. Carbonation produces carbonic acid and carbon monoxide, displacing your oxygen. (Too much and your blood doesn't get enough oxygen.).

The average soft drink's pH is 3.4. This high acidity dissolves teeth and bones. (The citric acid in Coke removes stains from your toilet. Pour in coke, let it sit an hour and flush clean). Put a human tooth into a soft drink and within weeks the tooth completely dissolves! This acidity plus sugar effects natural bacteria and causes cavities.

Soft drinks with acidic food can dissolve 8-18% of your bones per year! Dissolved calcium compounds accumulate in arteries, veins, skin and organs and form kidney stones.

Caffeine is listed as an addictive drug by the US Food and Drug Administration (FDA). Sodas, fruit bottled teas and even water may have large amounts added. Yet this added white "chemically-pure" powdered caffeine is notably not noted on the ingredient list. Beverages are not required to report the presence or amount of caffeine added. Why? Could it be that the measured amounts of caffeine is calculated to keep us addicted; the same way nicotine is measured by cigarette manufacturers?

As little as three to five cans of cola (not including chocolate or tea and coffee) can make a person caffeine dependent, according to the Center for Science in the Public Interest. In 1996 the average American threw down over fifty-three gallons of soft drinks.

An American child drinks an estimated thirty gallons of soda a year, or about a can a day. If you add up the caffeine in chocolate, soft drinks and tea, your little tyke may ingest hundreds of milligrams of caffeine and ten teaspoons of sugar a day. If this gives junior a headache, and we slip him an Anacin he gets another 30 to 150 milligrams of caffeine, bringing his total even higher! Because kids weigh less, the caffeine ratio is greater. Attention deficit disorder? I think not.

I used to be a TWA flight attendant. I wish I had a nickel for every grown-up who asked me to put Coke into his or her baby's bottle. I'd be rich.

Have Lithium In Your 7-UP® and Take the 'Ouch' Out of Grouch.

In1929 Charles L. Grigg marketed a beverage called Bib-Label Lithiated Lemon-Lime soda, with the slogan, "Takes the 'ouch' out of 'grouch.'" Wildly popular during the depression, it contained lithium, the powerful drug now prescribed for manic-depressives. Lithium was listed on the label until the mid 1940's. Is there still lithium in it? Somewhere along the way, the drink's name was changed to 7-Up. What's up with 7-Up now?

Don't Drink the Fire Water

I was recently given a bottle of "pure caffeine charged" water. The amount of caffeine was listed as "mineral enhanced" "Great for anyone who wants a get up and go from their drinking water" the label read. Today, it is common practice for software companies to have refrigerators full of "jolty" soft drinks and water, loaded with extra caffeine, (the amount not labeled) so that programmers can stay awake all night writing or debugging software. Truckers keep on truckin' with "leaded" from 24-hour coffee shops. And students pop No Doz.

How Does Caffeine Affect You?

Caffeine is considered the most abused drug in the world.

Ironically, the very substance that wakes you up, lets you down. "The best part of waking up" over time wakes up arthritis, stress and depression. Varying amounts strain the liver, pancreas, glands, nerves, digestion, circulation and distorts brain chemistry.

No matter the source (coffee, tea, or soft drinks) within 5 minutes the "psychoactive drug" caffeine hits your brain. A caffeine high peaks in 30 minutes and lasts from twelve to twenty hours after ingestion. Its toxicity is cumulative. In about five hours, half of the caffeine ingested is eliminated. By then, caffeine addicts have taken in more caffeine.

Caffeine's chemicals stimulate a temporary antidepressant response in the brain and fools the body into thinking it's not tired. Here's how:

When you need rest, your tired brain releases a chemical called adenosine. It plugs into special receptor cells to tell the brain to slow down. Adenosine says, "It's time to rest" and mildly depresses. Caffeine mimics adenosine, plugs up the receptor cells, and prevents the cortex from receiving its chemical signal. This feels like stimulation. That's why pharmocologists classify caffeine as a stimulant. The caffeine in a couple of cups of coffee can knock out half of your brain's adenosine receptors. That's what keeps your brain on high alert.

Caffeine constricts the blood vessels in your brain, while adenosine expands them. Hangovers are caused by alcohol expanding the blood vessels in the head. People with a hangover drink coffee because it constricts those swollen vessels.

Adenosine (a-den-o-sin), blocked by caffeine, floats homelessly around the nervous system and builds up. Then you crash. Neuro-scientists speculate that the reason we build up coffee tolerance is that the brain creates more adenosine receptors. Think of caffeine as a burglar with skeleton keys that fit perfectly into the receptor cells. With the bogus keys, the brain doesn't get the response it needs, rest and sleep. After a while, your clever brain figures out what's going on and increases the number of receptor cells, so it will have enough for both caffeine and adenosine. When this happens, caffeine won't keep you awake any more, unless you take more.

Caffeine also over-stimulates the parts of the brain that regulates heart rate, breathing and muscle activity.

Caf-fiend Gets On Your Nerves

☆ *"Doctor, I can't stop my hands from shaking."*
"Do you drink a lot of coffee?"
"No, I spill most of it."

Caffeine overtaxes your nerves. People who are anxious or have panic attacks are usually highly caffeine sensitive. Like sugar, caffeine over-stimulates and weakens the adrenals fight, flight, fright, excite response causing exhaustion, chronic fatigue and an inability to handle stress.

Caffeine, like speed, unnaturally accelerates your thoughts and physical ability to do things. You work faster and do more, until you crash and feel let down. It causes blood sugar to quickly rise and fall and stimulates the release of adrenaline. Too much insulin is produced and blood sugar levels fall to a low level. That is why caffeine has been linked to diabetes. "Coffee nerves," include anxiety, irritability, lightheadedness, nausea and diarrhea. Caffeine can trigger facial spasms or tics especially in children. The older you are the more caffeine sensitive you become.

Caf-fiend Crazies

For susceptible people, even the smallest amount of caffeine produces "Caffeine intoxication," a psychiatric label for nervousness, excitement, restlessness, tachycardia (irregular heartbeats), insomnia, psychomotor agitation, rambling speech and thought.

Caf-fiend Dries You Up

You need water to think, move and live. For every cup of coffee you drink; you lose approximately one and one-half cups of fluid. If you drink a caffeinated beverage while eating, you deprive yourself of food's nutritional value.

Caf-fiend Breaks Your Heart

A rapid, racing or irregular heartbeat is one of the most common effects of caffeine. It raises blood pressure; elevates cholesterol and triglyceride levels. Additional norepinephrine secretion into the blood causes constriction of blood flow.

Cholesterol levels are dramatically higher in people who drink two or more cups of coffee a day. A Finnish study found that dripped coffee increased cholesterol levels even more than perked coffee. All this may increase your risk of heart disease.

Caf-fiend is Indefensible

Children need minerals for healthy growth and so do you.

Caffeine contains negative nutrients that deprive the body of vitamins, minerals and water while requiring extra resources to combat its toxicity. As a diuretic, it depletes your nutritional reserves and lowers resistance to illness. Magnesium, potassium, B vitamins (especially B-1) and C are leached from your body. Your ability to absorb iron and calcium is impaired, which increases the chances of osteoporosis, anemia and kidney stones.

It removes zinc that your pancreas needs to process food and nourish you.

Caf-fiend Irritates

Caffeine raises the secretion of acid in the stomach. That's why abdominal pain is the other most common side effect of caffeine. Caffeine dries out the intestinal lining, and irritates bowels and intestines, leading to hemorrhoids. Caffeine may make you "regular." It does this by impairing your colon's normal peristaltic action. This artificial stimulation causes diarrhea and stomach cramps. As with all addictive drugs, the amount of caffeine needed to move your bowels increases with regular use.

Tea and coffee, both caffeinated and decaffeinated, contain tannic acid, which irritates your gastrointestinal tract, kidneys and liver, by increasing your stomach's production of hydrochloric acid. This is why there is a strong correlation between ulcers, gastritis and caffeine.

Tannic acid prohibits absorption of calcium and B vitamins. Milk added to override the harmful effects of the tannic acid can't override caffeine.

Caf•fiend Adds Insult to Injury

Caffeine raises blood sugar levels and makes you feel warm. It temporarily increases mental clarity and energy. Initially, like marijuana, alcohol, sugar and tobacco, caffeine gives a feeling of well being and artificially satisfies hunger pangs. Then, when blood sugar dips, it depresses, increases hunger and leaves you craving sweets.

Caf-fiend Loses Sleep

Caffeine interrupts sleep patterns. For the sensitive, just one cup of coffee at breakfast can make the difference between a good or poor night's sleep 12 to 20 hours after it is ingested. If you are a heavy sleeper, you may not notice. But if you are a light sleeper, you really notice.

INTO•GREAT POWER EXERCISE

Take It Zzzzy

Caffeine and sugar are the main causes of sleeping disorders. If you have trouble sleeping, try this simple experiment:

1. For the next five days, take no sugar, alcohol or caffeine (coffee, tea, chocolate, soft drinks or cocoa) after 3:00 p.m.
2. Sweet dreams.

Caf-fiend Goes to Your Head

The let down can change the flow of your blood and evoke TMJ, teeth grinding, pancreatic cancer, fibrocystic breast disease and birth defects.

Lady Be Ware!

Lumps in the breast? Give up caffeine and they usually go away. Caffeine inflames female sweat glands, and this may modify breast tissue. Caffeine has been suspiciously linked to fibroid cysts in women's breasts. It is not known whether the risk is a result of the caffeine itself or the chemicals used in its processing.

Like alcohol, caffeine has a more pronounced effect on women with PMS. Caffeine nerves can ruin relationships. Perhaps caffeine should be considered grounds for divorce.

Caffeine leaches calcium from your bones via the kidney; a serious problem for menopausal women.

Colic? Maybe Not!

Caffeine crosses the placental barrier. Fetal distress or caffeine distress? Pregnant women raise their chance of miscarriage 22% with one eight-ounce mug of coffee a day. Caffeine is often found in mother's milk. Mommy takes coffee, tea, a soft drink, or chocolate, and so does her babe.

I was horrified recently to see an Australian magazine advertisement for chocolate baby food "Made with the freshest ingredient and a touch of imagination." The photo showed a baby bathing in rich dark chocolate.

Caf-fiend is a Chemical Nightmare

Chemically, caffeine resembles uric acid by stimulating the flow of electrical impulses to your muscles. That's why you feel the caffeine buzz, hands and fingers shake, heart and respiratory rate rise and sometimes your ears ring.

Caffeine is an alkaloid. So is cocaine, strychnine (used for rat poison) and atropine (poison from the deadly nightshade family). Caffeine may not be as harmful gram for gram but regular use generally leads to deadly problems; heart rhythm disturbances, stomach problems, anxiety and breast disease.

Other harmful chemicals in chocolate, cocoa and tea are the xanathines: theobromine and theophylline. These make the body acidic and can cause acid stomach, heartburn and ulcers. Theophylline is the active ingredient used in asthma medicine to smooth the muscles of the lungs. Headache, nausea and vomiting are the common side effects of theophylline overdose.

Caffeine Addiction is Easy

☆ *"Caffeine produces effects similar to low doses of cocaine and amphetamine-feelings of increased energy, well-being, decreased sleepiness, talkativeness, more sociability and better concentration."*

—Roland Knight, Ph.D.
John Hopkins University School of Medicine

Within one week, most become a caffeine addict, which means your brain has restructured itself to run on caffeine. This includes children. Eighty percent of Americans who consume caffeine become clinically dependent and trapped in a vicious circle of sleep deprivation and over-stimulation within one week.

INNER•VIEW QUIZ

Are You Hurt by Caffeine?

☆ *"People who get panic attacks are usually highly sensitive to caffeine."*

—Alexander Bystritsky, MD

☆ *"Caffeine raises cholesterol, impairs fertility and continues to be the world's most widely used beverage and drug."*

—Sid Kirchheimer

Put a T if you have these symptoms:

___ Abdominal Pain
___ Anxiety and the Jitters
___ Bed wetting and hyperactivity (especially in children)
___ Depression
___ Diarrhea
___ Elevated blood pressure
___ Fatigue
___ Frequent urination, loss of urine control
___ Headache
___ Heartburn and/or indigestion
___ Hemorrhoids
___ Hypoglycemia and sugar imbalances
___ Increased cholesterol
___ Increased or irregular heart rate
___ Insomnia, disturbed sleep
___ Irritability
___ Muscle Tension
___ Nervousness and/or shaking
___ Poor concentration
___ Tobacco, sugar, and/or alcohol addiction
___ Upset stomach

The more T's you answered, the more caffeine harms you. If you suffer from these or are pregnant, quit caffeine immediately.

Caffeine, alcohol, sugar, tobacco, drug and preservative toxicity have these same symptoms.

Caffeine plus tobacco is said to increase the risk of ovary, pancreas, bladder and prostate cancer.

How Much Caffeine Do You Take In?

Even those who do not drink coffee may unsuspectingly ingest several hundreds of milligrams of caffeine daily. A gram is about the weight of a small paper clip. Over 100 milligrams spells trouble.

Beverages milligrams (mg) of caffeine per six ounces.
(Amounts vary depending on brewing time and amount used)

	Caffeine (mg)
Coffee, drip	120-150
Coffee, percolated	80-110
Instant coffee	60-150
Decaffeinated	3-10
Black tea	50-60
Chai	40
Green tea	30-40
Cocoa	10-40
Chocolate milk	2-15
Colas (regular and diet)	33-67 (12 ounces)
Jolty-type colas	120 (12 ounces)
Mountain Dew	50 (12 ounces)
Slice of Chocolate cake	15+
Chocolate bar	25-90 6-8 grams fat + 19-70 grams sugar

Medicines That Contain Caffeine (milligrams per tablet):

Anacin	30-150
Aqua-ban	10
Dexatrim	200
Dietrac	200
Dristan	16
Emperim	32
Excedrin	65-150
Fiorinal	40
Midol	32
No-Doz	100-200+
Vanquish	33
Vivarin	200

From Haas; Young, Klein, and Beyer; Kirchheimer and the editors of Prevention magazine.

Some are unable to tolerate caffeine.

Consider Ida's story told just before she died:

A TRUE STORY Ida

"When I was 23, I married a young lawyer and moved to a small town in California. My neighbors were always inviting me over for a friendly cup of coffee.

Eventually I drank 20-cups-a-day and started taking diet pills. The pills added to the caffeine buzz.

I was able to function in public; in private, I bounced off the walls. I started taking downers at night to sleep. When I really got stressed, our friendly neighborhood pharmacist gave me tranquilizers.

Fifty years later, I got cancer and stopped caffeine, pills and the hysteria.

If I had my life to live over again, I would never have had a single cup of coffee or a single pill. My biggest regret is that I yelled at my children. They turned out OK, but I still have a lot of issues with the way I treated them."

How Much Caffeine is Harmful?

☆ Question: *"Every time I have a cup of coffee, I get a sharp pain in my eye. What can I do?"*
Answer: *"Take the spoon out first."*

More than 100 milligrams or the equivalent of one cup of coffee or two colas daily make problems. 250 milligrams or more per day, translates into extreme nervousness, irritability, anxiety, moodiness, poor sleep, headaches, stomachaches, bleeding hemorrhoids and early death.

Any caffeine above 250 milligrams a day raises blood pressure, intensifies digestive disorders, ulceration and heart stress.

500 milligrams or more of caffeine a day is dangerous.

A lethal dose of caffeine is 10 grams of caffeine in a four-hour period.

Candy, soft drinks and medicine do not label caffeine content. Why isn't it on the labels?

Withdrawal: What Goes Up Must Come Down

☆ *"Caffeine withdrawal is not in any way just a psychological phenomenon. Withdrawal is very real. Performance is impaired in withdrawal."*
—John Hopkins University Study

Over time, caffeine's addictive nature requires more to keep you "up" and causes greater withdrawal when you quit. If you "cold turkey" stop caffeine, free-floating adenosine floods receptors, your brain veins swells to a painful degree and may attempt to shed excess receptor cells. This causes withdrawal headaches and sleepiness until caffeine is cleansed from the body.

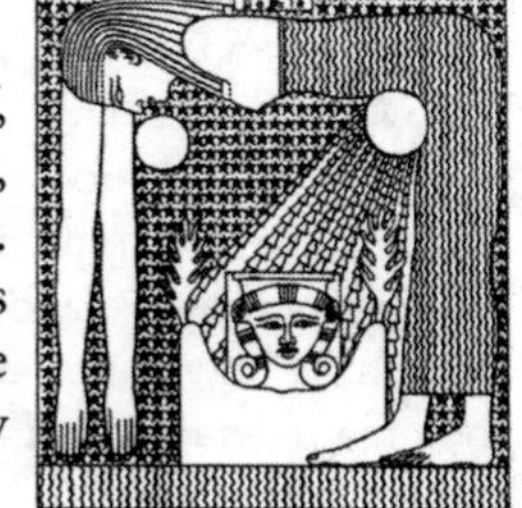

Completely stopping coffee, rather than tapering off, may produce throbbing and pressure headaches, generally around the temples, eyes and back of the head. It also can disrupt sleep patterns for weeks to months until it is completely out of your system. To avoid the following list of withdrawal symptoms, gradually decrease caffeine intake.

Withdrawal Reactions After Stopping Caffeine

___ Body temperature changes
___ Cramps, Constipation and/or Diarrhea
___ Cravings
___ Drowsiness
___ Dizziness
___ Depression
___ Fatigue
___ Frequent urination
___ Headache
___ Heart Palpitations
___ Lethargy
___ Inability to Concentrate
___ Insomnia
___ Irritability
___ Irritable bowel syndrome
___ Muscle tension and decreased strength
___ Nausea and/or vomiting
___ Restlessness
___ Runny nose
___ Sluggishness
___ Shakiness
___ Stiffness and/or flu-like symptoms
___ Trembling

Withdrawal symptoms begin an hour to twenty-four hours after stopping. For a few days to as long as two weeks, "withdrawal" sends out distress signals.

Heavy caffeine use indicates a drug-taking tendency and often occurs along with other substance abuse, nicotine and sugar most commonly. Caffeine users are more likely to take uppers for a familiar buzz or to take tranquilizers and sleeping pills to help them sleep.

A TRUE STORY Paul

"Almost every day, I had to lie down in a darkened room because of my awful migraine headaches. My whole family's world revolved around my headaches and me. We could not figure out why I got them. These just seemed to strike randomly. I went from one doctor to another and none of them could tell me what was wrong. Then I went to a brand new intern who had recently seen a study connecting caffeine and migraine headaches. He told me that my headaches were from caffeine withdrawal. Once I learned that, I stopped drinking coffee, had a horrible headache and after it was over, I never had another one."

How to Detox: Break the Pause that Pollutes

It is definitely easier to quit over a few week period that to quit all at once.

Drink more water. Substitute herb tea or water with lemon. Water down your coffee. Drink decaf. Drink half the cup instead of the whole cup. Replace drinks with water, fruit juice or herb tea.

Whether you reduce intake or stop "cold turkey," you need to support yourself with nutrition that supports your adrenals. A diet rich in fruits, green vegetables, whole grains, soy, nuts and seeds helps.

Avoid meats, sugar, baked goods (even if made with whole grains). A green drink like green Magma (available from the order form at the back of this book) is loaded with amino acids, calcium, B vitamins, magnesium and zinc. Take a one a day vitamin like Centrum to supplement your resources.

Wean yourself off over a five-day period or tough it out for the short-term. If you suffer from a headache and choose to take a mild pain reliever, make sure it doesn't contain caffeine. The more water you drink, the faster your head clears.

Here's an affirmation that will help you quit:

AFFIRM SUCCESS: Get over Caf-Fiend

I give up the drug of caffeine. I enjoy the ritual of having a break. I give myself an herbal tea break. I sit down, relax and destress. Herb teas or water help me detoxify; chamomile and peppermint teas are excellent. Hot water and lemon juice is delicious. I make sure that whatever I drink is caffeine free.

I can wean slowly, first by taking in less each day. If I choose decaffeinated, I use those processed with a steam method. That way I avoid toxic chemicals normally used in leaching. I love to drink water. It cleanses and renews me. I like feeling good. Fruits, vegetables, whole grains, nuts, seeds and of course, lots of water cleanses. I avoid meat, sugar, refined flour, baked goods and of course MSG. A high-fiber diet cleanses me more. I'm so glad I've gotten a grip on myself.

I drink six to eight glasses of water a day, and more when I exercise or perspire. I take vitamin C supplements and potassium, calcium, magnesium, zinc and B complex vitamins to replenish my body. I feel great.

INNER•VIEW QUIZ

Are You Allergic to MSG?

__ After eating Chinese food, I get a migraine or feel light-headed.
__ I wake up with a swollen face and bags under my eyes.
__ After eating peanuts or packaged snacks.
__ I have itchy eyes, a runny nose or dry mouth.
__ Some canned soups make me nauseous.
__ I get diarrhea, "irritable bowel syndrome," or an upset stomach.
__ I feel lousy a few hours after I eat gelatin.
__ I sometimes have mood swings, depression, partial paralysis, shortness of breath and balance difficulties.
__ Protein powder can give me allergy like symptoms.
__ I suffer from asthma.

Common MSG Reactions

Cardiac:
Arrhythmia
Extreme drop in blood pressure
Rapid heartbeat (tachycardia)
Angina
Circulatory:
Swelling
Muscular:
Flu-like ache-ness
Joint pain
Stiffness
Neurological:
Anaphylactic Shock
Dizziness
Disorientation, confusion
Balance difficulties
Dry Mouth
Mouth lesions
Flushed Skin
Skin rashes
Seizures and death can result.
Heart palpitations or rapid, irregular heart beat
Heart attack like symptoms
Hyperactivity
Lethargy, sleepiness, insomnia
Migraine Headache
Numbness or paralysis
Slurred speech
Seizures, epilepsy
Gastrointestinal:
Diarrhea
Nausea/ vomiting
Stomach cramps
Irritable bowel
Bloating
Respiratory:
Asthma, shortness of breath
Tightness of chest
Runny nose, sneezing
Spasms of the larynx
Skin:
Hives or rash
Mouth Lesions
Temporary tightness or paralysis, numbness or tingling of the skin
Flushing, itching
Extreme dryness of the mouth
Visual:
Blurred vision
Difficulty focusing
Emotional:
Anger, rage
Anxiety or Panic Attacks
Behavior problems (especially in children and teens)
Depression
Mood Swings

It's unknown whether MSG aggravates or "causes" the condition that underlies these reactions.

▲ MSG Conspiracy

Whatever you put in your body, you must read the label.

MSG, or monosodium glutamate, is the sodium salt of glutamic acid. This flavor-enhancing drug crosses the blood brain barrier, excites neurotransmitters and tricks the brain to believe food tastes good. MSG enhances your brain; not the food you eat.

A tiny amount of MSG can cause violent and devastating drug reactions for the sensitive. 30% of the population may not feel up to par.

Excess MSG causes brain cells to die through over-stimulation.

Children whose blood brain barriers are not fully developed and those weakened by age, are seriously at risk. MSG crosses the placental barrier and enters the brain of the fetus.

Elevated levels of glutamic acid or glutamate are found in brains of those who die with Alzheimer's, Lou Gehrig's (ALS), Huntington's and Parkinson's Disease. MSG has been known to cause asthma attacks.

Reactions show up immediately to over forty-eight hours later.

Hidden Danger

MASSIVE amounts of MSG are hidden in almost all processed food. The FDA says that only additives that contain 99% MSG must be identified on the label as MSG, so manufacturers slip lower percentages into some 40 different additives. If you buy a product that has three or four MSG containing substances, you get more than you would believe. A can of soup may have five different MSG substances!

MSG sensitive people may also react and become seriously ill from the artificial sweetener, aspartame (Nutrasweet).

The words "natural," "all natural' or "no preservatives" does not mean that the product is free of MSG. MSG is commonly used in health food, regular food, diet food, frozen food and fast food. DON'T BE FOOLED.

Any product with hydrolyzed protein, textured protein, sodium or calcium caseinate, yeast extract, autolyzed or hydrolyzed yeast or gelatin, contain MSG. Those with natural or artificial flavorings may also be loaded with MSG.

Protein, which occurs naturally in food, is not harmful, but when protein is hydrolyzed, MSG (free glutamic acid) is formed. The FDA says that MSG may cause "mild, transient reactions in some portion of the public" and is "naturally occurring" so it is not a problem.

Alias Names That Hide MSG:
Protein, Textured Protein, Plant Protein, Hydrolyzed Plant Protein

Hydrolyzed Protein: Creates MSG in the chemical process. Manufacturers may add pure MSG without saying so on the label; and they do.
Sodium Caseinate: The sodium salt of a hydrolyzed milk protein. Contains MSG. Found in milk powder and solids.
Calcium Caseinate: The calcium part of hydrolyzed milk protein. Also found in milk powder and solids.
Yeast Extract and Autolyzed Yeast: When yeast is "autolyzed" it releases MSG similar to hydrolysis. Pure MSG may be added without designating it on the label.
Natural Flavors, Flavorings: Both autolyzed and hydrolyzed yeast are labeled under this category. Not all products labeled natural flavors have MSG. Consumers must proceed at their own risk.
Carrageenan: Contains pure MSG or hydrolyzed milk protein added. It is used for the slimy or smooth feel in food.
Gelatin, Stock, Broth, Seasoning, Bouillon, natural pork flavoring, natural beef flavoring, natural chicken flavoring: all contain MSG.
Kombu Extract: MSG is extracted from kombu seaweed.

Names That Often Hide MSG

The following contains MSG or form MSG in the manufacturing process:
Gyanylate/Disodium Insolate: are flavor potentiators most commonly used with an ingredient that contains MSG.
Malt Extract, Malt Flavorings, Barley Malt: May contain small amounts of MSG resulting from enzyme reaction.
Maltodextrin: A hydrolyzed corn product. Possibly either contaminated with MSG or has MSG added to it.
Whey protein, Whey Protein Isolate, Whey Protein Concentrate: May contain MSG in the form of hydrolyzed milk proteins. Some claim to be free of MSG. Beware!
Pectin
Protease Enzymes, Enzymes, Protease
Soy Sauce, Soy Sauce Extract, Soy Protein, Soy Protein Isolate, Soy Protein Concentrate.

Anything protein fortified, enzyme modified, ultra pasteurized, fermented.

Binders and fillers for medications, nutrients and supplements, both prescription and non-prescription, enteral feeding materials and some fluids administered intravenously in hospitals may contain MSG, as well as soaps, shampoos, hair conditioners and cosmetic s labeled hydrolyzed and amino acid.

For more information about MSG, visit www.nomsg.com

▲Drug Store Seduction

We are hypnotized to run on drugs. Every town has its drug stores, with glaring signage: "DRUGS" and "DISCOUNT DRUGS." There are drive-through drug stores and internet sites.

Magazines sport full-page ads for prescription drugs. The drug companies hype drugs on television, radio, in magazines, and sell hard to doctors and pharmacists who dole out drugs like candy.

RIP
Here lies the body of
Samual Young
Who came here
and died For the
benefit of his health

Tombstone in Ventnor Isle of Wight, England

We're told to say "no" to drugs in multi-million-dollar advertising campaigns, while we're told to say "yes" to over-the-counter ones: Aspirin, Nyquil, Mylanta, Pepcid, Tagamet, Zantac, Ibuprofen and Pepto Bismo.

Over 22,000 American children, in a vast experiment take Ritalin, Dexadrine, Adderall, and other stimulants and antidepressants to manage "behavioral problems." As many as 1.5% of children between the ages of 2 and 4 are given these stimulants as well as antidepressants and anti-psychotics. Most were evaluated by pediatricians who generally have little training in mental health.

Your body is constantly growing and regenerating. In fact, 98% of the atoms in your body renew yearly.

Perhaps you never thought twice about taking over-the-counter medications. After all, everyone takes them, don't they? Many over-the-counter remedies are merely lower dosages of prescription drugs. How many drugs have you sprayed, swallowed, inhaled, inserted, or rubbed on you? Did you know that if you are sensitive, you might easily become addicted to nose sprays or other over-the-counter drugs?

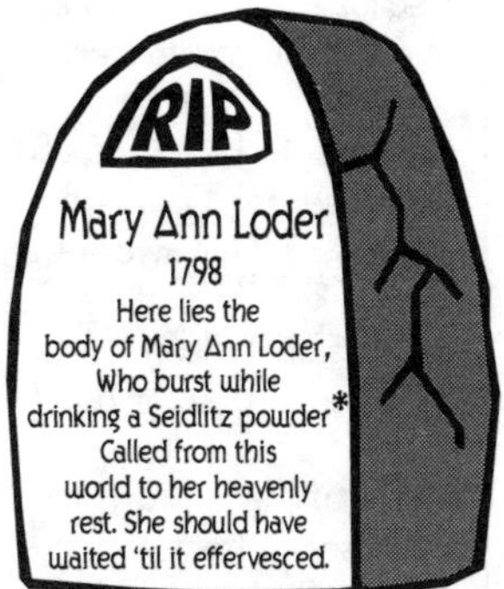

Tombstone from Burlington, New Jersey

**Seidlitz powder is a laxative containing Rochelle salts, sodium bicarbonate and tartaric acid. Named for the spring waters at Seidlitz, Bohemia.*

Do you use medicine for one symptom and inadvertently create a need for more? If drug reactions are strong, doctors often prescribe other drugs to alleviate the symptoms of these side effects.

At menopause, we are hard sold on taking "necessary hormones" and other drugs until we wind up wretchedly hooked on rows of medication. The elderly are most vulnerable. Do you know someone who "lives" on bottles of pills?

Designer drugs are legal substances produced by only slightly altering the chemical structure of illegal counterparts.

Since designer drugs are not prescription, we don't think about how they interact with prescribed, health food and over-the-counter medication. This could be a deadly mistake.

How many remedies do you take from the HEALTH food store? Dietary and fitness supplements can't hurt; can they? "After all it's only an herb" we rationalize. Besides, it says "healthy, pure and natural" on the label. But what are the active ingredients? How do they interact with what else is in your system?

It's Enough to Give You Indigestion

—by Shelley Stockwell

Egyptians used honey for heartburn. Greeks liked powdered coral.
Chinese chose seaweed or ginger, and Victorian cures were moral.
"Elevate the head with bricks for a bed.
It will make your stomach calm down," they said.

Pepto-Bismo made the 1919 scene.
In 1931 Alka Seltzer reigned supreme.
Zantac for ulcers in '92 was the best selling drug on earth.
And though it brought in $8 billion that year, it's easy to question its worth,
because ulcers are caused by bacteria called helicobacter pylori
(Now treated with new drugs like Prilosec; but that's another story).

We bought bicarb of soda, Maalox, Rolaids, Tums,
Bromoseltzer, Gaviscon, Mylanta by the tons.
Advertisements swore they'd comfort and relieve your malady.
$1.6 million in profits went to Pepcid A & C
In '98 $229 million came from Prescription Pepcid pills
And we all bought our Tagament and they profited $89 mill.

None of these drugs will cure you, yet can damage your urinary tract,
adversely effect kidneys and bowel and cause heart and blood pressure to react.
Aluminum compounds rob calcium. Phosphorous constipates.
Overuse and interactions may kill or aggravate.

What you eat and what you drink really is the stinker.
Alcohol and tobacco effects the lower esophageal sphincter.
Fat makes your sphincter slimy and slick so acid floods your esophagus quick.
If you get heartburn, avoid tannic and citric acid.
Eat bran, bananas and bland foods and delay upheaval gastric.

If you suffer from heartburn, avoid chocolate, coffee, alcohol, peppermint, onion, tomato and fatty food. If it's too late, eat a banana, it's a natural antacid, with no side effects.

Drugs are Big Business.

☆ Dr. S: *"That operation was done just in the nick of time."*
Dr. J: *"Yes, in another 24 hours he would have recovered."*

Americans spend $49 billion on nearly two billion prescriptions a year. According to a survey taken by Families USA, the annual incomes of CEOs of drug companies are some of the highest in the nation. In 1991, the CEO of Bristol-Myers-Squibb earned $12,788,000, Abbott Laboratories CEO $4,213,000, and Eli Lilly $2,802,000.

It is estimated that the average drug user costs an employer at least $7,000 in medical expenses and theft a year.

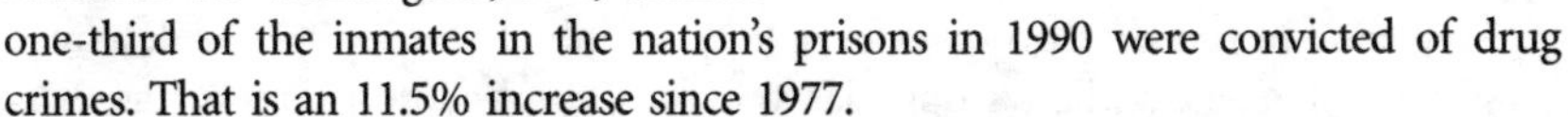

According to the Bureau of Justice Statistics in Washington, DC, almost one-third of the inmates in the nation's prisons in 1990 were convicted of drug crimes. That is an 11.5% increase since 1977.

Janus Joplin, John Belushi, Elvis Presley, Jimi Hendrix, Jim Morrison and Howard Hughes all succumbed to drugs and died. Actor Tony Curtis' son died from a drug overdose. And Tony himself considers himself a "recovering alcoholic." His daughter Jamie Lee Curtis says that she used cocaine with her dad. Singer Tony Bennett admits that he almost killed himself with a drug overdose. Nat King Cole's daughter, singer Natalie Cole, used drugs and became a dealer.

Untimely Rip Off

Ever notice the expiration date on prescription drugs? Manufacturers must date stamp each batch they produce and they do it conservatively. Pharmacists often ignore those dates and put their own "earlier" date on it, ostensibly to discourage patients from hoarding meds they should finish in a short time. This misinformation causes us to throw away and replace expensive drugs.

Ill Pill Mill: Cures That Kill

☆ *"Doctors and nurses are people who give you medicine until you die."*
— Deborah Martin

☆ *"I told the doctor I broke my leg in two places. He told me to quit those places."*
—Henny Youngman

☆ Bill: *"The doctor told me to take one pill three times a day."*
Lil: *"How can you take a pill more than once?"*

Eighty-percent of US citizens regularly take prescribed medication.

How often has a well-meaning but perhaps not-so-well-informed physician pulled out their prescription pad and offered you, your children or parents pain pills, muscle relaxers, anti-depressants, sleeping pills, hormone replacements, antibiotics or other drugs?

Ten-percent of US hospital admission result from adverse drug reactions caused by prescription drugs.

Cetirizine HCI for allergies, for example, causes mild to moderate side effects like drowsiness, fatigue, dry mouth, headaches, sore throat and stomach pain in eleven to fourteen percent of the takers.

The Fen Fen frenzy halted with reports that it caused severe heart and lung damage. Phenylpropanolamine, found in Acutrim diet gum, Alka Seltzer Plus, BC cold powders, Comtrex relief remedies, Contac, Dexatrim, Dimatapp, Robitussin, Triamenic, and others was recalled because of brain bleeding in women 18–49.

Has your health care provider ever told you about the possible side effects, long-term dangers, addictive qualities and drug combination risks of the drugs they prescribe?

Were you given the medical literature, that delineates the risks of drugs? Was the print too small and the words too big to understand? Did you read it at all? Illegal drug users never know what is in their street drugs. Neither do most legal drug users.

Have you been prescribed one drug to alleviate the symptoms or the side effects of another?

Drug interactions are a serious problem. Has anyone asked, when prescribing medication, what other prescription, over-the-counter or illegal drugs you take? Are the combination of drugs that you take compatible? Have they asked how much alcohol, caffeine, nicotine or marijuana you take in? Do you volunteer this information?

Food inter-actions are a serious problem, too. Has anyone asked you what you eat, how much you sleep, what vitamin supplements or exercise you do? Did anyone question how much sugar, salt or preservatives you use before giving drugs? Some conscientious doctors do.

Has a physician recommended that you stop taking a prescription or over-the-counter medication and use a natural solution instead? Have you been put down, poo-pooed or insulted for using alternative modalities like acupuncture, chiropracty, massage, faith-healing, bio-feedback or hypnosis?

The Pharmacists' Rule of Thumb:

If it's a drug it has side effects.

So What's The Problem?

☆ Doctor: *We can operate or you can go on a healthy diet.*
Patient: *Operate. My insurance doesn't cover a healthy diet.*

A 1998 report in the Journal of American Medicine estimates that around 15 percent of all hospital patients experience adverse drug reaction. A Harvard University study reports, "Twenty-six percent of all people in hospitals are dying of iatrogenic disease, which is a disease caused as a direct result of medical intervention." Forty-percent of all deaths result from damage caused from drug and medical intervention. Doctors are hypnotized to go for the most dangerous, expensive, and/or painful solution first:

Most Dangerous: **Drugs & Surgery**

Safer: **Herbs, Vitamins, Natural Remedies**

Safest: **Nutrition, Exercise and a Healthy Life Style**

Why on earth would they offer or use the most dangerous approach first? Because THAT'S WHAT OUR CULTURE HAS HYPNOTIZED THEM TO DO.

Most well-meaning western doctors and pharmacists are trained to use drugs and surgery first. Natural cures are not part of their background. Drug companies vigorously sell them their wares. Most medical professionals sell you what they know. It wasn't too long ago blood letting was standard medical procedure.

Overwhelmed with hundreds of patients and relying on scant information, many physicians prescribe medications as a way of doing something. Insurance companies often dictate treatments based on cost rather than effectiveness.

Buyer beware. Martha Ann's story is a perfect example:

A TRUE STORY Martha Ann

When my periods stopped, I was diagnosed with a thyroid condition and sent to an endocrinologist. He said that I had Graves disease which is hyperthyroidism. He advised me to take radioactive isotopes to kill my thyroid and convert me to hypothyroidism, an easier ailment to treat. "Don't be around anyone else for nine days," he said. "You will be radioactive."

I said, "no way" and went to an acupuncturist.

After eight months, I went back to the endocrinologist and there was no change in my blood. He said: "At this point it would be bad medicine if I don't treat you with something." And he gave me Tapazole. "You'll have a eight percent chance of turning jaundice. It's a low risk." he said.

The pharmacist gave me a pamphlet listing the potential side effects of Tapazole. I was hesitant but took the medication. Two weeks later I developed a sore throat, diarrhea and the whites of my eyes and the rest of me turned dayglow yellow.

When I called the doctor, his nurse said "You need to take something for the flu." The doctor prescribed an antibiotic.

I couldn't keep anything down. Four days later, I called the doctor again. He didn't get on the phone but the nurse referred me to a general practitioner. I felt totally betrayed. He dumped me. The general practitioner said I was in total liver failure; just like the warning side effects of the Tapazole literature. I stopped the Tapazole.

I went to a naturopathic physician. He gave me vitamins and milk thistle to cleanse my liver, pancreas and kidneys. I remained jaundice for three months and lost eighteen pounds. After six months, my jaundice is gone and my thyroid is greatly improved.

Antihistamines: Nothing to Sneeze At

Who wants to take a pill for hay fever or a cold and wind up with cancer?

Recent reports say that antihistamines (such as Hismanal (astemizole), Claritin (loratadine) have accelerated tumor growth in mice and rats and may also promote tumor growth in humans. "Those who take antihistamines regularly are at a higher risk of stimulating cancerous tumors" notes Lorne Brandes, MD, oncologist at the Manitoba Institute of Cell Biology in Canada. Antihistamines also exacerbate glaucoma.

These connections are still being debated but nobody is debating the common side effects of antihistamines: sleepiness, restlessness, agitation, dry throat, mouth and eyes, and difficult elimination.

"Antihistamines are misused by people with colds, flu, sinusitis and should only be used to alleviate severe allergic symptoms" says Kimmelman, MD, Manhattan Eye, Ear and Throat Hospital, New York City.

Antihistamines increase the sedative effect of pills for motion sickness, intestinal problems, alcohol, narcotics, sleeping pills and tranquilizers. Thus impairs motor skills, blurs vision, dries the mouth and causes constipation.

What's This Got to Do With You?

The biggest problem is that you never know how a drug will affect you personally because affects vary from person to person and will vary for you each time you take it. At best, drugs relieve symptoms, make you high and don't hurt you.

At worst, they exacerbate or create problems. Fifteen million Americans for example, take highly addictive prescription medication to sleep. A study by Dr. Anthony Kales at the Hershey Medical Center found that insomniacs who took sleeping pills woke twice as often during the night as the insomniacs who didn't take the medication.

Drugs Can Kill You or Your Spirit.

Your reaction to drugs depends on your genes, what you took, your stress level, how much sleep you've had, your state of health, what you drink and eat and what other drugs are in your body.

Even the most tried, tested and approved drugs can devastate some. You could be one of those unfortunate ones. FDA approval offers no assurances that your chemistry will react positively, what the long term and side effects will be and how what you take will interact with your system at the time. Some meds are time bombs causing no problems the first dozen times and then on the thirteenth go round, send us to the emergency ward in a coma.

Medications you took in the past can translate into damage or drug dependency in the present. Drugs given to your mother could still effect you (LSD for example impacts the unborn eggs in a woman's body). What are the long-term effects of your childhood vaccinations and flu shots? Someone told me that mercury and other toxic substances might be part of the vaccination concoction. How do we know?

Drug Inter-Play

☆ *"The more drugs you take, the greater the potential for serious interactive reactions."*

—Lynn Willis, pharmacology professor
Indiana University Medical School

Do you play Russian Drug Roulette; spin the barrel, pull the trigger and take your chances?

The interplay of chemicals in the body can be devastating or deadly.

Drug store computers list some 17,000 potentially harmful drug inter-actions. Chemical interactions can increase or decrease a drug's effects.

Sudafed, has eleven different products with the name "Sudafed" and each contains varied ingredients in their formulation: alcohol, caffeine, acetaminophen, guaifenesin and dextromethorphan are some. How do they interact with other drugs in your system?

Elizabeth Taylor, addicted to prescription drugs, was given over 1000 prescriptions of 28 different tranquilizers, painkillers and sleeping pills. Combined with her drinking, they could have been lethal. The California Medical Board reprimanded three of her doctors.

Viagra sounds like a great idea unless you suffer from side effects like headache, flushing of face, upset stomach and blurred vision. The small print warns, "In rare instances, men have reported erections that last for hours. If not treated right away, permanent damage to the penis could occur." And, "Taking Viagra (sildenafil citrate) with other medicines, and most specifically those that contain nitrates (amyl nitrate or nitrite called "poppers," nitroglycerin, isosorbide mononitrate and isosorbide dinitrate), could suddenly cause your blood pressure to drop to an unsafe or threatening level." "Heart attack, stroke, irregular heart beat and death have been reported rarely." "Viagra may cause other side effects besides those listed on this sheet."

Even the wrong food and drug mix can trigger unwanted side effects. For example, high potassium food like broccoli and "potassium-sparing diuretics" may interact causing irregular heartbeat and palpitations.

Antacids can interfere with the effectiveness of certain antibiotics. If you take Tagamet HB for indigestion and have the prescription drug Coumadin in your system, you may suffer from internal hemorrhaging and bleeding from mouth, nose, rectum and urinary tract. Not a pretty picture.

Overuse of acetaminophen (Tylenol's main ingredient) is said to be the leading cause of acute liver failure. A heavy drinker using Tylenol is at an even greater risk for liver failure.

We all know that alcohol on an empty stomach effects you more than if you've eaten. But did you know that alcohol in combination with pain-relief and fever-reduction products is potentially dangerous? If you take Glucophage or Glucotrol XL to lower your blood sugar and you have alcohol in your system, your blood sugar may dip dangerously low and fatal high levels of lactic acid can occur.

One drug may cancel out another one. Blood pressure medicine (Accupril, Prinivil, Monopril and Vasotec) lose effectiveness with aspirin. Beta-blockers like Inderal, Visken and Lopressor should not be taken with Aspirin, Advil, Aleve, Motrin, Ibuprofen and Nuprin. Rolaids and Tums reduce the effectiveness of the antibiotics, tetracycline and flouroquinolones.

Appetite suppressants amplify the decongestants, causing nervousness, agitation, high blood pressure and heart palpitations. Decongestants and appetite suppressants interfere with hypertension medication. Pain relievers decrease the effectiveness of hypertension drugs and diuretics. Conversely, pain relievers increase the effects of anticoagulants and put the user at risk of internal bleeding and hemorrhaging. If you take an oral contraceptive along with a blood-thinning drug, the blood thinner will not work.

If you take antibiotics, your birth control pills may not work.

The Antidepressant Racket: The Pros Who Con

Seventeen million Americans are prescribed antidepressants (seratonin reuptake inhibitors or SSRI's) like Prozac (Fluoxetine Hydrochloride), Zoloft (Sertraline), Paxil (Paroxetine hydrochloride) or Luvox.

SSRI's are said to make you less depressed by increasing the concentration of seratonin in the brain. They are given as treatment for depression, obsessive-compulsive behavior, anxiety, panic attacks, hypochondria, PMS, to lose weight and eating disorders (bulimia). Some call it prescribed ecstasy in a pill.

Grounds for prescribing antidepressants have shifted to PMS or to alleviate the discomfort of life's regular challenges like "dysthymia" which means moodiness and sensitivity to rejection of lonely, divorced and single people. "My doctor gave me Prozac when I told him that I was nervous about going to our company holiday party," one of my clients told me.

"Amazing pill can help 32 million crippled by shyness" was the caption in an article in a major publication. The pill: the antidepressant Zoloftin (sertaline).

Recently, Prozac's manufacturer, Eli Lilly, ran full-page ads in several medical journals asking doctors not to "trivialize" the seriousness of depression and proclaimed that their drug is intended "only where a clear medical need exists." Yet, non mental-health specialists dole out sixty-three percent of antidepressant prescriptions.

A study published in the Archives of General Psychology claims that more than half of all anti-depressants are prescribed by doctors after only a three-minute discussion with the patient. Two-thirds of all anti-depressants, sleeping pills and tranquilizers are prescribed to women between twenty and fifty, supposedly to help them relax.

If the poor woman's pregnant, drugs go directly through the placenta to the fetus and are excreted in breast milk to baby. Mommy takes a pale blue Prozac, so does her little one.

A TRUE STORY Shelley

"A national magazine and media blitz announced a "free" screening test to determine if you were depressed. It was sponsored by the American Psychiatric Association and the National Depressive and Manic-Depressive Association. I signed up. My appointment began with the request that I read a brochure on the symptoms and cures for depression. Cures included therapy, drugs and in or out patient hospitalization. The information brochure was printed by an educational grant from a division of Eli Lilly, the drug manufacturer of Prozac.

Next I was shown the movie, 'The Storm Within.' The video featured severely depressed people telling their tragic tales. According to the credits, the American Psychiatric Association and Upjohn Pharmaceutical Company paid for this beautiful mood setter. Immediately after, I was given a written test to determine if I was depressed. After that movie who wouldn't be!

My test results were evaluated and although I was judged only 'mildly depressed', I was referred to 'a member therapist' in my town, and told that I definitely needed care. Antidepressants, I was told, would be my treatment of choice. When I vehemently objected to that idea and made note of the movie's production credits, the counselor wrote in bold letters across my file "Do not offer drugs."

I wondered if the sad, anxious and depressed souls who shared the waiting room with me that day were given the same sales pitch.

Later that afternoon, my friend Barbara went to the clinic. They showed her the same video but, this time, the receptionist scurried in to turn off the VCR before the credits of the drug companies were shown. Though Barbara's test proved her to be "within normal range" and she did not request help, she was nonetheless referred to a psychiatrist in her hometown for depression counseling.

What's The Problem With Antidepressants?

One third of over 10,000 antidepressant users studied developed "allergic reactions" like rashes, fever, leukocytosis, water retention, carpal tunnel syndrome, respiratory distress and vascular problems that seriously involved the lung, kidney or liver. "Death has been reported to occur in association with these systemic events." Unforeseen damage from antidepressants may emerge years or decades from when taken.

Most amazing of all, the common side effects of antidepressants are the very things you take the pill for in the first place. Downers like Valium often trigger hostility, severe depression, seizures, nausea, diarrhea, headache and/or loss of sex drive.

Prozac has serious drug interactions with most over-the-counter, prescription, street drugs, alcohol, and especially, anti-convulsants, anti-psychotics, benzodiapines, lithium, anticoagulation drug and other antidepressants. Prozac used within five weeks of taking a monoamine oxidase inhibiting (MAO) drug, like Warfarin, can be fatal.

Prozac takers, who have electro-shock therapy, may suffer prolonged seizures. If you take Prozac or other monoamineoxidase inhibitors and a cold remedy that contains the cough suppressant dextromethorphan (like Nardil, Parnate and Sudafed), watch out! You could evoke seratonin syndrome or vomit blood, sweat, shake and be confused, followed by highly elevated blood pressure. The US Institute of Mental Health says, "All antidepressants may create: headaches, nervousness, insomnia and agitation."

Other Mood Boosting Supplements

Health food stores peddle a panoply of mood boosting supplements; kava root, L-tyrosine, amino acids, 5-hydroxy-tryptophan, SAMe (S-adenosyl-methionine), the hormone pregnenolone, and the most popular, St. John's Wort (hypericum perforatum).

Two-thousand years ago the Ancient Greeks used St. John's Wort's yellow-flowered plant to "drive away evil spirits." 300 milligrams of extract contains .3 percent of the active ingredient. Hypericum is taken three times a day and is said to relieve depression starting in a few weeks. Even with St. John's Wort, or any other natural remedy, no one knows much about the long-term effects or how they interact with other drugs.

Side effects, at this time, appear to be less serious than those reported with Prozac. In a study of depressed patients, well over half experienced side effects like restlessness, gastrointestinal irritation and allergic reactions. St. John's Wort has caused photosensitivity in some animals and, for that reason, fair skinned users are asked to avoid the sun and not take it at all if they are taking photosensitizing drugs like tetracycline.

In Italy in 1973 SAMe was used with schizophrenia patients and they reportedly were less depressed. SAMe is thought to work by making brain cell membranes more elastic which allows neurotransmitters like serotonin, norepinephrine and dopamine to travel with ease. This is different than antidepressants like Prozac that make these neurotransmitters remain in the brain longer. SAMe comes on within five days. But be warned, SAMe makes the manic phase of manic-depression "overexcited and irritable." Buying SAMe is risky, too. Last year, Columbia University psychiatrist, Dr. Richard Brown had 8 major brands of SAMe analyzed. Two brands had no SAMe at all, and several others had less than half the amount claimed.

Just because a pill "ups" you, don't deduce that you were sick in the first place.

We all go off center occasionally. It doesn't mean that your body has failed. We have emotional "seasons," mood and positive stress. In a UCLA study by Lewis Baxter, MD, two treatments were given to people with fears and uncontrollable urges. One group received Prozac and the other learned behavior modification to modulate upset impulses. Two-thirds of both groups improved and both groups showed identical physiological changes in their brain stem. So why risk putting a drug in your body?

A drug for depression is like putting a Band-Aid on a festering boil. Not only does it not solve a problem, it may in the long run cover it up and make the problem worse. Let the miracle of your body heal itself. Take positive action steps to balance your body and activate your innate alchemist to do its healing work.

Antidepressants cover up your problem without going to the source and clearing it, and they create more problems. Many drugs cause depression: Xanex, Valium and other sedatives list depression as a side effect, and even worse, are highly addictive. When you stop the medication, you may get depressed all over again because you didn't develop the tools to make yourself happy on your own.

The most effective way to get your body to produce more seratonin is to train your mind to engage in positive thoughts and behaviors, and to avoid depressing foods and toxins. Adjust your diet before you mess with yourself chemically.

Depressing Side Effects of Antidepressants
The "ZAC" WHACK and "SPAR" JAR

☆*"Any man who goes to a psychiatrist should have his head examined."*
—Norman Zierold

Prozac's listed possible side effects and interactions include:

Anxiety, Nervousness, Agitation
Activation of Mania and Hypomania
Amnesia, Confusion
Insomnia, Dizziness, Tremor
Increased Appetite and Weight Gain
Suicide
Interference with Cognitive and Motor Skills
Abnormal Vision
Hemorrhage
Heart palpitation, Seizure and Convulsion
Worsening of other Illnesses
Headache, Flu symptoms, Chills, Fever,
Nausea, Vomiting, Diarrhea
Hypertension
Ear Pain, Tinnitus

Imipramine: Dry mouth, low blood pressure and constipation.
Monoamineoxidase (MAO) inhibitor: Can cause violent reaction when combined with cheese, wine, nut,s pickles or other drugs.
Tricyclics: Can cause dry mouth, constipation, bladder problems, inhibit sexual functioning, blurred vision, dizziness and drowsiness.

Buspar's literature:
BUSPAR (an anxious, anxiolytic drug advertisements say: "Have you been bothered by unrealistic, uncontrollable and excessive worry for the majority of days over the past 6 months? Do you also suffer from three or more of these symptoms: Are you irritable, have difficulty falling asleep, feel keyed up and restless, difficulty concentrating, are you easily fatigued and have muscle tension? Persistent anxiety is a medically treatable condition...BuSpar is a non habit forming medicine for the treatment of persistent anxiety." "Some people experience side effects like dizziness, nausea, headache, nervousness, lightheadedness and excitement." [Note: The same things you take the pill for in the first place.]

The Fine Print Says:
With the help of a magnifying glass, the next page suggests: "For complete prescribing information please consult official package circular." And continues: When you stop taking Buspar it is common to experience:

SIDE EFFECTS OF BUSPAR
Dizziness (12%)
Drowsiness (10%)
Nausea (8%)
Nervousness (5%)
Excitement (2%)
Depression (2%)
Headache (6%)
Anger/Hostility (2%)
Confusion (2%)
Light Headedness (3%)
Insomnia (3%)
Dream Disturbances
Interference with cognitive and motor performances

Insomnia	**Headache**
Nervousness	**Fatigue**
Dizziness, Lightheadedness	
Nausea	

Withdrawal or rebound reactions: In "sedative/hypnotic/anxiolytic drug-dependent patients:"

Irritability	**Abdominal cramps**
Anxiety	**Vomiting**
Agitation	**Sweating**
Insomnia	**Flu like symptoms**
Tremor	**Seizures.**

Aspirin and Other Pain Relievers

Willow bark (nature's aspirin) has been used by the indigenous ones for as long as they can remember. Some twenty-five hundred years ago, the Greeks extracted salicylic acid by boiling willow. A man-made variation was developed in France in 1853 and rediscovered some 40 years later by German Chemist, Felix Hoffman. Synthetic aspirin—acetylsalicylic acid—is the most widely used drug in the world. Analgesic rubs applied to the skin contain aspirin. Aspirin has never been approved or rejected by the FDA.

Taken orally, aspirin is absorbed into the stomach and small intestine.

A TRUE STORY Jimmy

"Although the label warned me not to take more than eight tablets a day and to not use for more than 48 hours, I used over 200 Excedrin Migraine tablets a week for nearly a year. The worse my pain, the more I took. It turns out it was the acetaminophen, aspirin and caffeine in the product that made me suffer more and more. I over did it, like I overdo everything. When I stopped the pills and started drinking water and exercising, I felt well again."

Take an Acetaminophen and Call Me in the Morgue

1994 NEWS ITEM: A Virginia man won $8.8 million in damages when he claimed that taking standard doses of Tylenol, along with drinking several glasses of wine, had destroyed his liver. Acetaminophen, a main ingredient in Tylenol and 100 other drugs, is being investigated for its potential link to liver damage, when taken with alcohol or during a fast. This case has an appeal (provided it's not your liver).

Aspirin is a psychologically addictive "numb-her." Ten-percent of all adverse drug reactions in the US are attributed to aspirin. Prolonged use of aspirin can cause many serious problems, including gastro-intestinal abdominal bleeding, irritation of the stomach lining (possibly leading to ulcers), thinning of the blood (which interferes with your blood's ability to clot), and potassium depletion. Many deaths, mainly children's, are attributed to aspirin.

It appears that regular doses of aspirin may reduce the risk of heart attack in people with systolic blood pressure but with those with higher blood pressure it doesn't seem to do anything…except lead to internal bleeding and hemorrhagic stroke. If you want to keep your heart healthy, quit smoking and eat better, lose weight and exercise.

If you mix alcohol and aspirin (or alka seltzer that has aspirin in it), serious bleeding from the stomach wall can occur. Since aspirin is a blood thinner, blood thinners and aspirin don't mix; they can cause massive hemorrhaging. Combining aspirin and arthritis medication can cause ulcers. Diabetes medication combined with aspirin may seriously decrease your blood sugar.

Hey Girlfriend

Millions of women are told by doctors to take cholesterol-lowering drugs, despite evidence that these drugs do not increase life expectancy and have very unpleasant side effects.

"Hypertensive drugs that doctors give women patients, were tested only on men. Studies now show that these drugs actually increase mortality rates in women by 26%."

—Dr. Susan Lark, M.D.
Woman's Health Companion

Sharon & Maureen

Women are twice as likely as men to suffer adverse drug reactions. Obesity, liver damage, hypertension, are stronger in women drinkers than men drinkers for example.

Cough Medicines (Antitussives)

☆ *"It's not the cough that carries you off,*
It's the coffin they carry you off in."

Egyptian doctors produced the oldest known cough drops three thousand years ago: honey, herbs, spices and citrus fruits were blended into hard candies. These worked by moistening irritated dry throats. Later, we added morphine

(A bitter crystalline narcotic and the main alkaloid of opium) and heroin. Morphine and codeine are still popular today. High doses of morphine cause death by arresting breathing...which, truly does stop coughing.

Coughing is the body's natural cleaning response to remove congestive mucus from your lungs or to clear your windpipe. Cough medicines act on your brain to depress the cough center, with the idea of reducing your urge to cough.

☆ *Come on, Mom. Don't be mean.*
Think about my self-esteem.
You complain because I party
am sometimes stoned and often tardy.

Yet, you dropped acid, you took speed
and toked a toke, when you felt the need.
You sip wine so you'll relax
No need for you your brain to tax.

Let's face the facts we know are true
I'm growing up a lot like you.
—Shelley Stockwell

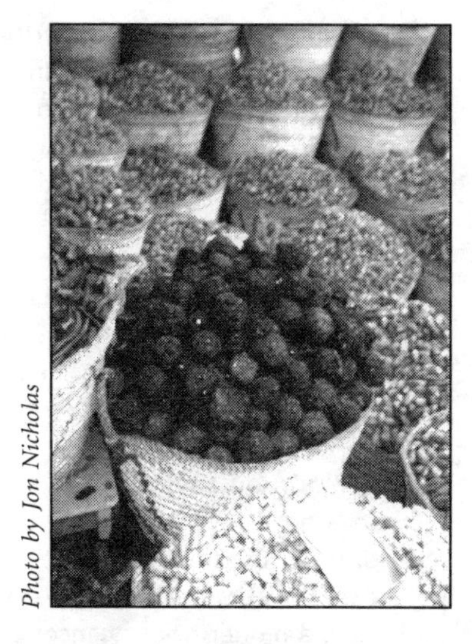
Photo by Jon Nicholas

Buyer Beware

☆ Dynamite Tester: *"That's me all over."*

It is your responsibility, as the treatment recipient, to always ask for and pursue positive solutions to physical problems. Many home remedies are excellent. Many holistic medical doctors and healing arts professionals teach common sense solutions that heal and don't make you worse.

Instead of taking a sleeping pill, which makes sleep disorders worse, eat bananas, figs, dates, warm milk and yogurt, which contain tryptophan, a natural relaxant. You can avoid sugar and alcohol, which may conk you out only to wake you up several hours later.

Trials and Fibrillation

"Coronary artery bypass operations have no proven effect on life expectancy, in men or women. 300,000 angioplasties (balloon expanded to clear arteries to the heart) were performed in 1990. Yet not one study shows that this procedure is any more effective than non-surgical therapies."

—Susan Lark, M.D.

Hormone Replacement HRTs Women

Hormone Replacement Therapy (HRT) is sold to millions of menopausal women to prevent osteoporosis, avert hot flashes, moisten the vagina and keep up vitality. Early "studies" claimed that hormones would reduce a woman's risk of heart disease. Major woman's magazine sports a multi-paged advertisement to motivate women to ask their doctor for such drugs.

The manufacturer, Eli Lilly writes:
"ESTROGEN IS BAD. It can include irregular bleeding, spotting, bloating, breast tenderness and migraines. Many women have serious worries about a possible link between estrogen replacement and cancer....It's a decision every woman has to make with the help of their doctor."

And: "Unfortunately, recent studies show that hormone replacement therapy increases the risk of endometrial cancer and has been linked to breast cancer [now an epidemic affecting one in three women], gall bladder disease, blood clots in the lungs and legs, heart disease, heart attacks, strokes, too much calcium in the blood and enlargement of benign tumors..."

A Premarin ad says:
"One side effect of estrogen replacement therapy is the possibility of developing cancer of the uterus." And "The risk of cancer of the uterus increases the longer estrogens are used and when larger doses are taken. There is a higher risk of cancer of the uterus if you are overweight, diabetic or have high blood pressure." "Most women have none or only mild menopausal symptoms and do not need estrogen. Other women may need estrogen for a few months while their bodies adjust to lower estrogen levels. The majority of women do not need estrogen replacement for longer than six months for these symptoms."

"Sometimes women experience nervous symptoms or depression during menopause. There is no evidence that estrogens are effective for such symptoms. You may have heard that taking estrogens for long periods (years after menopause) will keep your skin soft and supple and keep you feeling young. There is no evidence that this is so and such long term treatment may carry serious risks."

Shelley says:
Herbs, such as licorice, a healthy diet, lots of water, exercise and avoiding alcohol, caffeine, stress and hormone-laced food is the only solution. Your ovaries, adrenal glands and other tissue allow you to grow, reach puberty and mature gracefully. Don't insult them with drugs.

How Drugs Seduce
"Come dance the dance of pain.
It's the dance of drug by any name."

1. Honeymoon Phase

A friend or medical person supplies the drug, shows you how to use it, and makes sure that your first experience is pleasurable. This sets the stage for the next phase.

2."Play it Again, Sam" Phase

During this phase, you use the drug without becoming chemically addicted. This interval varies from person to person, even when using heroine. However, the younger you are, the more quickly you're likely to get hooked.

3."Gotcha" (or denial) Phase

The initial two stages give you the illusion that you are in control of your intake, that the substance is not addictive. You think you can stop any time you want. Using drugs is a personal right. It is the symbol in this stage of your individuality and your supposed control over your body. This "Stinkin' thinkin'" brings you to phase 4.

4."No exit." (Oy, Phase Mere)

You feel awful. You can't see past your nose.
You hurt. You ache.
You want to make a prison break.
You give your power to a sick seducer
and every day feel worser and worser.

Jim Vogl Monitor's Over-Medication

To prevent the abuses here are Jim's recommendations:

Photo by Richard Vogl

Jim Vogl

1. Keep an up-to-date record of ALL medications you are taking, be it prescription or over-the counter.
2. Give a copy of the list to a pharmacist that you use. Do not use more than one pharmacy. Ask the pharmacist to examine your list and see if there are any conflicts.
3. Give the same list to your doctor and ask the same question.
4. Each time a medicine is added or deleted repeat steps 1-3.

Up Your Egypt

Egyptian Medicine

The Egyptian Petri Papyrus (1850 BC) and the "Ebers" Papyrus, (1550 BC) from Egypt's New Kingdom list hundreds of remedies for every imaginable ailment. In 1872 Georg Ebers procured the Eber's Papyrus, a sixty-six foot scroll written in Egyptian hieroglyphics. Its eight hundred medical recipes along with incantations are amazingly similar to modern medicine.

Eyes Refined: Get the Lead Out

A hundred recipes to cure eye trouble are listed after the section on crocodile bites. Also, both male and female Egyptians wore eye-makeup to kill germs and heal conjunctivitis. Eye make-up, called mesdemet (or kohl in Arabic), was derived chemically from the lead compounds galena, (a dark sulfide of lead) phosgenite, laurionite and cerrusite (a white carbonate of lead). These were mixed with 7-10 percent animal fat (usually goose fat) for creaminess (this is the same percentage of fat used in makeup to this day.) Eye infections like conjunctivitis called for "genite" formulated in a drawn out chemical procedure.

Oil

Take castor oil internally as a laxative, rub it on the scalp to promote hair growth and put on warts and moles to remove them.

Red Then Dead

Pomegranate root expelled intestinal worms.

Squilly Me

Heart patients were given the juice of the Mediterranean sea onion or squill, a heart stimulant as powerful as digitalis. (A paste of squill is still used by tribes in South America and Africa on the tip of poison darts used in hunting).

Poppy Kaka

To quiet a restless child "take pods of poppy plant and add fly dirt that is on the wall..." (The opium content would mellow anyone down.)

Wouldn't it Be Liverly

Roasted ox liver improves night vision they wrote. (That makes sense because of it's high vitamin A content).

Jewish Penicillin

Moldy bread on wounds or taken internally (penicillin comes from this).

Circumcision was the only decision.

Contraceptives

- Douche with honey and natron (natures sodium carbonate)
- Insert crocodile dung (the alkalinity of this may have actually promoted pregnancy)
- Use a tampon of ground acacia leaves, dates and honey (Lactic acid is a good spermicide)

INNER•VIEW QUIZ

Are You Faux Real?

___ I'm not in denial. I'm not in denial. I'm not in denial.
___ I'm not compulsive. I'm not compulsive. I'm not compulsive.
___ What's happening isn't.
___ What happened didn't.
___ I'm confused.
___ I'm spaced.
___ I'm in the mirror without a face.
___ I can stop my bad habits any time I want.
___ Every one else does it so it's ok for me to do it too.
___ They 're not such bad habits after all.
___ I do what I do because I'm concerned about what other people will think.
___ I must do what I'm supposed to do.
___ I have to be careful not to put my foot in my mouth and prove I'm foolish.
___ I always have to defend myself.
___ He only beats me a little.
___ I only beat myself a little.
___ My problems are their fault.
___ If I ignore it long enough, it will go away.
___ I was kidding. Can't you take a joke?
___ I am not going to die.
___ I have a "bullet proof" attitude.
___ I'm not in denial. I'm not in denial. I'm not in denial.

If you answered yes, no, or maybe to any of these questions, you could be in denial.

D on't
E ven
N otice
I
A m
L ying

Denial: Refusal to admit truth or reality. Negation of logic.
Denial: Resistance to change.
Denial: Eternal sleep. The opposite of wakefulness.
Denial: Living in the parenthesis. (Jean Houston)
Denial: Ignore-ance.
Denial: No matter how thin you slice it, it's still baloney.
Denial: Is not a river in Egypt.

"Kaffer" is the Arabic word for denial.

We use words like: disavow, refute, disaffirm, disallow, disclaim, abnegate, ignore, belie, disown, pretend, pull the wool over your eyes, self-deceit, the lights are on but no one is home. "If I ignore it long enough, it will go away."

Chapter 10
Denial

Confidentially, This Lion Sphinx

When your inner wisdom cries, "Stop hurting me! Listen to your truth!" and you answer; "Shut up!" You deceive, avoid and you feel worse than ever. This chapter is your wake up call to feel better.

Photo by Neredah Bradstreet

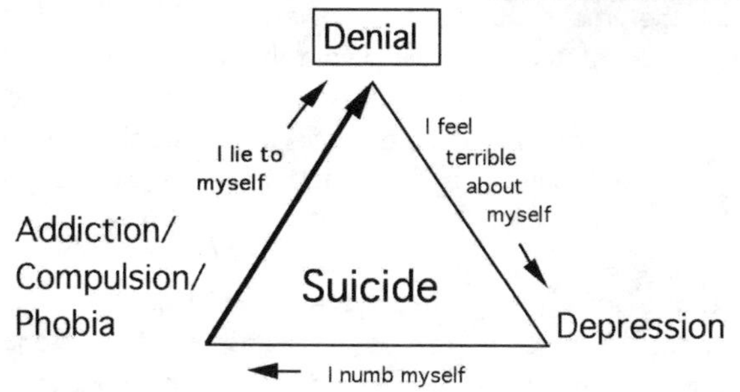

THAT'S CLEAR; I'M OBSCURE

☆ *To tell the truth (and that's no lie)*
I wouldn't feed some alibi.

No, I ain't joshin' (and that's no bull)
I wouldn't think to pull the wool.

Of course I'll give it to you straight.
(Really, I won't hesitate)
Avoid the issue? Fake, deceive?
Why, honestly! Who can you believe?

—Shelley Stockwell

Up Your Egypt

This Lion Sphinx

The word sphinx comes from the Egyptian word *shesepankh* meaning "living image of a ruler or god." The sphinx represents wisdom, strength and eternity. The Greek word "Sphinx" meant "the strangler" because they said that if you could not solve her riddle, you would be strangled.

Thousands of sphinxes were built in Egypt. Some are lions with ram heads and others are lions with hawk heads. A stone sphinx with the face of the female Pharaoh Hatshepsut can be seen in New York City's Metropolitan Museum of Art.

Sphinx Links

The most famous sphinx of all is the Great half-human, half-lion Sphinx in Giza. This Great Sphinx is said to be the statue of the goddess Armachis. Some say that it has the face of the Pharoah Chefren. Said to have been built over 5000 years ago. At one time, it was lusciously painted, perfumed and sported a nose and ceremonial beard. It was rebuilt during the reign of Khafra (2575-2467 BC) and was joined to the three great pyramids, Khafre, Khufu and Menkaure of the Giza complex. Her face looked at the Nile and the rising sun. A long stone causeway leads from Khefre and is joined to a labyrinth of underground temples.

Sphinx Facts

Sixty-six feet, or over seven stories tall, she is some 200 feet long, or about 3/4 of a football field. The sphinx is made of 70-ton solid limestone blocks, with exception of the paws that are built of brick. Her cobra head, once worn on the royal headcloth or nemes, is now displayed in the British Museum.

Cleaning Up Plaque

For centuries, the Sphinx was covered in sand and only her head was visible. It has now been uncovered and her body almost intact.

A plaque between the sphinx's fifty feet long paws, known as the Dream Stele, was carved by order of Thutmosis IV around 1400 BC. It tells the story of Prince Thutmosis after a tiring hunt, falling asleep beneath the head of the Sphinx. In a dream, the Sphinx told him that if he swept away the sand that choked the great monument that he, Thutmosis would be a great king. He did and became Pharaoh Thutmosis IV. When Napoleon visited Egypt 3000 years later, the sphinx was again buried up to her neck in sand.

▲ Veiled Glimpses

☆ *TAKE THE TIME TO LOOK*
Look, down here, it's me.
Yes, look closer. Can't you see?
It's me, buried deep.
I've been away for awhile, asleep.

Slightly weary, slightly wise. Wait! Can't you hear?
It's me, just me. Look. Down here.
It's me, buried deep
Beneath my smile.

—Erin Clary, age 16

Tombstone in Hell

Denial Tombstone

In 4000 BC, people stayed away from graves and took drastic measures to keep the dead from haunting the living: nailing down the lid of a wooden coffin, lowering it six feet under, covering it with earth and placing the biggest, heaviest stone they could find on top of the lid.

Ancient Egyptians invested in after-life insurance by building fabulous tombs to assure eternal life. Today, advanced reservations for a funeral plot is our after life insurance. Some traditions die hard.

Many of us, while still alive, nail our coffin lid, lower ourselves six feet under, and buried in denial, hide under the biggest, heaviest stone we can find. We deny that we die and we deny that we deny.

Do you live life like the walking dead?

Do you kill your vitality with hurtful behaviors?

Do you turn your head the other way and pretend that whatever is happening isn't or whatever happened didn't?

Do you go to unbelievable lengths to arrange life so that you don't have to be present?

Lies seem to be based on good reasons. But over time, old reasons don't make sense. Living a lie teaches us to do things we detest, like remaining in a unchallenging jobs, hurtful habits and toxic relationship.

When we are out of integrity, we despise our selves.

In China, the normal greeting is "Have you eaten yet?" "Yes, thank you" is the proper response, even if it's not true.

In Kyoto, Japan, the greeting is, "How's business?" "Just awful" is the expected response.

If someone asks "How are you?" do you answer "Fine" even if you're not?

The next time somebody asks you, "How are you doing?" Why not tell them the truth? If you're feeling fine, say "Fine." If you're feeling crummy, say, "Crummy." Then add, "I choose to feel great in this moment."

▲ What is Denial?

Denial is when you turn your head the other way and pretend that whatever is happening isn't or whatever happened didn't. When you unknowingly create suffering for yourself and say the universe caused it, you are in denial.

Shelley, Betsy and Jill

Liar, Liar Pants on Fire, Hanging Off the Telephone Wire

☆ Judge: *"O.J. I find you innocent."*
O.J.: *"Does that mean I can have my gloves back then?*

In the book *The Day America Told the Truth,* thirty percent of Americans say they are having extramarital affairs; and, 93% of Americans said they have lied at work.

How accurate are your income tax filings?

Do you tell the cashier if they hand you extra change?

Do you pad expense reports?

Do you keep little secrets from yourself?

Do you lie to yourself as you go unconscious, light up a cancer stick, throw down a beer, eat candy bars, binge or hurt your body? Do you pretend that a terrible thing will change for the better if you ignore it long enough?

Do you ignore someone beating you or the kids, rationalizing, "He was under stress. It won't happen again."

If self-deception hides an elephant under your emotional living room rug, you are not alone. Lying is too often, individually and globally, socially acceptable and a regular part of social interaction.

A criminal is the one who gets caught or has the worst attorney. And, if they are caught, they are wise to keep the books right.

INNER•VIEW QUIZ

Is That You Lion?

You know you're lying or withholding your truth when you:

Clear the throat

Throat clearing means you're withholding something you want to say. Conflict causes throat constriction.

Finger over the mouth

"Well, shut my mouth."

Hold your breath

Smile with tight lips

When you deceive, smile corners tighten, lips compress, or lower lip pushes up slightly. There is no eye crinkle when lying.

Photo by Neredah Bradstreet

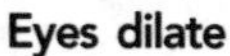

Eyes dilate

Dilated and enlarged pupils. (This also is a sign of being in love).

Glancing up and to the right (if right-handed)

Looking up and to the right is our natural response when creating a new story.

Not looking others in the eye or maintain a steady gaze

(except in Japan where this is a sign of respect).

Less movement

Body positions become less fluid when lying.

Shoulders slouch

Head angles to one side

Body turns away

Stomach aches

A body cannot stomach a lie. "Gut truth" is in your gut.

You feel dizzy

Dizziness means, "I've heard something I don't want to hear or am confused about."

No Lion

You know you're telling the truth when you:

▲ **Genuinely smile** The whole upper half of my face smiles and eyes crinkle.

▲ **Look directly into another's eyes**

▲ **Look up and to the left** (if right-handed). A natural response when recalling something from truth

▲ **Relax** Hands are relaxed, often slightly curled at chest level in front of heart.

▲ **Stomach Talks** Borbourigme or stomach gurgles are true. They happen to you.

Tabloids and main stream newspapers indict, convict and entertain with creative writing from "unnamed or anonymous sources." The great Thomas Jefferson categorized newspapers in four parts: "The first part is truth, the second possibility, the third probability and the fourth lies." "The forth section would be the largest," he said.

Here are some real-life examples of denial in action:

A secretary croons, "I'm sorry, Mr. so-and-so is in a meeting," as the boss whispers, "I don't want to talk to him."

A person breaks an agreement to meet you, doesn't call and blames it on circumstances.

A woman fights pornography for a living and then secretly begs her husband to take naked pictures of her.

A priest preaches about the sin of unmarried sex and the sanctity of marriage, vows celibacy and has an affair with a married church-goer.

A radio talk show host, who repetitively warns callers to not "shack up" or "fool around" before marriage, is shown on the internet seductively naked in pictures taken by an ex-boyfriend.

Parents tell their children that drugs are terrible, and then proceed to take medication, smoke marijuana or get drunk.

Many vocal "impeach-Clinton" congress people got caught in their own indiscretions: illegitimate children, affairs. Speaker of the House, Livingston quit his position when his affairs were revealed. The head of the House Impeachment Committee, Henry Hide, tried to hide and dismiss an extramarital affair in his forties as a "youthful indiscretion." "Do you kiss and tell? How about in front of a grand jury?

A person who drinks all the time says, "I don't have a drinking problem."

A person blames their mate for their own unhappiness and indiscretions.

A person who's smoked for 20 years says, "I'm not hooked. I could quit."

Or "I don't smoke that much."

Business As Usual

☆ Question: *"How can you tell if a lawyer is lying?"*
Answer: *"His lips are moving."*

Anorexic models slurp ice cream and soft drinks. Magazines have cover photos of decadent desserts bordered by articles headlines like, "How I Lost 60 pounds in 10 days!"

Used car salesmen or insurance agents "exaggerate" to close a deal.

Business associates feign teamwork while stabbing each other in the back.

TV evangelist Jim Bakker received $100 million a year as donations for "God's work," which he "invested" in womanizing, a theme park with 25 boutiques and an amphitheater. Some still sent him money while he was in jail.

Major corporations bribe and connive; business as usual.

The tobacco industry got busted for "false claims" and lies they used to sell cigarettes. Chemical companies knowingly lied about vinyl chloride causing cancer.

Politics As Usual

☆ *"When Richard Nixon spoke, he would look people in the face, but would angle his body away, telegraphing the signal that he wanted to escape. His 'squirming' cues gave the impression that he was hardly friendly and a liar of sorts."*

—David Givens, Ph.D.

☆ Question: *How can you tell if a politician is lying?*
Answer: *"His lips are moving."*

An "honest politician" is an oxy•moron. Society expects politicians to lie; say one thing and do another.

"Read my lips" George Bush

"I am not a crook" Richard M. Nixon

"I did not have sex with Miss Lewinski" Bill Clinton

We take for granted that the CIA and the National Security Agency spend billions on subversive machinations.

We turn a blind eye as the military, FBI and CIA lie about their actions and foreign politics. We secretly suspect them of murder and revolution in developing countries.

We accept statements like "Roswell was just a weather balloon."

Do you think the Secret Service and Mafia are linked to the assassination of President Kennedy?

This general deterioration of integrity creates a destructive superstructure for society and you.

Where are your role models? To cope with this loss, you may go numb and not even notice lies any more. Stop living in neverland!

A TRUE STORY Mary Bontempo

(No names have been changed to protect the guilty).

"At 21, I was a straight 'A' student and decided to be a Peace Corps volunteer. Robert Kennedy, a friend of a family friend, wrote a letter of recommendation.

Off I went to train in East Lansing, Michigan. My unit consisted of 49 other volunteers. Our training was intense. We had to learn Spanish, since our assignment was to be in Chile. Frei was the president of Chile at the time. We were told we were training to assist civilians with agricultural reform. We were therefore taught to cut off chicken's heads, plant corn, press grapes and build outhouses.

We remained in class for over 12 hours a day. At night, we were required to attend "parties" where they served us large amounts of alcohol. We were exhausted.

One of our instructors trained us on special procedures, which included 'learning how to steal without being caught.' To pass that segment, we were required to go to local supermarkets and stores in East Lansing and remove several items without being caught. We were taught how to avoid security devices. It was called "market research."

On a rare day off, a girl friend and I hitchhiked to a local town. On our return hitchhike, a nicely dressed young man picked us up.

'Where do you need to be dropped off?' he asked.

Since we were told not to mention our Peace Corps assignment, we simply said, 'We're students at a local university. Please drop us there.'

'Where are you going?' we asked him.

'I'm an administrator in the Peace Corps and I'm here to observe a Peace Corp training group.'

'Oh, what's that like?' we asked.

'They're pushing this particular group of volunteers to the limit. They're seeing how much pressure they can take before they crack. Their hours are unbelievably long, and they are feeding them large amounts of alcohol to see how they operate under pressure. We have a psychologist at the parties to observe their behavior'

We didn't say a thing, but smiled sweetly.

The next morning in class, our driver, was our new instructor. The following day, we were given seven days off and chauffeured to the beach.

A few week later, we had to "drop in" and live in a local Michigan town and observe the "demographics"—how the politics, businesses and religions operated. We had to pinpoint who was in control of the politics, economics and the media and what priests or ministers had any weight in town. Two of us were assigned to a town over 30 miles away. The first night we slept in a cornfield. A Catholic priest asked one of their parishioner's to put us up for three days. A Peace Corp supervisor marched into this nice lady's house without even knocking and demanded that we give them our research immediately. The lady threw them out.

When I got back to Lansing I was suspicious. This seemed much more than market research. It didn't seem right. So upon my return, I went out of town to a library to research the Peace Corps. Imagine my surprise when I found a national news magazine article about "project Camelot" in which the CIA used the Peace Corps to gather information. I came back to the facility. My roommate, who was having an affair with one of the married teachers, was all ears, as I told her my findings.

The next morning, I went to breakfast and was greeted by the psychologist in our program. With tears in his eyes, he told me: 'Mary, I don't understand this, but you have been dropped from the program. Your bags have been packed for you, and a limousine will pick you up in the front of the building in ten minutes. I can't understand it. You're the best student.'

I was devastated. What was I going to tell my folks back home? The driver of the limousine told me I was to pick up my tickets at the American Airlines ticket counter and that all the arrangements had been made for me to fly home.

I came up with a plan. As soon as he dropped me off, I went to a phone booth, and called American Airlines and said,

'I'm with the Peace Corps, we just ordered a ticket to Cleveland for Mary Bontempo to pick up at your ticket counter. We'd like to change the routing and send her tomorrow morning to Detroit with an open ticket for her to go to Cleveland when she decides. I leisurely strolled over to the ticket counter, picked up my new ticket, got in a cab, and then went shopping for groceries. I wasn't going to leave without a celebration.

When class ended, I returned to the facility and invited everyone in my class to a party. At the party, I announced my findings to everyone and explained to them why I imagined I had been dismissed. Most of them didn't believe me. The next day, I went to Detroit and visited friends. This gave me time to pull myself together before facing my family.

Years later, I visited one of my classmates who had taken the assignment to Chile. He flatly refused to say anything about his experience. He said he was too frightened. He did, however, say that in Chile my roommate had roomed with our married administrator and that the Chilean government was on to all of them. He said they were literally political prisoners while they were there. It wasn't without perks, however; they lived in a gorgeous place, had fine food and went everywhere in chauffeur-driven vehicles.

Some time later, I requested a copy of my Peace Corp file with my letter of recommendation from Robert Kennedy. I was told there was no record of my ever having been admitted to the Peace Corps or ever having attended training.

▲ Why Deny: Under-Lying Reasons

☆ *Little Miss Muffer caused directors to suffer*
Blowing her lines every day.
A mime sat beside her, now with him to guide her
Miss Muffer has nothing to say.

—Pat Cotterell

☆ *"We don't see things as they are, we see them as we are."*

—Anais Nin

There are three kinds of people. Those who make things happen, those who watch things happen, and those who don't know what's happening!

We lie or withhold truth from ourselves because "everyone else" does.

We lie to circumvent rules.

We lie to survive, protect family secrets, keep up appearances and cope with pain.

We pretend to do what society expects from us.

Were you told that saying "yes" rather than "no" is good manners?

We lie to protect ourselves from hurt, abandonment and even death.

We fudge to ourselves when we eat fudge. "One little piece won't hurt." "If no one sees me eat it, it never happened."

We hold back feelings to protect our "image?"

We lie to avoid unpleasant consequences; judgement, wrath or recourse. "What you don't know won't hurt me."

We lie out of habit or convenience, "Just a little lie to not have to explain."

We lie to protect ourselves from shame.

Some lie to protect an abuser. "Grandpa was the only one who was ever there. I can't let them know what he did."

We lie to show them or get even.

We tell "little white lies" to "protect others" from hurt.

Al Neuharth, the founder of USA Today, tells this story about Billy Carter's mother Lillian:

A TRUE STORY Oh Those Lilly White Lies

A reporter came to visit President Jimmy Carter's mother Lillian.

"Tell me Mrs. Carter, when Jimmy was a little boy, did he ever lie?"

Miss Lillian (after a long pause): "Only little white lies."

Reporter (trying to hide her glee while imagining the headlines this was going to make): "Can you give me an example?"

Photo by Nica Lee

"Well," Mrs. Carter replied, dripping in southern sweetness, "Like when you came to the door a few minutes ago and I told you how nice you look and how glad I was to have you drop by."

Denial is a necessary stage that helps us deal with trauma. It offers "time out" to regroup when the small, wounded inner-child can't bear the hurt. It's our attempt to function; go to work, raise a family and carry on in a world that also may pretend that everything is "just fine." Family secrets keep up images.

The Best Defense is the Offense

☆ Judge: *"Doctor, you took these x-rays. Tell us about the injury."*
Doctor: *"Which side am I testifying for?"*

If your hidden truth is revealed, do you get defensive, make up stories or flood with rage? Such reaction diverts attention away from real problems. If you are ready, you can wake up and just tell the truth.

When a drug taker in denial is confronted, they often argue that they have no problem. To everyone but themselves, they are obviously ill. "I'd be fine, if you will just leave me alone." Later, when these beautiful people are clean, sober and in control of their life, their viewpoint shifts, "I understand. I was blind. Now I see." Amazing grace, indeed.

Audrey Kishline wrote a book, *Moderate Drinking: The New Option for Problem Drinkers.* The book advocated a quota of 14 drinks for men and nine for women per week. Six years later, a drunken Kishline, driving on the wrong way on a state highway, killed a man and his 12 year old daughter. She now says that to continue drinking was a "program for alcoholics covering up their own alcoholism." Drinkers may trick themselves into "controlled drinking" but such an approach is doomed to failure.

Why Would You Trick Yourself?

Deceiving yourself serves a purpose. Have you lied to yourself to:

___ To look good?
___ Have fun?
___ Numb pain and stay tranquil?
___ Escape?
___ Override worry, anxiety or depression?
___ Reduce guilt and shame?
___ Help control your environment?
___ Avoid confusion and boredom?
___ Keep yourself from feeling inadequate or imperfect?
___ Avoid consequences of your actions?

Mummy's the Word: From One Degeneration to Another

☆THE NAKED I

Take off your dark glasses,
Take off your mother's glasses, your fathers' glasses
Your blind theories of everything you know,
What the hell, take off your clothes.

From bare trees, green leaves will fall
And you will read them like a gypsy with crystal vision.
All over town you'll see nothing but naked children: bankers, lawyers & doctors
(Who otherwise appear so permanently dressed) show their soft bellies and secret scars.
Teachers strip their curricula and instruct children only to keep their eyes naked
To see for the first time what they have always known.

—Annie Reiner

Lying is often taught us in childhood.

Children eagerly mimic life's lessons from their most intimate teachers, the big people.

Children believe that what their parents do is appropriate behavior. They believe what their parents say is real.

Much compulsive behavior is a direct result of imprinted information that the child within us accepted as the gospel. You may not be consciously aware as you repeat and carry on these family traditions.

Mom and Dad may teach their own deceptive actions. "Do as I say, not as I do."

Older siblings train younger ones to, "get around Mom and Dad." Kids catch on fast: a well-placed lie covers your ass. "It wasn't my fault, Johnny pushed me."

Did you fear feeling and expressing grief, because you thought no one would like you if you were sad? Did you fear that you would be abandoned? Or even killed? If so, you most likely shut up and shut down. These imprints may be unconscious and pervasive.

Keeping quiet in the world often translates into quietly withholding the truth from yourself. Where did this all begin? If you were trained to appear strong, silent or unemotional, no matter how you really felt, you may now have no idea how you truly feel or if you are lying to yourself.

Shut Up and Shut Down

☆ *"Back in a moment..."*

—Godot

For a child, telling the truth to a big person in denial is risky business. Imagine for example, what happens to a child who stands up to a freaked-out parent. The parent may yell louder, hit harder or abandon more. We shut up rather than tell the truth; "You big bully. How dare you treat me with such disrespect? I'm a helpless child, my very survival depends on your love and care." "You're whacko to insult and violate me, something is wrong with you."

The consequences of this withdrawal is immense. Bits of our vitality, passion and life force split from us and hides away, guarded by stern sub-personalities.

Protecting Family Secrets

☆ *"If you've lost your memory, forget it."*

Skeletons in your family closet? Protecting family secrets may be essential for remaining alive. Family secrets are enforced by guilt trips and/or threats and punishments. "Don't air your dirty laundry." "Don't let the skeletons out of the closet." "Think of the family name."

A TRUE STORY Shelley Lessin

OH BROTHER
My brother Marc told me he was a drug dealer,
Swallowed prophylactics filled with substance abuse to bring the stuff in.
He made those runs with other parents' nicest sons
(Subsidized his monthly allowance)
Became a lawyer and a medical doctor.
He sued me and our older brother
To pocket more money from the estate of our mother.
My brother is handsome like Omar Sharif and says he's out to bury me.
When he was small, I was like his mom and he said he wanted to marry me.

My brother Marc is reputable (used LSD occasional)
Beat his girlfriend Linda (only once) and has good manners at the table.

My brother Marc, in his doctor's smocks is admired and respected.
He writes prescriptions, pays his bills and is societally protected.
Seasons change us in our lives (It's amazing what we discover)
That little boy I once adored; He's heavy, he's my brother.

Gold Guilt

If you were abused or taught to feel guilty or responsible for another's abuse, you may hold back your feelings and/or pummel yourself.

Cope With Pain

"Don't cry."
"Stop crying or I'll give you something to cry about."
"You're a big girl now."
"Calm down."

Conspiracy of Silence

One-third of all injured women who go to emergency rooms in the United States are victims of family violence. Yet many shield the person who has beaten them to "protect" their abuser, themselves and /or their children.

Keep Up Appearances

"What would the neighbors think?"
"Don't make waves."
"Be seen, not heard."
"Be ladylike."
"Save face."

We embellish to make ourselves look better to others. How exaggerated is your resume? Is the weight on your driver's license the truth? Do you make up stories about how much you eat (or don't eat), drink (or don't drink)?

How to Create A Void: Avoid

☆ *"When I read about the evils of drinking, I gave up reading."*
—Henny Youngman

According to a study conducted at the University of Virginia and Texas A & M University and published in the Journal of Personality and Social Psychology; we lie to embellish the truth more than we lie to protect another.

Unmarried romantic partners lie to each other, with the intent to mislead, at least once in three encounters. College students lie in almost every interaction with mother and members of the general community reported fibbing once in every five interactions.

A TRUE STORY Fly Lie

To join the airlines you had to have 20/20 uncorrected vision. I didn't, so I lied on my application and was accepted. On the last day of training we were given a physical exam. After I removed my contact lenses I couldn't even read the big "E" at the top of the chart.

I flew for 20 years. I would have never even made it through training if I had told the truth.

Up Your Egypt

Blind Justice

Ancient Egyptians conducted their trials in a darkened chamber so that the judges could not see the witnesses, pleader and prisoner. They felt this would make the judgment impartial; although it must have also resulted in an occasional mistake.

Greeks later depicted Justice as a statue wearing a blindfold and holding a pair of scales. Hence, we get the term "blind justice." The ancient Egyptians believed that the soul of the deceased was weighed and its weight determined the fate they would experience on the other side. This is where the expression "tried in the balance" comes from.

Judgment Day

☆ *Carving a turkey is like parallel parking: you do it perfectly when no one is watching.*

If you lied to protect yourself and others, or to keep up an "image," your denial may be used to avoid unpleasant consequences and the harsh judgment of others.

Curse and Way

☆ Elephant #1: *"What is it we never do?"*
Elephant #2: *"Forget."*

Rebellious deception motivates us to circumvent roadblocks to get what we want. Aren't rules meant to be broken? Lying also allows us to rebel. "Screw 'em, I'll tell 'em what they want to hear and do it my way."

Breaking rules gives us a charge.

What?

☆ Doctor: *Do you have trouble with your urine?*
Patient: *No, my hearing is fine.*

—Sophie Lessin

After a while we don't listen or hear. When you are out of it and defending, you stop getting into adventuring.

Denial Works For A While

☆ *"I gave up drugs because I didn't like what it did to my friends when I was stoned."*

—Wendy Liebman

It's not worth lying if you can't tell the truth. It may seem more comfortable to lie rather than face harsh truth. When lying becomes a habit, you may not even notice self-deceit.

Over time, denial makes us feel more alone and hurt than any hurt or rejection we fear.

The more you ignore pain, the more it hurts. The more you avoid issues, the more issues you create. The more you stuff down truth, the more it tries to make itself known. Illness is a tip-off that you are deceiving yourself. Your body often expresses what you will not.

The truth sets you free. Even when you are afraid to tell the truth about what you are thinking or feeling, truth sets you free. Even if you think your thoughts are unacceptable, overwhelming or that maybe you're nuts, the truth still heals. To tame ugly emotions or feelings first acknowledge them. What are you really thinking and feeling? Then decide how you would rather think and feel?

Two Pharaoh Tales

1. A Crone of Thorns

Mohammed wanted to know the truth. He visited gurus and soothsayers. He read self-help books and watched Oprah Winfrey. His quest took him to the highest mountain in the Himalayas. There, in a dark cave, before a flickering fire, sits the wisest of wise; a wizened old lady with craggy teeth, pocked skin, crossed eyes, dressed in filthy rags and tatters.
"Tell me, oh wise one, what is the truth?"

The hag looks up. In a thin cracking voice replies:

"Tell them that I am beautiful."

Moral: 1. Truth ain't always truth.
2. Truth ain't always pretty.

2. Out Right Judgements

Two men went to court in Egypt to settle an argument.
The first man made his case and the judge said: "That's right"
The next man tells his side of the story and the judge said: "That's right."
The court clerk blurts out: "They can't both be right!"
and the judge says: "That's right."

Moral: Truth is where you put your focus.

Incongruity

☆ *"I had to stop jogging. It made the ice jump out of my glass."*
—Martin Mull

Psychologist Carl Rodger called denial "incongruence; having one feeling but acknowledging another, or not feeling feelings at all. The more incongruent we are, the more confused we get and the worse we feel," he said.

An incongruity tip-off is a sentence like "My mother was so good to me." Yet, when you think of her you feel distraught over her insults, her abandonment or her insensitivity. Or the reverse, "It's all my mother's fault I have these problems; she was a bitch." Yet when you check into your heart, you discover she was always on your team.

A TRUE STORY: Shelley

☆ DIRTY LAUNDRY

When I turned 40, time inversed, back to the time I felt the worst.
Paralyzed in a quiet collision of rules, diversion, indecision.
My life wasn't happy any more. No matter how I shut the door,
My childhood pains spread like cancer, pushing that door, demanding I answer.
So, I chose to be taller than my defenses, regardless of the consequences.
If I stayed trapped in family lies, I might as well lay down and die.
So this is how it really was; straight from the fist—not from the glove.

"It must be a girl," Mom screamed at my birth. She had her game to play,
And a baby girl, all plump and round, fit in her scheme some way.
I was the doll to live her drama of little sister, big bad brother,
Love and hate, compete with father and her own abuse from Dad and Mother.

Dad fed her chocolates to keep her fat so he justified his lover
And working late, he left us home to be cared for by our mother.
His buddy, Barney the pharmacist, kept her stocked in diet pills
Which she drank with pots of coffee to add more caffeine thrills.

For six or seven hours she would scream out words of hate.
"I don't deserve you stupid kids. You're mean. Oh, what a fate."
She'd hold me down, rubbing raw, my "filthy" female parts
And told her friends, with dewy eye, that I was her sweetheart.
She stuffed down cake and ice cream and slept with sleeping pills.
My dad worked late at the office so he could pay the bills.

My brother tortured bugs and ants and threatened me with no second chance.
Our house was a box with holes punched in it. Life was a contest:
No way to win it.
The sky was Mom's scream-ramble-talk around my ears and eyes
As everything I experienced, she interpreted and analyzed.
"Pretend to do what your husband says ... love is a competition."
"Manipulate and get your way; control all the decisions."

I learned to please with a passive grin as Mom's voice reverbed in my head.
Until I turned 40 and paralyzed in pain and nearly half dead.
If you're saying, "Get off it; that was then. Why turn 40 and live it again?"
Perhaps, you're not caught in self-denial or have another cure
Or maybe you were fortunate or maybe you're not sure.
As for me: ignoring pain caused my pain to stay and when I fully felt my hurt
And pain, it went away.
That was then and now I'm free, honest, liberated.
I love myself, forgive the past and I am consecrated.

"My childhood was an obscure mist of forgotten time. I couldn't remember anything before the age of 12. I even had trouble remembering things from the week before. The most disturbing thing though, began when I was 19 years old. Inexplicably, I felt a mental fog roll in, swallowing up the world. I worried about this mental fog for some time. Then I realized that my mental fog was not rolling in, it was rolling out. I was coming back to bright spots, moments of clarity.

I dragged myself to a self-help seminar. Perhaps I would gain insight on how to be happier. The climax of the seminar was when participants claimed their personal mantra, an affirmation that embraces their gift, their path, and their goal.

I was stymied. As hard as I TRIED. Not one affirmation popped into my head. I even tried to steal other people's. But they didn't fit.

Hopeless and helpless, I started to cry. It began like ancient wailing from another dimension. I shook uncontrollably and cried until I thought I would die. I was out of control. The leader came and put me on her knee. 'What's going on Shelley?' she asked. 'I feel like my heart is breaking,"' I answered.

'No,' she said, 'that's the feeling of your heart opening.'

After that, an affirmation filled me with light: 'I am Shelley. I am perfect just the way I am, feeling so glad to be alive, deeply loving me and deeply loving you.'"

Obviously Ill, Seemingly Well

☆ *"Would someone the gift agi us, to see ourselves as ethers see us."*

—Robert Burns

☆ *I have to live with myself and so, I want to be fit for myself to know.*
I want to be able as days go by always to look myself in the eye.
I don't want to sit with the setting sun and hate myself for deeds I've done.
I see what others may never see. I know what others may never know.
I have to live with myself and so,
Whatever happens I want to be
Self-respecting and conscience free.

—Author Unknown

Psychosomatic illness is all in your head. You may bury your needs, but your body clamors for attention with physical symptoms. Mind and body are one. Your body expresses psyche's pain. To be heard, sometimes a body has to shout. Illness and pain are friends that come with messages for renewal.

Does your mask reflect how you feel inside? How you portray your "okay-ness" is an act. Everyone on some level, knows the truth. If you pretend, you only fool yourself. Even if the outside world doesn't seem to notice, you know if you hurt and are out-of-control.

A TRUE STORY: Judy

"**I was a prisoner of my body.** For thirty years I suffered from fibromialgia, chronic fatigue and irritable bowel syndrome. I was in constant pain while walking, standing and/or moving. My life was a predictable pattern of work, fast food on the way home and taking prescribed pain medications.

A 'loner' in a rigid world; 'I can't' was my incantation. I did not allow myself to push the boundaries that fenced me in. Even after eight years of psychotherapy, I was still depressed. During hypnotherapy regression with Shelley, I tracked the cause of my irritable bowel syndrome. This is what I discovered under hypnosis:

'I'm five years old and mother says I'd better go to the bathroom before we go on a car trip.'

I can't go, so I'm afraid I'll have an accident the whole trip. It's terrible.

I'm in my first-grade class and I go to the toilet. When I return, my teacher asks (in front of all the kids); 'Where have you been?'

'I've been in the bathroom but nothing would come out.' I answer. Everyone laughs and I'm humiliated.

As I continued my hypnotherapy session, I heard how negative I've become. I learned negativity from Mom. I give it all back to her. She lived in fear and anxiety. That was her choice. I lived in fear and anxiety, too. Now I change 'I can't' to 'I can.'

These insights helped me take responsibility for feeling good.

Painkillers add to pain and depression so I'm coming off them and I feel better. I eat healthy foods, fresh fruits and vegetables and drink water. I no longer am a little girl with a sad mother. I'm growing up...at 45!

If I feel debilitated, I pick that little girl up and give her attention, support and respect."

Mirror, Mirror On the Wall

☆ *"Pretending is fun except for the part of living the mask instead of my heart."*

—Dennis Briskin

How do you look to yourself? Your face and eyes mirror everything about you inside. If your face looks sad in the mirror, you wear a sadness mask. Hurt that you hold inside is written all over your face. If you want to see how far back any sadness goes, look at childhood photographs. If your face has a "flat" expressionless mask-like appearance, it is quite likely that you were sexually or otherwise abused.

You can change your face and things will shift inside. Look in the mirror and smile, and you will see it is true.

▲ Playing the Lyre: Dis•chord

☆ Jon: "*There are three things I can't remember.*"
Shelley: "*What are they?*"

☆ "*The shabbiest truth is always better than the best-dressed lie.*"
—Ann Landers

Expression Junkies

For compulsive talkers, talk is cheap. Sometimes, words mask and substitute for feelings. Overly analytical folks often hide feelings behind a barrage of abstracted rationalizations. They speak from the mind, not the heart. Emotions often get lost behind words.

Both big and small lies chip away at joy and make us bitter and resentful. To numb the pain of lying, we often use destructive behavior. Honesty grows where honesty shows.

Up Your Egypt

Don't Lose Your Head Over a Lie

Hieroglyphics from 2600 BC say that a conjurer came to the Pharoah and appeared to cut off the head of a goose who then walked about crowing. After this fine display, the goose was miraculously restored. The Pharoah was so impressed he asked the conjurer to perform the same trick with a person from the court. The conjurer refused.

Photo by Jon Nicholas

SPLATTERY WILL GET YOU EVERYWHERE

A man lay down by the sewer
And by the sewer he died
They didn't know what to call it
So they called it sewer-side.

—Irv Lessin

Chapter 11

Slow-Motion Suicide

Rubble Without A Cause

A person may lose their child and people will weep for them. A person may lose their arm and we cry for them. But, a person who loses themself slips away as silently as a marshmallow into a cup of hot chocolate.

The Denial Triangle is slow-motion suicide. It breaks hearts. Self-destructive behavior cause more pain than any you escape. Even with denial, you suffer ill effects. No matter how you pretend, the denial triangle makes you feel awful. If you've been self-destructive, you can stop now before it's too late.

So, if your broken heart needs repair, I'm the one you'll need. I'll whisper sweet things you tell all your friends and they come running to see. Oh, Oh, Oh…There is no denying, reading this chapter could save your life.

▲ WELLNESS VS ILLNESS
▲ D.K.
▲ WHAT TO DO IF YOU'RE SERIOUSLY SUICIDAL: No Exodus
▲ HOW DO YOU GET OUT OF DENIAL: The Last Straw

Death is Nature's Way of Telling You to Slow Down

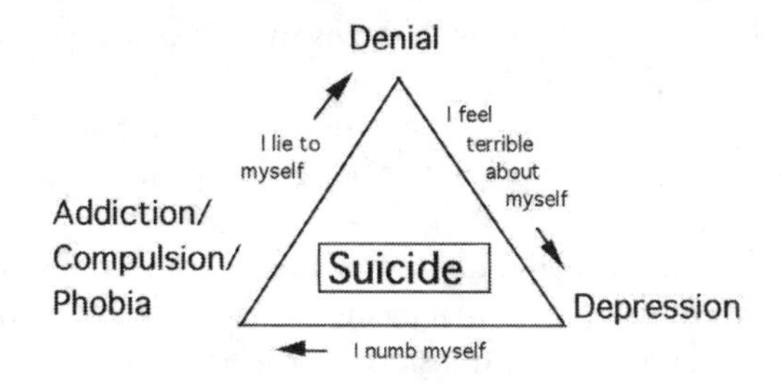

▲ Wellness Verses Illness

☆ Lion: *"I am king of the jungle. Stately, strong, powerful. And you. You are pathetic, weak and scrawny. What do you have to say for yourself?"*
Bedraggled Mouse: *"I've been sick."*

☆ *Is illness a statistical mistake?*
Unfair ordeal? The fickle finger of fate?
Surely it is no debate that illness pains and irritates
Yet, illness is a wake up call
To love yourself; warts and all.
A chance for profound transformation
Shedding old skin, regeneration,
Count your blessings, honor life,
Slow right down and avoid strife.

—Shelley Stockwell

Do you act as if you're a brain with a body dangling from it? If your body gets sick, do you get angry? Being alive requires you to accept and own your body. You are your body. You are every cell, muscle, nerve and organ.

The world's first doctors were shamans who believed that physical, emotional and spiritual energy were inseparable.

Photo by Grant Stockwell

Cari-on

In shamanistic societies, the holiest person is the wounded healer; for in wounding, gods are summoned for healing to take place. Those who overcome are gifted with a God Power to heal others.

Chinese healers say that illness is blocked energy within the body, and resistance to change. "Don't go with a positive flow and you get stuck in a hurtful past," they say.

Illness is a blip on your blueprint of perfection; usually a rigid souvenir from the past that manifests in the present. What causes pain and stress? Old habits? Patterns from your family?

I see illness is a transformative opportunity for self-love and spiritual openness and a shocking wake-up call. With ailments, we face inner demons and discover profound inner resources. Some transform and give up a lifetime of bad habits.

Some change stifling jobs, relationships and locations. Illness forces you to slow down, take responsibility for joy, change behaviors that aren't working and refocus on a bigger picture. For those who have made pain their lifestyle; giving up pain, means giving up the suffering lifestyle as well.

Dr. Bernie Siegel formed a group called COPE "Cancer Offers Precious Experience." Illness may be just what the doctor ordered for you to dump toxic attitudes and habits and connect with your higher self.

Welcome illness as a wake up call that alerts you to what you need to do to free yourself from limits. Honor pain as your teacher who allows you to discover your inner and outer resources.

When in conflict, ease becomes dis-ease. Explore illness and you may discover that you inadvertently created it. For example, to cope with stress you stuff in your mouth often triggers migraine headaches. Not enough water can also cause headaches. Constant stress causes emotional and physical "stress fractures."

Lots of people appear well, but are really very sick. Their true condition is repressed, ignored or used as an excuse to indulge in more drugs or self-destruction.

When ill, your brain secretes chemicals that affect your mood and personality, so it is challenging to get a clear perspective when your chemistry is out of whack.

Up Your Egypt

Ancient Egyptian Psychic Surgery

Close your eyes and imagine yourself standing upon a hill, arms outstretched and hands open toward the sun. As you hold the sun's rays in your palms, the energy circulates through your body and radiates out from each fingertip; then breathe. The more you breathe, the more sun you draw in and radiate out.

Now gently take your hands back and notice that they continue to radiate energy. Each fingertip is a laser beam of healing light. Within this laser light are golden scalpels, cleansing brushes, powerful ointments, healing herbs and golden threads.

The sun fills your crown.

Place your fingers toward any part of your body or mind that needs healing, and the beams of laser light now do their work. Say:

"I am healed. Any confused cells are now released from my body and mind, positively renewed by sun and earth."

▲ D. K.: When Ease Becomes Dis-Ease

☆ *"He lost his health getting wealthy, then his wealth getting healthy."*
—Irv Lessin

Photo by Jon Nicholas

Many of us forget about the body/mind connection. Everything you think and do affects your mental and physical being.

A German study of 2,000 people over a thirteen year period found that those who kept emotions bottled up, experienced anger, depression, hostility and despair, were more likely to get cancer and heart disease. Most illness is the result of suggestion, stress, unresolved conflict and/or blocked energy.

Krazelneck's Killer Thoughts

You can literally program your mind to kill you.

In a bizarre 1942 study conducted by Dr. Krazelneck at Indiana University School of Psychology, ten guys scheduled to be executed on death row were offered the privilege of having their body given to the family for a proper burial and $50 to help the family pay for the services, if they would experience their death while under hypnosis.

All agreed and were individually put into a deep trance and blindfolded. They were "tricked" to believe that they were being executed. Their wrists were very slightly cut and saline solution was poured over it to emulate a feeling of blood pouring from their veins. "With so much fluid leaving your body, your heart will stop pumping and you will die," they were told. Eight of the ten died on cue.

Doctors and families are amazing hypnotists. What they suggest, positive or negative, is often realized. Unreleased energy is like putting your foot on the brake while stepping on the accelerator full throttle. Here is how Deanna "welled" herself:

A TRUE STORY Deanna

"I suffered from numbness in my throat and had difficulty swallowing. My doctor said I had nerve dysfunction and an impaired gag response. When I heard the word 'gag,' I put two and two together. What was it I didn't want to say?

I didn't want to admit that my husband was sexually abusing our two young children. Rather than voice my suspicion, my throat closed up. I guess it was hard for me to swallow the truth. Finally, I spoke up. I confronted my husband.

It ended my marriage, and saved my children. The most amazing thing happened: My throat was just fine."

What Are Your Options?

☆ *"I'm dying to find out."*

—Mort Tality

If you are ill, you have many wellness options. Some are dangerous; others are safe and easy. The most dangerous options are drugs and surgery. A healthy diet, exercise and healthy life style is your best approach. Try saying and doing good kind and nourishing things to and for yourself. If necessary, give herbs, vitamins and natural remedies a go.

Illness and emotions are similar. When we suppress them, they travel deeper into our being and increase discomfort. As we get healthy, such putrefied tensions unravel much like a ball of yarn. Honesty and positive thinking cleanse the mind of denial, illusion, destructive patterns and release symptoms and sickness.

Detoxifying and cleansing old compulsions and addictions is like being under reconstruction. Change may make you confused or unsettled. But it won't last forever.

Be patient, in no time at all, you'll feel human again and enjoy life. In some ways, change is like starting life all over again—vulnerable and naive. Be gentle with yourself. It is precious to learn to be you again. New skills and behaviors open you afresh. Nutrition too can make a great difference. Susan Lark, MD tells this story:

"During my internship in obstetrics and gynecology at the University of Oregon Medical Center, I by chance, spotted an article on the use of nutrition to treat breast cysts in an obstetrics and gynecology journal. I had never been exposed to the concept of nutrition as therapy before; in fact, it hadn't occurred to me that what I ate could affect my health.

That article was a real breakthrough for me. For the first time, I realized that there was something substantial I could do myself to alleviate symptoms and improve my health."

Red Herings

Herings Law of Cure says that stopping toxic behaviors can cause a "healing crisis." That's why people getting well sometimes feel sicker first. We may re-experience past pain, symptoms and dis•ease. Our bodies heal from the inside out, from top to bottom, and from the most important organ to the least.

Headaches happen when toxins are released too fast. The body says, "No more poison. Oh good, let's clean house and release stored toxins into the bloodstream." To get through any crisis: cleanse, drink lots of water, acknowledge each condition, hang in there and be enthusiastic about wellness.

Everything you've ever done in life began as a thought. The work you do, the place you live and the clothes you wear, are all a result of a thought that you manifested into action and reality. In order to choose wellness, joy and peace, you must choose to think wellness, joy and peace. Think it with all of your senses and all your being.

What would full wellness be like for you? How would it taste? How would it smell? How would it sound? How would your body feel? What would you look like? What proactive steps can you take right now to feel well?

Stop Withdrawal Headache

☆ *"If we tread our path with heart; illness' dark passage may give us a glimpse not only to what it is like to become whole but what it means to be fully human."*

—Mark Barasch, New Age Journal

Three Headache Remedies

Drink as much water as possible to flush your system. Then try these three remedies:

One: Tell the Truce
Imagine a war going on in your head with guns, cannons, warriors and bombs. Focus your attention on your feet and imagine the soldiers marching...and running. Count from 1 to 3 and the war is over.

Two: Magnetic Magic
"My hands are giant magnets and as I pull them from your head all pain and tension will move from your head to my hands."
One two three the war is over.
(Draw hands away and say:)
"I feel better."

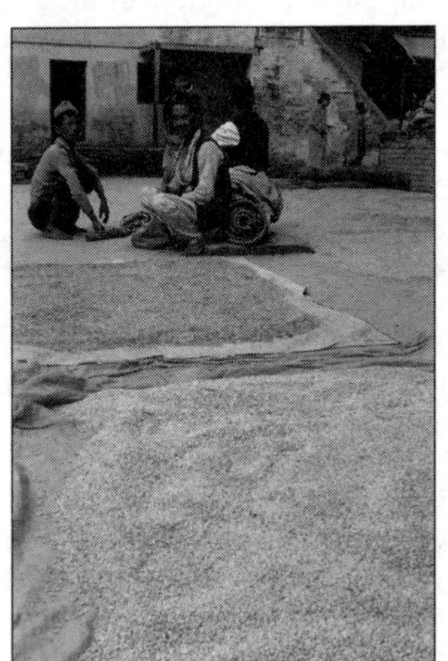

Going against my-grain

Three: Hocus Focus
What color is it? How much does it weigh? Where is it located? Is it transparent, translucent or opaque? It's moving. Where is it now? What color is it? How much does it weigh now? Is it transparent, translucent or opaque? Keep going asking more and more detailed questions as you interject suggestions like: "It's getting smaller. What size is it now?" Finall,y as it shifts, say, "I'll take it now" and sweep your hands upward from the crown of the subject.

Pain Management

☆ *"There is no illness of the body apart from the mind."*

—Socrates, 6th Century BC

Laughter Fights Infection

Laughter is contagious; not infectious. Studies at the Loma Vista University School of Immunology show that laughter increases your body's natural toxic-attack killer cells (T lymphocytes) and helper receptive cells. Laughter lowers cortisol levels, which keeps you healthier.

Laughter may really be the best medicine.

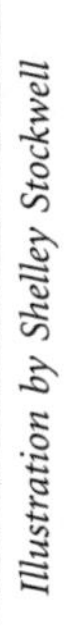

Illustration by Shelley Stockwell

☆ SOBRIETY

I looked into the morning and all I could see was sadness
Sorrow, for me, my friends, my angel, anyone that had
the bum job of caring for me.
I guess when you do sober up, and see how you have lived,
It can be the worst and best feeling you ever have.

—Chris Aguilar

It is estimated that 63 billion people a year in the United States are dealing with pain. Be comfortable within the pain and anxiety by moving into it and noticing the "still point." If pain is present, don't will it away. Work with it.

How to Solve a Painful Problem:

1. **Identify what is wrong.** Subconscious come forward and tell me now. (Pause)
2. **Identify the payoffs.** Does the problem serve any useful purpose? If so, what? Did it serve a purpose in the past? If so, what? What needs healing? Go to that place.
3. **Pinpoint a problem area.** What do I notice? I describe it to myself? What shape? What color? What texture? How does the blood supply flow?
4. **What do I need to do?** To help, do I cool it down, warm it up and bring more blood there? Less blood? Do I need to release it and let it go?
5. **Do it!** I do what needs to be done and I notice when it is complete. Great!
6. **Anything else?** Is there anything else that needs to happen? Make it happen now.
7. **Affirm: "All levels of my body, mind and energy promise to do what is necessary to be at peak performance."**

INTO•GREAT POWER EXERCISE

Burmese Pain Control

Take a deep breath, and notice the part of your body or mind that is uncomfortable. Notice the size, shape, color texture and areas that surround this problem spot. Now call in the carpenter, who sands, slices, planes and shrinks this uncomfortable place from your awareness. Continue to breathe and relax.

AFFIRM SUCCESS: Healing Harmony

Here is the affirmation that works miracles. Read it and let its power work wonders:

Breathe. If pain is present, notice and feel it as it comes and goes. Ride the sensation as it comes and goes. I observe my thoughts as they shift and change. I escort my mind to mindful breathing.

Thoughts, like a monkey, jump from idea to idea; chattering and influencing. Notice thoughts and say, "Oh that was just a thought." And return to breath.

I notice the still point within or below any discomfort and let go. I savor each moment of my life.

I choose to live. I am healthy.

I do what creates good health for myself. When I am awake, I create wellness. When I am asleep, I create wellness. I am perfectly healthy.

I am true to my natural rhythm, my real self.

I release any habit or emotions that cause issue to my tissue. I'm healthy and unlimited.

If I "spring a leak," I examine it and recognize its cause. I discover new personal strength and this heals. I completely and absolutely release any and all limits. I am unlimited. I return to balance in my body, brain chemistry and mind.

I focus all levels of myself upon one cell in the part of my body that is renewing. Hear me cell:

Go back to your innate coding. Return to the blueprint that allows you to do your job most efficiently. Return in full balance, fullness and harmony. Restore

your original and most perfect imprint, coding and function as it was meant to be. Restore your natural ability for even more efficient functioning. You are now restored to your full and perfect functioning. Cell do you understand? (Pause and listen)

You are now restored renewed and regenerated. You are restored renewed and regenerated.

I speak to my endocrine system:
Glands and immune chemical responses, go back to your original and perfect state. Heal ______ (give specific instructions).

My body is now fully activated and producing all you need to be entirely restored. I have now accomplished a lot and am very proud of myself.

▲ What To Do If You're Seriously Suicidal: No Exodus

☆ *Razors pain you; Rivers are damp;*
Acids stain you; Drugs cause cramp;
Guns aren't lawful; Nooses give;
Gas smells awful; You might as well live.

—Dorothy Parker

INTO•GREAT POWER EXERCISE

Exercise to Exorcise Obliteration

Take a mental time out; sit up straight and think about the real consequences of killing yourself.

If you kill yourself, you will be dead. It's so final. You can't change your mind. You can't come up with a great new solution. Think about what you will do to those who love you.

Imagine yourself five years from today, looking back on this moment, "I'm so glad I didn't do it," you say. Now take a deep breath, get up and drink a glass of water, then take a nice, warm bath. Have yourself a good old-fashioned cry if you want, and know that you are participating in change and growth. Get a grip and be well.

If you are afraid you might really kill yourself, here's what to do:

▲ Even if you think there is nothing you can do, hang in there

You always have options, even if you are too upset to see them. If you really believe you don't have options, get help now. You'll be so glad you did when you're feeling better. By all means, don't let your panic, despair or helplessness get the best of you. Hormones, chemicals and pain influence your negative thinking. Soon you'll be on center again.

☎ Pick up the phone

Immediately call 911 or a crisis hot line, support organization (any 12-step program), minister, therapist, a helpful friend, or doctor. If you're away from home or in another country every city has a suicide hot line. Call it.

▲ Get help

Drag yourself to a local emergency room. Turn to the resources section at the end of this book for a list of organizations to call. Ask a friend or neighbor to just sit with you. No matter how depressed you get, do not take drugs or alcohol. If you can't think of anyone to help you, go out on the street and stop a stranger. Everyone is human; they will care for you. Help and change come from unexpected places. Be on the look out. Get help from yourself.

▲ Talk to the part of you that wants to live

Sit down with that part of you that wants to live and have an uplifting conversation.

▲ How Do You Get Out of Denial: The Last Straw

☆ Question: *How Do You Get Out of the Denial Triangle?*
Answer: *Reed on!*

HYPNOSIS HELPERS

Resources available from Creativity Unlimited See back of the book.

The Wellness Tape, (audio cassette) Stockwell, Shelley, Ph.D. and Dr. Lilia Prado, D.O.

Peace and Calm (audio cassette) Stockwell, Shelley.

Yes I Can! (audio cassette) Stockwell, Shelley.

Enter the Great Pyramid of Truth

▲

Yes
New
Peace
Health
Unlimited
Happiness
My true self
Positive action
Kings Chamber
Healthy choices
I live my dreams
I'm a new person
The land of my soul
Nourishing life style
I gift myself with joy
Vital and enthusiastic
Positively feeling great
My essential loving self
Embracing my innate talents
I use my strength for positive action
I release hurt to the past where it belongs
Guided up the stairs of higher consciousness
I teach myself positive ways to be in the world
Right here, right now, I meet my higher self & fall in love
All celebrate! I am whole and holy. I love myself completely
Hear this all parts of myself, I extend to you unconditional love
My readiness for change and commitment are my key ingredients

Step Three •●.●.•●

ENTER the GREAT PYRAMID

How to Feel Terrific!

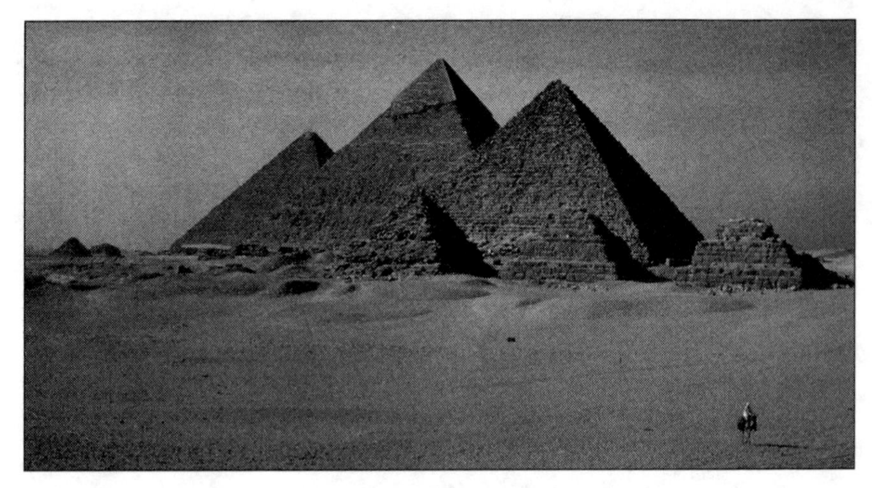

Pyramids at Giza

Up Your Egypt

What Is The Truth About Pyramid Power?

Forty-six known pyramids cover 40,000 years of history. The Great Pyramid of Cheops, made of limestone, calcite and granite, weighs an estimated 6.6 million tons. It has enough stones to build a wall three feet high around the borders of France. The highest building in the world for 4000 years, its base area equals ten football fields. The Hebrew Bible says that Moses, raised as an Egyptian Prince, was taught spiritual and technical knowledge from priests who watched over the pyramids.

Pyramids purportedly amplify vibrations of anything placed under them. Razors sharpen. Produce stays fresh. Seeds found in the Great Pyramid have grown in laboratories thousands of years later. Five-thousand-year-old flower essences found in pyramids still retain full aroma. What is the purpose of pyramids? Many theories abound:

Sundial Theory Some say that the Great Pyramid of Cheops is the biggest sundial in the world.

Power Plant Theory Slots in the ramp to the grand gallery of Cheops, show heavy scorch marks and heat damage suggesting that the Great Pyramid was a power plant. The passages and chambers were precisely constructed by an unknown advanced technology using mathematical constants like pi and the golden proportion. This geometry and composition creates an energy injection system for phononwave and acoustic excitation.

Structure and Function Theory The pyramid shape is said to mimic the shape of the molecules of the calcite and red granite of which it is constructed.

Astral Transmitter to Other Dimensions Astronomical alignments of passages to the Pole Star, Alpha Draconis, The Pleiades and Orion imply to some that the pyramid and sphinx were built and used for astral or extra-terrestrial communication. Pyramid placements of Giza, perfectly align with the three stars in the belt of Orion. 10,500 years ago the air shaft from the king's chamber of the Great Pyramid would have pointed directly to Orion. The "face on mars" as seen in photos from our space shuttle suggests a similar configuration on the planet, Mars.

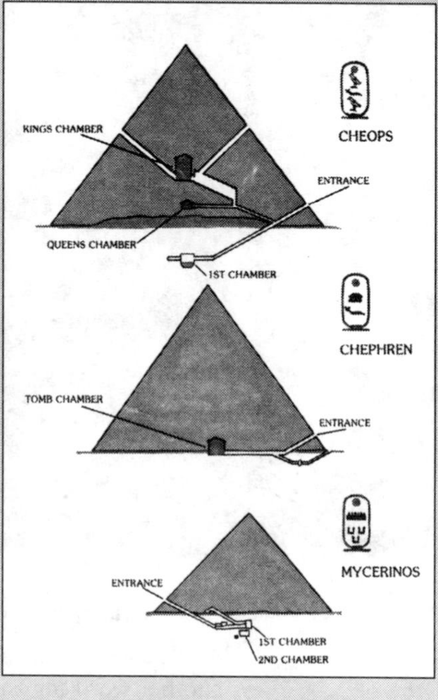

Ka Theory Ancient Egyptians called their pyramids "houses of eternal life" and built them so pharaohs could both receive and transmit energy. The "ka," or soul of Pharaoh, received energy from the sky through this transmitter. Pyramid power kept pharaoh's soul essence in full vibration. Loved ones would visit the burial chamber, or the linking tunnels beneath the pyramids, Sphinx and other buildings. Booby traps, fake doors and fear of evil curses were meant to dissuaded grave robbers. None of these worked too well.

It was common for priests to bring bread (the staff of life) and sacrifice meat next to the pyramid. This food nourished the departed pharaoh. The priests and royal family then ate this food and took on the blessings of eternal life. This tradition is still carried on today when we pray before eating and "bless" bread and wine.

Initiation Temple The King's chamber was the site of the most sacred initiation rites. Hypnotic regression and rebirthing took place here. In one rite, initiates were to sleep inside a pyramid and unfold lucid dreams of other life times. If you managed to remember them all without getting caught in a *dream trap* (forgetting that it is a dream), then you transcended the reincarnation dream for enlightenment.

Photo by Jon Nicholas

Maat, Mother, Milk

Maat meaning truth, justice, or judgment is another word for Isis. Maat is the original all-seeing eye of mother. The word Maat comes from the verb "to see" and sounds suspiciously like our words "mother" and "milk."

Chapter 12
Truth Pyramid
Turn On Your Pharaoh Faucet

Truth is the opposite of denial. Truth unburdens and unveils your resplendent innate talents, interests and personal gifts. This chapter has simple exercises and ideas to help you get out of your own way and get you what you want...what you really, really want...JOY.

- ▲ BARGE AHEAD: Certifiably Committed
- ▲ SEVEN EASY STEPS TO LIVING WELL: Raised From The Dead
- ▲ MOVE INTO ACTION
- ▲ IN TRUST WE GOD
- ▲ TRUTH: Bone-A-Fied
- ▲ DR. STOCKWELL'S TEN COMMANDMENTS FOR PEACE & FUN: Icon Do It

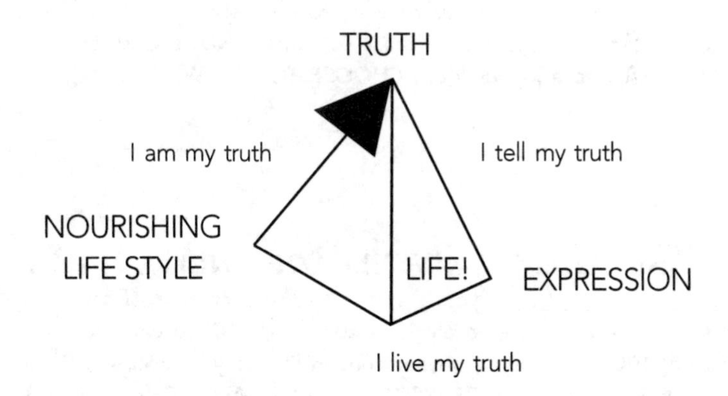

Awake and alive you listen, hear and live your truth

▲ BARGE AHEAD: Certifiably Committed

☆ *"Every morning you are handed 24 golden hours. They are one of the few things in this world that you get free of charge. If you had all the money in the world, you couldn't buy an extra hour. What will you do with this priceless treasure? Remember that you must use it, as it is only given once. Once wasted, you cannot get it back."*

—Shayne Marchand

☆ *"Be what you is, not what you ain't. If you is what you ain't, you ain't what you is."*

—Bernie Siegel

Be as stubborn about being happy as you are about defending hurtful behaviors! Make well-being your truth. Sign this affidavit and you'll be certifiably committed:

HAPPY NEW ME
A SWORN AFFIDAVIT

I am ready to rebirth my joy, love, peace and bliss. To prove it to myself, I fill out this affidavit and sign my name. (JUST DO IT!)

I CHOOSE TO LIVE!

I ____________________ joyously swear, to the very fiber of my being, to all those of my lineage and all those to come, AND to God, that I am dedicated 100% to a joyous life. I CHOOSE TO LIVE WELL.

Signed____________________

I CHOOSE TO LOVE MYSELF UNCONDITIONALLY

I ____________________ joyously swear, to the very fiber of my being, to all those of my lineage, to all those to come, AND to God, that I am dedicated 100% to loving myself unconditionally. I EMBRACE ALL ASPECTS OF MYSELF WITH RESPECT, KINDNESS, AND LOVE. JOY IS MY COMPASS. It's the truth, it's actual...everything is satisfactual!

Signed____________________
Date____________________

▲ SEVEN EASY STEPS TO LIVING WELL: Raised From the Dead

☆ *"Are you God?" they asked the great Buddha.*
"No, I'm just awake."

☆ *"When your heart is in your dream, no request is too extreme."*

—Jimminy Cricket

Step One: ·· HONESTLY CLARIFY Your GOAL

Positive change begins with a straightforward conversation. Honestly tell yourself what makes things worse and or better…for you. Answer these questions with the first thing that comes to mind. If you are not sure what the right answer is, make one up. Your subconscious mind will spontaneously communicate.

What can I do to take charge of my joy and life? ______________________
What do I want? ______________________
What blessings help me have what I want? ______________________
What obstacles keep me from having what I want? ______________________
What steps can I take to overcome those obstacles? ______________________
What one action step will I take today? ______________________
If not today, exactly what day will I take it? ______________________

Step Two ·.·· ☼ CLAIM Your POWER

Pretend that you are the *All-Powerful Omnipotent Leader of the World.* Hold the thought that YOU create everyone and everything in your life. With this in mind, take this quiz for fun; it's all a game.

As the all-powerful:

I choose my mate (or to be alone) because: ______________________
I choose to be ill or suffer with __________ because: ______________________
I choose to be well because: ______________________
I choose to feel strong because: ______________________
I choose to fail at ____________ because: ______________________
I choose to succeed at ____________ because: ______________________
I choose to punish myself for__________ because: ______________________
I choose to forgive myself because: ______________________

Think about your answers before you proceed to step three…

Step Three ..·•.. ☺ OWN Your WEAKNESSES

☆ *"I see what others may never see. I know what others may never know. I have to live with myself and so, whatever happens I want to be self respecting and conscience free."*

Check any behaviors you have or substances you use that are unhealthy for you and give yourself the reason you do it anyway:

Overboard Behaviors	**I Do It Because** (payoff):
Lying to Myself	______________________
Lying to Others	______________________
Chaos	______________________
Cleaning (over and under)	______________________
Cluttering	______________________
Co-dependency	______________________
Computers	______________________
Control	______________________
Counting	______________________
Eating (over and under)	______________________
Exercise	______________________
Exhibitionism	______________________
Eyebrow plucking	______________________
Foot tapping	______________________
Gambling	______________________
Gum chewing	______________________
Hit me, hurt me	______________________
Hoarding	______________________
Hypochondria	______________________
Hysteria	______________________
Leg jiggling	______________________
Lip biting	______________________
Love obsession	______________________
Lying	______________________
Nail biting	______________________
Neatness	______________________
Nudity	______________________
Pack-ratting	______________________
Perfectionism	______________________
Picking	______________________
Rage	______________________
Religion	______________________
Scamming	______________________
Sexual compulsion	______________________
Shoplifting	______________________
Shopping	______________________

Songs-in-my-head ______
Sports ______
Thrills ______
Ticks ______
Video games ______
Washing (over and under) ______
Workaholism ______
Worrying ______
Name your own ______

Over Used Substance	**I Use It Because** (payoff):
Artificial Sweeteners	______
Aerosol sprays	______
Alcohol	______
Antidepressants	______
Aspirin	______
Barbiturates	______
Caffeine	______
Chocolate	______
Cocaine	______
Cold remedies	______
Decongestants	______
Ecstasy	______
Hair Dye	______
Heroin	______
Inhalants	______
Laxatives	______
LSD	______
Marijuana	______
Mescaline	______
Methadone	______
Morphine	______
MSG	______
Nose sprays	______
Peyote	______
Prescription Pills	______
Salt	______
Soft drinks	______
Sleeping pills	______
Solvents	______
Steroids	______
Sugar	______
Surgery	______
Tobacco	______
Tranquilizers	______
Name your own	______

Step Four ..·•..·• Review Your "Becauses"

Review the reasons that you give yourself for any of the above overboard behavior.

Answer the following questions for each "reason" you gave yourself:

Is your reason a way to justify hurtful behavior? ______________

Is your reason an excuse for something you are avoiding? ______________

Does the reason make sense? ______________

If reason doesn't make sense, what's your underlying payoff or motivation? ______________

Is there a healthier way to meet your need? ______________

What is your bottom line? What do you really want or need?

Here is an example of the layers and the bottom line of wants or needs:

"I choose to junk out on sugar" because:

Layer 1: <u>It tastes delicious.</u>

Layer 2: The delicious taste <u>reminds me of my father, who gave me candy.</u>

Layer 3: When I think of my father, <u>I feel loved.</u>

Layer 4: <u>Sugar makes me feel loved.</u>

Bottom Line or payoff: <u>I want to be loved.</u>

The bottom line or payoff in this example is, "I want to be loved."

Step Five ..·•..·•.. ⇨ REPLACE NEGATIVE PAYOFFS

Replace negative bottom lines or payoffs with constructive ones.

If "I want to feel loved" is the bottom line; what other things could you do to be loved? How about speaking lovingly to yourself? Eat healthy foods, lose weight, get exercise and attract a new mate (or turn on the mate you have). You could ask someone for a hug. You could look at yourself in a mirror and say, "I love you." "I am enough." "I'm great." You could treat yourself as if you were your own best friend.

Replace helplessness	⇨	with responsibility
Replace ignoring self	⇨	with honoring self
Replace need for approval	⇨	with self-approval
Replace lack of boundaries	⇨	with clear boundaries
Replace guilt and shame	⇨	with forgiveness and pride
Replace self destruction	⇨	with healthy habits

You create your reaction to circumstances. Forcing and reinforcing positive thoughts, attitudes and behavior makes you happier. If there is anything that you do each day that you judge yourself harshly for, say to yourself, "What did I learn. I will do better in the future and I forgive myself. "

Most pain and illness is the result of unresolved or buried conflict. When you tell yourself the truth about things, you stop the war within and feel well.

Step Six ..·•.. ·•..·• MOVE INTO ACTION

Action means to:

- Δ Tell yourself the truth by opening your eyes, ears and consciousness
- Δ Replace negative thoughts with positive words
- Δ Honor yourself with a nourishing life style
- Δ Live your dreams
- Δ Do one thing at a time and organize
- Δ Divorce destructive patterns
- Δ Forgive
- Δ Celebrate and count your blessings

Step Seven ..·•.. ..·•..·• CELEBRATE YOURSELF

☆ *Propel, propel, propel your craft*
Gaily on liquid solution.
Joyfully, joyfully, joyfully
Life is but an illusion.

Photo by Rayma Ditson

You are a miracle!

Over seven hundred million sperm fought for your egg. Only one hundred of those little guys survived the journey to YOU "the egg." You are the sperm that made it. YOU, The Egg, carefully chose You "the Sperm." From here, you spontaneously spread, divided and made Mom lopsided. Because your will to live was strong, you survived. You chose to live. You were born.

To live means to awaken in gratitude for your life and to follow your bliss, come to your senses in the here and now, listen to what you want for yourself, and do whatever it takes to get it. To live means that you tell yourself the truth.

☆ *THE MAN IN THE GLASS*
When you get what you want in your struggle for self and
the world makes you king for a day,
Just go to the mirror and look at yourself; see what that man has to say.
For it is not your mother, or father, or wife, whose judgment upon you must pass;
The fellow whose verdict counts most in your life is the one staring back from the glass.

Some people may think you're a straight-shootin' chum, and call you a wonderful guy,
But the man in the glass says you're only a bum
if you can't look him straight in the eye.
He's the fellow to please, never mind all the rest, for he's with you clear up to the end,
You've passed your most dangerous, difficult test, if the man in the glass is your friend.

You may fool the world down the pathway of years, and get pats on the back as you pass,
But your final reward will be heartaches and tears, if you've cheated the man in the glass.

▲ IN TRUST WE GOD

☆ *"Sit down before fact, like a little child, and be prepared to give up every preconceived notion. Follow humbly to wherever and to whatever nature leads, or you shall learn nothing."*

— T. H. Huxley

You can live and view life with profound clarity. Your inner wisdom knows exactly what you need to do to live life fully. LISTEN TO THAT STILL SMALL VOICE WITHIN. Call in The Creator, Ascended Masters, Mother Nature, Higher Self, Angels and Guides, and know that there is help.

Photo by Nica Lee

▲ TRUTH: Bone-A-Fied

☆ *Can't look another in the eye? Suspect a lie.*
Throat clears, stomach knot…it's deception you got.
Tellers of truth don't clear their throats
Or second guess or stab with jokes (just kidding).

Tellers of truth listen with their hearts, talk with their eyes,
Are often loved; seldom despised.
Truth sayers are awake
Aren't constipated, don't have bellyaches.
Attend self-conducted seminars.
Listen well to their inner voices.
Nude warriors, amidst manipulative finery, pretensions and illusion.

☆ *Tellers of truth are each one of us*
Before we learn to lie and deny.

—Shelley Stockwell

☆ *"If you tell the truth, you don't have to remember anything."*

— Mark Twain

In Greece in 400 BC, Diogenes went looking for an honest man. The modern word *diagnose* comes from his quest. The honest man is hu•man.

You are it.

Truth begins when you are aware of your truth and do the right thing even if nobody is watching.

Truth is cleansing. Say your truth to yourself and out loud to another.

Levels of Truth: Account-Ability

☆ *"Lying makes a problem part of the future; truth makes a problem part of the past."*

—Rick Petino

Lead To Succeed

The more you own your own process and reaction, the better you feel. Think about a time you were really upset with someone. Did you:

Level 1 Withhold Truth

"I don't care." You Lie like a rug, stew or ignore.
"I don't feel." You shut up and shut down. Nobody's home.

Level 2 Attack (Blame it on the bossanova): "You are..."

I reject you. You name call and blame saying out loud or in your head, "You are a jerk" or "You are a jackal!" or "I don't like you."

Photo by Jon Nicholas

Gouda's Shop

Level 3 Acknowledge Your Own Feelings "About you I feel..."

Recognize that your feelings are all about yourself saying out loud or in your head, "I feel annoyed with you and that's why I call you a jerk."

Level 4 Identify What Hurts "... because..."

Reporting observations from introspection, saying out loud or in your head, "My annoyance came because you were rude to me and that hurt."

Level 5 Bring it Home, "That means to me..."

You judge the meaning saying out loud or in your head, "You don't think I'm worthy of respect?"

Level 6 Own Your Own, "About me I feel..."

You tell yourself the truth about what's really going on, saying out loud or in your head, "I judge myself as horrible and unworthy of love and respect."

Level 7 Higher Truth "I create a better outcome."

Responsibility! You take charge of your inner harmony saying out loud or to yourself, "Cancel, cancel. I am a wonderful person; worthy of love and respect. I am centered and happy. Whatever you say and do is all about you. What I do with it is all about me. I learn better ways to stay centered. I learn from your point of view better ways to interact for my own wellness."

INTO•GREAT POWER EXERCISE

Truth Test: Bust Self-Deception

1. Take a deep breath and get into center.

2. Exhale, close your eyes, and think about someone you love. What's that like for you? How does your body feel? How does your mind feel?

3. Open your eyes and stretch.

4. We are going to do a mean trick but only for a minute. Take a second deep breath, close your eyes again and get into center. Now make up a gigantic lie. Tell yourself that you HATE this person; in fact, despise them. Notice how you feel when you lie!

5. Take a deep breath and go back to your loving thoughts. Notice the difference between the way you feel when you tell the truth and tell a lie.

6. Now, you can tune into your body and can tell if you are being honest.

AFFIRM SUCCESS: Transform Me Honestly
Put your hands on your heart and affirm these words. Let their meaning become your truth.

I tell the truth, the whole truth and nothing but the truth, so help me God. I congratulate myself for learning better ways of being and communicating. I promise to do whatever it takes to feel terrific and live my dreams. I'm aware of my true feelings, thoughts and heartfelt desires.

I speak my truth out loud and am more aware of hidden truths as I speak. I know what I really want for myself. I listen to myself. My truth sets me free. I'm free. I face problems head on and they fade away. I face the facts. I seek help for myself. I'm responsible for my actions. I choose healthy right action.

I come to my senses with each moment of now.
I trust my truth, which is my vow.
I agree to be me. I agree to be free.
I honestly live in ecstasy.

Truth expressed openly to others cleanses and heals. The moment I choose positive change, I am joy. I choose positive change. I get a grip, take control,

release habits that don't work and take on joyous behavior. I'm kind in my communication.

I love myself completely, as best friend and life-long companion. Joy is my goal. I follow my bliss. I'm strong and flexible. I weather life's tides. I enjoy the seasons of my life. I feel fine. I'm stubborn about feeling terrific. l commit to live well. The Garden of Eden is honestly within me.

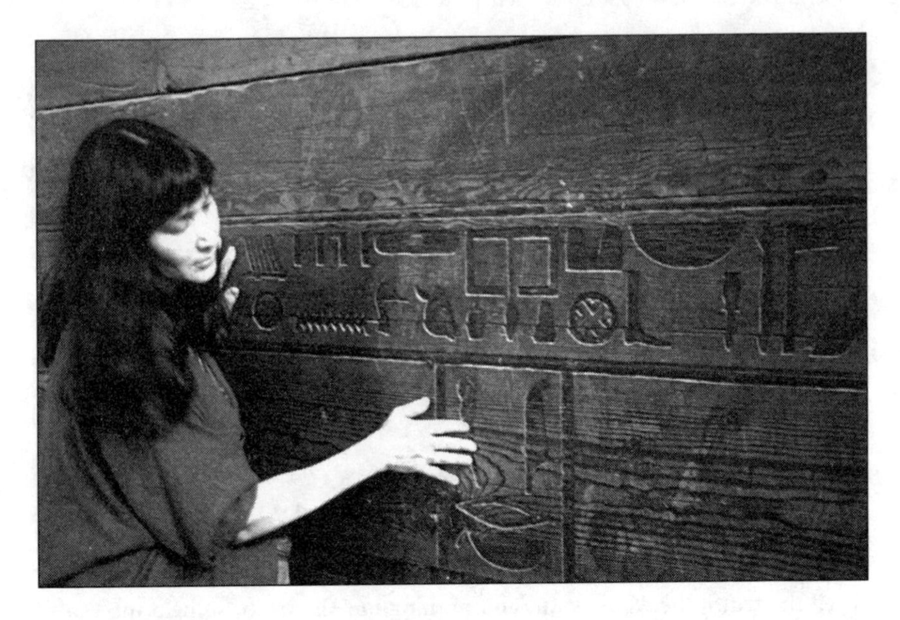

☆ *"To break the tangled web we weave,*
from the practice to deceive
Spin a yarn of bright ambition
Make a plan and good decisions and
live your dreams with great precision.
Your secret mind: uncharted, unscathed
Is golden light: Welcome Brave."

—Shelley Stockwell

☆ *"I was sixty-six years old. I still had to make a living. I looked at my social security check of $105 dollars and decided to use that to try to franchise my chicken recipe. Folks had always liked my chicken."*

—Colonel Harland Sanders

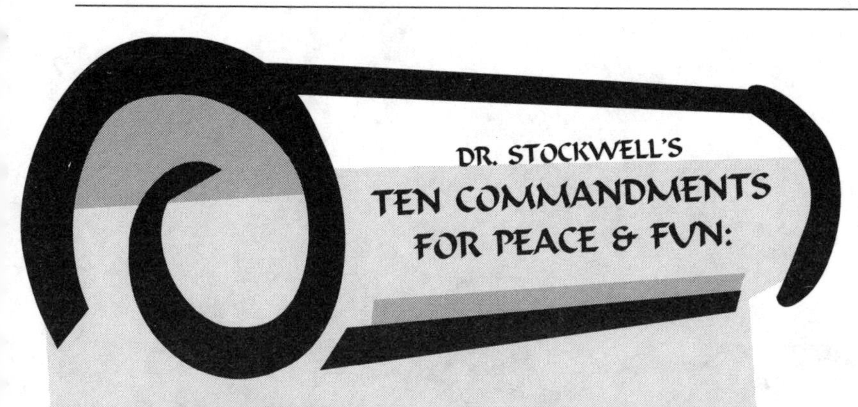

1. Tell The Truth
2. Enjoy Proper Nutrition
3. Avoid Toxic Chemicals
4. Breathe
5. Get Exercise
6. Get Support
7. Clear Your Mind
8. Relax
9. Make your dreams and plans happen
10. See The Humor

Choose joy. Life is hilarious. Discover the humor in every situation. You are part of a divine comedy. Enjoy yourself.

☆ Question: "*What do you do to get to heaven?*"
Answer: "*Die.*"

☆ Question: "*How do you get heaven on earth?*"
Answer: "*Live.*"

Photo by Jon Nicholas

Sufi Dancer, Cairo

Chapter 13
Expression
An Aye for an Aye

Expressing energy in positive ways liberates you. Expressing your truth to yourself and others gives your body, emotion, behavior, and vitality. That's what this chapter is about.

▲ HONEST COMMUNICATION: Give Up the Ghost

☆ *Express: To make known the opinions and feelings of oneself through words, gestures, actions or what one creates or produces; syn: vent, utter, voice, air.*
—Webster's Ninth (Dictionary)

☆ *"Beyond ideas of wrong doing and right doing there is a field. I'll meet you there."*
—Romee, 13th century poet

To heal and feel, GET REAL! Honest communication lets you clear inner conflict and recycle painful patterns into healthy new ways. It's difficult to love or trust a liar, even if it is yourself.

Express truth and you dislodge the wedge between yourself and others and ultimately clear stress. A rule of thumb is, "If it feels like it's important not to tell, tell." Or, if you mentally censor something more than three times, say it out loud. You can do it kindly, but do it.

It takes a lot more time *not* to say something than to just say it. Stuffing or ignoring feelings is stressful work.

▲ CANCEL! CANCEL! by Jillian LaVelle

☆ *Your mind is a garden,*
You reap what you sow;
If you see your life in a positive way
That's how your life will go.
—Shelley Stockwell

Thoughts are wonderful things. Through them you build your life adventure. Thoughts are positive when you brainstorm or problem solve.

Your thoughts are reflected in your attitude and response to life experiences.

Some thoughts run wild.

Some thoughts are negative. Focusing on things going wrong or a past negative experience are not productive; they are counter-productive.

Reoccurring negative thoughts interrupt work and play. They keep you awake nights. Repetitive negative thinking, and the resulting emotions, neuro-chemically impact your brain/mind as profoundly as any substance.

You can stop negative thoughts in their tracks!

Teach your mind to stop negativity by simply

Photo by Nica Lee

saying, "Cancel, cancel." This suddenly stops the thoughts, asserts your control and strengthens your decision to change the way you think. You have the right to do so. This is your life, this is your mind, and these are your thoughts. By interrupting a negative pattern, you train your mind to have less "worry time" and become calm. The trigger thought "cancel, cancel" brings you back to a centered feeling. It allows you time to change your thinking.

Affirm Success: Be Here Now
Use the following affirmation and embrace a more positive attitude about your true self. Read it slowly and take yourself to a new level. Take a deep breath, allow the oxygen to fill your head and feel free:

I train my mind for positive thought and right action. In this moment, I grow and mature with clarity, directness and wisdom. I call upon the Grace of God and the profound wisdom within me to keep me learning and maturing. I trust my inner wisdom to teach my senses to tell me the truth.

I know myself and what I need to do to make my life perfect. I give myself power to love myself, honor my body and be kind to me. I give any hurt to Mother Earth and a Higher Power and lovingly mourn its loss. Instantly, I return to joy and peace. All is well in my world.

▲EXPRESS HURT: No•mad

☆ *"The only way out is through."*
—Fritz Pearls

☆ *Once upon a time, on the eve of my childhood: I died at least one thousand times and one.*
So I left myself there on that one:
Somewhere in the long ago.
Never to be who once I was
In that olden, lost and golden
once upon a time.
—Dory McAuliffe

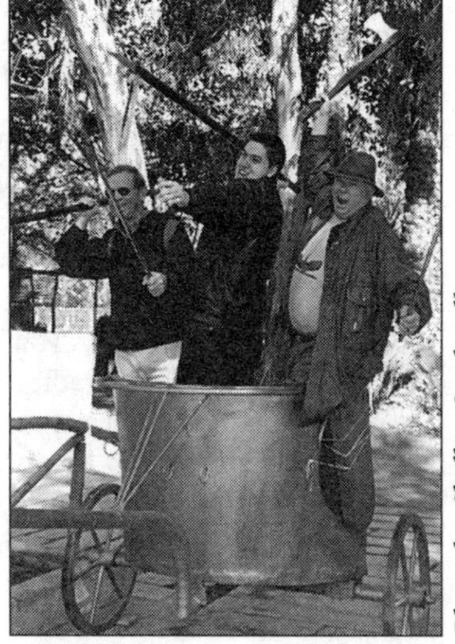

Photo by Shelley Stockwell

Warriors: Ross, Bryce & Jon

When you tell the truth and express rage in healthy, socially acceptable ways, you stop taking out rage (outrage) on yourself or innocent victims.

Hurt is remarkable; talk about it, release it

and heal. Expressing hurt lets it go and is quite a relief! Pain is trapped energy that causes more pain. Released pain takes with it mental limits and body aches, leaving you more time for fun.

Clearly and honestly expressed, pain extinguishes itself within 15 seconds. A little positively expressed pain never hurt anyone. The goal of expressing hurt is to let it go and get back to feeling good.

Affirm Success: What a Release

I am in control of my reactions and emotions. I consider the consequences before I act or react. I use healthy methods to release trapped energy. I ask for help and feedback from safe and appropriate people, and listen well to what they have to say.

As I change, some people grow closer while others may move away. This is healthy. Every day, in every way, I am better and better.

Avoid Scapegoats

☆ SNAKE

Sometimes my skin crawls so bad…
I just want to strike out at something.
Sometimes I get so irritated with my surroundings…I just want to strike out at something.
Then, if I do strike out, I get my fangs all a tangled and wish I just hadn't bothered...
Sleeping in the sun suits me better.

—Nica Lee

Photo by Nica Lee

Expression is not license to manipulate or to beat up yourself or another. It's inappropriate to yell, insult, snipe or be condescending to a human (or animal for that matter). Such aggressive acting out literally robs your energy and hurts you.

"Hate" organizations, radical religions or political activists attract angry people who loudly and repetitiously vent rage. This compulsive, socially acceptable negativity can be unbelievably destructive to others and the "true" believer. Burning crosses or hissing at your enemy's cat, makes you sick inside.

Covert venting of anger at football and soccer can be fun; so can bashing a tennis ball. Jane has a creative way to sublimate hurt and anger:

A TRUE STORY Jane

"Several years ago, I moved into a rambling old house in the country. It had a huge yard with a high wall for handball. In the basement was a warehouse of ceramic plates; not my taste. When I'm stressed, I grab a box of plates and head for the wall. Throwing plates saved my sanity and my marriage."

Appropriate Ways to Release Anger and Trapped Energy

Photo by Nica Lee

Bryce and Racheal

- Sing or yell at the ocean or in the shower,
- Hit a tennis ball really hard.
- Punch a punching bag.
- Pound a pillow.
- Run with a vengeance.
- Ride an exercise bike at high speed.
- Do martial arts.
- Pound a drum.
- Kick, scream, and/or cry.
- Make passionate love.
- Write rage on paper...then burn or destroy it.
- Destroy your old phone book with your bare hands.
- Take a deep breath and feel so much better.
- Bring yourself back to peace and joy
- Don't go down that road. Find a more fun road.
- Change your environment.
- Eat happy food and avoid stressful habits.
- Wash that man right out of your hair

AFFIRM SUCCESS: I Grow Up

I remember every moment of my life. I take the good and let the rest go. I surrender negative behavior into positive grown-up actions. I'm proud of myself. As I explore my attitudes and beliefs, I show myself compassion. Many patterns were created when I was small and most likely saved my life. Now that I am grown, I find new behaviors that serve me better. I support and respect my expanding awareness. I'm kind to myself. I live in the present.

▲ THE ART OF SAYING "NO": Against The Grain

☆ *"Art is not truth. Art is a lie that makes us realize truth."*
—Pablo Picasso

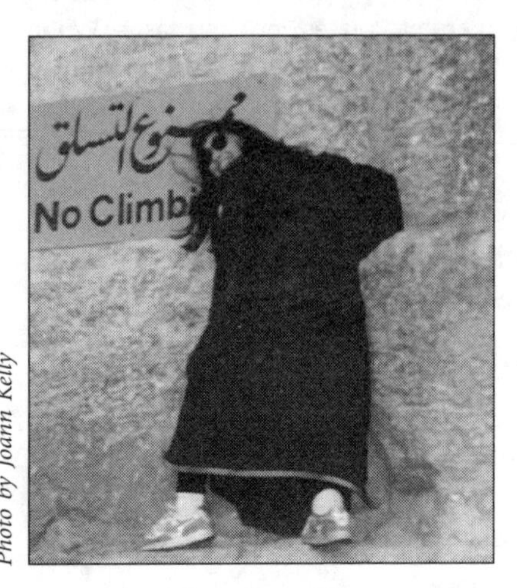

Photo by Joann Kelly

Positively Not!

Saying "No" in the right place frees you and keeps you on course. "No" establishes boundaries. When you say "No" to hurtful behavior, you give yourself a space to be healthy and say "yes" to what nourishes.

A well placed "no" eliminates things that bog you down and gives you time to move forward, clearing the way for you to do what you want to do. Pulling weeds in the garden leaves room for flowers.

"No" Rules: Don't Give Me Any Flax

If someone wants you to do what is not right for you, these "No" rules rule. Here's what to do:

1. Thanks but No Thanks
Thank that person for thinking of you and explain that you choose not to do that now.

2. No, Baby, I Don't Mean Maybe
When you say no, give a crisp, clear, final answer. "Maybe" is not final and leaves the question open.

3. Trying, Trying, Trying, It's Frustration, There's No Denying.
Just say, "no." The word "try" means to fail. Just say "no."

4. If You Don't Like The Heat, Get Out Of The Kitchen
Actions speak louder than words. If you don't want to be interrupted by phone calls, don't answer the phone; let the answering machine do it. If you don't want to kiss the toad, wart him off.

5. Don't Get Toad In
Remove yourself from situations that force you to say "no." A toad can ask you out, until they croak. If you don't want to donate money to bible zealots at the door, don't answer the door. And definitely, don't attend their fund-raisers. If you don't want to buy your children cookies...don't buy them cookies.

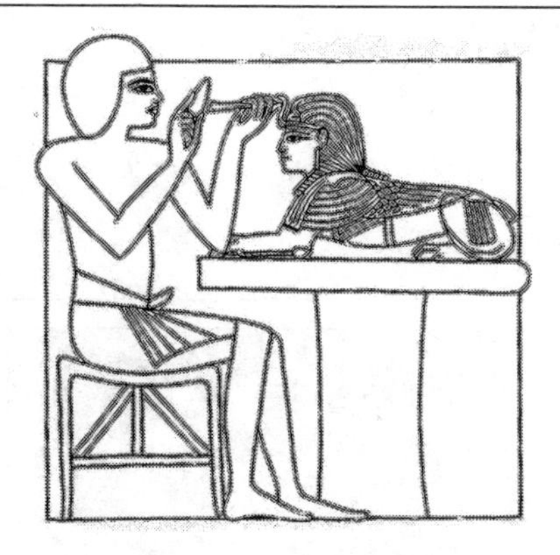

Tapping Techniques

Tapping is also known as EFT *(Emotional Freedom Technique)*, ET *(Energy Tapping)*, TFT *(Thought Field Therapy)* and BSFF *(Be Set Free Fast)*. It's a powerful tool to balance mind and body. A different system of tapping is found in chapter 8.

Here's how you do this one:

1. Think about an issue that you want to resolve.
2. Say the sentence "Even though drinking (money, obsessing, worrying...) is an issue, I deeply and completely accept myself," three times, as you gently tap your finger several times at each of the location below:
3. Tap the palm of your hand.
4. Tap above your eyebrow.
5. Tap your third eye (between your eyebrows).
6. Tap your temple.
7. Tap the side of your nose.
8. Tap underneath your nose.
9. Tap under your mouth.
10. Tap your collarbone.
11. Tap the back of your head.
12. Tap the back of your hand.
13. When complete say, "I now permanently release this and any related issues and permanently install my desired outcome."

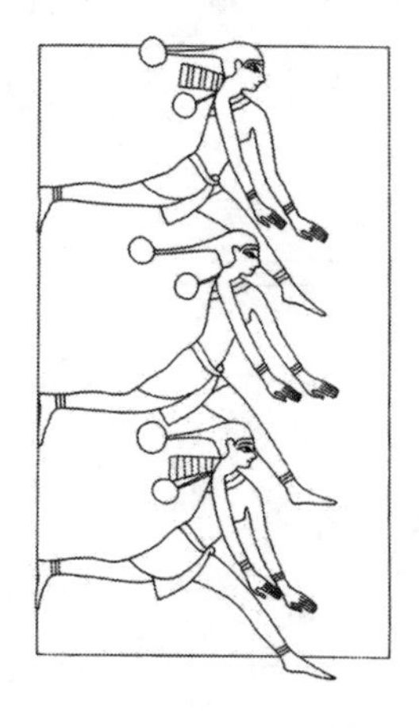

▲ JOY: Grave Robber

☆ *The funnier it gets, the funnier it gets,*
Your cells remember what logic forgets.
To laugh is to live from the inside out,
and that's what ecstasy is all about.
You are the light. You are the laughter,
And that's how you get to happily ever after.
Giggle, chortle, chuckle, grin,
That's how happiness begins.
Laugh, guffaw, slap your knee,
And you'll achieve high-larity.

—Shelley Stockwell & her guide Kendra

☆ LAUGH 'TIL THE COWS COME HOME
Silly Shelley's slaphappy
Milk comes out her nose.
Hay, she's an udder riot
Wouldn't you suppose?

—Shelley Stockwell

INTO•GREAT POWER EXERCISE

The Inner Smile 

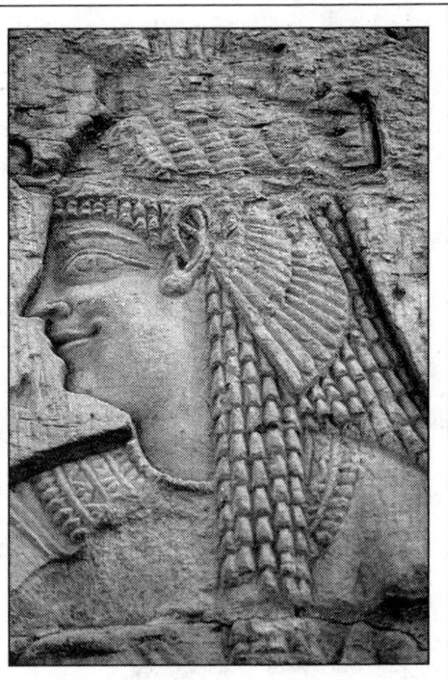

Ptolemaic Queen Smiles at Kom Ombo

How to Make A 1000-year-old Taoist Yogi Smile

- Close your eyes, sit tall, palms facing upward and breathe.
- Scan your body, focus energy on your face and imagine it gently melting.
- Recall something that feels good.
- Bring that memory to the corners of your mouth.
- Bring that memory into your right eye and then into your left eye. Feel your eyes start to smile.
- Bring that memory into your right ear. Now your left ear. Feel your ears smile.
- Bring that memory into your tongue, voice box, heart and smile out "thanks."
- Bring that memory into your lungs and smile out "thanks."
- Bring that memory into your organs, bones, nerves and into your whole body.
- Let your whole body smile.
- Come back to your eyes and let them smile.
- Let your whole being smile.
- Open your eyes. And Smile at your world.

Smile Exercises

1. Keep a humor journal.
2. Write down a pet peeve and think of five ways to deal with it.
3. Collect cartoons that make you laugh. Write your own captions for them.
4. Make a collection of absurd newspaper captions.
5. Write down funny things that you hear.

Humor lightens your emotional load and makes you more positive. Laughter lets you play. Laughter helps you cope. Laughter brings joy.

A real or imagined, smile or laugh tickles the release of positive chemicals into your brain. These are the same chemicals (endorphins, dopamine and seratonin) that you experience during orgasm, peak experience, an "ah ha" or runner's high. "Endogenous" opiates peek under the skirt of depression by suppressing stress-related hormones. That is why, after the guffaw, stress is reduced, muscles go limp and blood pressure drops.

Laughter reverberates your brain. John D. Petegrew, a neuro-biologist at the University of Queensland in Brisbane, Australia, says that the vibration re-balances the brain to more easily use the right and left hemispheres. Usually, we see though one eye, then the other, every few seconds. A good belly laugh obliterates or reduces this binocular rivalry causing you to see simultaneously through both eyes, for up to an hour and a half.

SMILE...NOW.

A smile is a God hook that lifts you up. Smiling feels good, relaxes you and puts others at ease.

Love to Laugh, Laugh to Love

☆ *If you don't laugh you may be suffering from humorhoids or hardened attitudes, which may actually lower your laugh expectancy. I suggest taking a laughative daily and restore your regul-hilarity."*

—Steve Bhaerman, aka Swami Beyondananda
Driving Your Own Karma

Babies start laughing at ten weeks. Navajo Indians say that a baby's first laugh is sacred and that the person who evokes that laugh will be forever connected to them.

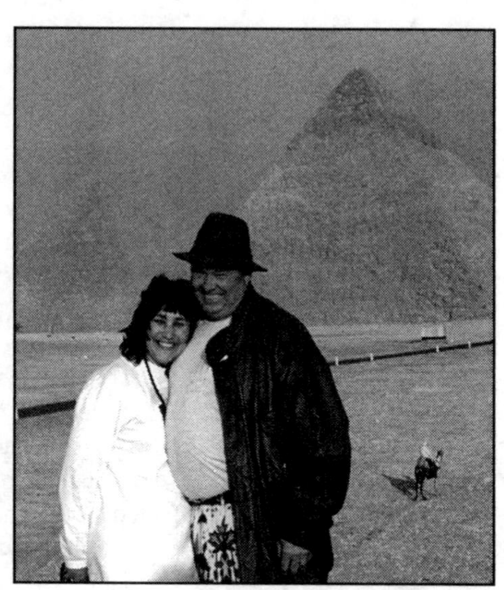

Shelley & Jon

The average kindergartner laughs 300 times a day!

Laughter is contagious and brings people closer together in chuckle-belly bonding. It gives us a time-out from problems. In business, a good laugh cuts the tension of serious issues and tough decision-making. When you come back to a problem after laughing, you see it more clearly. In a study of CEO's, 98% said that they would rather hire someone with a sense of humor than someone without one.

Nancy, Barbara, Phran, Sandra, Tamara, Shelley, and Diane

Laughing is the Aphrodisiac of the Mind

Paraplegics, paralyzed from the waist down, can achieve orgasm by stimulating their mind with glee. Some say that having sex while laughing is the highest high (seriously)!

Seven Days Without Laughter Makes One Weak

☆*You don't stop laughing because you grow old. You grow old because you stop laughing."*

—Michael Pritchard

Photo by Jon Nicholas

Studies show that most adults suffering from acute seriosity laugh less than fifteen times a day. YOU need to laugh approximately 300 times a day to be your best. If you "wiped that smile off your face," paint it back on.

Laughter: Jest, the Best Medicine

Laughter is contagious but not infectious. In fact, laughter literally fights infection. Blood tests show that laughing releases and increases antibodies, white blood cells and molecules like immunoglobulins, which find and destroy tumor cells and viruses.

Laughter helps your body fight bacteria and infection.

Studies at the Loma Vista University School of Immunology show that laughter increases your body's natural toxic-attack killer cells (T lymphocytes) and helper receptive cells. Laughter lowers cortisol levels, which keeps you healthier

Patch Adams (played in the movie by Robin Williams) was right; laugh just for the health of it. A University of Maryland study says that laughter relieves the pain of arthritis and hypertension.

Norman Cousins, *Anatomy of an Illness,* cured himself of an "incurable connective tissue disease" by checking himself out of a hospital and into a hotel (the hotel's lower cost would make anyone feel better). Norman only invited uplifting people who told him funny stories and read funny passages. He watched amusing movies (Candid Camera and the Marx Brothers), took vitamin C and discovered that for every 10 minutes of belly laughter, he had two hours pain-free. Within a short time, his "incurable" illness vanished. He died of old age, many years later, and a happy man.

Our Tickle Ate

Laughter aids digestion by stimulating enzyme secretions. It even acts as a mild laxative, cleansing you more. Laughter neutralizes acid/alkali imbalance in the body.

Photo by Jon Nicholas

Whirling Dervish at Guada's

Hilarious Workout

Sometimes called "internal jogging," laughter works like aerobic exercise. A hearty chortle a hundred times a day equals ten minutes on a rowing machine.

A belly laugh improves muscle tone and breathing. Research by William Fry and Lee Berk of Loma Linda Medical School, reports that a good laugh improves circulation, increases heart rate and afterwards, lowers blood pressure. More oxygen is delivered to your blood and brain, refreshing your mind and relaxing stress-cramped muscles.

Long bouts of laughter can temporarily make you less coordinated and weaken bladder control. A small price to pay for a great time!

Laughter the Healthy Escape

☆ *"Laughter is like changing a diaper —it may not permanently solve a problem, but it makes things acceptable for a while."*

—Red Williams

Enjoying yourself is a delight-full escape from problems. People who use laughter are less likely to be upset by negative situations.

▲ WHAT'S SO FUNNY: A Serious Analysis of What Makes You Laugh

☆ *"Everybody's got a laughing place, a laughing place to go."*

—Uncle Remus

☆ *"Humor is a safety valve from constraints, restrictions and taboos and a logic-free burst of extra intellectual energy."*

—Dr. Victor Raskin

Humor is anything that you think is funny. What tickles you and makes you laugh reflects your inner attitude.

Truisms of Life

☆ *By the time the meek have inherited the earth; our inheritance will have been squandered.*

☆ *"Death is just nature's way of telling you, 'Hey, you're not alive anymore.'"*

—Bull, Night Court

Many a truth is said in jest. Most humor centers about fate; death, love, sex, bodily functions, work, play, religion and each other. Humor at best reduces stress, clears the mind and unites us in rapport. Will Rogers said, "I don't make jokes, I just watch the government and report the facts."

Surprise, Does This Catch You Under-wares?

☆ Question: *George Bush has a short one. Gorbachev has a long one. The Pope doesn't use one. And Madonna doesn't have one. What is it?*
Answer: *A last name.*

—Dr. Victor Raskin

If you think that joke is funny, you like a surprise ending. Jokes like this, build tension then pause before the punch line. Your laughter releases the tension. The game of "peek-a-boo" delights babies in the same way.

Juxtapose, You Think This Is Funny

☆ *"Leave it lay where Jesus slung it."*
—Carol Burnett's grandmother

Photo by Jon Nicholas

Combining and contrasting ideas and teasing juxtaposition delight us.

Shelley: *"Do you love me?"*
Jon: *"What day is it?"*
Shelley: *"Friday."*
Jon: *"Brigitte?"*
Shelley: *"I'll kill you!"*

Incongruity

☆ *Lack of decisiveness is probably a bad trait...on the other hand, maybe it's not.*

If this makes you smile, you like the unexpected and to laugh at the absurdity of a position. I often do stand up comedy as a character named Shell Bell who "was a flight attendant for one day but doesn't know why." She says things like; "A lady asked me to put her baby stroller in the overhead compartment. And when I did she went hysterical; I didn't know the baby was still in there." This naïve presentation of an obvious mess-up, brings gales of laughter.

Absurdity

☆ *"House for sale, some assembly required."*
—Earthquake Victim

If this joke tickles you, you enjoy a fresh viewpoint about frustrating situations and relationships. Understatement, exaggeration, reversal of familiar roles (a dog acts like a cat), and plays on word absurdity, lets you enjoy new observations, laugh with yourself, release frustration, and puts things in manageable perspective.

A TRUE STORY Shelley's Bust Up Bus

My mother and I were in Holland looking for a multi-syllabic street name, something like Fredricksgartenstadbergaad.

My mother stopped a man on the street "Excuse me sir, can you tell us where we can find...Shelley, what was the name of that street?"

"Rumplestiltskinbergaad" I answered.

"Yes sir, Rumplestiltskinbergaad...I'll kill her."

At that moment, the seemingly right bus drove up. We jumped on, took a seat and started to laugh. My mother's unique laugh, made me laugh more. I too have a unique laugh. Pretty soon, the people behind us laughed, and the people in front of us, and then the bus driver and the entire bus.

When we got off the bus, several blocks later, it went laughing down the road without us. In 1986, my mother got off life's bus, but this memory always makes me chuckle.

Words

Certain sounds and words tickle us. Tickle has a sound "k" that makes us smile. We laugh at repetitive sounds and punny plays on words.

Exaggeration

☆ *"I'd give my right arm to be ambidextrous."*

The story of Paul Bunion and Babe The Blue Ox is hilarious in its exaggeration.

Out-Rage-Us: The Hit of Wit

☆ *He's a couple of guppies short of a school.*

☆ *Joke be nimble. Joke be slick.*
Joke fly over the not so quick.
—Pat Cotterell

Laughing at another's misfortunes offers a false feeling of superiority and sometimes compassion.

There's a fine line between teasing and cruelty. Petty, persistent and annoying teasing puts a wedge between you and others. Kindness in humor makes you closer.

On a Miami Beach bus, I sat across the aisle from an elderly man with his fly open. Not to embarrass him, I was quietly getting up to tell him, when the senior citizen next to me said out loud to him, "Your fly is open."

The old fellow looked up and said, "What?"

In slightly higher volume, he repeated, "Your fly is open."

"What?"

In the loudest voice I have ever heard in a public place, he bellowed, "YOUR FLY IS OPEN."

Barbed humor is negative, and both creates and reduces tension. How it goes is culturally influenced. Trobriand Islanders play a uproarious game of "cricket" punctuated with mocking dances and put-down chants and everyone is delighted. Their insulting humor is a civilized replacement for physical hostility.

If "You've been whooped with an ugly stick" cracks you up, you have thinly veiled rage and aggression. To wit, the point of a practical joke or jestful put-down, is to embarrass someone. Aristotle, Plato, Charles Darwin and Thomas Hobbs, underscored hostility as the root of an insult.

Humorous insults are an unconscious (or conscious) wish to destroy another's confidence and the confidence of others in them. If people are awake, they view the prankster as the butt of their own put down and lose confidence in them.

Ethnic, religious or racial humor insults groups and promotes bigotry and stereotyping. Such exclusive humor shuts out or isolates someone while giving the teller a superior feeling. Sexist, vulgar humor bashes another's fixtures.

The person or group maligned changes with the times.

☆ Question: *"How can you tell the bride at a _________ wedding?"*
Answer: *"She's the one with the braided armpits."*

If you are on the receiving end of a sarcastic, caustic comment, say, "When you said such-and-such, it hurt me." And don't back off if they come back with, "Just kidding. Can't you take a joke?"

☆ He: *"I see you're still on your diet."*
She: *"We suffer from the same problem- we both have trouble keeping our mouth shut."*

INTO•GREAT POWER EXERCISE

I Am De Light

The key to joy involves a secret mantra that has been passed down through the infinite wisdom of the ages. It has been whispered in the secret huts of shamans. It has been chanted loudly from mountaintops by peoples of many lands. This special mantra is so powerful and sacred that it's a secret. Don't tell anyone else... unless you want to.

When you chant this mantra, do it loudly. If you feel foolish, that's excellent; it increases its power.

Relax your eyes so they don't feel like opening.

Stop testing them.

Imagine white light coming down upon you, maybe from the sun. The light bathes every hidden part of you.

Take a deep cleansing breath and hold it in. Let it out.

On the exhalation, chant the mantra.

The mantra is: HA, HA, HA, HA, HA.

Repeat as needed.

Stockwell's Joy Therapy: Ha! That's a Laugh!

☆ *"You grow up the day you have a real laugh at yourself."*
—Ethel Barrymore

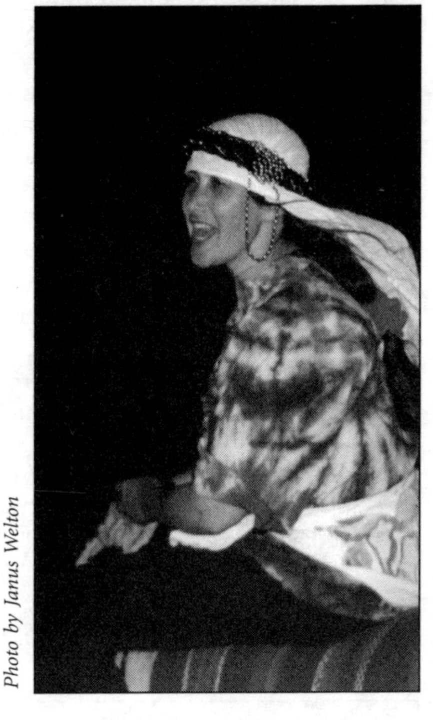
Photo by Janus Welton

Are YOU READY TO HAVE FUN?

Fun Step One
Replace gloomy movies, depressing news broadcasts, tabloid newspapers, gory books and sad people with hilarious movies, delightful books and funny TV shows. If you hang out with joyous people, there won't be time to hang out with sad sacks.

Silly Step Two
Think of a time when you laughed real hard; a funny incident, scene in a movie or television or a joke you heard. Even if you can't remember what was so darn funny it doesn't really matter, does it? As you think about it, relax your jaw and tip up the corners of your mouth. COME ON; SMILE.

Yuk It Up All Over Step Three
To let yourself YUK IT UP as you activate your chakras

Problem Solved Step Four
Now, if you can, think of a problem…laugh. Really let out a laugh. What happened to your problem?

AFFIRM SUCCESS He Who Lasts Best, Laughs Laughs

I lighten up and lighten up. Pain as a lifestyle sucks. I give up suffering...and have fun. Fun as a lifestyle suits me. Fun may be a tough job, but someone's got to do it. I love to laugh. I live to laugh. I am the laughter.

Shelley's Yuk It Up Chakras

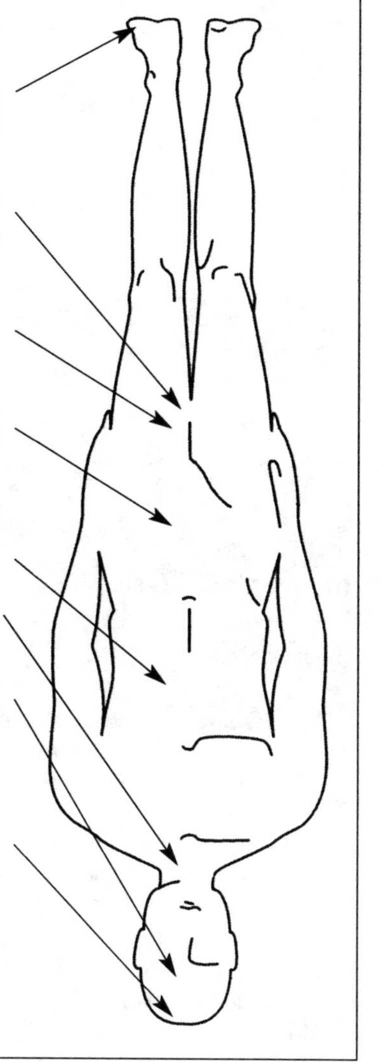

Something's Afoot. Breathe to the bottoms of your feet and tickle them. Smile and chuckle.

Smiling Asshole. Picture a smile on your anal sphinx-ter and laugh out loud. This stimulates your base chakra.

Tickle Your Fancy and Funny Bone. Let your sexual organs giggle.

Belly Laugh. Tweak your belly button. It's the pick of the tweak. Let your belly jiggle and laugh.

Hearty Har Har. As the laugh moves up to your heart, let your heart dance and In-joy.

Say Ahh-Haha. Your throat vibrates with glee; tee, hee, hee.

Eyes Laughing. Your third eye, and jovial pineal gland behind it, laughs. You are making a spectacle of yourself. Your laughter now moves to your:

Clown Chakra. The top of your head bursts forth in a crown of de-light. You lighten up and laugh over the top.

Whole Body Hilarity. Now combine all the laughing chakras and feel great all over more than any place else.

Stockwell's Joy Therapy Helpers:

Joy Therapy Video
An hilarious happening, sure to make you laugh.

Joy Therapy Audio Playshop
Riveting demonstrations of Shelley Stockwell's Joy Therapy Process, In less than 30 minutes, seven people completely heal core issues with a laugh. It is awesome.

These are available at the back of this book.

▲ Good Vibrations: Sound Advice

☆ *"The human voice is the ultimate healing instrument "*
—Ancient Sufi proverb

☆ *"Sound will be the healing of the future."*
—Edgar Cayce

Photo by Jon Nicholas

In harmony we come to resolution. Speaking, like laughter, is the art of breath, release and vibration. Your voice or another's offers natural ultrasound that heals and soothes.

You have a signature sound that reflects your brain wave patterns. Your voice, vibrations and tone allow energy and expression to flow. Without breath, you cannot speak. When you learn to positively use your breath and voice, you take back a sense of personal power.

There are many good ways you can use your voice.

Move Your Vowels and Relax

Sighing, moaning, yawning, crying, laughing and burping release trapped energy. That is why crooning, lullabies and humming relax. Those who wish, always find a song.

Stronger vowel sounds like "ow" and "ah," regenerate.

The simultaneous layering of several sounds, called overtones, heals.

Music is fun that's why we "play" music.

Sound impacts your moods and emotions. Feelings and behavior are the chemical result of thought and energy. That's why companies spend millions on environmental sounds like Musak. Have you ever been "seduced" by the sounds of a slot machine?

Music, words and sounds coax your brain to imitate patterns and create new neural pathways. Melodic music overrides anxiety, loneliness and depression. Try this experiment: Listen to a slow peaceful tune without words (words can be loaded with associations.) and notice how you feel as you listen. Are you more relaxed?

Now put on something more upbeat. Notice how your feelings shift.

Photo by Jon Nicholas

Sufi Dancers, Cairo

INTO•GREAT POWER EXERCISE

Shelley Stockwell's Good Vibe System

In harmony, come to resolution.

▲ Music:
Play relaxing music and stretch out comfortably on your back, feet 8-10 inches apart and arms loosely and limply by your side.

▲ Bless You:
Bless me on all levels, physically, mentally, emotionally, and spiritually so I may truly recognize and fulfill my life's purpose. Let all teachings be for my highest good and the good of humanity. Help me reconnect with my special gifts and lovingly shed any negative messages given by insensitive people. Thank you. Ahmen. Ahwomen. Ah life.

▲ Breathe Out Loud:
Notice each breath. How it smells, how it tastes, how it feels, any colors, textures or sounds. Let your breath out with a gentle sound. Let the sound lace gently in and out of the music of your thoughts.

▲ Chakra Penetration:
Focus attention on the base of your spine. Notice the energy of that place. Now take a deep breath and release any sound, as though it is coming from that part of your being. Be aware of the vibration of the energy, color and sound of that place.
Now bring your attention to your sexual organs and release another sound.
Do the same moving up to your solar plexus, heart, throat, third eye and the top of your head.

▲ Resolution:
Now combine all the energies, colors and sounds from each part of your being. Let out the full tones of your entire self. Feel your body vibrate. Relax and repeat two more times.

Photo by Grant Stockwell

Baby Bryce

Love a Lullaby

Research suggests that exposing a baby to classical or soothing music, as well as touch, taste and sight, makes baby more intelligent. This "Mozart Effect" activates the brain's math, spatial and complex reasoning. Premature babies who listen to classical music are calmer, gain weight faster, use oxygen more efficiently and are more tuned in. Soothe your inner child with a lullaby.

Magnetic Mind Toning

☆ *"For an anxious patient, music can have a comparable effect as taking five milligrams of Valium. When music plays in the operating room, anesthesia requirements drop 10 to 20 percent."*

—Dr Fred Schwartz, Anesthesiologist,
Piedmont Hospital, Atlanta

INTO•GREAT POWER EXERCISE

A Real Hum Singer!

Hum!

Hum...
Oh, go ahead no one will notice. It doesn't have to be a tune or even on key. Feel the vibration as it moves through your body. See if you can balance the sound between your throat and nose.
Now bring the vibrating hum down into your chest.
Now to your stomach.
And now a deep breath and relax.
Don't you feel better? Now...

Sing!
Now sing! Any nonsense song will do.
Be in the center of your breath. Breathe to your body and let go of any tightness in the body. Now breathe to your mind, letting go of any tight thoughts.

AFFIRM
I am a stream. I go everywhere with a thousand voices singing.

Viennese physician, Friedrich "Franz" Anton Mesmer (1770) perpetrated a theory he called "animal magnetism" in which he used magnets, healing hands and suggestion. "Planetary magnetic-pull influences us through an invisible fluid [gravity?]" he said. The sick, he reasoned, had less energy or unequal distribution of this joy juice and magnets restore the balance. Modern quantum physics has since shown that electromagnetism does effect body chemistry.

Doctor's don't usually say "play a CD and call me in the morning," but music truly heals. Sound helps Alzheimer and stroke victims remember and move. People who listen to music after surgery require less pain medication.

Alpha-Theta Sound

Ormond McGill and Joseph Worrell created the Serenity Resonance Sound, a psycho-acoustic recording that calms and alters brain wave activity. Alpha and theta sound pulses coax your brain and influence your mind to relax. They claim that harmonic binaural frequency patterns help your brain stay focused for faster memory and learning.

(The Serenity Sound is available on tape or CD. A second version overlaid with music and human heartbeat sounds, called Entrancing Music, is also available in the resources section in the back of this book).

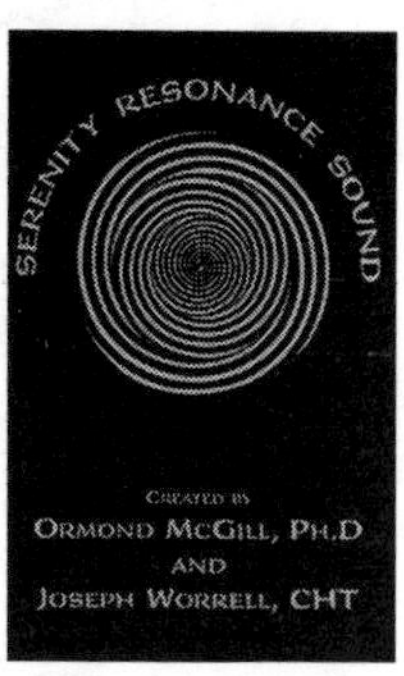

Serenity Resonance Cassette

▲ OPEN YOURSELF: It's A•Peeling

☆ *Energy*
Watts up!?
As I volt out of bed
I've got Ohms in my heart
and amps in my head.

—Joellen Natow

As you express yourself; sad, frustrated, old patterns die. Pay your last respects, mourn and then rebirth joyous new patterns.

You may also mourn antiquated relationships to begin new, more fulfilling ones. Empty your basket of rotten apples so you have room for fresh oranges.

Photo by Jon Nicholas

▲ Positive Disposition

☆ *"When life hands you lemons, stick them in your bra."*

—Trudy Grossman

(After finding out she had breast cancer)

Being positive during a challenge, tough time, illness, or catastrophe motivates you to be more flexible, use your resources and integrate. Ask yourself, "How has my predicament enhanced me?" "Hoe did it awaken me to be a better person?"

Positive questions like: "What did I enjoy most yesterday?" "What are the high points of my life?" " What am I good at?" "What is fun for me?" change your perception. Such appreciative inquiry works wonders with others as well.

An American Medical Association study of Americans over one hundred years old, attributed their longevity to an "easy-going disposition, quick sense of humor and a desire to stay alive and active." "Don't fight your enemies; outlive them," was their message.

▲ Play: A-Muse

☆ *"The family that plays together, stays together"*

☆ *"All work and no play make you a dull boy (or girl)."*

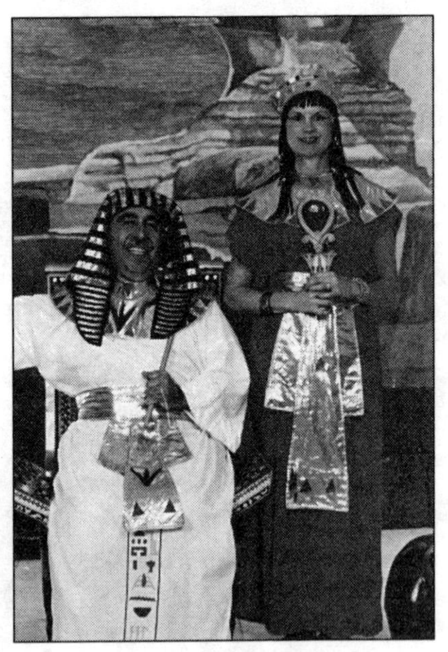

Ernie and Sally

Who was your best friend when you were a kid? Was it someone you played with? Of course! Playing was the central focus of your life back then. Admit it, you still love to play. Playing is what you want, what you really, really want. Playing is fun.

Play opens you to others. Cooperative play stops competitive behavior and creates deep permanent bonds. If you were taught only competitive play without supporting others, you may not know how to play just for fun. Learn how and life becomes richer.

Natural play is communal and supportive. Find healthy people and ways to play.

Up Your Egypt

Bored Game

Mancala was game played by Ancient Egyptian Pharaohs. Two players used strategy to collect as many stones as possible. Draughts and Senat were popular too. Senat means "passing" and is the forerunner for modern checkers. The game pieces are called "kelb" and the squares "ooyen" meaning eyes.

A lot of drug activity is healthy play gone awry.

Play helps you see yourself in a new way. Play makes deep, connected relationships to others. Play is one of the most creative things you'll ever do.

▲ Fan

☆ *"Give love an inch, it will take you a mile*
Like a trickling stream, that swells to the Nile."
—Susan Luesinger

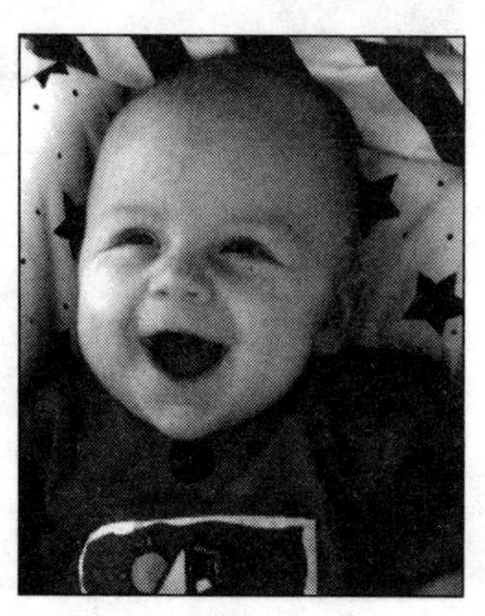

Peter

Unconditional self-love and self in-joy-ment may require new skills. If your childhood role models didn't love themselves, how could they teach you? Your job is to show yourself and others healthy, happy, loving and loved ways. Do you remember the expression, "Be good to yourself?" Now's your time to do just that!

Photo by Jon Nicholas

INNER•VIEW QUIZ

Finger Food for Thought

1. Relax and, with your non-dominant hand, grasp a finger on your other hand. Note which one/ones you grasp.
2. Hold your pinkie finger and notice the first word to pop into your mind. Write it ______________________________
3. Hold your ring finger. What word comes to mind? ______________
4. Do the same with the middle finger, and the word is______________
5. Do it with the pointer finger, the word is ______________
6. For your thumb, the word is ______________

What each finger represents:
Pinky = Money, intuition, spirit
Ring finger = Relationship
Middle finger = Balance
Pointer = Authority, leadership
Thumb = Foundation, will, intellect

Chapter 14
Nourishing Life Style
Consecrate Your Temple

A nourishing life style takes your body, mind and emotions out of the snake pit of self-destruction and into delight and spiritual upliftment. Nothing to hide, no need to numb, positive patterns replace negative ones. As you integrate body, mind and spirit, you learn to love yourself, rise above your story and embrace life's gifts. This chapter motivates you to take excellent care of yourself. Living well is the best revenge!

▲ **MIND YOUR MIND: Positive Thoth**
▲ **MIND YOUR BODY: Feast**
  Water: the Solution
  Eat For Fuel: E•luxor
  Exercise: Met•a•physical
  Sleep: The Cradle of Civilization
  Sunshine: Ra, the Supreme Beam
▲ **MIND YOUR EMOTIONS**
▲ **SOUL SUPPORT: De Fruit of De Vine**
  Creativity: Fertile Valley
  Spirituality: Fruit of De Vine
  Nature: Tree's Company
  Right Work

Photo by Tamara Thomas

What would you do if you took excellent care of yourself?

(Take a minute and tell yourself exactly what you'd do. Listen well to what you answer.)

What *wouldn't* you do if you took excellent care of yourself?

(Pause and answer).

What does a nourishing life style mean to you?

(Pause and answer).

You instinctively know that a healthy life style includes being a good citizen, good parent, good partner and good friend to *yourself.*

INTO-GREAT POWER EXERCISE

Garden of Weed-in: Replant and Sin No More

It's easy to extinguish limiting behaviors. Here's how:

SURVEY

List limiting behaviors and the positive ones to replace them.

Weed: Negative behaviors	Flowers: Positive behaviors
______________	______________
______________	______________
______________	______________
______________	______________

ONE WEED AT A TIME

Choose a weed you want to replace. ASK YOURSELF:
When did such a negative pattern begin?
How did you reinforce it?

PLANT A FLOWER

Choose your flower...a positive behavior you'll use instead of the limiting one. Plant a new, big dream (sunflower) or a baby-step dream (ground cover.) Ask yourself "How will my magnifi-scent Flower enhance my life?
Am I willing to nurture this new behavior?
Double check. "Is this what I really want?"
Ask your heart of hearts.

BENEFITS

What benefits will this new approach bring me?

REPLANT

Write the action steps you will take to support your positive growth.

Action step	Time goal
______________	______________
______________	______________
______________	______________
______________	______________

DO IT!

▲ Mind Your Mind: Positive Thoth

Action and reality results from thoughts. Say good and kind things to yourself and you point your mental compass toward peace and joy. Diligently look on the bright side.

Do not permit stinkin' thinkin.

If you find yourself in negative thought, say "stop" or "cancel, cancel, cancel" and then change to a positive thought. Positive thoughts give you the gift of time and energy you might have spent in defensive thought and behavior.

If you find yourself dwelling on a negatives, ask yourself: What's really the problem? How bad is it really, in context to everything else in my life? And what action can I take to start making things better?

Live lovingly in the moment. Promise, right now, to focus on the positive blessing of life. It's not a tall order and happiness will come in short order!

Up Your Egypt

Positive Thoth

Thoth, the ibis bird or baboon headed deity, was considered the god of speaking, learning and wisdom and lord of the moon. Thoth invented writing and protected all scribes. Our word "thought" comes from this fellow. Thoth was often depicted as a scribe.

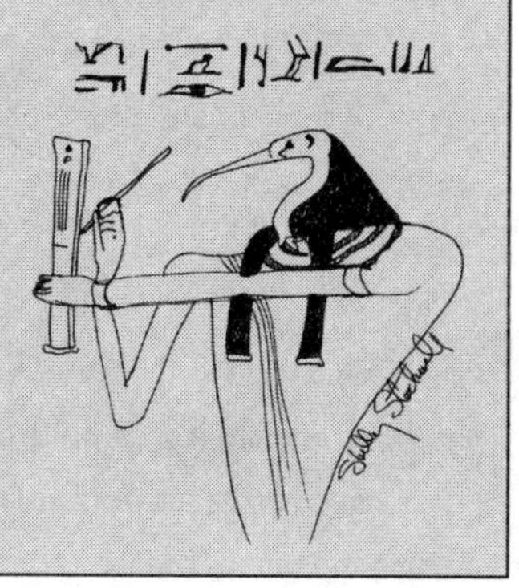

Illustration by Shelley Stockwell

Affirm Success: Affirmation for Mental Bliss

Here is your Affirmation for mental bliss. Repeat it three times to yourself, click your heals and then read on.

I am my thoughts. My self-talk is positive and creates a positive environment and situation. I make positive choices. I have fun. My thoughts create right action. My mental self-awareness brings laughter, play, right work and loving relationships. I enjoy my own company. Emotions are just energy. I recycle emotions into intense joy.

I say 'Yes!' to wellness. My healthy body results from my healthy mind. My body is well and renewed by my positive thinking. Inner Knower, thank you! I awaken positive thinking and positive life choices.

UP YOUR Egypt

The Story of Seth, Isis, Osiris and Horus

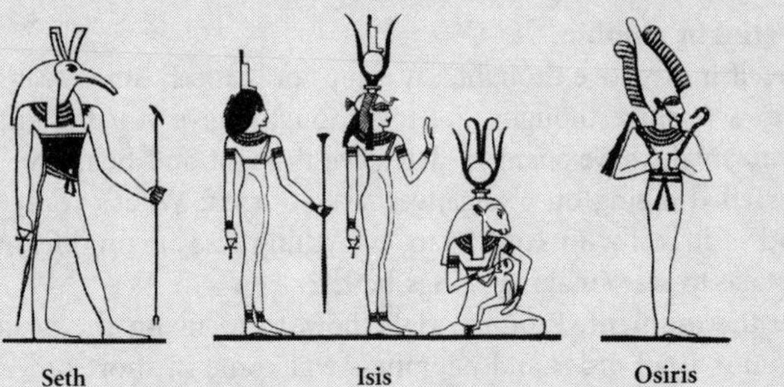

Seth Isis Osiris Horus

Seth is often depicted as a male hippopotamus or a human with a big-eared, donkey head. Called the "god of the desert", the "god of chaos" and the "lord of all non-Egyptian lands", Seth murdered his brother, Osiris. Seth dismembered poor Osiris into fourteen pieces and buried each segment in a different part of Egypt.

Isis, Osiris' wife (and also his sister and mother), re-collected his pieces and re-membered him by putting him back together, like Humpty Dumpty. The last piece of him that she found was his phallus. When she recovered it, she conceived their son Horus. (The word horus evolved into our word "hero"). Horus is depicted as a man with a falcon head. He was considered god of the sky and was dead-icated to avenging his father's death by Seth.

Isis and her magical powers were used to protect children and heal the sick. She is considered the "creator of the land".

Osiris is regarded as the "god of death and rebirth, earth and vegetation" and the "one who gave birth to the Nile". He was a most popular and powerful god. Egyptians believed that Osiris was the first living thing to die. Legend has it that Osiris civilized his people by discovering methods of organized agriculture and the cultivation of corn and barley.

▲ Mind Your Body: Feast

Honor your body with good breath, water, nourishing foods, exercise and proper rest and sleep. And avoid substances that you know hurt you.

Water: The Solution

☆ Question: *Do you like shaved ice?*
Answer: *No, I like mine with beards on them.*

☆ *Be at peak, suck a creek.*
Clearly think, drink.
Eight a day, makes you okay.
Go with the flow, drink H2O.
—Shelley Stockwell

Rumor has it that, since creation, the amount of earth's water hasn't changed. It still exists in abundance. You can live for weeks without food and only a few days without water.

Over seventy-three percent of you is water. Ever since you were a baby, you have needed fluid for survival. Mother's milk is *perfect* fluid food. It supplies water as well as natural digestive carbohydrates and proteins. Mother and milk meant survival and made you feel secure, and salivate.

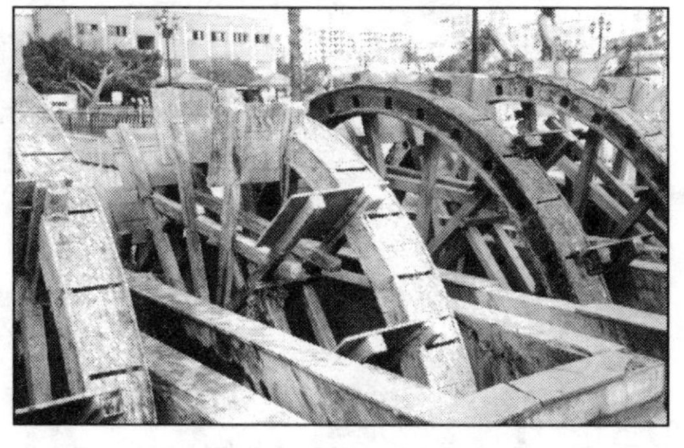

Photo by Jon Nicholas

The combination of drinking water, bathing and exercise, along with organic fruits and vegetables works healthy miracles.

You're All Wet

Water is the lubricant of health. You have water in your blood and in and around your cells. Cells, especially nerve cells, must be immersed in water. You are like a mobile aquarium with organs and cells sloshing around inside, cushioned and protected. Water allows osmotic pressure, cell vibration and filtration, tissue function, blood flow, nutrition, oxygenation and reproduction.

Up Your Egypt

Sab-bath

☆ Doctor: *"Did you take a bath today."*
Patient: *"Why? Is one missing."*
Doctor: *"I can't examine you, you're filthy. Bathe and come back."*
Patient: *"That's what the last doctor said."*
Doctor: *"Then why did you come here?"*
Patient: *"I wanted a second opinion."*

Bathing cleanses your body of negative energy, grime, pollution, toxins and germs. Make your bath or shower a holy ritual. Egyptian physicians and ancients from East and West made bathing a requirement. Ancient Jews initiated a purification ritual called Mikvah that reminded people that personal health is a celebration of the holy day, or Sab•bath. By 1500 BC, elite Egyptians had hot and cold running water, delivered to their houses by copper tubes or pipes.

Photo by Jon Nicholas

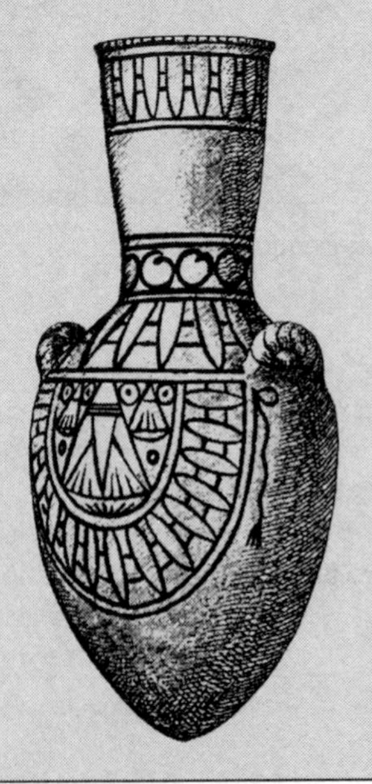

☆ *"I gave my cat a bath the other day...He sat there, he enjoyed it, and it was fun for me. The fur would stick to my tongue, but other than that..."*

—Steve Martin

Jesus; Cleansed Out of His Gourd

Rumor has it that Christ went into the desert and used gourds to purge himself. Colonics were thought to avert disease by quickly sending toxins out of the body.

Water heightens sexual desire and all of your senses; hearing, taste, smell, sight and touch. It hydrates your skin, keeping it from wrinkling and sagging. Without water you can't concentrate or think clearly. Studies show that a reduction of four to five percent of body water results in a decline of twenty to thirty percent of your work performance.

Water flushes toxins such as alcohol, pollution, waste products and food additives.

Constipated? Drink water! If your body gets too little water, it steals it from the colon and dehydrates. Water makes your body more flexible, allowing muscles to contract and expand, giving you more muscle tone.

Without water, your body goes into survival mode and stores available fluid outside the cells. This causes water retention and swollen hands and feet. If you are swollen, the worst things you can do is take diuretics or eat salt. They cause more water to leave, along with stored nutrients. The more salt you eat, the more water your body retains to dilute it. More water flushes sodium from your kidneys and eliminates water retention.

When the kidneys don't have enough water to properly flush toxins, the liver takes over. The over-worked liver now cannot do its job of metabolizing stored fat. Therefore, fat is stored as a wall about you and you put on weight. Heavy people need more water than light people do. Water helps everyone properly metabolize stored fat into usable energy.

You lose about a pound of fluid overnight. Wastewater is siphoned from your blood to the surface of your skin and wafts away. Your lungs expel water vapor. Your eyes tear and cleanse. Your kidneys draw water and produce urine. You know that you are getting enough water if you urinate every four hours during the day. Urine that looks like lemonade is beautiful. If it looks like dark apple cider, you are dehydrated.

If this is making you thirsty, go get a glass of water, right now.

Drink to Think

☆ *"I have water on the brain & in winter it freezes & everything slips my mind."*
-Irv Lessin

Pour a glass of water and think about its energy. It gives you the life force to move and think.

Drink the water slowly and with reverence. Imagining, as you do, that each water molecule stimulates your brain with clearer thinking. Imagine it activating the emotional parts of your mind, so that you make good positive decisions and responses.
(Pause)

Everything is energy. The water you just took in energized your body, mind and spirit.

Good Tidings: How Much Water Do You Need?

Does the adage "six-to-eight-glasses-a-day for good health" hold water? Yes!

You lose approximately ten cups of water a day, two cups by sweating and evaporation, two cups in breathing, and six cups in waste removal. And, that's not counting excess loss from perspiration during exercise or from dehydrating things like caffeine, sugar or alcohol.

Photo by Nica Lee

THE WATER TABLE; Water out	
Sweat	Minus 2 cups
Evaporation	Minus 2 cups
Waste Elimination	Minus 6 cups
Water Out Total:	-10 cups or more

To replenish lost fluid, you "drink" approximately three and half cups in a floating smorgasbord. Milk, juices, soups, yogurt, potatoes, fruits and vegetables give you fluid. Cucumbers, lettuce and tomatoes are ninety-five percent water. Chicken is sixty-percent water. Your body's metabolism supplies another half cup.

THE WATER TABLE; Water in	
From Food	Add 3.5 cups
From Body metabolism	Add .5 cups
Water In Total:	+ 4 cups

GRAND TOTAL	-10 cups out
	+ 4 cups in
	-6 cups

The grand total: you lose approximately 10 cups of water a day and take in about 4 cups leaving you a daily deficit of 6 cups. You need to replenish loss by drinking fluids, and water is the natural choice.

Wet Doesn't Always Hold Water

☆ *"Drinks containing concentrated nutrients, such as milk, sugar-sweetened soft drinks and salty tomato-based juices, count more as food than drink, because they themselves increase your body's water needs."*

—New York Times Guide to Personal Health

Caffeinated or chocolate drinks, coffee, tea, or cola, actually dehydrate. Every cup of caffeinated beverage robs the body of approximately one and a half cups of fluid. As fluid leaves your cells, it takes with it stored nutrients, thereby weakening your immune responses.

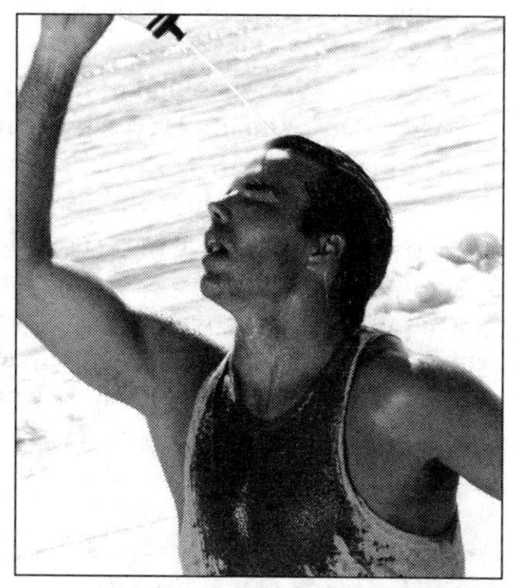

Every Day Is Thirst Day

Thirst is a sure sign that you are already partially dehydrated and need water. Many people who are addicted to sugar, over-eating and alcohol, are simply thirsty for water.

When it's hot, or we perspire, we particularly need water. When it's cold, we also need more water.

Where you sweat on your body depends on why you're sweating. Cooling sweat shows up on the forehead, upper lip, neck and chest. Nervous sweat occurs more on the palms, feet and arm pits. During strenuous exercise, we can sweat away as much as two quarts of water and hour.

A fit athlete starts sweating earlier and sweats more. A college football player might lose as much as eight pounds of fluid an hour. This temporary weight loss comes right back when they drink water. The more you exercise, the more water you need to regulate your body temperature and nourish cells. This is how many glasses of water you need when exercising:

Your Weight	Light Exercise	Moderate Exercise	Strenuous Exercise
115	9 glasses	9.5 glasses	10 glasses
125	9	10	11
150	9	10	11.5
175	9.5	10.5	12.5
200	9.5	11	13.25

If you are an overboard kind of person, don't get carried away and drink more than is reasonable or they may carry you away.

Water From Your Eyes: For Cryin' Out Loud

☆ *"A lot of illness is our body's way of crying. High blood pressure is an unheard cry. And when someone hears, the pressure comes down. That's one reason why people who feel sadness, spill tears, and accept loving support from others, water longevity's garden."*

—Gurney Williams III

Crying is a powerful form of communication that brings help. When we cry alone, we ask for God's help, another's help or help from within ourselves. The benefits of crying depends on whether you imagine someone is hearing you and recognizing your sadness.

The chemical composition of tears of laughter is different then tears of sadness.

When Dr. William Frey, Ph.D. did a research project in Minneapolis, Minnesota there wasn't a dry eye in the place. Frey collected and analyzed human teardrops. He brought his subjects to tears with a sad movie or sniffing onions. Emotional movie tears showed higher protein and hormones than onion tears. Emotional tears caused heart rates to rise, finger temperatures to drop, perspiration to increase and greater sensitivity to pain. Dr. Frey concluded that emotional crying doesn't necessarily lead to calmness. Yet, ask yourself; hasn't a good old-fashioned cry cleansed you?

Up Your Egypt

The Nile

☆ *"Egypt is a Gift of the Nile."*

—Herodotus

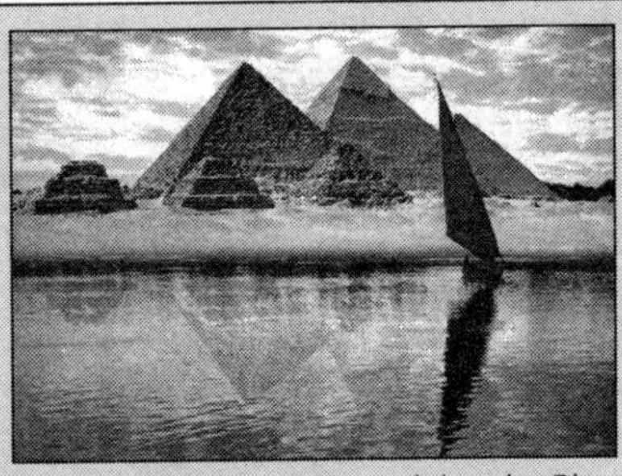

The White Nile (Bahr Ghazzal) begins at a Tanzanian stream, the Kagera River. It flows 2,285-miles and is joined at Khartoum, by the Blue Nile (Bahr el Azrak), from Ethiopian Highlands. Together they are called simply, The Nile. Ancient Egyptians said that the Blue Nile brought silt and the White Nile brought nutrients. In the middle of the Nile is the Sudd, a huge impenetrable swamp.

Before the Aswan High Dam was built in 1964, the Nile rose about 27 feet each year, flooding the Nile Valley. The flooding coincided with the star Sirius in a position at daybreak called sopdep. The flood flowed about 3 miles an hour and create a lush 8,500 square mile fertile green corridor called the Nile Delta. If it were not for this flooding, the great Egyptian valley would be a sterile desert.

Nile Delta farmers (fellah, from which we get our word fellow) celebrated the flooding, which was heralded by the coming of the Ibis. To assure its rise, the chadouf, or "water raising song," was sung. To this day, the weight pivoted water bucket that scoops up water from the Nile is called a chadouf. The unification of the upper and lower Egypt is symbolized by intertwining serpents like the turns of the Nile with beast heads. This image is very much like the modern caduceus, the symbol of the American Medical Association.

Eat For Fuel: E-Luxor

☆ *You are what you eat, that's all you need to know*
Good food is fuel that makes you laugh and grow.
Eat lean and green, feel strong and tall
Good for you, good for me, good for us all.

—Shelley Stockwell
"You Are What You Eat" audio cassette

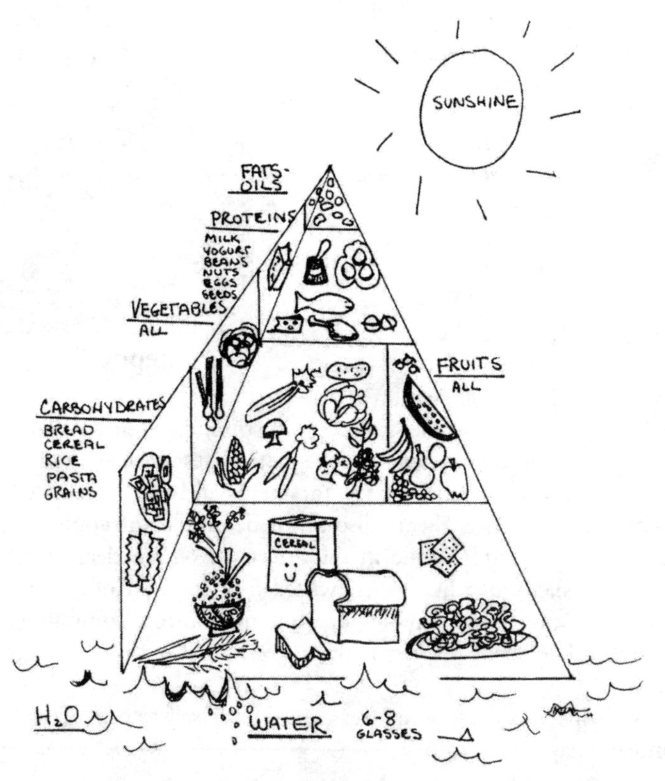

Illustration by Shelley Stockwell

We must eat for fuel. Real food contains fiber, carbohydrates, enzymes, proteins and obscure, but essential, nutrients like lutein and phenols. Vitamin and mineral supplements can add balance and fortify a good diet, yet never replace it. The use and amount of vitamin supplements is a subject of hot debate.

If you eat a healthy breakfast you boost your mood. Start each day with protein, complex carbohydrates and fiber. It not only fuels you, it keeps your blood sugar stable for the rest of the day. Within 15 minutes you should notice that you feel better. Conversely, if you eat a donut or Danish, you most likely will feel depressed.

Vitamins too can help. Take a good multivitamin that contains antioxidants and you will notice that within a few days you will be generally happier.

Exercise: Met-a-physical

☆ *"Are you from around these parts?"*
"I live smack dab in the middle of these parts."
—Shelley Stockwell

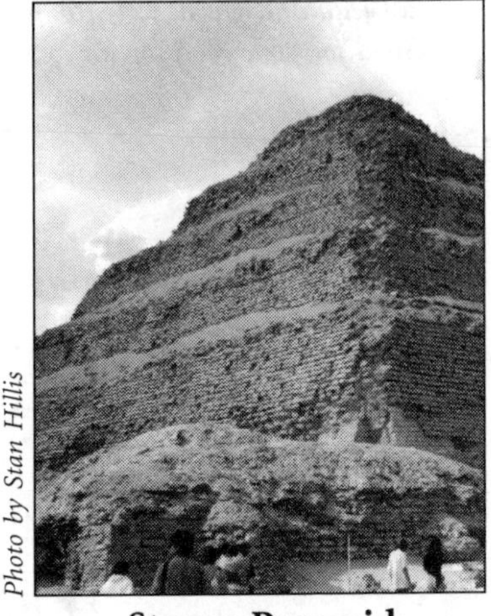
Photo by Stan Hillis

Steppe Pyramid

☆ HOW EXERCISE EFFECTS YOU
Six months ago I would have died
For greasy bites of something fried.
Or chocolate or big desserts
Or bite sized chunks of stuff that hurts.
But now I want to exercise
To build my arms, reduce my thighs.
I'm at the gym at eight each night
And exercise and eat what's right.
The only part that's really hard
Is squeezing into leotards.
—F. Douglas Moeller

Movement is living. Stagnation is strange. With exercise, you come to life, because you stimulate your circulation, lymph, respiratory and nervous systems. Movement tones muscles and strengthens bones. Exercise gives you more oxygen for energy and fuel for new cells. Exercise reduces the risk of cancer, heart disease, diabetes and infection. It lowers the cholesterol in blood and plaque in the arteries. Exercise cleanses toxins from muscles and tissue, much like water twisted from a washcloth.

Energy from movement allows your spine free-flowing communication with your brain and internal organs, making you more optimistic, energetic and creative.

Exercise helps you cope with stress and builds self-esteem. Thirty to forty-five minutes a day makes you healthy and keeps you mentally sharp and slim.

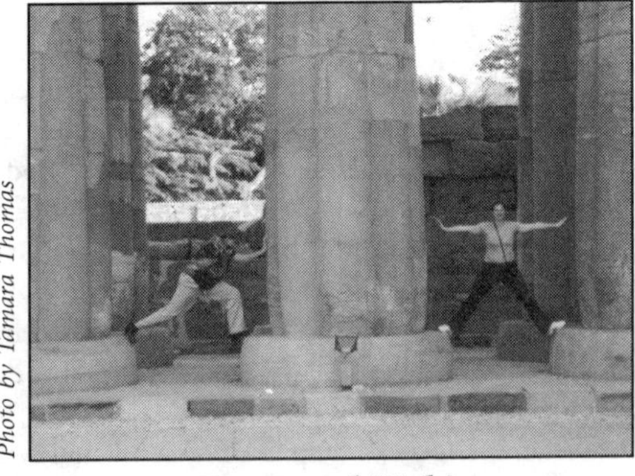
Photo by Tamara Thomas

Bryce and Vicki

For females, movement alleviates PMS, water retention and prevents endometriosis, which can cause infertility. Exercise helps prevent osteoporosis, arthritis, and keeps the over-forty crowd mentally sharp. A new study published in the *Archives of Internal Medicine* found that women who exercised while quitting smoking were twice as likely to quit and didn't gain as much weight as those who didn't exercise.

"Thirty to forty-five minutes of exercise reduces your risk of heart disease," says Neil Gordon, M.D., Director of Exercise Physiology at the Cooper Institute, "exercise lowers elevated blood pressure an average of ten points. That's enough to keep some people from ever having to take hypertensive drugs and suffer their side effects of fatigue, dizziness, swelling and even impotence."

During physical exertion, large amounts of endorphins (natural morphine-like hormones) are released. They shield the body from pain, reduce tension, tranquilize and give you a second wind.

Rules For Exercise:

☆ *"My grandmother started walking five minutes a day when she was sixty years old. Now she is ninety and we don't know where in the heck she is."*
—Ellen DeGeneres

1. **Do What Feels Good.** Don't force yourself. Some days, you are stronger than others; honor that. If it hurts or you are fatigued, you are doing too much.
2. **Build Up Gradually.** If you make exercise a compulsion, you could run yourself into the ground. It may have taken years to gradually get out of shape. Allow time to gradually get physically fit. If you are excessively tired and cranky after a workout, you are most likely exercising too hard or too frequently. Cut back a bit. Building muscles and getting in shape needs proper rest as well as a good workout.
3. **Drink Water** Before and during exercise, drink water. It keeps you from dehydrating when you perspire.
4. **Breathe** While exercising, breathe, it keeps the blood flowing.
5. **Don't Force Yourself** Some days, you are stronger than others; honor that. If it hurts or you are fatigued, you are doing too much.
6. **Cool Down** Afterward, slow the pace before stopping. This lets the blood circulate without over tasking your heart. Gentle stretching reduces muscle soreness or stiffness later.
7. **Warm Up and Stretch** Avoid injury before "going for it" by allowing your muscles, joints and circulation to come up to speed.

Exercise Your Body

Play ping-pong.
Go dancing.
Push the lawn mover.
Rake the grass.
Weed the garden.
Walk briskly.
Ride an exercise bike while watching TV.
Paint a room.
Chase someone you love around the bedroom.

Photo by Jon Nicholas

Shelley and Belly Dancer

Exercise Your Options

Condition your hair
Run at the mouth
Stretch a point
Let your fingers do the walking
Jog your memory
Lift your spirits
Lift paper weights
Bend the rules
Throw a party
Fish for compliments
Putter around
Twist the facts
Jump the gun
Gotta run

If You Don't Like Formal Exercise, No Sweat?

Create a positive attitude toward movement in everything you do. Moving your body is fun. Ask any kid. Children beg to go out and play. Physical activity can be gardening, housework, climbing stairs, parking the car that little extra distance, dancing the night away, ping pong or pushing a lawn mower. Accumulate thirty minutes or more in a day of physical movement and you're doing great.

Get up and move around at least once every half-hour. To motivate yourself, try my tape *I Love Exercise.*

Good Posture: Skeleton Keys

As an experiment, slouch and scrunch your body and notice how icky it feels in this position.

Now, take a deep breath and sit up straight and notice how good you feel. Your breathing is enhanced when you sit up straight.

Slouching creates up to fifteen times more pressure on the lower back than standing up straight. Your diaphragm collapses, leaving less room for your lungs to expand. This makes breathing shallow and gives your body less oxygen. That's why slouching makes you feel groggy. When you sit up or stand up straight, you actually permit more oxygen and blood to flow to your brain.

While seated, rest your feet on something that raises your knees slightly higher than your hips. Sit up straight with your back braced firmly against the chair back. If seated at a desk, pull your chair in close to avoid bending forward.

Up Your Egypt:

Pharaoh Posture Rules

In Ancient Egypt, the pharaohs sat upright in a straight-back chair so that their spine was straight. Their arms rested comfortably on arm rests, hands open, palms up or down, and feet flat on the floor. Umbrellas held by an attendant shaded them. Throughout time, royalty of all cultures, use the pharaoh's straight-back attitude to allow clear thinking and inner guidance.

When you sit or stand up straight, you actually permit more oxygen and blood to flow to your brain. Breathing is enhanced and you breathe fully.

Take a deep breath,
sit up straight.

Pillow Talk

Ancient Egyptians used a stone for a pillow. The Goddess of strength and air, Shu was carved into King Tut's headrest. Legend says that Shu ended chaos by raising the sky high above the earth.

Tut's Pillow

Sleep: The Cradle of Civilization

☆ *SLEEP*

An exciting day, makes deeper sleep.
Don't give TV your soul to keep.
Don't use drugs to cut your zzzs,
And your body renews with the greatest of ease.

Your time in sleep is blessed
Time to put your mind at rest
Free to roam without restraint
Through subject, energy, time and date.
A space to dwell inside your being
To be with the spirit of eternal seeing
When your knit-picky brain tries to stand in your way
The you of your core lets it just fade away.

Sleep is where we all live.
Where miracles are true
It's your daily rebirth
While home here on earth.

—Shelley Stockwell

A third to half of your life is spent sleeping and nobody is really sure why.

We do know that in sleep your body digests, cleanses stress and renews its power. Your pituitary gland assists you to manufacture seratonin.

Millions of years ago humans ate every two hours and slept afterwards, the same way primates do today. Night was a dangerous time to forage for food, so people slept at night and stayed awake during the day. This conserved energy and kept them safe during darkness. We are genetically programmed to daydream (alpha state) into a waking trance every two hours and, dream during sleep (theta state) every two hours. This is probably your accommodation to our ancestors' two-hour sleep cycles.

How long you sleep doesn't depend on how tired you are. How long you sleep depends on your body's natural rhythm, and how much toxin you have in your system. Sugar, sweeteners, caffeine, nicotine, processed food, salt, soy, dairy, meat and drugs and an un-cleansed bowel can disrupt sleep patterns.

Newborn babies sleep sixteen to eighteen hours a day. By age two or three,

State	Behavior	Brain Wave	Hertz (HZ)
Conscious	Active	Beta	13-26
Daydream	Relaxed	Alpha	7-13
Deep Hypnosis	Dreaming Sleep	Theta	4-7
Sleep	Dreamless Sleep	Delta	.05-4

sleep drops to twelve hours and by age five, naps usually stop.

Adults sleep anywhere from four to ten hours, with the majority sleeping seven to eight hours per night. The elderly average six and a half hours. Only a small percentage of people function well on four to five hours of sleep. How much sleep do you need to feel refreshed?

Occasionally, everyone has a sleepless night. Odd schedules, sleeping with the TV, poor eating habits, caffeine, sugar, stress and drugs, especially sleep medications, can certainly unwind your body clock.

The more all-nighters you pull, the more catnaps you take. If sleep-deprived for two to three days, we micro-sleep and doze for a few seconds with eyes opened or closed. When your body clock returns to a normal cycle you crave a good night's rest. Conduct your own "sleep study" and see how many hours *you* really need.

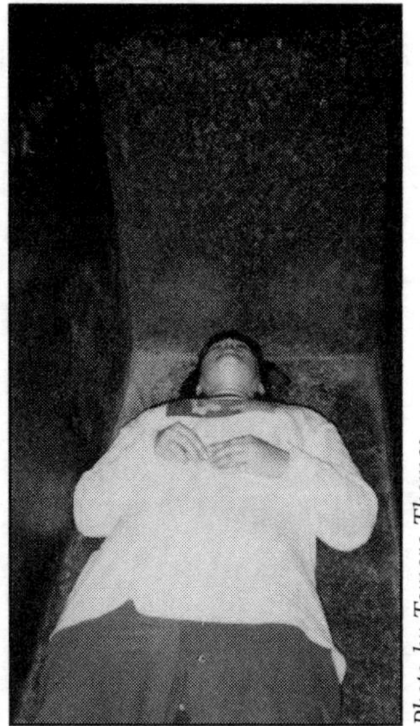

Photo by Tamara Thomas

Shelley in the King's Chamber, Cheop's Pyramid, Giza

Stress and Forgetfulness

Sleep's periodic suspension of conscious awareness paralyzes the body and activates the brain. Cortisol, the hormone your adrenals release as your fight, flight fright or flight response, lowers during sleep. This may be a reason why sleep helps you overcome stress. If you do not sleep, cortisol levels remain high. This stress damages and shrinks the part of your brain (hippocampus) that remembers and learns. That is why you don't think well when sleep deprived.

Eating To Exhaustion

That tasty dinner and dessert, innocently eaten hours ago, may stoke your metabolic furnace and increase body temperature instead of lowering it for sleep. Gas and indigestion interrupt sleep. So do obsessions about work, family, money or anything!

Diabetes and Obesity

A University of Chicago study had healthy subjects sleep four hours for six nights straight. The result was an inability for their body to break down sugar, which produced a rise in serum glucose and serum insulin levels. This risks adult onset diabetes and weight gain.

Call Me a Somnambulance

Sleep-deprived folks talk about sleep the way starving folks talk about food. The word insomnia used to mean "the total inability to sleep." Now insomnia is used to describe difficulty in falling asleep, waking during the night, or getting up too early in the morning. Those who have disrupted sleep for over three weeks are said to have insomnia.

Sleep Apnea and Narcolepsy

Poor breathing disrupts sleep. If your airways repeatedly collapse or are obstructed by enlarged adenoids or tonsils, the brain does not receive proper oxygen during sleep. You can tell if someone is suffering from sleep apnea because of repeated stoppage of breath while sleeping. If that's one of your problems, it might be worth a dietary shift or corrective surgery. But, before going under the knife, it's best to check out what goes in your mouth. Sleep difficulties could be a reaction to sugar, smoking, bingeing, boozing and allergies. Some folks have great results using little nose shields that football players wear. Others attend sleep clinics, or wear a mask that shoots air up their nose.

Narcolepsy, or nodding off to sleep at the wrong times, is a sleep disorder that is helped greatly by diet, hypnosis and biofeedback.

When Sleep Solutions Intensify Problems

Sleeping pills, sedatives (barbiturates) and hypnotics (benzodiazepines), must be taken in ever-increasing dosages to remain effective. They actually make sleep problems worse, because they backfire and disrupt sleep. Because of the addictive nature of sleeping pills, stopping usage can cause insomnia. Alcohol and sugar, knock you out only to wake you up mid-sleep. It is estimated that 4.3% of Americans take prescription sleeping pills and even more buy sleeping aids over the counter. If you are one of them, you know the price you pay in stress.

Even if sleeping pills increase the number of hours you sleep, they decrease deep REM (rapid eye movement) sleep. REM sleep is essential for clear thinking and coordination when you are awake. That's why folks on downers feel confused after a drugged night's rest. Older folks on downers (that's what sleeping pills really are) have a higher incidence of falling down and hurting themselves.

Nightmare

Over time, the body develops tolerance for sleeping drugs and requires more and more to get the same effect. Such addiction eventually contributes to illness and injury. When this happens, folks tend to move on to different medications. If you are a sleeping pill junkie who has tried to stop, you know how addictive these drugs are. Withdrawal often causes a kind of healing crisis, where sleep problems worsen for a short time, excessive REM sleep occurs, and nightmares may ensue. For more information about getting off downers read chapter 26, *Downers: The Shaft.*

Get the Picture: Get Sleep!

To get the renewal rest you need, be consciously aware of anything you do that interferes with sleep, and stop it. Heavy meals, sugar, alcohol, and drugs especially after five p.m. mess up your sleep rhythms.

Daily exercise deepens sleep. There is a hot debate on whether exercise just before bedtime helps or hinders sleep. Decide for yourself.

A glass of warm milk, with its natural l-tryptophan, the same amino acid found in mother's milk, beans and turkey, helps you get drowsy. If sex comforts you, it's a great nightcap.

Insomniacs frequently lack thiamin, riboflavin, B6, B12, folate, pantothenate, potassium, magnesium and iron. Some swear that the right vitamins are the ticket to a great nights sleep. I prefer hypnosis. It helps you develop healthier habits.

Honor Circadian Rhythms

Set a sleep goal and stick with it. Sleep, at regular times, and in a darkened room, allows normal body rhythm.

Morning sunlight, has one hundred times the intensity of indoor light. It interacts with your body's release of melatonin, a neurotransmitter that your body releases when you sleep. If you expose yourself to light a six a.m., your melatonin will release earlier the next evening and make you sleepier sooner. Some folks swear that melatonin tablets, taken just before bed, counteracts jet lag and sleep pattern disruptions.

Photo by Shelley Stockwell

Night owls are more suited to shift work than morning folks are. Rotating work shifts that move from day to evening to night (clockwise) are easier on sleep patterns than counter-clockwise shifts. It's easier to keep regular sleeping patterns by maintaining the same schedule on days on and off work. Studies suggest that people get better shut-eye by sticking to a regular bedtime and waking schedule and not watching television in bed.

Catch a Few Zzzs with Ease

1. Refuse to let work and family get in the way of a good night's sleep.
2. Make the bedroom a cozy sanctuary.
3. Invest in a good bed; not too hard, not too soft, just right.
4. Don't sleep with the TV or radio on.
5. Make sure to have the proper amount of covers.
6. Avoid heavy foods, alcohol, sugar, caffeine (cola, coffee, chocolate) and salt after 5:00 p.m.
7. Light evening meals helps sleep and help slim.
8. Put the body on a regular schedule by going to bed and getting up at the same time each day, even on weekends.
9. Develop a pre-sleep routine to tell your body that it's time for bed. Warm baths, gentle stretching, and soothing music help.
10. Avoid or stop sleeping pills; they make matters worse and are highly addictive. If you've been using sleeping pills, go on a lifelong drug holiday. A good way to do this is to reduce pill dosage to half, and gradually wean yourself off. The best sleeping aid is stress reduction. Find ways to take it easy.
11. Treat yourself to sleeping in at least one weekend a month.
12. Schedule extra sleep on vacation. An extra 30-60 minutes makes a vacation a vacation.
13. If traveling, factor in extra sleep time to help with jet lag and time zones.
14. Exercise 30-40 minutes three times a week.
15. Listen to the hypnosis tape, "Sleep, Beautiful Sleep," available from order forms at the back of this book.

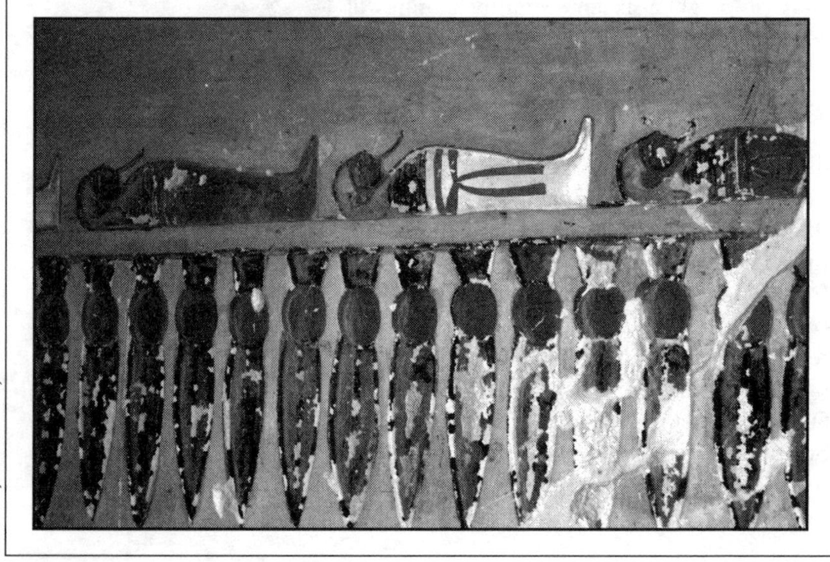

Photo by Joann Kelly

Dreams: Bed-Rock

☆ *You've got to have a dream, if you don't have a dream*
How you gonna have a dream come true?

—Richard Rogers & Oscar Hammerstein

☆ HOW DO YOU GRAB A DREAM?
Say, "I want to grab my dreams" then enter the space between words.
Hold your heart at even beating; then your dreams are heard.
Let your mind dance helter-skelter, let your day begin.
Dreams return on kitten fingers, and take you home again.

—Shelley Stockwell

As brain waves shift throughout wake and sleep, you access and process memories with mental images, emotions and physical changes. These wafting images have amazing power. They reflect your inner feelings and thoughts, and offer keys to resolve unresolved issues. Dreams are symbolic clues of your history and imprints.

Stress and drugs often interrupt dream and sleep patterns. That's why they are so harmful.

Some societies believe that your waking state is the dream and your sleeping state is reality. Aborigines travel the dream-time and heal. Patricia Garfield studied the Senois society in her book Creative Dreaming. Senois are happy, peaceful and well adjusted and thought to be "too magic to fight" by their aggressive neighbors. The key to Senois "magic" is their deep respect for the dream state. A Senois is taught from birth to manipulate their dreams into a positive outcome. The positive goal of Senois dreaming is to fly, receive gifts, or have sex to orgasm. In pursuit of these goals, there are no taboos.

Dreaming in western civilization is often a nightmare, repeated. Let's say you are being pursued by a big, nasty, ugly brown bear to the edge of a cliff. You fall off the precipice, and awaken in a cold sweat. Fear never gets resolved. Learn to reconnect with your dream world and reframe old pain.

Highly Senoi-ing

A Senois child has the same big nasty brown bear chasing him to the edge of a cliff. At breakfast he tells his family. His Aunt Tilly says, "That was a wonderful dream, but you should not have awakened. The next time you have such a dream, make sure you hit the ground. And if you die, be sure to ask the bear for a present. Or you could turn around and fight the bear. And if you kill the bear, be sure to ask for a present. The next time you have the dream, everyone wants to hear about it." That day is spent celebrating your gift. Songs are sung, dances are danced, and paintings are painted; all to celebrate your dream.

Embrace these same goals. Each night, fly anywhere and any way you want. Have sex with any recipient you want, any place, and any time. There are no taboos when you're deep in sleep. If dreams frighten you, the trick is to not wake up but to take the dream to its completion and then, ask for a present. Before you go to sleep, request beautiful, restful slumber, flying, sex to orgasm, and to remember your dream. Ah. Zzzzzz.

INTO-GREAT POWER EXERCISE:

Catch a Dream

Analyzing dreams lets you discover your beliefs and solutions. We all dream. The trick is to train yourself to remember. As you drift to sleep tonight (in that hypnogogic state between wakefulness and sleepfulness), give yourself the suggestion, "I will remember my dreams and write them down."

Keep a notepad or tape recorder by your bed. Dreams quickly slide away from conscious memory unless you record them immediately upon waking.

Shape Shift a Nightmare

While still dreaming an upsetting dream, immediately say, "Enough of this dream." And replay it in your mind with a happier ending.

Shape Shift in Wake-fullness

If you awaken with unpleasant dreams say: "Enough of these defensive patterns." And replay it in your mind with the ending you prefer.

How To Gestalt A Dream: Arabian Nights

☆ *"To Sleep: Per chance to dream."*

—William Shakespeare

☆ *"God speaks in dreams and visions."*

—The Holy Bible

☆ *Your dreams are the daddies of real*
How much you love equals how much you feel.
Easy, slow, watch you grow
Time moves us gentle in his palm
As our faces wrinkles some
And you and I our dreams become.

—Shelley Stockwell

Gestalt therapist, Fritz Pearl said that you are every character in your dream. His process of "gestalting" a dream resolves inner conflict. To use this process you imagine yourself as each character in your dream and retell the dream from each viewpoint. Then have each character converse with each other. This re-frames uncomfortable images.

Ross and Friends

Here is how to do it: Let's say you dreamt: "Two people are riding on horses. One, looks good from the outside but is really hurt. My horse, is sick and tired and can't move. He is dying. I realize that I am dying."

1. Magnify Your Dream Look more closely at the dream. What is it trying to tell you? Is this dream about two horses or is it talking to you about relationships?

2. Become The Elements or Characters in the Dream Speak out from the voice of each horse, and the voice of each of the two people. Tell the dream from each of their viewpoints. Have each element talk to the other characters.

3. Ask Ask yourself; "What do these images tell me about my feelings. In this horse dream, do I feel sick and tired and want to quit?

4. Play it Again, Fritz Make a new script that creates the story the way that you want it. In this case, bring your horse to a gorgeous brook, let him rest, brush his coat and feed him a fresh apple. Both you and your horse will be revitalized.

Sunshine: Ra, The Supreme Beam

☆ *Sun, god of all light,*
You bring me energy, warmth and sight.
Sun, god of all power,
Daily is your finest hour.
You touch Cheops, these folks and me.
You take the edge off frigidity.
Each day you shine in your full spectrum
At night you offer a time of reflection.
You're the source, from you I come and return,
Grow and flourish, live and learn.
Fiercely independent, radiant and strong,
Father sun I sing your song.
In love and light, I chant, I cheer,
(For you are the one who brought me here):
Ra, Ra, Ra, Ra, amen, Ra.

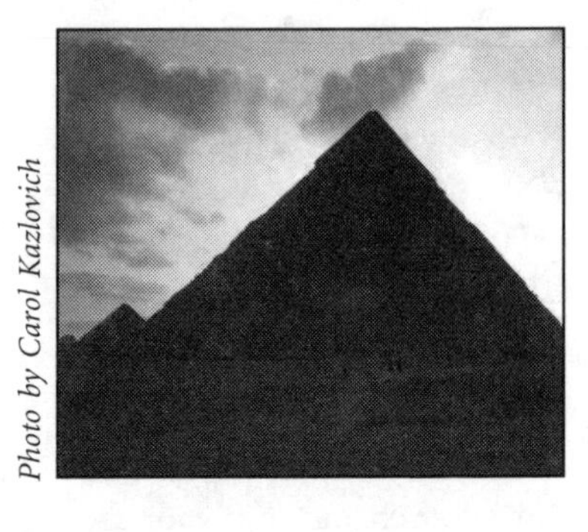
Photo by Carol Kazlovich

See the light! Sunshine and natural lighting make you happier and healthier. Make a sunny window or a walk outside part of your day...every day.

7 Steps to Expand Your Spirituality: Gold Rush

☆ Question: *Why did the Ascended Master cross the road?*
Answer: *To return from the other side.*

1. Take a deep breath and imagine a golden sun flooding your crown spreading light through your mind and body, and radiating out your hands and fingertips.
2. Imagine a golden cord of light surrounding and connecting you to all; for you are each golden light, nourished by the great orb, the sun.
3. Notice the feeling as the warmth spreads through your body.
4. Notice colors radiating within and without.
5. Imagine that you hear the light, like golden rain.
6. Smell and taste delicious light.
7. You are luminous.

AFFIRM SUCCESS: My Body, Myself

When you claim your body and learn to cherish it, it works well. Read this affirmation slowly and let its truth bring you supreme health.

I am my body my body is me. We live together in harmony.
I am healthy. Proper nutrition, sleep, movement, fresh air, light and water, fuel, refresh and cleanse me. I enjoy my many hobbies, interests and talents. I listen

to my body's great wisdom. I satisfy my body's healthy needs. It feels good! I feel good. I am grateful to be alive.

Food fuels me. Eating is a precious time when my body and I commune, refuel and nourish. I eat with reverence. Whole foods are holy. Real food, fresh fruits, vegetables and whole grains are rewarding and fun. I drink lots of water. It's "alimentary" dear Watson. I eat for fuel. I make good healthy food choices.

I permanently and easily quit bad habits and replace them with terrific healthy habits. I'm sensitive to my environment. Toxic substances are gross. I'm sensitive to my body. Chocolates, sugar, caffeine, alcohol, salt, fatty foods and drugs disgust me. I don't want them or need them.

I avoid toxic people. I choose the company of positive, healthy, nourishing people. I keep firm boundaries between myself and others. I love moving my body. I love nourishing my body. I love resting my body. I love cleansing my body.

Movement is living. When I move, I come to life because I stimulate my body's five important systems; circulatory, lymph, respiratory, muscular and nervous. Moving my body gives me more oxygen for energy and fuel for new cells. I exercise three times a week for thirty minutes and I feel healthy, energetic and happy. I love to move my body. I make an appointment with myself to exercise at least three times a week. It's fun! My spine has a free-flowing communication with my brain and internal organs. Moving my body makes me healthy. I love to move my body.

I sleep soundly through the night. My mind balances and renews positive gifts.
I enjoy and learn from my dreams.
I love my body, my body is me.
We live together in harmony.

▲ Mind Your Emotions

Seek out things that please the real you. Surround yourself with nourishing people. Demand that you focus on happy things. Be stubborn about joy.

1. Cleanse Express, any rage, release the past and forgive.
2. Purify Make a new start. Light a candle and count your blessings. Take a long bath. Change your clothes. Occasionally dress as if you are attending your own wedding.
3. Integrate Pool your learning from the past into the present.
4. Affirm Success: Repeat this affirmation three times and let its truth sink into your sweet mind.

AFFIRM SUCCESS: Joy is my Compass
If it is not fun, I don't do it. I choose joy.
The past is just a memory. I diffuse any negative emotional spin on the past. I am neutral about the past. My life is now and I now, in this moment, direct my feeling toward upliftment. I am happy each moment.

I easily express my feelings. My emotions flow toward the great sea of joy. I'm peaceful, happy and positive.

▲ Soul Support: De Fruit of De Vine

You gather strength and upliftment from soul searching, prayer, meditation, nature and creativity.

Creativity: Fertile Valley

☆*CREATIVITY*
Dehydrated thoughts,
saltine crackers in the desert,
ideas gone dry,
scattered,
spinning in lost wind.
Settling like dust.
And each is a seed that any instant,
blooms tender in the wastelands.
What a wonderful idea!
(It grows on you.)
—Shelley Stockwell

Photo by Jon Nicholas

Sacred Ceremony, King's Chamber, Cheop's Pyramid, Giza

☆ *"You can't depend on your eyes when your imagination is out of focus."*
—Mark Twain

☆ *"I just had another twisted idea."*
"So was the light bulb and look how far that's come."

☆ *"The gift of fantasy has meant more to me than my talent for absorbing positive knowledge."*
—Albert Einstein

You are only limited by how you use your creative imagination. The dictionary says creativity is "to bring about through imagination." Creativity allows you a new vision now and a new creation of your future.

The creative artist in you is your life force.

Creativity comes like a flood and breaks the logjam of mental blocks. Unlimited creative energy brings recovery and joy and makes you are the artist of your life.

Illustration by Shelley Stockwell

The creative mind is a double-edged sword: it can lift you to the heights of bliss or dash you to the pits of despair. You must use your creative mind in a positive way. When you open the realm of creativity, you have mystical experiences and encounters with the divine. Here's how a young man used creativity to his advantage:

A TRUE STORY Chris Aguilar

"I overcame addiction, alcohol, and serious sadness by tapping my creativity and expressing myself through poetry and music. I witnessed the collapse of my family, and it wasn't long before I collapsed myself. Poetry was the only way I could express the way I really felt inside. My life goal is to reach out to people and let them know that no matter what the situation is, someone else in this world feels the same way.

REJECTION
You can only try
to be a part of someone's life.
If they spurn you away
at least you know you tried." —Chris Aguilar, Age 18

The best highs are the highs of dreaming and creating living poems and living songs. Some say that getting stoned makes you more creative. But, over time, artists who take drugs get wise to this gigantic lie. Drugs and toxic substances cloud thinking and eventually make you dull, unimaginative and lifeless.

Up Your Egypt

Wall Art

Egyptian art is called "aspective" because of its lack of perspective. The gestures on the hieroglyphic figures indicate specific words or phrases. Two hands raised with palms facing out means adoration to the gods. Two hands held out with palms facing up means an offering a gift to the gods. And one hand raised in front indicates the person who is doing the talking.

The most important things to the ancient wall artist was that each body part was presented from its most identifiable view. A person's face was presented in profile, eyes and shoulders from the front and the waist line in profile. Body proportions were idealized. The "perfect proportions" were eighteen fists tall, from foot to hairline. One third of the body from foot to knee, the next third from knee to armpit and the last third from the arm pit to the hair-line.

Apprentices first drew wall art in red. The master artist would then correct the work with black. The stone cutters then carved the images and the artists returned to paint the figures.

Egyptian wall art and hieroglyphics reads from right to left, left to right, up to down or down to up. You can determine the way to read it by the bottom line of the accompanying cartouche or the direction that the figures are looking.

Rule of Thumb:

Big toes and thumbs are always visible.

The Ancient Egyptian word for artist means "the one that keeps things alive."

Colors had meaning:

BLACK came from kohl or charcoal and meant, "underground."

WHITE came from limestone and represented life beyond.

RED came from red ochre and symbolized the desert and the West Bank of the Nile. The inside of the sarcophagus was often painted red.

Tomb of the Unknown Artist

GREEN came from turquoise or malachite and represented youth and eternity. Osiris the god of the other world was often depicted with a green face.

BLUE came from lapis lazuli or azurite and stood for godliness. Godly images often had blue eyebrows and hair.

CREATIVELY AFFIRM SUCCESS

Read the following affirmation and your life will sparkle:

I think freely and unleash my inherent creativity. I'm balanced in reality and creativity. My past and future thoughts merge. My ideas flow. I notice the obvious. I notice the subtle. I'm creative. I'm a keen observer of myself and life.

Great ideas are all around me. I keep my mind, eyes and ears open to the great ideas waiting to be discovered. I enjoy turning a concept upside down and re-examining it. The make-believe of my childhood is now a beautiful part of my life. Everything inspires me, from the silly to the sublime.

I send limiting voices to wait in the car. They are not needed while I explore unlimited possibilities. I let go and proceed. I give myself small breathing breaks so new ideas 'cook.' I enjoy many playful and recreational activities. I take up creative hobbies. I write a journal, paint a picture, mold with clay, sing, and dance. I express my true self.

Into-Great Power Exercise

Re-Write Your Life

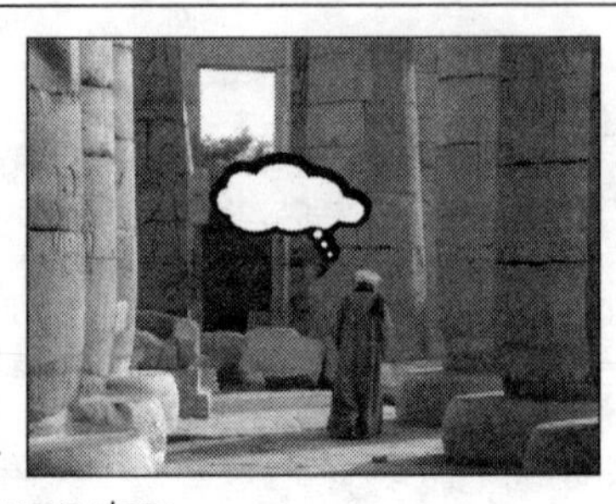

Luxor Temple

A beautiful way to use your creativity is to reframe negative memory to positive ones. Change your future by changing your imagination. Change your life by changing your story.

Take Write Action

Write down deep disturbing thoughts and feelings. All words are acceptable. All thoughts are fine. Just get it down on paper. Some like to throw the papers away; some prefer to keep them forever as a marker of how far they've come. For write action, rewrite thoughts and feelings from the viewpoint of how much you've learned by the experiences or feelings that upset you.

Name Four Creative People

____________________ ____________________

____________________ ____________________

(Hint: Put your name on one of the lines.)

Up Your Egypt

Scribes

Egyptian scribes had to master more than 750 hieroglyphics, representing sounds, objects and ideas. A successful scribe enjoyed soft hands, white linen kilts and no manual labor. They also served as a tax collector, quartermaster, treasurer or architect.

At first, scribes carved hieroglyphics onto slate or ivory, then they moved on to papyrus. Beginners practiced on an ostraca, a flat stone or pieces of clay pottery.

Papyrus is made from water soaked slices of the inner pith of the papyrus reed stalks that were pounded with a mallet and dried flat under a weight. Once the plant juices evaporated, the scribe burnished it with a piece of wood or ivory. Ink was made from soot, water and diluted vegetable gum from trees and plants. A sharpened reed served as a writing stick.

The God Head

☆ SERENITY PRAYER

God, grant me the serenity
To accept the things I cannot change,
Courage to change the things I can,
And wisdom to know the difference.

☆ SOCRATES PRAYER

Beloved Pan, and all other gods
who haunt this place
give me beauty in the inward soul:
may the outward and inward
person be as one

Photo By Nica Lee

Alexandria

☆ GRACE

You pulled me up though I tossed myself down.
You gave me wings, though I hugged the ground.
You taught me to fly through the fog of my fear,
up to the clouds and the sky so near
You lifted me up and gave me the wings,
to fly away from earthly things.
You pulled me up though I tossed myself down.
Then you gave me wings though I hugged the ground.

—Byrne Offutt

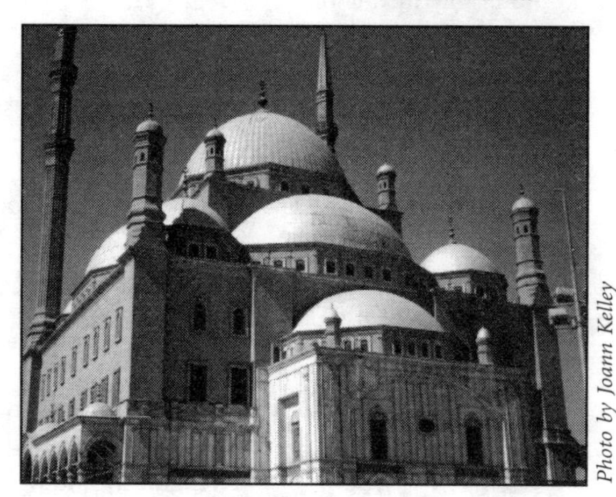

Photo by Joann Kelley

Citadel

The word enthusiasm comes from the Latin "en Theos" meaning the God within.

Your true self, your human potential, includes amazing spiritual energy. If faith is missing from your life, find something, anything, to believe in. Attach yourself to a higher purpose, love and beauty. You'll be glad you did. Higher consciousness makes you blissful.

The right, spiritually uplifting faith, religion or support group can help you "let go and let God." The wrong one can exacerbate neurotic fears and games and stifle your true spiritual self.

Some take drugs to uplift themselves spiritually. But instead of fulfillment, you get a short-lived physical thrill that never satisfies a gnawing-void emptiness. Drugs can open the door to heaven but then slam it shut even faster.

A Yale University two-year study of the elderly, concluded that strong spiritual or religious beliefs make you live longer. This was true for elder cigarette smokers as well.

A simple meditation or prayer increases your sense of well-being. You can sit in a chair, listen to soft music and just chill out, go for a stroll or close your eyes and count your breath.

What Does Faith Mean to You?

☆ *"My religion consists of a humble admiration of the illimitable superior spirit who reveals himself in the slight details we are able to perceive with our frail and feeble mind."*

—Albert Einstein

What beliefs bring peace in your heart and restore you? Faith means different things to different people. For some, formal organized religion satisfies their needs. Others enjoy a more personal, eclectic approach to faith or take their illumination into their own hands, practicing what feels right for them. For some, a walk in the woods and communing with nature is a religious experience.

"Let go and let God," says AA.

"Awaken your light body," says New Age.

"Aum," say meditators.

"Take Jesus as your savior" say born-agains.

"Activate the Chi" say the Chinese.

"Listen to the Great Spirit" say the Indigenous Ones.

"Thank God I'm an atheist," say others.

Great Good, Supreme Being, Nature, Creator, Truth, Wisdom, Love, God, Atman, Artemis, Dewa/Dewi, Christ, Krishna, Buddha, Vishnu, Yahweh, Allah, Kwan Yen, Diana, Madonna, Saraswati, Sophia and Isis; Call it what you like, your personal spiritual expansion will make you feel lighter, more energetic and in tune with a larger picture. Spirituality is your doorway to the room of light.

Don't Confuse Faith With "True Believership"

Overboard beliefs add stress to life by fanatically and religiously indulging in compulsive thoughts and behaviors. True believers often become enmeshed in co-dependent, guru/subject, and all knower/sinner relationships. religion is hypnotic. Make sure it's a positive trance.

A person of faith feels balanced, positive, uplifted, peaceful and sees bigger pictures. A person of faith honors differing opinions.

AFFIRM SUCCESS: Let Go and Let Light

To embrace your spiritual self, read the following affirmation slowly and often. Make it's truth your own:

I open and expand my awareness in every way. I'm grateful for my life. I'm a reflection of perfection and my higher purpose. Discovering and living my higher purpose is my priority, my mission, what I came here to do. My quest for righteousness uplifts me.

Every day I talk to God in my own special way. I rise above my stuff. I pray and am blessed when I eat. I'm one with Great Mystery, All That Is, the Ascended Masters, my Higher Self, God, Goddess, and consciousness as I envision him/her/it to be. I'm the true manifestation of all ascended masters. I co-create heaven on earth. Humility, pride, wisdom, creativity, courage, focus, energy, patience, strength and peace keep me in rhythm with the divine plan.

My Prayer:

'Dear One, assist me to honor my emotional, mental and physical self. Help me celebrate my body with full breath, refreshing sleep, water, healthy food, cleansing, exercise, good posture, fun and laughter. Help me to avoid toxins and seek nourishment.

Heart of my heart. Heart of my mind. Heart of my divine being, help me to embrace my true self. Let me manifest grace, harmony and unity inside and outside of myself. I connect with all life. I honor life. Let me follow my spirituality without need for approval and allow others to follow their spirituality in their own way. I honor the holiness of each person's individual quest. I'm positive and optimistic and develop my innate ability to love.

My body radiates love and light. Pure energy from my soul shines through my eyes making me well and vital. I am whole and holy, aware of all aspects of my perfection: muscles, nerves, ligaments, bones, organs, blood, emotions; my soul, aura, chakras, meridians, guidance and vibration. With this awareness, I balance my strength, speed, endurance and energy.

I give myself time to be creative. I am creation itself, a never-ending flow of inspiration and creativity. I co-create art with word, song, paint, clay, music, dance, thoughts, action, love and light. I know the name of my true self.

My life is meaningful and fun. I hire myself to get high with my higher self; that's the best high. I humbly learn from any mistake I have made. I am grateful that I will never make that mistake again. I make choices based on the highest good and by the laws of love. I spend time in nature.

Up Your Egypt

Ankh If You Love God

☆ Question: *What is the world's oldest profession?*
Answer: *Being God.*

The Ankh means key or hand mirror and is the ancient Egyptian symbol of the union of male and female, god and goddess, and our gift of eternal life. This symbol of human perfection was often crafted as a mirror or tuning fork.

The Ankh reminds us mortals to attune to a higher power, to balance our male and female side, and to reflect beauty. Later religions modified the Ankh into various crosses.

Hand mirrors were made of polished bronze and often adorned with the ankh. The word ankh is intrinsic in names like Tutankhamun.

Time in Nature: 🌴🌴🌴 Tree's Company

☆ SPHERE

Earth is worth her girth in mirth.
The merry land where we lie and stand.

She sucks us all in gravity, regardless of color or depravity.
Glues us on water, snow and ground,
Regularly makes us come around.
She runs hot and cold,
Is third from the sun,
And weighs in at 6.6 sextillion short tons!

For her global support and latitude
(Forgive me for the platitude)
I offer Earth my gratitude.

—Shelley Stockwell

Photo by Nica Lee

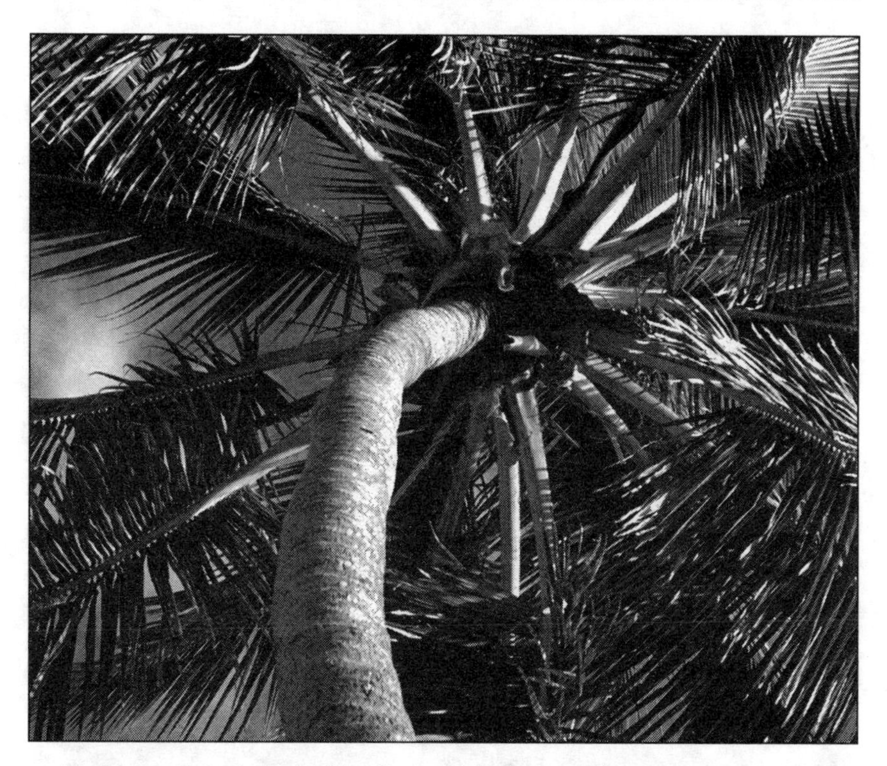

Mother earth has a way of healing and renewing. When you take time in the natural world, you recharge your batteries and the sky's the limit. Ecopsychology, a psychological specialty, says that stress is the result of a disconnection from nature. Peace of mind it's said, results from natural harmony and respect for nature. Positive ecology lets you prefer the smell of moist earth to car exhaust fumes and the sound of the ocean to the telephone ring.

Rachel Kaplan, Ph.D., at the University of Michigan, found that workers with a view of greenery experienced less job pressure and fewer illnesses. Women recovering from breast surgery heal faster and feel better when connected to nature. A view of nature from a hospital window can contribute more to recovery from surgery than most drugs. As my friend James Demirjian says, "Nature is the window into the soul of the Creator."

☆ *Lift all your vital tricks that hide forever loneliness*
Strip them as a dress and find yourself pink and mottled.
Let the sun touch you with remember.
The winds, the stars, turn your soft belly to the earth.
Return to your mother's womb and stay.
It is safe here. You've come home.

—Shelley Stockwell

Up Your Egypt

Honored Animals

The ancient Egyptians created a society and a religion that blended humans and nature.

Indigenous cultures around the globe celebrate earth and her bounty. Like the Indian totems, the Egyptians attached human characteristics to the animal kingdom. That's why they have so many animals as their gods. Sacred animals were painted in all the tombs because they were said to accompany the dead to the after life. Thousands of mummified Ibis (heron) birds, horses and cats were mummified with loving care.

The giraffe represented foresight, the female hippo (Goddess Tauret) childbirth, the male hippo (Seth), chaos. The lion was king. No wonder the Sphinx looks the way he does.

The water buffalo had aggressive power to the Egyptians. Like Norseman, Bulls horns upon a king's head represented power.

Bast was an Ancient Egyptian black cat/goddess. Reverence for cats was so strong that Egyptians shaved off their eyebrows as a mark of respect when the family cat died.

Photo by Neredah Bradstreet

An Attitude of Gratitude

☆ *"Recite prayers while driving home from work."*

—Halla Lou Yah

Find a place in nature and do a personal invocation to honor the blessings of your earth home. Thank earth; air, soil, water, vegetation, hill, valley, sky, wind, sun, moon, stars, rain, clouds, lakes, streams and oceans.

Thank each season.

Thank the four directions.

In gratitude, light a candle, burn incense, bury a rock and make this place in time a sacred moment that you'll always remember.

Sip herb tea and look out your window.

Sing, dance or chant.

Symbolically wash away any negativity, and come to your mother earth with clean hands and a pure heart.

☆ GREEN WILLOW ONE, WILL YOU DANCE?

I look into your one thousand, two hundred and fifty-one mostly small petal eyes.
You're limitless spine nods ever so slightly. "Hello," you fuzz, in purest green.
Brown and amber hue evaporates into the open window of my eye.
Moving into caves between soft lobes into the space between thought, tissue and patterns of my day.
Your voice, the philharmonic (with Arthur Fielder conducting)
Echoes through the hall.
My love, (in the rapture of your delicate arms) I swoon.
As we (ever so quietly) dance the minuet.
Have we never met?

—Shelley Stockwell

Add Structure to Your Life

☆ FILE

Don't pile, change a sloppy style.
Throw things away. Leave space for play.
Get off the dime; pay bills on time.
Get taxes done. Organization is fun.
Return calls, answer letters.
Get it together and life works better.

—Shelley Stockwell

Clean your closet and you do so much more than organize your physical space, you actually renew your psychic space.

AFFIRM SUCCESS: Get It Together

I handle things that need handling in the now. I map out my dreams and goals for the future.

I love to eliminate clutter. I throw away things I don't need and give myself space to function. Put your priorities in order. I schedule time for play, pay bills on time, get taxes done, answer letters. I write a will so my heirs and affairs are in good repairs. Organization is fun.

RIGHT WORK

☆ *"I got this fantastic job because I went to bed with the right person, myself."*

The perfect work lets you do things you enjoy most. Make your work your play and your play your work. Learn to "plerk.' Here is an affirmation to help you manifest the perfect job:

AFFIRM SUCCESS: Right Work
Right work, works right. I create and manifest right work.

When on the job, I schedule more important work first. I think before I begin. I complete one job before going on to the next and delegate to another person rather than do everything myself.

I stay on track and get the job done well. I keep records simple. I give myself reasonable deadlines. I don't duck with denial or paralyze with perfection. I am realistic. I don't put off 'til tomorrow; I do now. I use peak times, time lines and do it now. Everything is attitude. I am positive. I accept my work with an attitude of gratitude.

I take charge. I'm responsible. I'm organized. I see bigger goals. I say 'yes' when I want to and 'no' when necessary. I focus upon completion and success. I'm a winner in my work.

How To Cool An Interview

Make a great impression at the beginning and at the end.

1. Take a deep breath, look with soft eyes directly into the eyes of your interviewer for two seconds and notice any information about how that person feels in your presence. Remember to breathe.

2. Let the interviewer start the conversation (sit when told).

3. Actively listen and determine what they are looking for. Repeat back key phrases. Be what they say they want.

4. Have a strong departure, again, with direct soft-eye contact, a warm and firm handshake and smile.

5. When they ask "Do you have any questions?" Take this chance to give a commercial. Say "No but I'd like to remind you that I am terrific for this job. I am focused, hard working and you'll be glad you hired me."

Photo by Jon Nicholas

The Pledge of Self-Allegiance

Place your hand over your heart and read this pledge:

I pledge allegiance to myself
And the united states of my sub-personalities.
And to the life for which we stand,
One person, Under God, Into-Greated.
With liberty and justice for my True Self,
My Country, and my loved ones.

Chapter 15
Great Relationships
Statue, Dearie?

Why be lonely when a great relationship can be fun, exciting and rewarding? All great relationships begin with your relationship to your own magnificent self. This chapter gives you easy-to-learn communication skills to cultivate a great relationship with yourself and others.

▲ BE A FRIEND TO YOURSELF
▲ SHELLEY'S TEN COMMITMENTS FOR LOVE
▲ DATE A HONEY: Man-a-Feasting
▲ FAIR FIGHT: Humm•Us
▲ SIX STEPS MAKE A GREAT FIGHT
▲ INTO-MATE RELATIONS: Going to Bedoin
▲ CHILDREN: Little Lambs

☆ LOVE
Love's the apex, the zenith from A to Z
Turns homo sapiens to chimpanzee.
It's love we inscribe on our paramour's heart.
Love draws us together; love tears us apart.
Love is a butterfly that can't be pinned down,
a dream drifting past the far side of town,
slanty-eyed lust, a powdery cradle,
a pat on the back, and food on the table.
Love is enough to make grown men cry,
color their hair, and cheat or lie.
Nothing's too much for a woman to do
To attract a sole mate whose intentions are true.
Without love we die, we war and we rage
and make sour faces alone in a cage.
So look all about you (if you want to survive),
if it's love that you see here, you'll know you're alive.
—Shelley Stockwell

Photo By Jon Nicholas

▲ BE A FRIEND TO YOURSELF

☆ *"It is only with the heart that one can see rightly; what is essential is invisible to the eye."*

—Antoine de Saint Exupery

☆ *"Learning to love yourself is the greatest love of all."*

Loneliness has health risks. Studies suggest that people, who need people, are the luckiest people in the world: they live longer.

During a six-year Swedish study of 17,433 men and women ranging in age from 29 to 79, "four times as many antisocial people died than social ones." A similar nine-year duplicate study in Alameda County, California concluded that those with fewer social ties were twice as likely to die younger.

Up A Friend

Imagine yourself having only one day to enhance a friend's self-esteem. What actions could you take? What gifts would you give them? What would you say? Make a list of five things that you could say or do.

1. ______________________________
2. ______________________________
3. ______________________________
4. ______________________________
5. ______________________________

Now, look over your list and circle any of these things on your list that you have given yourself in the last two weeks. Great relationships begin at home with honoring yourself. Commit yourself to doing at least one of the things on your list for yourself…today! When you do you practice kindness that is easier to give outside of yourself.

To be a love magnet you must give yourself great reasons to feel loved. Here are some great reasons why YOU deserve love. Of course, you can add your own good reasons too:

I am loved because I love myself.
I am loved because someone loves me now.
I am loved because someone loved me in the past.
I am loved because God loves me.
I am loved because I choose loving people to be around.
I am loved because I ask for what I want.
I am loved because I choose to feel loved.
I am loved because I choose to be loved.
I am loved because my wonderful body loves me unconditionally.

▲ Shelley's Ten Commitments for Love

1. Be A Good Friend

What qualities do you want in a friend? Do you demonstrate them yourself? If not, improve your behaviors and attitudes. Monkey see, monkey do; if you want a friend, you need to be one.

Start by being a good friend to yourself. When you respect your own beauty and uniqueness, it makes it easier to appreciate others' beauty and uniqueness.

Friends, family and mates bring out your best and worst so you can learn how to love. Relationships require you to look at your "stuff." When you observe yourself in relationship with others, in good times and bad, you grow in wisdom and peace and are better equipped to have fun and love.

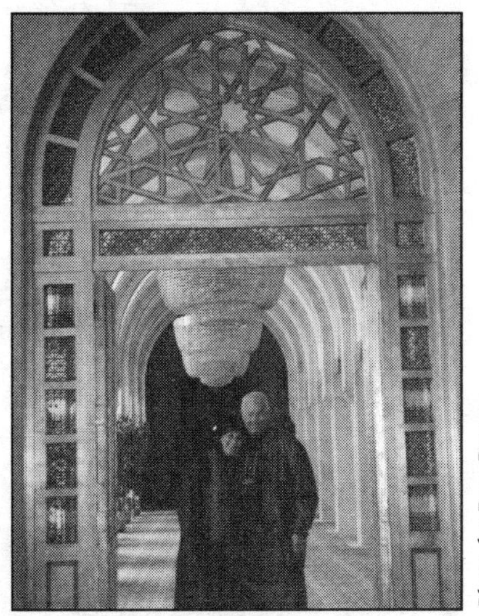

Photo by Ross Prowse

Mina House, Giza

2. Tell the Truth

If you tell the truth to yourself and your partner, you'll never go wrong. Truth is the gauge of friendship.

3. Make Time for Togetherness

☆ *"When was your baby born?"*
"The year the TV broke"

An average married couple spends six hours a day watching TV and less than 25 minutes talking together. Friendship needs time to develop. Make time to talk and listen to yourself and your beloved.

4. Celebrate Uniqueness

☆ *"How did you stay married to the same woman for 50 years?"*
"Hell, she's not the same woman. Every couple of years she changes."

Viva la difference! A true friend encourages the other to grow, learn and pursue their unique purpose. *Resist the temptation to create a replica of yourself.* Differences in attitudes and behaviors enhance. Honor different inner voices in yourself and others.

5. Compliment Your Friend and Yourself Often

☆ *"People don't care how much you know until they know how much you care."*

Almarie and Bam Bam

"I want you to know that my life has been enhanced by knowing you." "I'm a better person because I know you." "I like the way you think." "You light up my life." "Brilliant!" "You're terrific!" "I love YOU."

When you catch someone being wonderful, tell them. When you catch yourself being wonderful, tell yourself Doing something positive for another makes you feel great.

6. Listen to Oral and Non-Verbal Messages

Photo by Neredah Bradstreet

☆ *"The real voyage of discovery does not seek new lands, but sees with new eyes."*

Be aware of feelings and actions as well as words. When you do, your friend knows you are a friend. Listen to yourself. Be your own best friend.

Buds Listen in the Third Degree

The flip side of generating sound is receiving sound. How do you listen?

First Degree Listening: *Listening Just to Agree* When you listen and agree just for the sake of agreeing, you give up power, and personal expression, only to yield to someone else's energy.

Second Degree Listening: *Listening Just to Disagree* If you listen just to take an opposing viewpoint, you again give away your power and personal expression. Your reaction becomes only in response to someone else's energy.

Third Degree: *Aware Listening* When you listen from a place of neutrality, simultaneously listening to your own reactions and responses and the words spoken; you hear. Another's words come from outside of you. Your reactions come from inside you. Listen from the heart to yourself and the other.

7. Be Positive in Communication

Folks stay close to you when they associate more pleasure than pain in their relationship with you. Sour faces, talking about problems and negativity turn others off. Positive strokes and attitudes make positive memories. Acknowledge the efforts and steps another makes to satisfy your requests.

8. Don't Criticize and Judge

☆ *"Advice is like snow, the softer it falls, the longer it dwells upon, and the deeper it sinks into the mind."*

—Coleridge

Photo by Nica Lee

We are only mirrors for each other. If you judge another, you too, are judged. Your actions and who you are sometimes differ. You don't have to like your every action, to like yourself. You don't have to like someone's every action, to like him or her. Keep a positive attitude toward yourself and others and you promote positive change.

9. Notice Needs and Meet Them

☆ *"I don't know why he dislikes me. I never did him any favors."*

Walk in your mate's shoes and empathize and support them in having what they want. Encourage them and yourself to ask for what you want.

10. Always Allow Time For Play and Relaxation

The family that plays together stays together. People having fun love themselves and others. Quiet time is important too. Spend time listening to music. Allow yourselves time to be quiet.

Shelley's Ten Commitments for Love

1. Be a Good Friend
2. Tell the Truth
3. Make Time for Togetherness
4. Celebrate Uniqueness
5. Compliment Your Friend and Yourself Often
6. Listen to Oral and Non-Verbal Messages
7. Be Positive in Communication
8. Don't Criticize and Judge
9. Notice Needs and Meet Them
10. Always Allow Time For Play

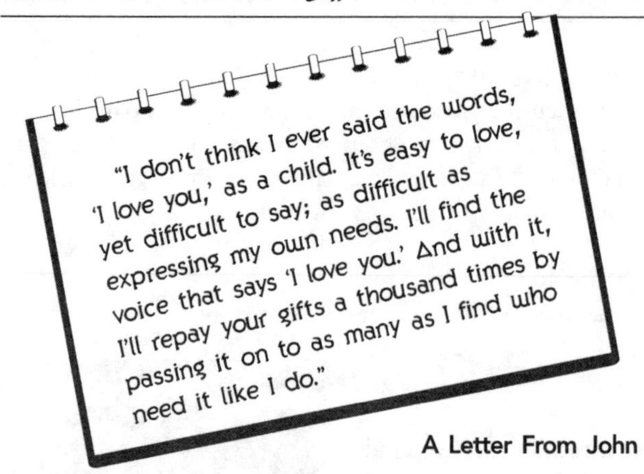

A Letter From John

▲ Date a Honey: Man•a•Feasting

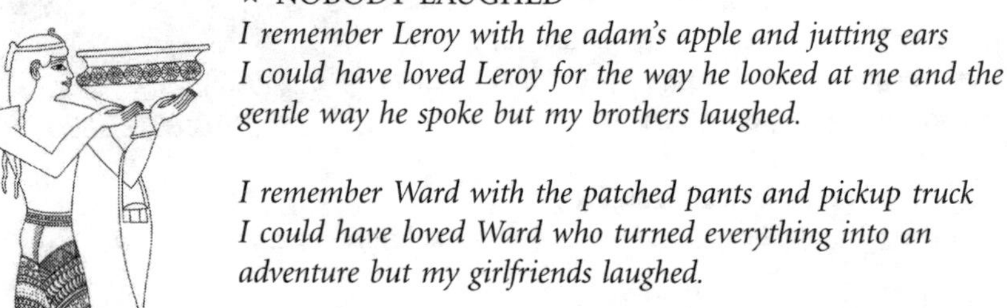

☆ NOBODY LAUGHED

I remember Leroy with the adam's apple and jutting ears
I could have loved Leroy for the way he looked at me and the gentle way he spoke but my brothers laughed.

I remember Ward with the patched pants and pickup truck
I could have loved Ward who turned everything into an adventure but my girlfriends laughed.

So I married Trump who went to Princeton and belonged to the right clubs.
Nobody laughed—least of all me, hardly ever again.

—Elizabeth Whittaker

☆ *"Life is a banquet table and some poor suckers are starving."*

—Mame

☆ My friend Sara is wailing: *"I want a man bad."*
"Maybe that's your problem." I say, *"Want a man good."*

Here's are the six steps to create a mate, Sara:

1. Ask and Ye Shall Receive

Most importantly, clarify for yourself what you want and prioritize your list. Decide what's important to you. What are your priorities? Do you want a companion who enjoys your same spiritual beliefs, work and activities? Do you want passion? Romance? Emotional closeness? Companionship? Humor? Intelligence? An instant family? Money?

What qualities in another make you happy? What kind of person brings out the best in you?

Write a list of exactly what you are looking for in your mate. Be as specific and detailed as possible. Don't be concerned if you are not 100% committed to what you write, just write down the first thing that pop into your mind.

Then ponder each one and decide if you really want that quality. If not, cross it off. You literally get exactly what you consciously or subconsciously request. If you want your mate to have $1,500,000+, write that down.

List your "unacceptables." Mine are: "Drinkers, druggies, smokers, liars, sneaks and sad sacks need not apply."

2. Help Your Thoughts Be Things

☆ BEING MYSELF

As I was letting down my hair,
I met a guy who didn't care;
He didn't care again today—
I love 'em when they get that way!

—Hughes Mearns

Put your list somewhere where you see it every day. The universe, guides, and all the powers that be are in a full-fledged conspiracy to grant your wishes. If you don't believe it, look at your life right now.

Illustration by Shelley Stockwell

You create your life by your thoughts and requests. How did you start doing the work you do? You said, with a thought. ' I think I'll do...' Seeing your list keeps you conscious, so when Mr. Or MS. Everything walks by, you'll recognize them.

3. If You Want To Have The Perfect Mate: Be One

Be every quality you can be on your list. If you want a lean, healthy specimen, *you* be lean and healthy. If you want him to tell the truth, always tell the truth. Become the mirror for beauty to reflect upon.

Do you expect others to do things you don't or wouldn't do under the same circumstances? Do you expect others to reach your unrealized goals? Do you want to change someone?

4. Hear Ye, Hear Ye

Let your availability be known through every middlesex, borough and town. Tell others about your specific requirements. The world is full of yentas who get off on matchmaking. Friends love to help you win but often don't know how to help. Give them a chance to feel useful. If you meet someone you find attractive, tell *them* what you are looking for. It pays to advertise. My friend printed her "man ad" on the back of the tee shirt she wears when running marathons. She's looking for a runner.

5. Let Go and Don't Be Attached To The Outcome

Joyfully return to your life. Follow your bliss. Fall in love with yourself. Become your own best friend and an unabashed pleasure seeker. Get happy. Nothing attracts an uplifting partner more than pure unadulterated joy. No need to wait for Mr/Ms Right or settle for Mr/Ms Right Now when you are so busy enjoying your many interests and hobbies. Relax. The universe is taking care of things for you.

6. Stop Being Defensive: Dis•are•me

It's not fun to play army when you're always the enemy. How you talk to yourself makes a big difference in your attitude and actions. In•fighting and in•sulting create insecurity. Self respect requires that you honor your true selves. All of them: the child, the teenager, the grown-up, the old crone, the naughty, the angel, the aggressive, the timid (we all get the idea.) It is essential that each part of you be acknowledged. Each subpersonality has an important reason for being and they come into alignment when you listen respectfully to all of you.

Imagine yourselves at a large conference table, having a board meeting. Your profound wisdom, or master self, moderates a discussion where all parts of you have equal voice. *Together*, peacefully re•solve conflict as a team. As you master self-love, you are ready to enjoy loving others.

7. Celebrate Your Mate When You Find Them

Once you find your sweetheart celebrate and love them. Don't put off your loving 'til tomorrow for tomorrow never comes. Take a chance and just love.

Up Your Egypt

Charming Egyptian Women

☆ *"She is like the rising morning star, at the start of a happy year.*
Shining bright, fair of skin, lovely the look of her eyes, sweet the speech of her lips.
With graceful step, she treads the ground, captures my heart by her movements.
She causes all men's necks to turn about to see her. Joy has he whom she embraces.
He is like the first of men!'

—Egypt, New Kingdom

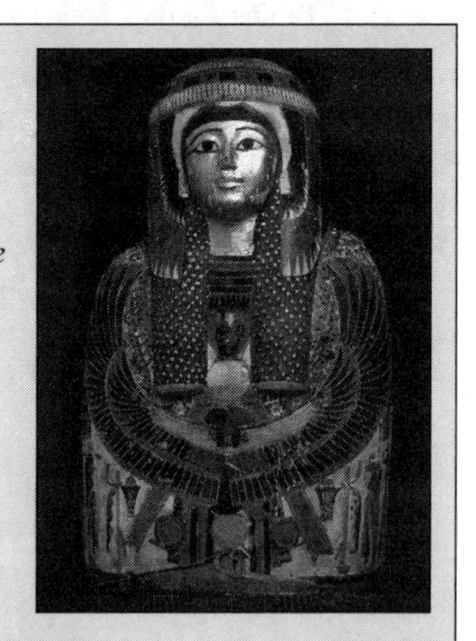

The famous Cleopatra was the last ruler from the Ptomaic dynasty and ruled Egypt from 10 to 30 AD. Cleopatra married her brother Ptolemy XII. She had affairs with Julius Caesar and Mark Anthony.

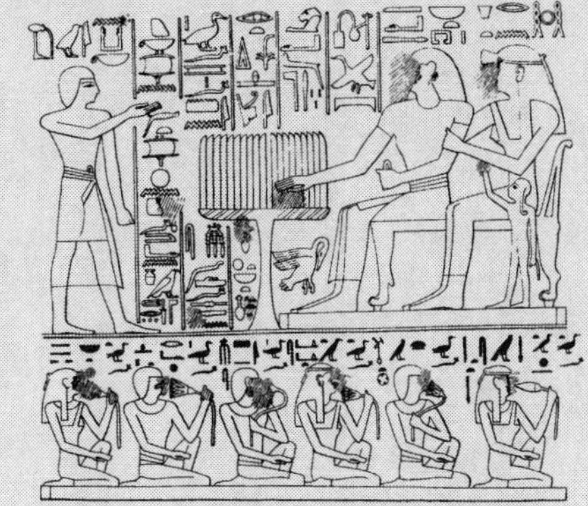

Cleopatra understood the power of aroma and seduced Mark Anthony in knee-deep rose petals, as they sipped pearls dissolved in vinegar. Her make-up was scented with cedar wood. She even had the sails of her barge soaked with perfume so that the breezes would let folks know that she was on her way.

Blue Blood

"Since we are painted blue, you may take away our clothes, our homes, our valuables but you cannot take away our dignity."

—The Brits, when captured, according to George Bernard Shaw

While performing her duties as queen, she sometimes wore a fake beard and a shend'eet or skirt/kilt. Because of her royal status, she painted the veins on her breasts blue. Perhaps that's where the phrase bluebloods comes from.

The blue used for this came from ground up lapis lazuli mined in Afghanistan. Lapis was considered the sacred stone of Isis and was used for jewelry and to paint the rich blues of wall adornments as well. Lapis was said to bring good luck, love, power and wealth. In powdered form it was also used for treating skin diseases, epilepsy and anemia. Like all women in those days, Cleo also painted her eyes with lapis or kohl, wore a corset and dowsed herself with fragrant tree resin.

Mummies were cedar-scented, too, for eternal bliss. Ancient Egyptians wafted Sandalwood to the gods to turn them on.

Nefertiti Queen Nefertiti was the wife of King Tut's elder brother pharaoh Akhenaten. The word Nefertiti means 'the beautiful woman has come' or ' the beautiful one.'

Close Shave It was the custom in Cleopatra's Egypt to shave the body all over. 5,000 year old bronze shavers have been found.

▲ Fight Fair: Hummous

☆ *"Yield: When push comes to love."*

—Shelley Stockwell

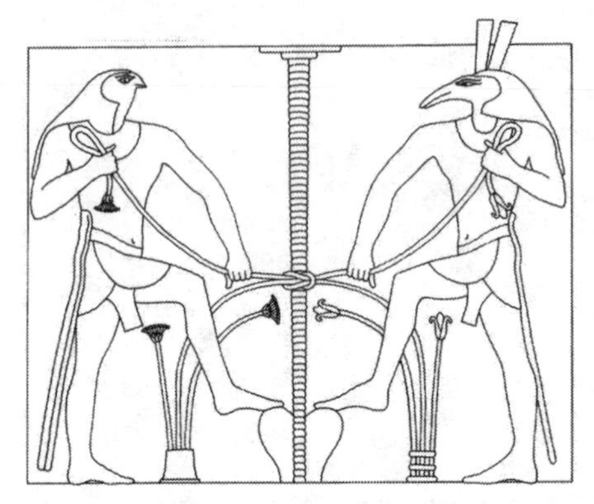

Whose Problem Is It?

Everyone involved in a problem, contributes to the problem. Be aware of how you contribute to a problem. Do you reward others by giving positive or negative attention when their behavior is unacceptable to you? Do you think of problems as a personal attack and retaliate? Ask yourself, "whose problem is it?"

If it's your problem, solve it. Ask yourself "What could I do to improve this situation?" and "What is the positive lesson here?" Write down possible solutions and choose one. Afterwards, evaluate how your chosen solution worked.

If it is their problem, let them solve it. Or be willing to assist them in solving it if they ask.

Encourage Acceptable Behavior

☆ *"It seems that I have never been the popular height, weight or color. Please Windex your eyes and look at me."*

—Nica Lee

Be specific about behaviors that you don't like, and lovingly tell your partner what behaviors you prefer. When you catch yourself being wonderful, tell yourself so. When you catch others being wonderful, tell them so. Acknowledge efforts and steps taken to satisfy your requests.

Avoid Power Struggles

Is being right more important than solving the problem? Of course not! No one wins. No one loses. No one is right. No one is wrong. Do not demand that others agree with you. Find creative ways to solve disagreements. If your partner says something that you don't agree with, avoid saying "You are wrong." Instead use the *and approach* "You said that (for example) the sky is green AND I perceive it as pink.

Use "I" statements instead of "you" statements. "I feel angry" rather than "You make me angry." "I'm upset" rather than "You make me sick." "My ears hurt when there is so much noise" instead of "You are making too much noise."

Play to Your Partner's Dominant Senses

Photo by Shelley Stockwell

Mismatched communication makes people feel unloved and misunderstood. Listen to another's words and you will hear their way of operating. As subtle as these differences seem, they can be used to connect, persuade, heal or sell you to your loved one.

"Something *feels* funny. I can't *put my finger on it.* I want my house to *feel* like a home" lets you know that they are dominantly a feeler.

"I *see* what you mean, I view it this way…" lets you know that they are visual.

Match their words and phrases and they will feel like you really understand them.

Talk to them in words they relate to. Most people are unconscious about their sub-language preferences.

Anger usually grows from hurt feelings. If you think your needs are ignored, you assume that others don't care enough to meet them.

When having a fight, do you listen yet not hear? Are you too busy thinking about how to respond or defend yourself to really absorb your partner's words? Join the human race. But don't despair. There is hope. Learning to fight fair just requires that you practice active listening. And, practice makes perfect!

Walk In His Sandals Strategies

Imagine that you are the person who ticked you off or who is angry with you. From that viewpoint, figure out why I/they behave the way they do, feel the way they do, act the way they do. Usually, they have the same fears you do.

Papyrus Plan A good way to settle hassles is to organize your thoughts on a piece of paper. Write down everything that is bugging you about the other person. Then step into their sandals and write their name and everything you can imagine that is bugging them. This way, you explore in writing both your and their needs and concerns.

Time Out Take yourself out of the situation and it sometimes puts emotions under control. Reschedule a time to communicate rather than hassle. Don't use time outs to punish another or ignore a problem. Use time outs to cool down and get space to clarify what's going on.

Keep Boundaries If you get yourself into center, you won't respond in crazy ways. Rather than defend yourself, and escalate a hassle, pull in and regroup. If someone acts aggressively toward you, sometimes a simple gesture, like taking his or her hand or offering a hug, or apologizing, can diffuse aggression.

Visual cues create 80% of our perception. We send dominant and submissive signals to each other. If a wild wolf approached another, it would immediately decide which was dominant and which submissive. The dominant wolf sticks his tail in the air (humans stand tall). Subordinates keep their tail down (we slouch). When your boss, parent or teacher pats you on the back, they are asserting their dominance. If you respond by pigeon toeing your feet inward, as they toe out, you yield.

The more you clasp your hands, cross your arms and legs, crouch or touch your throat, the more self protective and submissive you become. When interpreting what other people are saying, visual clues are most important and make up some 80% of our perceptions. When you want to get along with someone stay in positive neutrality and good posture. Communication is an equal footing experience.

Rules of a Fair Fight

☆ Larry King: *"You're a manic depressant."*
Jonathan Winters: *"Yeah, but not all the time."*

Any fight that lasts longer than a day, lasts too long.

Communication is simple when you know the rules. If someone is angry, they may raise their voice, say accusing and nasty things, or name-call. They may punish by shutting down and cutting off communication. Being angry or having someone angry with you feels terrible. And even worse, it keeps you from meeting your needs. Here are the ground rules of successful scraping:

No hitting below the belt or biting off an ear.
No "hit and run" tactics.
No playing to an audience or grandstand plays.
If you have an issue, go directly to him or her in the appropriate setting.
No name-calling.
No silent treatment, pouting and "punishment."
No "nuclear threats."
No weapons are permitted.
No person or personal property can be damaged.
The fighters may declare a truce, time-out or surrender at any time.

▲ Six Steps Make A Great Fight

Step One:

Agree To Disagree

I/we agree to disagree and fight fair. To begin a fair fight we agree on a time and place. We each agree to communicate clearly, no hitting below the belt, no name-calling, put-downs, or insults.

Step Two:

Lay It on the Table

If something is bothering you, report it, even if you do not know exactly what it is. For example, "I'm feeling distant from you right now and I'm not sure why, can you help me figure it out?" If you called the fair fight, be brave enough to reveal how you feel. Don't hide behind anger or fear, be brave and say what's going on with you emotionally. Take time to express *clearly*, so that you are understood.

Step Three:

Listen

Listen well. The key to a fair fight is to listen and repeat what you have heard. Called active listening, each "parrots" back what the other says. Use their same words and inflections. Sometimes that alone ends an argument. Conflict is often missed communication.

Active listening makes an issue clearer. Sometimes people simply want their viewpoint heard. When truth is expresses, no one is "right" or "wrong." Each says what is right for them.

How you perceive others listening to you also influences what you say. Unfortunately what you imagine going on in other people's heads may not be what is going on at all.

Dale Carnegie tells of giving a speech where he focused on a smiling elderly woman in the audience. Afterward, he said to her "You're a wonderful listener. It really made a difference to me and I want to thank you." The old woman nodded, smiled and reached up to turn on her hearing aid. "I'm sorry, there's so much noise in here, I turned the darned thing off when I came in."

In a study of 4,000 young adults, Finnish researcher Mirja Kalliopuska found that highly empathetic subjects were more assertive, less self-obsessed, more sensitive, and less likely to smoke or drink than their less empathetic counterparts.

While listening, process and clarify what's going on with you. This gets you past anger and blame. Sweet Talk yourself and say, "Relax, let it pass, take it easy, chill out or take a deep breath, lower your voice, slow down."

Step Four:

Brainstorm

Brainstorm solutions. How can we solve this dilemma? Brainstorm for possible solutions. Say anything that comes to mind. Even if suggestions seem silly, illogical or impractical, just spit it out. One just might stick or give us a new perspective. How can you organize responsibilities? How can we negotiate things better?

Step Five:

Let's Make A Deal

I/we make a deal. Are we are both willing to try one of these solutions? If so, when do we begin? Should we try it for a day? A week? A month? Should we just shelve this fight for a day, a week, a month and bring it up again if it hasn't shifted satisfactorily on its own?

Step Six:

Appreciate

Show appreciation to your "fight partner." The person across from you cared enough to take the time to work out a problem.

▲ Into-Mate Relations: Going to Bedoin

☆ OF ALL MY RELATIONS, I LIKE SEX THE BEST

Of all life's interests and pursuits,
a quest for power, a quest for loot,
intellectual aggrandizement,
wearing labels for advertisement.
Doing drugs, doing religion,
procrastinating or making decisions.
Your line of work or philosophy,
loving your dog or your bonsai tree.

What you really want, what you're hungry for,
is touch, love, sex: toujour l'amour.
Nature commands life to make itself anew,
you are of nature and you know it is true.

So don't delay in deluded diversions,
getting lost in projected excursions,
love and sex is all there is.
Ask your heart.
Ask your kid.

—Shelley Stockwell

If your parents hadn't gone with the sperm of the moment, you wouldn't be reading this right now. Take the time and the effort to find out what your partner enjoys romantically and sexually. School yourself in being a great lover. Every body loves a lover.

☆ FOREVER IN LUST AND TRUST

My new mate I will marry. His eyes dark and bright:
Shining with whites pure light.
Clean and sober, high on joy;
a friend, a man, a little boy,
a lover of nature, a lusty sort,
kind to children, bored by sports.
He will not seduce another one: Will love me as his sole mate.
And as we make our wedding vows; My loving heart he'll take.
He'll sit with me at twilight and I will stroke his skin
and fall in love with his words and tunes over and over again.

He loves to throw a party, has many old, old friends,
laughs in screwy places and never does offend.

He walks his talk, is generous, enjoys the finer arts.
He loves to explore the world with me.
He calls me his sweetheart.
And when we're in our 90's, I'll sit upon his knee.
And we will leave together for all eternity.

—Shelley Stockwell

Up Your Egypt

Familiar Ring

We wear a wedding ring on our ring finger because the Egyptians believed that a "love vein" extends directly from that finger to the heart.

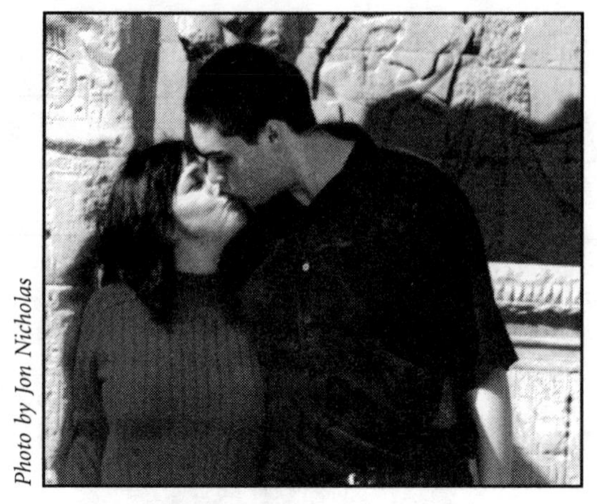

Photo by Jon Nicholas

Shelley with son, Bryce.

▲ Children: Little Lambs

A Parent's Prayer

Dear God, make me a better parent. Teach me to understand my children, to listen patiently to what they have to say and to answer their questions kindly. Keep me from interrupting or contradicting. Help me to be as courteous to them as I want them to be to me. Forbid that I should ever laugh at their mistakes or resort to shame or ridicule. May I never punish them out of anger or spite or to show my power.

Help me, dear Lord, to demonstrate by all that I say and do that honesty does produce happiness. Reduce the meanness in me. And when I am out of sorts, help me to hold my tongue. May I be ever mindful that my children are merely children and that I should not expect them to have the maturity and judgment of adults. Let me not rob them of the opportunity to do things for themselves or to make their own decisions. Help me to grant them all reasonable requests and give me the courage to deny them the privileges that I think may be harmful.

Help me to be fair and just and kind so that I will earn their love and respect and they will want to imitate me. This is the supreme compliment. Amen. Awomen. Ah life.

A TRUE STORY: The War of the Pennies
by Alex Lessin, Ph.D.

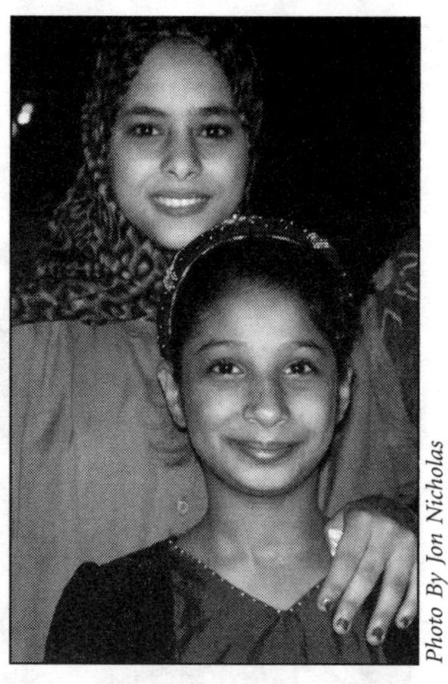
Photo By Jon Nicholas

Wager of War My little sister Shelley and I fought the "War of Pennies." I was 9 and she was 4. I hoarded pennies Mom, Dad, and my grandparents gave me. I pilfered pennies guests lost in our overstuffed chairs.

I started the war when I conned pennies from my sister and also sneaked into her room and stole them outright. When I wasn't home, she took them back—and dozens more from my hoard. Outraged, I purloined more of hers. She made off with more of mine. Over the next year, I kept pirating and hiding her pennies. She matched and often beat me as we swiped each other's cents.

Then, on Valentine's Day 1950, Shelley gave me all her pennies as well as the ones she'd stolen from me. She glued the coins into the shape of a heart and in its center she spelled in pennies, "I love you." My heart warmed and opened; tears ran down my cheeks.

We became best friends and confidants, sharing our deepest feelings and concerns and modeling the kind of loving bond two people can share. This model let me, as an adult, commit to my wife.

Love comes as an unexpected gift. Receive it gratefully and feel yourself grow. Thank God for love.

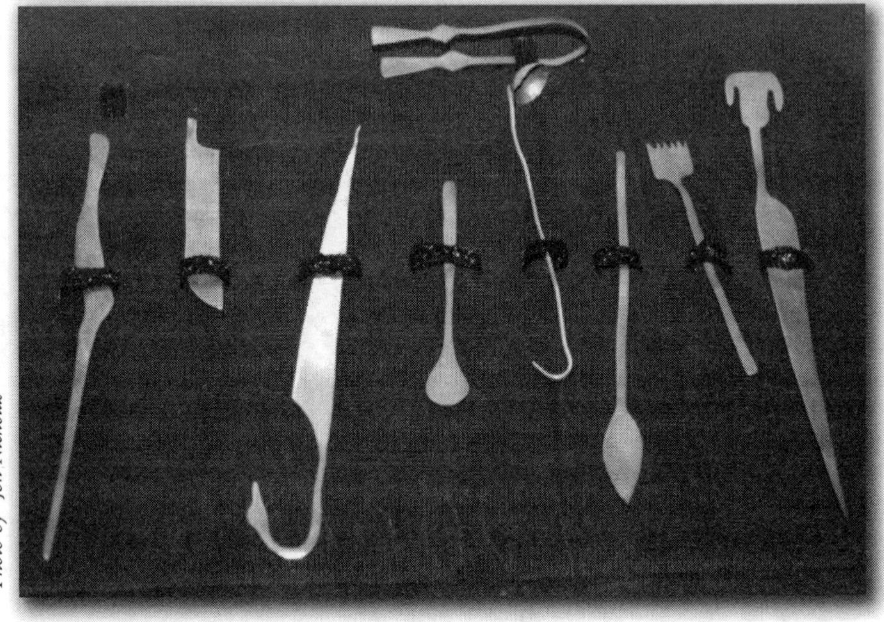

Photo by Jon Nicholas

Tool for Mummification

Step Four •●.•●•●.•●

TOOL TIME

Hammer It Home

Easy Guides That Get Results

Photo By Jon Nicholas

YOU
Have Faith
Love Yourself
Choose your Actions
Pleasure is an Attitude
Dreams Do Come True
Give More Than Expected
You Have the Power to Choose
Today's Dream is Tomorrow's Reality

Chapter 16
Help:
Peer-Amid the Others

Purge past pain and percolate pleasure with self-therapy or with a loving friend, sensitive therapist or support group. This chapter helps you help yourself, get help or help your helper. (For a detailed, professional referral list, see Chapter 30).

▲ SELF-HELP

☆ Customer to bookstore clerk: *"Where's the self help section?"*
Bookstore clerk to customer: *"If I told you, it would defeat the purpose."*

Inside you live a medley of inner voices. Sub-personalities or states of mind comprise hundreds of "you's." Your best counselor, of course, is the voice of your own inner wisdom. Listen well to it and you will give yourself great counsel.

Subpersonalities

☆ *"I am one with my duality."* —Barry E. Smith

When you pay attention to the chatter in your head, you hear them; the wisest of wise, angel, naughty, humorist, child, teen, mature one, crone, seducer, prude, the feeler, the thinker, creative one and the inner critic. Conflict is these inner selves dukeing it out. Activate and integrate positive sub-personalities to work together and they will. Then you become a happy, many-faceted jewel.

If a faultfinding sub-personality gets overly controlling, you need to diffuse or balance it with more nourishing sub-selves. Why let one out-of-control voice rule all your other voices? Tough love for yourself is the way to tame that voice.

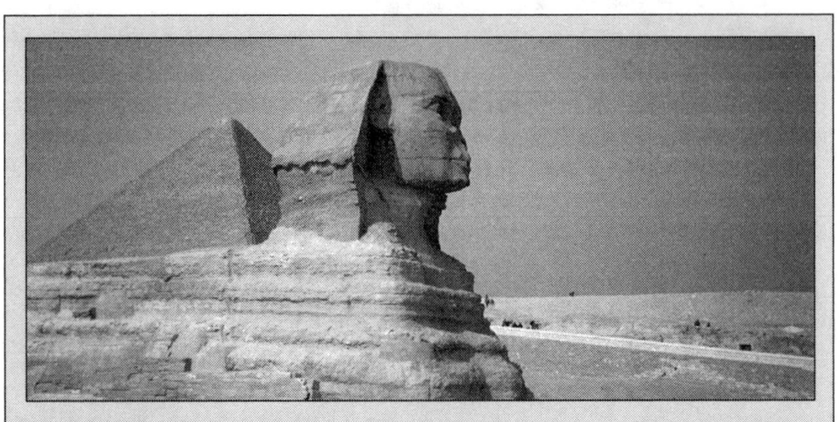

Photo by Tamara Thomas

Up Your Egypt

Message From Abraham

This automatic writing message was written through me the morning I was to give a speech at a 1995 'Past Life Conference' below the great pyramid at Giza, Egypt. I included it in my lecture. I found out months later that Abraham was the Semitic version of the Hindu god Brahma and the Islamic founder of Mecca, Abrama as well as the well Judeo Christian, Abraham. It is a great allegory for you to understand how a subpersonality can get out of hand.

Automatic Writing by Shelley Stockwell

"I am speaking to you today because of permission given from my warden, Valerie Jacobson, of the Cairo Prison. Valerie, please stand up so you may be publicly recognized. Give her a hand.

Why am I in the Cairo prison? I have committed the crime of not upholding the rule. The rule I have not upheld was that of pharaoh. He rules and I have broken rule. My truth varied from his. My truth spoke of the pharaoh in each. He grew angry: 'I am Pharaoh. How can I be in each? I talk. All listen. I have a direct line to the sun. I am the son of the sun.'

I, as scribe, said on my scrolls:
'All are pharaoh, for all can talk to the sun.'
My crime is that I have broken rule. Valerie Jacobson has a job to do; she is to punish me for my crime to not uphold the rule of her pharaoh and she does a good job. This morning she told me that I could council you today on the wisdom of Pharaoh and talk with you later, individually at the Holiday Inn (I agreed). Now she says to me and all other breakers of rule:
'No talking to the individuals; It gives too much power.'

My warden honors power. So I am here to talk to you as a group. I am here to talk about simple things like myself.

I am a simple man, Abraham. I live in donkey town.
We eat and sleep and enjoy breath. We laugh and cry and do our best.
I learned to scribe at my fathers knee; Shiny eyed Joseph; man of integrity.

To be a scribe means to place sounds upon the page, so that each, in turn, can lift them up and the words live again; come to life through the eyes of others. I was to place the words of my pharaoh upon the pages. You as a group (For I am told not to talk to individuals), have you a pharaoh? One who makes your rule? One who will imprison you if your rule is broken? Think now of a word of your pharaoh so you will understand this simple scribe, Abraham.

As a scribe, my job is to take the words of Pharaoh and record it to the letter so no utterance shifts meaning, below my stick. Can you put down on the tablet the exact word of your Pharaoh? Pharaoh says, 'Eat happy food to break fast with sun' and I write 'eat cheery oats'. I have betrayed Pharaoh. That was my crime.

I could not record the letter of the rule. I had my own ideas that interfered and I was punished for my impudence. My warden is an honorable woman. Each time she feels I trust my thoughts and words above those of Pharaoh I am punished more and more severely. Valerie Jacobson follows rules.

Each house of Pharaoh had different rules. Djoser would have asked me to speak to you today individually but my Pharaoh does not. That is all."

Edit the Editor

☆ *"If someone with multiple personalities threatens to kill themselves, is it considered a hostage situation?"*

—George Carlin

Do you live with your worst enemy?
Are you very hard on you?
Do you blame yourself for failing to be perfect?
Do you call yourself names like "moron," "idiot," "pig" or "stupid"?
Is there a part of you that goes haywire and out of control?

A limiting sub-personality says things like, "I'm going to keep you sick and debilitated," "You don't deserve any better," "You'll fail." "This is silly." "What will other people think?" "You're worthless." "How dumb can you be!" "You can't do anything right."

Who is this untamed inner critic, or limiting character? I call them the Editor. There to protect you, this sub-self can get cocky and out of hand. Left unbridled, they may constantly lend a hand that slaps you down. This critical parent is often more negative than your actual parents ever were.

Untamed critics take as much power as you give them. Then they overtake thoughts and behavior. The Editor isn't hell bent on stomping you; it's just that they have been given too much power. If you let them, they inner-fear with your happiness. Here's how my brother Alex and I tame them:

1. Describe the Perfect You

The first step in unhooking yourself from the Editor is to simply be aware of them. Think about yourself as if you were perfect. Use 10 words or less to describe your ideal self. For example; "I am sweet, slim and loving. And I get things done." Write your positive AFFIRMATION of self here: ____________________

____

2. Check in with your Limiting Character

What did your Editor/Critic say when you wrote your affirmation? If a part of you complained or criticized, write down what they said:

____

____

3. Reverse the Curse

Take the Editor's negative comment and turn it around into a positive remark. If it said "You never finish anything you start." Change it to "I always finish what I start." If you said, "You are stupid" change it to "You are brilliant and learning more each day." Great! ______________________________

____

4. Personify Your limiting Gal or Guy

Now that you have become acquainted, let's proceed.

Imagine your Editor in a physical form and describe them. Answer each of the following questions with the first thing that pops into your head. Dare to give outrageously brave and ridiculous answers:

What is your editor like?
What clothes do they wear?
How do they smell?
What kind of vibes do they give off?
How are they built?
What kind of a voice do they have?
Do they remind you of someone you've met before?

5. Interview The Limited One

Ask them, "What do they do for fun?"
"When did you come into my life?"
"What brought you into existence, Editor?"
"What is your job? Do you like it?" "What would you rather do?"
"Editor, how do you protect me?"
"How does what you do serve me?"
"What would you like me to appreciate you for?"
"What am I doing or not doing that concerns you?"
"What do I do (or not do) that gives you what you want? (Or, "What is the least wrong thing I do?").
"Give me one small doable thing that I can do to improve in this regard."
"How can you, do a better job of critiquing me and yourself?"
"Where are you located?" (Are you in my body or in an object?)
"How would you like me to contact you in the future?"
"Thank you, Editor, for talking to me and doing a diligent job."

6. Assign a New Job Description

You are going to have a new job. Sit in the car or wait outside the door when I tell you to. I will call you in when I need your keen observations.

AFFIRM SUCCESS: Tame the Shrew/Critic/Editor
OK inner wise guy this affirmation is for you...listen up.
"I am speaking directly to the Editor: When you are present, affirm with me these ideas: 'I am a masterful critic. I give loving critiques; I'm ever improving. To get my host's attention, I address them with terms of endearment. I address my host lovingly. I praise their progress and suggest small improvements. In this way, I protect them well and help them get the love they need.' This frees me to have a well earned vacation."

NLP Gives Sub-Personalities A Hand

Locate the parts of you that are in conflict; and envokes unwanted behavior (like smoking, for example). Locate other parts that have your highest good in mind. Put out your hand and place into one hand the negative parts and in your other hand the positive voices.

Photo by Jon Nicholas

Close your eyes and identify each part with a visual, feeling and sound image... describe each carefully to yourself. As you do, your hand will take on the weight of each personality grouping and will respond to the weight. That way, you feel the balance or imbalance of your opposing viewpoints. When both sides have said everything they have to say about the situation, take a deep breath and let them discover any points that they agree upon. When ready, bring your hands up until they touch and merge both attitudes. Congratulations, you have resolved your conflict.

▲ OUTSIDE HELP

☆ LISTEN

Hear me crowing. Hear me squawk.
Time to listen. Time to talk.
Take me easy. Take me slow.
Savor life, ripen, grow.
Share a sorrow to ease your pain.
Share a joy, more joy you gain.

—Shelley Stockwell

Photo by Nica Lee

When another "holds the mirror steady" for you, you can reflect on limits and change them once and for good. Friends who "knew you when" can really help you explore your truth.

If you choose another to hold the mirror, it is imperative that they do **not foster co-dependency.** Such misguided help may intensify problems. A person's credentials are irrelevant. A helper who disempowers you is not a helper at all. A real helper teaches you to be self-reliant.

Make your helper the kind of person you would like to model, one who walks their talk, loves themself and is positive and nourishing. Make your helper someone you like.

▲ Friend Rules: A•Sister

☆ *"A friend: Someone who has the same enemies as you do."*

—Irv Lessin

☆ *Try a hug like a prescription, the cost is right.*
To see if it works you don't have to be bright.
Hugs come with a money back guarantee
So if you don't like it, bring it back to me.

—Bill Erwin

Photo by Jon Nicholas

A true friend is a great mirror with valuable reflections that heal hurts. They can offer a different perspective. A helping friend needs to be sensitive and solution-oriented. They must agree to allow you full expression, listen with their heart and promise to tell you when they've had enough.

How to Choose a Supportive Friend

This quiz helps you choose a worthy friend for advice and support.

___ Is this a positive person?
___ Do I like and respect them?
___ Do they like and respect me?
___ Do they act kindly toward me?
___ Do I feel safe with this person?
___ Have I been able to discuss my feelings with them before?
___ Do they agree to be a good, receptive and available listener?
___ Do they feel good to me on a gut level?
___ Are they a good role model for me?
___ Will they keep confidentiality?

Get by with a little help from a friend who scores 100% yes on this quiz.

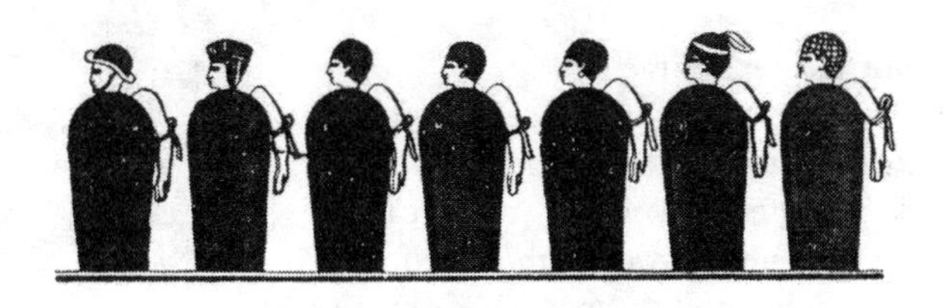

Fan Club

☆ *"The only way to have a friend is to be one."*

—Ralph Waldo Emerson

It's fun to exchange healing sessions—one hour for yourself, one hour for your friend. Here are some guidelines:

- Agree on a time and place free from distractions. That may mean turning off the answering machines, not answering the door, sitting in a park, or walking and talking.
- Communicate how you each want to be supported.
- Decide which responses you want to hear or not hear, and let each other know how they can be a good listener, ask the right questions, and/or give suggestions.
- Tell each other if you want to be held or touched, or not.
- Agree to keep your experiences confidential or not.
- Choose to write down or tape-record your sharing.
- If you are the listener, be loving and supportive. Do not stifle them. Regardless of what they say or do, it is simply an outward expression of their inward awareness. Keep things simple. Show your support with a smile or a hug. You don't have to press them for a long talk, just be there.

Four Friendship Guidelines

☆ *Advice is what we ask for when we already know the answer, but wish we didn't."*
—Erica Mann Jong

Use these guidelines when getting assistance from a friend:

1. Don't Wear Out Your Friend

Remember friends are not therapists. Don't wear them out with your pain. Lasting friends are those with whom you associate positive memories. A friend is fun. If not, move on. Balance your "therapy sessions" with time for fun.

2. Honor Differences

Viva La Difference. A friend is different from you and may not act the way you would if you were the helper. If your friend turns out to be insensitive or harsh, let them know that your feelings are hurt and forgive and forget. Accept their viewpoint as just that; another way to look at things.

Photo by Jon Nicholas

3. Honor Your Helper's Time

Commit to being honest and open. Don't waste a friend's valuable time by telling half-truths or holding back. The more of yourself you reveal, the easier it is for a friend to reveal him/herself. Self-disclosure and vulnerability create a deep and lasting bond of love.

Tell your listening friend what you like. Supportive people who want to help often don't know how. And, they don't even ask. So know that they welcome your guidance.

4. Honor Your Helper's Advice

If you ask a friend for advice, listen well and honor their wisdom. Otherwise, don't ask.

In•tents Reward

In indigenous cultures, it's up to each person to solve their own problems. One is not allowed to enter another's teepee without leaving their problems outside in the burden basket—unless, it's the teepee of a medicine person, or shaman.

If a medicine person allows you to bring your burden into her teepee, you agree to do exactly as she recommends. She honors you by devoting three days of dream-time to your problem, so she may receive a vision on your behalf. You honor her by taking her wisdom and bringing her an offering for her time.

▲ Helpful Experts: The Helping Hand

☆ *Take a trip inside your head*
Replant weeds with flowers instead.
Listen well to your inner knowing.
Watch you blossom, you're a'glowing.

—Shelley Stockwell

Photo by Nica Lee

Putting a professional on your wellness team is very rewarding. Their titles may vary. The most important criterion when selecting a professional helper is their "mindset." Your helper must be sensitive, clean, sober, and respectful, or don't use their services. No matter what helper you chose, always get a second opinion…your own.

There are many loving and caring hypnotists, hypnocounselors, hypnotherapists, holistic healers, therapists, life coaches and support groups available to you. Hypnosis and self-hypnosis can regress you to your past so that you access buried memory and heal them. It can motivate you for action and put you in a happier state of mind. An ancient Chinese proverb puts it well "A single conversation across the table with a wise one is worth a month's study of books."

How to Choose a Supportive Professional

Express and heal by choosing a professional who scores 100% on this quiz:

___ Do I like and respect this person?
___ Are they a positive person?
___ Do they like and respect me?
___ Do they act kindly towards me?
___ I feel safe with them?
___ Do they respect my ability to heal myself?
___ Are they're within my price range?
___ They don't offer drugs as a solution? Is that what I want?
___ Do they look healthy?
___ Do they feel good to me on a gut level?
___ Is this person is a good role model for me?
___ Do they encourage me to make my own decisions and not stay "joined at the hip" to them.

AFFIRM SUCCESS: Help Buyer Beware
These affirmations help you avoid "helpers" that hurt. Not all caregivers are help givers. Chose a caregiver that walks the talk of health—a role model.

I avoid anyone who is off center, a druggie, liar or manipulator. Poor help demands a co-dependent relationship. I want to be self sufficient. I avoid any group or individual who sets themselves up as "owning" all knowledge or wisdom. Cults, gurus, organizations with "secrets" and those who play "follow the leader" and "mother may I?" and "give me more and more money and then I'll help" are icky. I avoid these types of people. Instead I find a sane, loving and straightforward counselor who "walks their talk." An excellent helper teaches me to stand on my own feet, function in the world and be joyous.

Is There Life After Hypnotherapy?

☆*Punch, pound, and fight it out.*
Rip, tear, scream and shout.
Pieces, bits, go flying by,
in this battleground called I.

My head said no, my heart said yes,
insides I was a royal mess.
The battle plan of this ancient war
acted out many times before,
left me smiling in a mold
hoping I would not explode.

Then I came across your door;
you bade me to "at least explore"
the place in me where I was snagged.
You didn't condemn, or scold or nag;
but listened long and listened well
to the morbid details I did tell.
Stale air seeped from my hot air balloon
as I sat and wept inside your room.
And bit-by-bit we slowed it down;
the blood war, the smiling clown.
And quietly put the soldiers to rest
with calm acceptance in my breast.

The warring factions they're each me:
We live together physically.
I'm a tapestry made of thread
woven perfectly in my head.
Tough and soft; girl and woman,
body, mind; now interwoven.

—Shelley Stockwell

Yes, there is life after hypnotherapy! Good help gives you coping mechanisms, ways to express feelings and tools that move you toward joy.

There's an antiquated therapeutic attitude that says, "After therapy, I don't have to express my feelings anymore." Not so. With a good hypnotherapist, psychologist or counselor, you learn to express your true self and go do your life. It's fun to express feelings. It keeps you vital.

Here is a real life story of how hypnosis helped Ryan:

A TRUE STORY; Ryan

"After four rehab programs for drugs and alcohol, hypnosis helped me clean up my act.

My parents said I was unmanageable because I'd do almost anything to get their attention. At four, I threw a vase on the floor and they took me to the doctor who put me on Ritalin. Ritalin made things worse. I escalated my behavior and the consequences. So they sent me to boarding school. There, I went from cigarettes, to marijuana, cocaine and then back to alcohol, and soft drinks, coffee and sweets.

By 32, every time things were going great, I'd sabotage it by getting drunk, crashing my car, or walking off a job. I stormed out of a $65,000-a-year job to get drunk. Jobless and hopeless I moved in with my folks. There I was staying in the same room they banished me to as a little boy. I said, 'Enough already' and got the help I needed with a hypnotist.

I haven't had a drink or drugs, including sugar and caffeine for three months. I feel great for the first time in my life. It's different than the rehab programs I've been in. This time I am committed to changing life patterns for good and It's working."

(For International Hypnosis Federation expert recommendations, see chapter 30).

▲ Helpful Warning: Sage Advice

☆ *"You don't have to suffer to be happy."*

—Sandi Medearis

☆ Client: *"I belong to alcoholics anonymous, gamblers anonymous, overeaters anonymous, and co-dependents anonymous."*
Hypnotherapist: *"How can I help you?"*
Client: *"I'm addicted to meetings"*

Photo by Shelley Stockwell

Sometimes crazy, co-dependent and/or addicted folks set themselves up to be authorities. Many teach what they need to learn at your expense. Many keep you financially and emotionally hooked to satisfy their own sick need for control or to be "needed." Twenty years of constant "therapy" is co-dependency, not help.

Some doctors and nurses who lock up "addicts" in clinics take anti-depressants, smoke a joint on the way home or get smashed at cocktail parties. Drug rehabilitation counselors are often druggies. (I have met judges at cocktail parties who smoked dope to "unwind" after sending marijuana offenders to jail.)

Jim Baker preached for the unity and sanctity of family while he defrauded followers and betrayed his wife. If you and your mate needed guidance, what kind of a pastoral counselor would he be? The point is this: *find a helper who walks their talk and makes their life positively work.* The following is sad, but true:

A TRUE STORY Franz, a "health-scare" professional

"I am the only one in our community who gives shock therapy. Any time I want, I can order a frontal lobotomy." Franz's words were slurred, and he poured another cocktail.

I felt nauseated. Drunken, 48 Year old Franz, was the psychiatric chief of staff of our local hospital. Electro-convulsive therapy (or shock therapy) kills brain cells. I remembered when Franz was brought before the medical board for misconduct. He had "cold turkey" removed a new patient from all drugs at the same time. She died. He did not lose his license. Hospital nurses refused to work for him because his behavior was "not rational." Other psychiatrists had to be called in.

His wife told me: "At five every morning, he goes to the trunk of his Mercedes and drinks from a whiskey bottle hidden in a paper bag. He takes Xanex and a nightmare of other pills. He goes into irrational rages, and on several occasions, he pummeled me awake from a sound sleep."

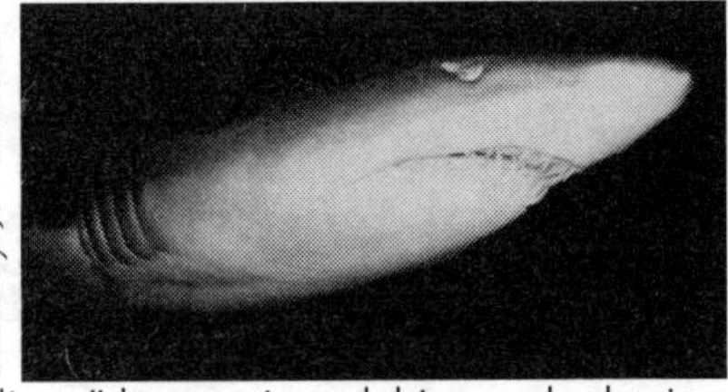
Photo by Jon Nicholas

"Yes, Shelley, I'm an expert on alcoholism," he continued, his words slurring more with each drink. "Anytime you meet someone with a drinking problem, think of me."

Several months later, after a powerful "intervention," Franz was admitted to the Betty Ford Clinic, where he got off alcohol. He continued, however, to take Xanex, and other self-prescribed "anti-depressants."

Sadly, two years later, after years of slowly committing suicide with drugs and alcohol, Franz hanged himself.

Some medical "helpers" are eager to give drugs and not sanction a healthy life style and common sense. They believe that medicine will solve problems. More often, this magic bullet approach compounds problems by numbing you more, harming your body and/or getting you more addicted.

What the medical establishment says is safe doesn't always turn out that way. Not so many years ago the medical community told us that cocaine and Valium were safe and non-addictive. Now they sing another tune. Kenneth Cooper, M.D. says "We would tell people after a heart attack to stop moving and take it easy. We were killing them. We now know that inactivity accelerates [heart disease and] aging."

December 13, 1999, U.S. News and World Report quotes the Institute of Medicine (of the National Academy of Science) estimate that 44,000 to 98,000 Americans a year die from preventable mistakes (from drug mix-ups to inattentive treatment) made in hospitals by physicians, pharmacists and other health care professionals. More than 7000 Americans die as a result of mixing up the names of the drug. Lower estimates rank *hospital error as the nation's eighth highest killer*, above car crash death.

A Check Up From the Neck Up

Medical Disclaimer

The medical community has many good people who believe that drugs and surgery should be an absolute last resort.

☆ *"Naturopathic physicians treat the whole person as a complex interwoven entity. They treat the root of the problem rather than treat the symptoms and mask the cause. If the sink is overflowing, some doctors just grab a mop and ignore the faucet. A holistic doctor turns off the faucet and then mops the floor."*

—Dean Ornish

Most drug side effects and problems come from high blood pressure medication, anti-arrhythmics, prednisone and other corticosteroids, glaucoma medication, oral contraceptives, antihistamines and of course, drugs given for depression.

A TRUE STORY Dayna's Thorazine Shuffle

"I was so anxious about writing a high school English term paper that the school psychologist suggested that I get therapy. I agreed so that I wouldn't have to write the paper. The therapist admitted me to a mental institution for depression. Since this was a county hospital, there were 50 patients to every one psychiatrist. I saw the doctor once a week for half an hour. When my insurance ran out, they released me.

As soon as I was admitted, they gave me drugs to help me 'think straight.' I did not believe that a pill would make me think straight. If it were true, everyone in the world would be taking this pill. I saw others who were taking that pill and not 'thinking straight' at all, so I threw them away.

I could tell the new people from those who had been there a while. The longer they were there, the more like zombies they became. They shuffled their feet. I called it "the Thorazine shuffle." Thorazine caused them to keep moving. That place looked like the night of the living dead, with zombies silently shuffling up and down the halls. I had to get out of there.

Many in the psychiatric hospital come from a disturbed environment, which they try to make right in their own way. In the hospital, they are drugged to shut up. The rationale is that the Thorazine will remove the symptoms so that the doctors can deal with the underlying problems. In truth, once medicated, no one helps them with their problems. The medicine may keep their pain away, but it also takes their life away and does not cure their disease.

I stayed in my room alone and smoked. They wanted me in the day room, not in my room. So they took away my cigarettes. I had to knock on their door to get one. I would sneak outside and walk in the snow at night. It was peaceful and I didn't have to deal with the pathetic system.

Once you enter a psychiatric hospital, the staff labels you as sick, whether you are or not. I think my diagnosis affected how they treated me. They saw me as sick. The hospital was understaffed and overcrowded; the staff was overworked. I wanted to be near the few who cared about wellness. They were sane. The others were nuts or just doing a job.

Leaving was like being paroled from prison. I was scared. I didn't understand what had happened. My biggest fear was going back. Most people who leave, can't cope in the real world without their medications. They have atrophied. So they come back to the safety of the hospital, even though they hate it.

I was lucky. I moved away from New York City after high school, and with the help of my hypnotherapy and sheer guts, I don't do drugs, I hold a good job and I'm learning to love myself.

What's the Solution?

Read books like this one. Take positive action to feel good. Get counseling. Then and only then, consider risking your health with drugs. A healthy diet changes your brain chemistry. Eat well. Take a spiritual vacation.

Photo by Bryce Stockwell

Move your body. Exercise balances you. Twenty to thirty minutes of strength-training, coupled with aerobic activity, three or four times a week strengthens your heart, burns fat and makes you feel happier. But for God's sake, don't take drugs that leave your body so overtaxed you get depressed.

Stop taking medication slowly; rapid decompression also can unnerve you.

Djoser's Step Pyramid

▲ Twelve Step Programs: Steppe Pyramids

☆ *"I'd go to Co-dependents Anonymous, but I can't find someone to go with me."*

Twelve step programs help countless people. Alcoholic's Anonymous was started in 1935 by two men, a New York stockbroker and a physician from Akron, Ohio. The only requirement for membership is an honest desire to stop destructive behavior. There are no fees, no dues and people's identity remain anonymous.

There are literally hundreds of twelve step programs that you can attend on any day or night of the week; Alcoholics Anonymous (AA), Narconon (for narcotic and cross-addicted folks), Alateen (for teens), Co-dependents Anonymous (CODA), Adult Children of Alcoholics (ACA), ALANON (for families of alcoholics), and Overeaters Anonymous (OA), just to name a few.

Is There Life After Group?

Many have benefited from these programs, and so can you. The only snag is that some people get addicted to meetings. They forget that they can take charge of their life without meetings. Use help, a friend, hypnotherapist, counselor, or twelve-step program as a tool to take back your personal power, joy and radiance.

Alcoholics Anonymous

THE THREE PRINCIPLES

▲ **I am alcoholic and cannot manage my own life.**
(This dis-empowering statement is supposed to humble you so that you take yourself out of denial. Of course, you can and will manage your own life.)
Affirm: I manage my life in a positive and nourishing way.

▲ **No human power can relieve my alcoholism.**
(AA relies heavily on belief in a Supreme Being; many find this comforting and uplifting. Naturally, it is within your human power to co-create with a higher power health, renewal, and joy.)
Affirm: The Higher Power and I co-create health and happiness. I stubbornly remain clean and sober.

▲ **God can and will, if I seek God.**
Affirm: I seek bigger pictures than old, limiting patterns. I get bigger than my "stuff." I discover what "God" means to me.

THE TWELVE STEPS

1. I admit that I am powerless over ________ and that my life has become unmanageable.
2. A power greater than myself will restore me to sanity.
3. I make a decision to turn my will and life over to God as I understand God.
4. I make a searching and moral inventory to myself.
5. I admit to God, myself and another human being, the exact nature of my wrongs.
6. I am entirely ready to have God remove all my defects of character.
7. I humbly ask God to remove my shortcomings.
8. I make a list of all persons I have harmed and I am willing to make amends to them all.
9. I make direct amends to these people wherever possible, except when to do so would injure them or others.
10. I continue to take a personal inventory and when I am wrong, promptly admit it.
11. I seek through prayer and meditation to improve my conscious contact with God, as I understand God, praying only for knowledge of his will for me and the power to carry it out.
12. Having had a spiritual awakening as a result of these steps, I carry this message to others and I practice these principles in all of my affairs.

Slogans to Live By

Easy does it
Keep it simple
Live and let live
Think

One day at a time
Listen and learn
Let go, let God
First things first

Don't sweat the small stuff
Chill out
Don't worry, be happy
Take baby steps

▲ Hypnosis Experts: Charming Help

☆ *"Movement has power and magic in it."*
—Goethe IV

Photo by Jon Nicholas

Referral Organizations & Services

For a detailed list of professional helpers in your area, see chapter 30, PROFESSIONAL HELP: Reef•For•All"

INTERNATIONAL HYPNOSIS FEDERATION® (IHF)
Shelley Stockwell, PhD, Founder
30819 Casilina, Rancho Palos Verdes, CA 90275, USA
Web Site: www.hypnosisfederation.com E-mail: sstockwell@earthlink.net
Phone: (310) 541-4844
Refers, promotes and acknowledges Body, Mind and Spirit Practitioners worldwide. Professional members are leaders in their fields of Therapeutic Hypnosis, Health, Brain Research, Bodywork, Life Coaching, Spiritual Counseling, Motivation, Psychic Development and speaking and entertainment. Offers a Motivational Speakers Bureau, Certification Trainings, Membership Directory, books and tapes. IHF Conference is held every July in Southern California.

INTEGRATED ASSOC FOR REGRESSION, RESEARCH & THERAPIES (IARRT)
Janet Cunningham, President
Web Site: www.iarrt.org E-mail: pastlife@empirenet.net
Phone: (909) 784-1570
This Past Life Researchers and Therapists organization since 1980, has members from 28 countries. Publication: *Journey of Regression Therapy.* Conferences and Certification Trainings available.

INTERNATIONAL ASSOCIATION OF COUNSELORS AND THERAPISTS (IACT)
Jillian LaVelle, CSMC, CHt, IHF Advisory Board & Fellow
Web Site: www.iact.org E-mail: iactnow@aol.com
Phone: (941) 498-9710
A fine referral service with an annual conference in May.

INTERNATIONAL MEDICAL & DENTAL HYPNOTHERAPY ASSOC (IMDHA)
Founder: Anne H. Spencer, PhD, CHt
Web Site: www.infinityinst.com
Refers excellently trained certified Hypnotherapists for healing body, mind and spirit, to work in harmony with health care professionals. Aids individuals with medical challenges and procedures.

PROFESSIONAL BOARD OF HYPNOTHERAPY
Alan R. Eastman, BA, MA, DCH, Executive Director
Web Site: www.hypnosiscanada.com Email: dreastman@home.com
Toll Free (403) 347-9019
Canadian based. Offers Mental Health Counseling and Clinical Hypnotherapy services. Eastman is the Executive Director of the Professional Hypnotherapy and the Therapist Directory Network.

☆INSIDES OUT

When I was just a weenie thing,
I had a sweet song I could sing.
It had no tune; it had no word,
It had no sound that could be heard,
But came from way inside of me.
It lifted me soft, it floated me free.
In my quiet waters I would lie
And my beautiful song would float me by.

And then, before I learned to think,
My river became polluted like a kitchen sink.
Rules of what were right and wrong
Quietly swallowed up my song:
How to smile, how to please,
How to bring men to their knees...
I struggled hard to learn it right:
Not to question, not to fight,
Not to be where I wasn't invited,
Never behaving less than delighted.

Then, ever so silently slipping on by, I would hear my insides sigh.
Oh my! Every cell alive, awake and high.
And flushed with the orgasm of my joy, I'd return
To the rights and wrongs that I had learned.

Thus it was and so it seemed,
My moment of song was a far away dream,
Made by a goblin in a far away land,
Where the tales they tell are always grand.

Yet again I exploded like a sack of duck down,
And again, and again.
So finally, I stroked each feather one by one
I didn't leave, deny or run.
I stayed, and invited the me inside to tea.

It was a warm and cozy room that day
Where we had our tea and decided to stay.
The sun was bright, the shades were drawn.
In the corner of the room I felt a song.

It had no sound that could be heard,
It had no tune, it had no word.
I had no choice but to go along.
The song was me, I was the song.

In my quiet waters I will lie
And my beautiful song will float me by.

—Shelley Stockwell

Chapter 17
How Your Brain Works:
Between The Temples

Your brain controls your mental processes and the mystery of imagination, memory, mood, behavior, consciousness and spirit. Your brain is infinitely creative and receptive to learning. Be a brain and learn from this chapter.

▲ WHAT MAKES YOUR BRAIN?
▲ HOW DOES YOUR BRAIN PROCESS THOUGHTS?
  Neurons
  Pyramid In Your Head
  Glial Cells
▲ YOUR CHEMICAL BRAIN
  What Kind of Dopamine?
  So What Does this Have To Do With You?
▲ HOW YOUR BRAIN IS ORGANIZED
  Reptilian, or Instinctive Brain
  Hindbrain
  Midbrain
  Forebrain and Cerebrum
  Limbic Some More
▲ CONNECTING LINKS
▲ MAGNETIC RESONANCE IMAGING

The amazing convoluted structure within your skull actually sees and reads this. Your eyes are merely windows and your eyelashes, window shades. Your perception of symbols on this page enters your windows. Your private, personal mind then identifies, categorizes and classifies these perceptions as language and meaning.

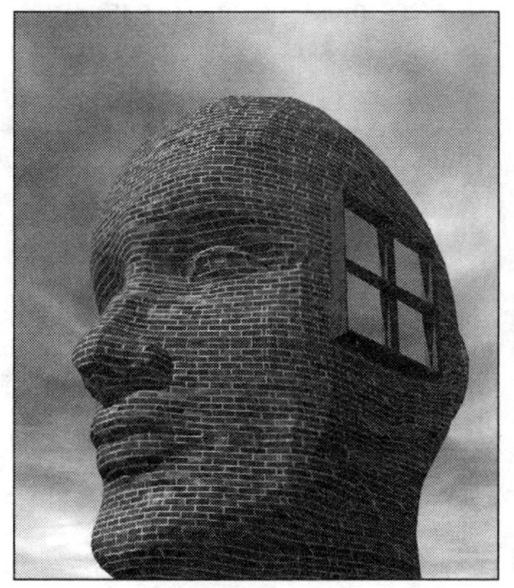

Illustration by Clark Dunbar (© *RF RubberBall Productions*)

Your brain knows how to encode, understand and utter sounds and words. It brain creates a three dimensional landscape from light that touches your two dimensional retina. One-forth of your brain is devoted to vision.

▲ What Makes Your Brain?

☆ *"I think therefore I am, I think."*

—Shelley Stockwell

We know very little about how your brain and mind actually work. Let's explore what we do know.

Your brain is a continuation and enlargement of the spinal cord or vice versa. It's composed of two main kinds of cells; *neurons* and *glial* cells, and three major subdivisions:

1) The crinkled outer surface, the cerebral cortex
2) The cerebral white matter
3) The brain stem that it encloses

Together, these regions yield the quantum elucidation called your mind. Your mind has never been physically identified.

▲ How Does Your Brain Process Thoughts

☆ *"The number of possible nerve cell interactions exceeds the number of particles of matter in the universe!"*

—Richard M. Restak, Neurologist

Your awesome brain weighs approximately three pounds (51 ounces) and holds perhaps trillions of cells that constantly change and modify themselves. At every moment, this dynamic organ alters the connections of countless neurons. This makes the counting the numbers of brain cells seem impossible.

Science has so far counted more than one hundred billion neurons each reaching out to thousands of other brain cells. The brain has more than 100 trillion connections-more than the number of galaxies in the known universe. Interestingly, only 50,000 genes are involved in your nervous system so there is not enough of them to specify your brains amazing wiring. The messages you receive via receptor cells from the outside environment shape these connections.

You were born with twice as many brain cells than you had at age three. With maturity, neuron loss became more gradual. As an adult you lose fifty thousand to one hundred thousand (50,000 to 100,000) brain cells and ten thousand synapses each day.

If you eat MSG, take drugs or drink alcohol, you lose even more. What cells remain you mentally into-great with more connections. As you get older, you find it's good to have connections.

UP YOUR EGYPT

Brains, Mummification and The Great Karnak

Illustration by Shelley Stockwell

☆ *"Not only our pleasure, joy and laughter; but also our sorrow, pain, grief and tears arise from the brain, and the brain alone..."*

—Hypocrites
Ancient Greek Physician
and Philosopher

The deceased was prepared for the after life by carefully placing his organs in ornate canopic jars. Each jar lid represented one of the four sons of Horus: Imseti or Amset, the human face,

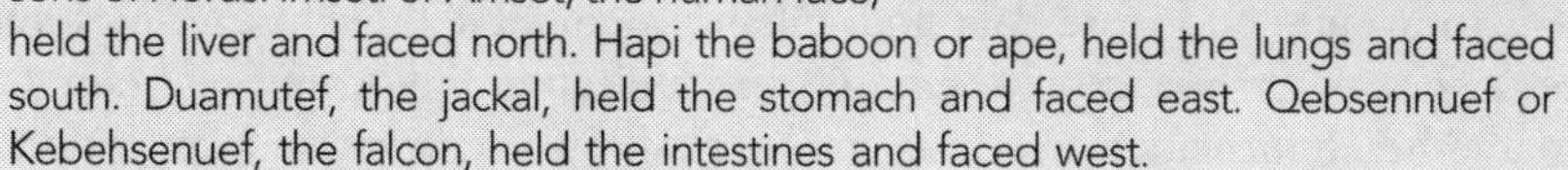

held the liver and faced north. Hapi the baboon or ape, held the lungs and faced south. Duamutef, the jackal, held the stomach and faced east. Qebsennuef or Kebehsenuef, the falcon, held the intestines and faced west.

The heart was the only organ left in the body, so the deceased would follow the path of heart. Statues always depict pharaoh walking with the left foot forward to symbolize leading from the heart. Said Solomon, in the Bible; *"As a man thinks in his heart, so is his life."*

Embalmers used the jelly like brain to preserve the body. Brain tissue was drained through the nostrils and mixed with herbs like cinnamon, cassia (leban dakar, a sap), myrrh, juniper berries and frankincense. The brain offers the exact amount of preservative to keep the entire body supple. This same recipe was later used by Native Americans to preserve hides of animals and today is called *brain tanning.*

The body was first dehydrated for 40 days in natron salt (a cross between baking soda and table salt), which came from the Natron Valley of the western dessert. Then for thirty days, the brain concoction was applied, followed by linen wrappings. Mummification rituals ended with the 'opening of the mouth' ceremony.

Bodies mummified in this fashion and dressed in the same style as Egyptian pharaohs, surrounded by similar rock art, have been found in the country we now call Sudan and predate Egyptian mummification by over 500 years!

The Egyptians had a great deal of interest in chakras of the body. Karnak, the largest temple complex in the ancient world includes the Temple of Luxor that symbolizes the human body. You enter the temple at the feet and each ensuing sanctuary represents each chakra. You wind up in the inner sanctum symbolizing the head. It reminds us that the human body is a spiritual temple.

Recently, science has proven that the brain, directed by receptors and ligands, creates new brain cells. Your brain likes to clone around.

No two brains are the same and your brain is not the same moment to moment. The hemispheres of your brain are different sizes and contain a varying distribution of gray and white matter, chemistry and structure.

Everything you create in life starts as a conscious or subconscious thought that manifests in your brain as a result of electrochemical responses. You were born programmed with some of these thoughts and behavioral instructions. No one had to teach you to lift your head, roll over and walk. It was hard wired into your thoughts. So was your ability to speak.

Everything that you see, hear, smell, taste, feel and intuit is received in patterned connections within a millisecond and placed into your memory. Nobody understands how decisions are made or how your imagination is set free. We can only observe physical structure and responses at this time.

Synapses

Per second, brain cells transmit billions of messages. These messages allow you to acquire and store data and enhance or inhibit thoughts, feelings and behaviors. A synapse is the chemical communication link from one brain cell to another. Information travels as an electrical impulse down an axon within a nerve cell and a chemical messenger between nerve cells via 'synapses.' Think of a synapse as a sort of telephone line that also stores information. If a synapse is destroyed, usually the information it stored slips your mind.

Neurons

Neurons are dark in color and, in clusters, appear gray. That's where we get the notion of *gray matter.* Neurons, brain, or nerve cells, collect, integrate and send information. They comprise the basic unit of your nervous system. Neurons communicate both electrically and chemically. A single neuron is capable of receiving more than fifteen thousand connections from other cells.

Each neuron is composed of a central cell body with branches (called dendrites) and long tendrils (called axons.) The dendrites receive information and the axons transmit information electrically releasing very small packets of chemicals with each electric pulse. The *in-formation* they send and receive is sent over long distances and form complex networks.

Networks of brain cells and synapses are called a neural web.

Glial Cells

Glial (meaning "glue," in Greek) cells support neurons. Glial cells are fatter than neurons, look whiter and, where they abound, is called white matter. Since we have an unknown number of these fat cells it gives a new meaning to calling someone a fat head.

Neurons send and receive information as glial cells insulate, and nourish them. Glial cells have different shapes, sizes and function. Microglia collect debris, astrocytes aid neurons and store some of the chemicals neurons need to do their job. Oligodendroglia nourish, insulate and speed communication among neurons. The more we learn, the more oligodendroglia cells we manufacture.

Pyramid in Your Head

There are several kinds of neurons: *pyramidal, granule* and *purkinje* cells. Pyramidal neurons are actually shaped like a pyramid, are larger than other neurons, and send information great distances from the brain, through the spine and to the muscles.

Photo by Barbara McNurlin

Motor neurons communicate with nerves. Sensory neurons bring information back to the brain from the sensory organs. Sympathetic and parasympathetic neurons communicate with nerves, glands and blood vessels. Some neurons specialize in communicating with other neurons.

▲ Your Chemical Brain

☆ Question: "*Who is the largest drug manufacturer in the world?*"
Answer: "*Your brain.*"

Trillions of molecules enter your brain via your blood. They evoke a cascade of biochemical messages that ricochet within your skull. They rearrange your mind, moods and physical self and determine your personality. This neurological chain reaction is associated with intelligence, creativity, emotion, consciousness and memory.

How you think, changes your chemistry. So does what you put into your body. When your bio-chemical balance is maintained, you can cope, learn, coordinate, remember and concentrate.

Recent studies by psychiatrist Eric Nestler, at the University of Texas Medical Center, show how a protein, called delta-FosB modulates the brain's sensitivity to drugs. And how the interplay of protein and neurotransmitters form the chemical basis for your actions and reactions. Neurotransmitters chemically ferry an astronomical number of messages per second from one brain neuron to another.

Pat Sweeting's Brain Chemical List

NEUROTRANSMITTER	FUNCTION	DRUG MALFUNCTION
Acetylcholine	Muscles, nerves, coordination, memory	Damages reflexes and memory
Dopamine	Moods, energy, pleasure	Depression
Endorphin & Enkephalin	Soothes pain, anxiety and stress	Pain, anxiety and stress
Epinephrine	Fight, flight, fright response, hunger, thirst, security	Paranoia, hunger changes
GABA	Calms, balances nerve impulses	Depression and seizures
Histamine	Immune response	Allergic reactions
Neurohormones	Growth and reproduction	Abnormal growth and reproduction
Neuropeptides	Relaxation and immune response	Weakened defenses, anxiety and stress
Norepinephrine	Heart, blood pressure, respiration, temperature	Withdrawal symptoms and hallucinations
Serotonin	The five senses, sleep, hunger, mellowness	Depression, aggression, sensory damage, sleep and hunger problems
Substance P	Calm and comfort	Stress and pain

What Kind Of Dopamine?

The chemical messengers dopamine, serotonin, norepinephrine, acetycholine, epinepherine, GABA, histamine, neophermone, glycene, neuropeptides, substance P and endorphins and enkephalin are some of the 50 neural transmitters associated with sadness and well being.

Dopamine molecules transmit pleasure and elation. They give us energy.

Dopamine levels rise with a hug, a kiss, sex, words of praise, a winning poker hand, chocolate and drugs. Dopamine can fool the brain into thinking that drugs are as beneficial as a kiss. From this, the body may remake itself to run on toxins and we get addicted.

We don't crave heroin, alcohol, cocaine, nicotine or caffeine. We crave the rush that these dopamine chemicals stimulate. A craving is receptor cells saying, "I need filling up."

Drugs and compulsions produce the same net effect by stimulating a reward pathway in the part of the brain that controls dopamine. Different drugs may affect responses elsewhere as well.

The chemical messenger dopamine is crucial for motor skills. It is relayed from the axon terminal of one neuron to the dendrite of a receiving neuron.

Too little dopamine in parts of the brain appears to trigger the tremors and paralysis of Parkinson's disease. They lose up to 80 percent of their dopamine-producing neurons in the midbrain. Too much dopamine causes hallucinations and bizarre thoughts.

So What Does This Have to Do With You?

Ingested drugs and drugs manufactured within the body/mind, and are responsible for addiction, compulsion and toxic cravings.

Heroin Alters at least ten neurotransmitters and trigger the release of great amounts of dopamine
Amphetamines Stimulates excessive dopamine and overwhelms reuptake and enzyme.
Cocaine and Crack Blocks dopamine absorption and the dopamine stimulates the receiver cells.
Alcohol Triggers dopamine and other neurotransmitters
Cigarettes Nicotine changes the level of at least five neurotransmitters. Triggers dopamine other substances block MAO
Caffeine Triggers dopamine

▲ How Your Brain Is Organized

☆ *Grey matter is the neurons, the cells within my brain.*
White matter is the bridges that connects this gray terrain.
Spine, medulla, pons, amygdala, mid-tissue
Glands, lobes and hemispheres work together when I kiss you.
—Shelley Stockwell

The brain works as a whole; yet various parts specialize in the job they do. These separate yet parallel processes are still little understood and offer quite a brainteaser. To date, this is how researchers view the brain:

Reptilian or Instinctive Brain

☆ Reporter: *"What's your hat size?"*
Yogi Berra: *"I don't know. I'm not in shape yet."*

Your brain stem is an enlarged spinal cord. It controls your blood pressure, heartbeat, pulse, breath, sleep and states of hunger, sex, thirst and temperature. It lets you fight for survival, protect and function. Thoughts buried in the unconscious and thoughts you reveal to your conscious awareness may be controlled here too. Your instinctive brain is straightforward and illiterate. It's often called the "primitive" brain because it evolved from your ancestors over billions of years.

Hindbrain

Located at the base of the brain, your little hindbrain includes the Medulla Oblongata, Cerebellum and Pons. These instinctive structures constantly interact with the rest of your brain.

The *medulla* is the first part of the brain coming up from the spinal cord. It regulates breath, circulation (blood pressure and heart rate) and, to some degree, digestion. In the Medulla, your axons create an anterior swelling called the pyramids or pyramidal tract!

The *cerebellum* controls balance and movement. It heads the committee of sensory motor coordination.

Latin for "bridge," the *pons* connects the hindbrain to the cerebellum on the opposite side. Here, signals cross over from the right brain to the left side of the body and from the left brain to the right side of the body. The place where this crossover takes place is called the "pyramids" or the "pyramidal deccusations." Cranial nerves (fifth through twelve) are found here. Sensations in your face, facial movement, outward movement of the eyes, taste, hearing and tongue movement enters the central nervous system as impulses via the pons, medulla and/or the midbrain.

Midbrain

Your *midbrain* is made up of the *tectum* and the *tegmentum* (wouldn't these be great names for fraternal twins). The midbrain mediates your response to visual and auditory input and houses the third and forth cranial nerves that control the reflexes of your eye movement and the size of your pupil (3rd cranial nerve only). This region is also the home of your *reticular formation* that controls sleeping and waking.

Forebrain and Cerebrum

The cerebrum and "fore"brain have five parts (go figure).

Cortex means "new bark" and describes your ordered, outer wrinkled forebrain layer. The cerebral cortex is largest in human and dolphin brains. It controls thought, language and the brain stem. This cortex lets you think, I think. It stores memories, makes plans, imagines and creates sound and language, music to our ear, calculations, spatial relationships, instinct, love and creativity.

Eyes, ears, nose, mouth and skin are converted here to images, language and thoughts that then command your motor responses. Each sensory stimulus seems to have its own pathway to the cortex.

The neocortex houses the right and left hemispheres.

A dopamine-rich area of the brain, the prefrontal lobe, controls impulsive and irrational behavior. Compulsions and drugs affect this area. That's why a cocaine user's emotions and behaviors go haywire. Drugs seem to impair the prefrontal cortex's ability to process its food; glucose.

Within the neocortex is thimble-sized nodule about 2-1/2 inches behind the bridge of your nose called the subgenual prefrontal cortex. This tiny nodule appears to be as much as "39% to 48% smaller in depressed people" according to Dr. Wayne Drevets from Washington University in St. Louis.

The frontal lobe controls social awareness, curiosity, foresight and understanding. It registers the consequences for your actions. The prefrontal circuitry determines how you act upon how you feel. According to Harvard Psychologist Dr. Daniel Coleman, the frontal lobe is not fully developed until about mid-adolescence.

The temporal lobe is located near the temple. Hearing and memory are its specialty.

The parietal lobe is involved to some degree with all sensory awareness except smell. (Smell is wired to the limbic system).

Deep folds separate the occipital lobes. This highly convoluted surface is concerned with vision and also allows us to plan, learn and remember. Neural pathways and connections between the emotional limbic and ordered neocortex seem to determine emotional self-awareness; empathy and impulse control (the ingredients for a sense of well being in life).

Limbic Some More

As the size of your brain grew, the emotional or limbic brain (Latin for border or seam) is said to have formed. It's now the center of your forebrain and contacts the outer portions of the brain. The limbic brain is said to have evolved into the larger cortex. The limbic brain stimulates the biochemical impulses that produce feelings, emotions and long-term memory. Lust comes from the limbic system, so does aggression. The actual seat (or heart) of your emotional life is found in the limbic systems. Malfunctions of the limbic system have been linked to panic attacks and rage. Smell is directly wired here. That's why a whiff of scent may bring forth a flood of memories and feelings about love, emotions and lust.

The limbic brain includes the basal ganglia and hippocampus, two structures with different functions. That "great basal ganglia of mine" is located directly beneath the neocortex. It is a collection of nuclei with intimate connections to the cortex.

An almond shaped knot of nerve cells by the brain stem, called your *amygdala*, scans incoming sights and sounds for emotional content. It specializes in memory, delight, disgust, fear and anger. The amygdala imbues mental stimulation with positive or negative emotions and is the center of right and wrong thinking.

Next to the amygdala, (also located in the cerebrum) is a crescent shaped collection of neurons called the *hippocampus* that coordinates and sorts memory retrieval.

At the top part of the brain is the thalamus, a main thoroughfare for receiving information from sensory and motor regions of the brain stem.

☆ *The Left Side Knows, The Right Side Understands*
The left brain maps from point A to B
It's the speaker and the "lister."
It can't be bothered with overviews
Like its right brained little sister.

The right brain sees the map as a whole
She decides and doesn't explain,
"Of all my relations I like spatial the best"
Intuits the right side of the brain.

Together they work in harmony
So I don't have two left feet
Connected by the corpus collosum
They make myself complete.

—Shelley Stockwell

Nobel Laureate, Roger Sperry (California Institute of Technology) discovered that the neocortex accesses information separately and uniquely with the right and left hemispheres. No body knows why each side has a different function, but it may be that such brain asymmetry gives us twice as many possibilities.

Left-handed? You are most likely dominantly "right brained." Each hemisphere directs the movement of the arm and leg on the opposite side of the body. The hand you prefer determines whether you are "right" or "left brained."

Right Side

The non-verbal right side makes order out of chaos as it synthesizes details into unity. The right brain is a "jack of all trades." It functions in pictures and symbols and perceives how parts fit together to form wholes. The right brain controls the left side of the body, as well as spatial and aesthetic perception and creativity. It's excellent at coping with the novel and unfamiliar and remembers places, music and faces.

Left Side

The left side is analytical and thinks in sequences. This hemisphere selects relevant details for point-to-point focus. The left brain controls spoken and written language. The left brain controls the right side of the body.

▲ Connecting Links

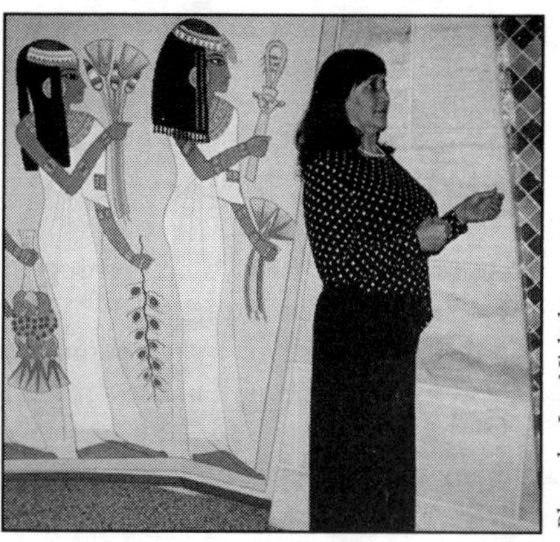

Photo by Jon Nicholas

The right and left hemispheres are joined together by mental bridges that transmit information and coordinate activities between the two sides. One of these bridges, the Corpus Collosum, is made up of some eight million bundled neurons. These nerve fibers are shaped like chubby curved worms.

THE MIND. Collectively, all regions of the brain create the mind.

▲ Magnetic Resonance Imaging: How MRI's Work

☆ *"I have water on the brain and in winter it freezes and everything slips my mind."*

—Irv Lessin

Over 53% of you is water. In the brain, gray matter contains 15% more water than white matter. Water's composition, H2O, show 2 parts hydrogen and one part oxygen.

An MRI image reveals the varying densities of the tissue. Protons, the nuclei of hydrogen atoms, spin like tops and point in random directions. Put one inside a magnetic field and they line up in the direction of the field's poles.

In an MRI, electromagnets (super-cooled by liquid helium), create a magnetic field as much as 30,000 times stronger than that of the earth's pull. This causes the nuclei of the protons to wobble at a specific rate or frequency.

When a radio pulse scanner (timed at the same frequency as the protons) excites the lined up protons, they wobble. The wobbling knocks them out of alignment and then, within a millisecond, they spiral back into alignment while "singing" out a faint radio signal of their own. A MRI uses a computer to translate the "singing" of hydrogen atoms into images. These images are now being used to "map" thoughts by charting which specific regions of the brain "light up" with various thought s and activities.

Recent brain imaging studies show that the nucleus accumbens, the brain area associated with drug addiction, lights up the same way for compulsive gamblers or when someone is shown a sexual stimuli.

AFFIRM SUCCESS: McGill's Three Minutes journey to Your Creative Mind
As a Child, I used my imagination all the time. Perhaps, I pretended to be Peter Pan, Wendy or a super hero. Maybe I went to the Emerald City to visit Dorothy. Dolls or trucks may have seemed real to me then as I pretended and dropped into complete fantasy.

Now that I am grown, I'm learning to use my imagination as I choose. If I leave my imagination unattended, it may take me to the heights of joy, or to the depths of despair. Imagination unattended can be like a blind Samson. I attend to my imagination. I use my imagination to take me into the glorious abyss of my inner mind. I enjoy being the master of my imagination.
Step by step by step, I enter the realm of absent-mindedness, into amnesia and finally I drop into the abyss of my inner mind. I allow myself to drop into complete fantasy and pretend that my eyes don't want to open. My eyes don't want to open. I try to open them and prove it to myself. They just don't want to open. When I've proven it to myself, I say 'eyes open' and they pop right open. The power of my creative imagination is very strong.

I begin a journey from the attic to the basement of my mind. When I reach the basement any command or demand from outside my consciousness of my true self will not disturb me. I enter the realm of complete amnesia, somnambulism and the inner mind. I like this place and remain here as long as I like. Down. Down. Down. From the attic to the third floor, down, down, down. To the second floor and finally to the first floor. When I'm ready, I ask myself to go into the basement. Here I become the boss of myself and anything outside of myself has nothing to do with me.

Illustration by Jon Nicholas

Illustration by Shelley Stockwell

I am a genius!

THE STORY OF CHANGE

—from the internet

CHAPTER ONE I walk down the street. There is a deep hole in the sidewalk. I fall in. I am lost...I am helpless. It isn't my fault. It takes forever to find a way out.

CHAPTER TWO I walk down the street. There is a deep hole in the sidewalk. I pretend it's not there. I fall in. I can't believe I did it again. It's not my fault. It takes a long time to get out.

CHAPTER THREE I walk down the street. There is a deep hole in the sidewalk. I see it. I fall in...it's a habit. My eyes are open. I know where I am. It's my fault. I get out immediately.

CHAPTER FOUR I walk down the street. There is a deep hole in the sidewalk. I walk around it.

CHAPTER FIVE I walk down a different street.

Hypnosis, self-hypnosis, suggestion, affirmations, monitoring your self-talk and reprogramming, help you get it together and walk down a different road. Hypnosis "ups" mental metabolism and stimulates natural highs with no harmful side effects! You master out-of-control compulsive impulses when you re-frame behavior patterns.

Chapter 18
Secrets of Change:
New Leaf

☆ *"Out on a limb is where the fruit is."*
—Robert Otto

You are the most important teacher in your own life. You decide what you want to learn. This chapter teaches you to change for your highest good. It includes:

- ▲ **How To Change Any Habit**
- ▲ **Pain Thresholds**
- ▲ **Results: The Inside Outside Action Plan**
- ▲ **Mind Patterns:**
  - Burial Chamber
  - Getting to Yes
  - Natural Highs: In Joy, Out Joy
  - Hire your Higher Self to Get High
- ▲ **How Your Mind Works: Manifest A Mirage**
  - Are you of two Minds?
  - Mind As Well
- ▲ **Your Conscious Mind: Ripples On The Nile**
- ▲ **Your Subconscious Mind: The Depths Of The Nile**
- ▲ **Your Super Conscious Mind: Oasis**
- ▲ **Get Hyp to Hypnosis: Brain Storms**

☆ *"You've brains in your head and feet in your shoes.*
You can steer yourself any direction you choose.
You're on your own and you know what you know.
And you are the one who decides where you go."
—Dr Seuss, *Oh The Places You'll Go*

UP YOUR EGYPT

The Song of the Blind Harpist (from pyramid hieroglyphics)

Spend a pleasant day! Be good to yourself in every way. Wear sweet oil and fine linen and feel the miracle of ALL of LIFE. Enjoy yourself every day. Do what you have to do, without complaining. Because no one comes back from the land of the dead to calm your heart. Let your heart be strong, Make yourself happy. Celebrate your life today.

▲ How to Change Any Habit

☆ *"Unless you change your direction, you might wind up where you're going."*
—Chinese Proverb

Change happens in an instant. Here are the steps to take that make good shift happen.

1. Decide to Change

Do you want to feel the way you are feeling now? Is your life working? Would your life be better if you changed these feelings? Do you want to change?

2. Choose What You Want to Change

I choose to change ______________________.

3. Come Up with a Plan

To take a trip you need a destination and a map to get there. Change things bit by bit, breaking down any patterns or behaviors into small pieces. For example, if you want to change feeling out of control with eating, change one attitude about eating.

Change "I eat everything on my plate" to "I always leave something on my plate."

Or, "I don't have time to eat" to "I make time to sit down and eat."

4. Stop It

☆ *"Failure is the opportunity to begin again more intelligently."*
—Henry Ford

Make a firm statement that reverses old behavior. For example, "I'm in control of my eating." "Candy is gross. I don't want it or need it."

5. Find Healthy Ways to Reward Yourself

All cravings for compulsions and substances produce the same net effect of stimulating a "reward pathway" of bio-chemicals. Therefore it's imperative that you become a pleasure seeker. Replace limiting patterns with emotionally healthy, fun and satisfying ones.

6. Move On

Decide how you would rather feel, what you would rather do, and make life about doing the "rathers."

"I would rather breathe than smoke."

"I would rather have a loving relationship with myself than insult my body."

7. Practice Makes Perfect

Practice your rathers. Each time, you get better and better. Before you know it, you are in control and feel great.

8. Use Mental Rehearsal

Imagining results gets results.

In 1969 an Austrian psychologist, named Richardson, reported a most remarkable twenty-day study. He had three, randomly chosen, groups perform basketball free-throws. The goal was to improve their free-throw scores. The first group practiced each day. The second group practiced on only on the first and twentieth day, and the third group imagined sinking baskets for twenty minutes a day, every day. The first group improved 24%. The second group showed no improvement while the third group-the mental rehearsal group- showed a remarkable 23% improvement!

Be specific in your thoughts. Specifically imagine feeling and being healthy and addiction free. Imagine yourself in a previously tempting situation, but this time, make healthy choices. Imagine yourself at a party drinking water instead of alcohol. Imagine yourself pain-free feeling great. Imagine yourself cool and collected in a situation that may have stressed you.

If you want to improve your tennis feel the weight and balance of the racket, feel the bounce of the ball before your serve, feel the ball hit the racket.

9. Be Grateful

Write a gratitude list and read it every day.

10. Stick With It

With reinforcement change becomes permanent. It takes about two weeks of a new behavior or attitude to be solidly embedded into your thoughts and actions. Behavior changes by repetition and reconditioning.

AFFIRM SUCCESS: Small Change
I actively recognize and avoid self-sabotage. I am self-supportive. I help myself succeed. I'm kind to myself. I treat myself with respect. I have high self-esteem. I lovingly learn my lessons. I positively change; one baby step at a time. Change is comfortable.

I put up a sign saying, DO IT NOW.

My creative self eagerly thinks of thousands of baby steps that move me into the driver's seat of my life. Each step I take springboards me into joy.

Right now, I think of three healthy things that I can do in this moment to feel great. (Pause)

I do one of these healthy things right now. (Hint: reading this affirmation might be one of them). **I count my blessings.**

Into Great Power Exercise

Unlimited You

1. **Think** Identify a limiting behavior.
2. **Breathe** Take a deep breath.
3. **Go Back** Without thinking, analyzing or judging, go back to the first time you remember having that behavior.

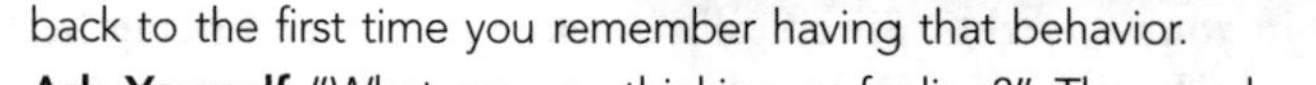

4. **Ask Yourself** "What are you thinking or feeling?" Then go back to the first time you had that feeling or thought.
5. **Bring it on Home**
   "What did you learn from that original experience?"
   "How is that lesson affecting your life and behavior right now?"
   "What do you get out of this behavior?"
   "How can I change my behavior to serve me better?"
   "Do I need to forgive myself or do I need to forgive someone else?"
   If so, do it right now.
6. **New Choice** What behavior or feeling will I adopt now instead of the old one?
7. **Affirm** Write and repeat an affirmation to reinforce your new attitude and behavior.

Change Is Uncomfortable...Unless It's Not

☆ *A man lived next to the train tracks and slept through the midnight train whistle for 50 years. One midnight, the train whistle did not sound. The man woke up with a start, "What was that?"*

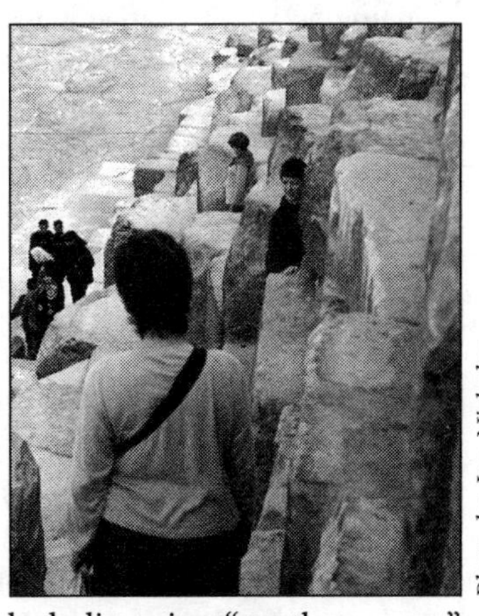

Photo by Jon Nicholas

Change may cause you to act funny. It may require that you lose control to gain it.

You may become temporarily uncomfortable as you change. Discomfort results from conflicting chemical responses and adjustment. Your body tells you that you are detoxifying.

If you choose to brush your teeth using the opposite hand that you use now, it would feel strange at first. Yet, within two weeks, it will feel normal. If you then returned to using the other hand expect the same readjustment period.

Withdrawal from compulsion is as real as withdrawal from addiction. For a workaholic, a vacation may evoke the same stress as an alcoholic going "on the wagon." When you stop caffeine, jitters, spaced-ness or yearning are the signs of withdrawal. Giving up poor eating habits can cause a "wellness crisis"—where a person re-experiences past illness as their body rids toxins. You make change easy or uncomfortable. Decide that the changes you make are well worth it. Tell yourself that it only takes a short time and that you are half way there. What are a few weeks when you have a whole life ahead of you? Tough it out and keep positive. As you release addictions, compulsions and obsessions, painful old patterns shift to rewarding new ones and things mellow out. My friend Jerome Beachum said it best, "Everything is smooth, even the bumps."

Honor the Change Process

☆ *"You have nothing to change but the fear of change."*

—Shelley Stockwell

The only thing certain in life is change. Nothing stands still.

Babies grow to children, children change into teens, teens to adults and adults to seniors. Families form, dissolve and reform. Jobs come and go. At work, we adjust to a new boss, a new job, a new procedure or a new computer system. You change shopping patterns as restaurants and stores come and go.

Do you eat out more than you used to? Do you spend your leisure time in different ways than you used to? Leisure time? Are you too busy to have any? You may have left your house and car unlocked. Now, do you lock them? Have you recently learned to strap your purse around your waist or wear a money belt? Has your attitude toward sex changed? Were you free wheeling in the seventies and more constrained in the 90's?

To successfully deal with change, stay below your change threshold. Handle each change separately and rationally, and you will be OK. If you become irrational, it means you are making too many changes at once. Take it slower.

Being aware of change helps you assimilate each one more easily. Limit the number of changes you make at one time. Don't pile change upon change. Emphasize a positive familiar habit as your touchstone.

Everything in moderation.

Up Your Egypt

Shape Shifting

Photo by Jon Nicholas

Similar to the American Indian totems, ancient Egyptians celebrated animals, stones, trees, sacred objects, symbols and the great forces of the universe (sky, stars, earth and the Nile). These images shape shifted into any form or name they wanted.

Every city, district, tribe and time frame created their own thought form of spirit. A universal eternal god, like the indigenous "Great Spirit" or "Waken Tonka" or our more modern "Father in Heaven," was called Atum, Ptah or Horus, depending on where you lived.

The Story of Creation

Atum created himself from Nun/Naunet, the great bowl of the primeval waters of the cosmos. Lying inert, he spat out Shu (air) and Tefnut (moisture and humidity). Then he rose from the waters and shape-shifted as:

1. The serpent Uraeus (cobra or horned viper, for boundaries)
2. The Benben stone hill (for land). A Benben stone was placed atop pyramids and obelisks.
3. The phoenix bird, Benu, (for soul, light and life).
4. As a scarab beetle, Khepri (for the rising sun).
5. As Ra (for the sun at its zenith).

I'll keep An Eye Out For You

The all-knowing Atum then sent his eye to find Shu and Tefnut in the Nun/Naunet. Human kind originated from the joy when he found them both. The eye of Atum gave each living thing hidden power in their heart and tongue to remember creation itself.

Affirm Success: In•formation Received
I gather all the facts I need to move into action. I consciously recognize what behaviors aren't working and I let them go and replace them with better action.

I choose attitudes and behaviors that work better. I begin now. What steps do I need to make to take back control? Enjoy a healthy life? Live my truths? If the answers are a mystery to me, that's fine. The answers will just pop into my head.

When I yield to the sweet mystery of the unknown, I visit a higher, brighter, more interesting world. The most important thing is that I move into action.

Action means opening new doors. I "will" do whatever it takes to feel great. The steps reveal themselves. I simply commit and open my mind to success.

▲ PAIN THRESHOLDS

☆ *"The door marked 'pain' on one side opens to 'relief' when you cross the threshold."*

—Shelley Stockwell

Some say they need to bottom out before they undergo reconstruction. Waking from denial gives you a near-death experience that brings life. Even if it took you some time to get to your turning point, actual change happens in an instant. Your awakening can be a dramatic "ah ha" moment of truth or as gentle as a new morning. My friend, Lloyd, tells of his threshold experience:

A TRUE STORY Lloyd

"In the 1970s, I joined a 'therapeutic community' headed by a psychiatrist named Betty. She doled out LSD and dictums to each of us. She told me who to sleep with and what choices to make. I guess I followed her direction because my mother died when I was a tot. Betty seemed to be the mother I desperately missed.

I remained 'under her spell' until the day she arranged for several of her men to beat me, as a 'therapeutic process.' I sat there on the floor; eyes blackened, head aching, and said to myself, 'I won't tolerate this any more.' I guess that's when I thresholded out.

Even so, it took me a year to leave.

It was a good thing I left, because the next year, a member of the commune was actually killed by the group during another 'therapeutic process.' And Betty went to prison."

(Lloyd was lucky that he woke up sooner than the followers of Jim Jones or the "Dividians" who followed religious leaders to their death.)

AFFIRM SUCCESS: Sweet Change
Read this affirmation slowly to yourself and it will be so.

I notice the lessons hidden in each challenge. I take responsibility for my happiness. It's normal to feel anxiety occasionally; it's just life. I change the word "anxious" to "excited". And the word stress to energy. I solve problems, as they arise, with solutions that work and clear the waters. My mind is clear. My positive attitudes and responses attract positive circumstances that assist me.

Inner View Quiz:

Are You Sick and Tired Of Being Sick and Tired?

☆ *"I'm making up a true story."*
—Richard Bach

Bravely put T for true for any statement that applies to you.

___ I rarely have a good time.
___ I'm jittery or nervous a lot.
___ My mood swings aren't working.
___ I'm tired of living in fear.
___ I'm out of control of my life.
___ I'm tired of being numb.
___ I don't want to fly off the handle.
___ I'm sick and tired of being sick and tired.
___ I go for the gusto and only get the foam.
___ I can't start myself without using stimulants like coffee, tea or soft drinks.
___ I have strong cravings for tobacco, sweets, caffeine, alcohol, and drugs.
___ I don't like the kind of person who would like me as a friend.
___ I want to stop calling myself names and attacking myself.
___ I'm ready to get off of the "pill mill."
___ It's time I take better care of my body than I do of my car.
___ I'm being abused. (Someone is harming me with insensitivity.)
___ I'm abusive. (I harm someone else with my insensitivity.)
___ I abuse myself. (I harm myself with insensitivity.)

If you answered "true" to **any** of these statements, there's a strong possibility that you've been **depressed, addicted, compulsive, phobic** and/or **fearful**. Enough already!

▲ Results: The Inside Out Action Plan

To have what you want, follow these simple steps. They give you everything you need to succeed.

1. **OUTCOME** Write down the result or outcome you want to have.

____.

(Example "I want to be happy/peaceful/healthy/wealthy).

2. **EXTERNAL ACTION** List actions you'd take if you were 100% responsible for that outcome:

____

____

____

Write, next to each one, when you will take that step.

3. **OMIT SELF-SABOTAGE** Write down the self-defeating things you say to yourself regarding the outcome:

____

____

____

Cross them all off, or if they are on a separate piece of paper, tear up your list.

4. **INTERNAL ACTION** Write positive statement about the results as if it has already happened.

____.

(Example "I am happy/peaceful/healthy/wealthy.)
Read this affirmation many times a day and its power will light up inside you.

5. **SUPPORT** Find someone to support and coach you to make sure that you stay 100% responsible for your external action. Then you can coach someone else to make their dream come real.

▲ Mind Patterns: Burial Chamber

☆ *"People can be divided into three groups: those who make things happen, those who watch things happen, and those who wonder what happened."*

—John Newbern

The power of thoughts and the way it affects your chemistry is dramatic. A false pregnancy creates the same hormonal changes as an actual pregnancy; milk secretion, swelling and changes in face pigmentation. A placebo can cure a disease.

The trick to mastering your life is to positively stimulate pleasure and avoid self-destruction. A positive mind dispels obsessions and compulsions. It also wakes you up from limiting personal and social trances.

Drugs are everywhere. A bong full of cannabis doesn't run around on the street forcing itself into your mouth. Syringes don't grab you and jam themselves into your vein. You make the choice for yourself and the choice is in your head.

Disempowering attitudes are everywhere too; in your past, and in society, education and religion. YOU chose to embrace or omit limiting beliefs and emotionally disturbing attitudes. The choice is in your head.

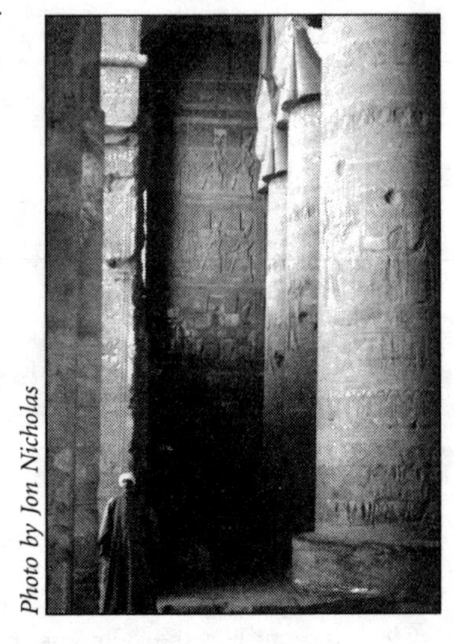
Photo by Jon Nicholas

Getting to Yes

☆ *"I know but one freedom and it's the freedom of the mind."*
—Antoine de Saint Exupery, The Little Prince

☆ *"Positive thoughts are prophylactic. Though it is yet to be proven, as you embark on the process of structural and bio chemical change, you protect yourself from upsetting or depressing reactions."*
—Joel Gober, Ph.D., Brain researcher

Train your brain to linger in a certain mood and its molecular and macro structure changes. Positive thought effects your synapses, axons and neural transmitters and makes you more receptive to positive thought.

Physical activity, love, touch, sex, sleep, learning, creativity, emotion and laughter stimulate endorphins and make you feel great! Hypnosis and meditation also evoke endorphins. As an experiment, notice how you're feeling in this moment. That's right, make a mental note. Between one and ten, how good do you feel right this instant? Ten you feel super, one, terrible. (pause)

Got your number?

Now, stand up. That's right, so what, what others think of you, this is an experiment. Put your hands over your head, palms wide open and smile. Make a big smile, not a wimpy one. Force a big grinner across your chops. Oh, go ahead! After all, this is an experiment. Keep smiling and notice on a scale from one to ten how you feel now? Get your new number. (Pause)

Did your number go up? How come?

Your facial expression instantly changed your brain chemistry and the temperature of the blood to your brain. Your facial expressions, voice and body posture effects your mood in a millisecond.

Moods are contagious. Ever notice how some people make you feel up and others bring you down? Others effect your happiness, and you effect theirs. The more intimate you are, the more contagious your mood. Don't worry, be happy.

Affirm Success: Program Yourself for Joy
Affirm these words slowly and have fun:

I listen to my thoughts for they become my words. Words become my actions. Actions become my habits. Habits become my character. Character becomes my destiny.

My brain is an amazing computer; designed to help me achieve all of my desires. One of its programs helps me relieve distress. I now activate it. Distress be gone! I am peaceful of mind. My mental patterns for joy are now fully activated. I am balanced and programmed for joy. With every breath I take I accept joy into my body and my life. I experience joy in everything I think, say and do. I am a miracle.

Natural Highs: In Joy, Out Joy

☆ *"Have a good one."*
"I've got a good one."

So how can you get it all together? Let's explore how your mind works.

Natural opiates are your body's painkillers and joy-bringers. Your brain and endocrine system manufacture them and distribute them throughout your body. You activate the release their bio-energetic flow with your thoughts, emotion and actions. Scientists have named them in three categories; endorphins, enkephalins and dynorphins.

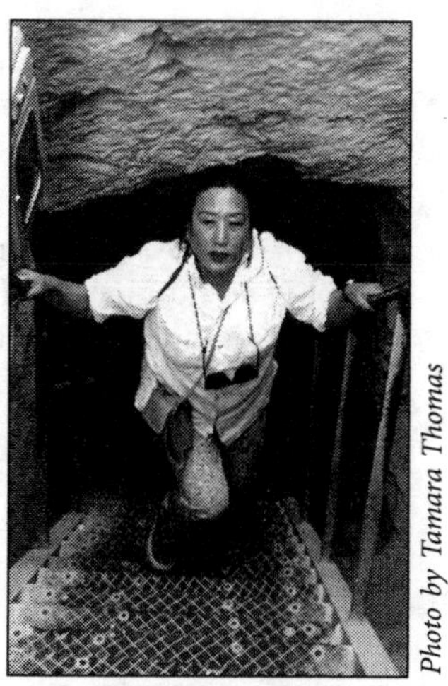

Photo by Tamara Thomas

If you don't go in, you can't find out.

You can activate a natural high by pinching the "web" between your thumb and forefinger (at the bottom the crease, when you put your thumb against your flat hand). This point is also used to relieve pain and headaches. Massage this sensitive point, close your eyes and feel the natural rush.

Hire Your Higher Self to Get High

The best high is when you wake up from the sleep-walk of old patterns and become awake to your inner resources. The small, still voice of your inner self brings self satisfaction and elation.

AFFIRM SUCCESS: Affirmations for a Natural High

Read the following affirmation slowly and often and you'll train your mind/body for feeling good:

I only do kind, considerate, nurturing things for myself. My higher self uplifts me. I learn new ways to love myself and others. My higher self makes me naturally high. I bring my precious body to radiant health and my mind to clear and positive thinking.

I'm a full-fledged pleasure seeker. I create a positive and happy life for myself. I put my hand on my heart and affirm that it is so: I choose joy. I choose wellness. I choose peace. I choose success. I only accept thoughts and ideas that are safe and appropriate for my upliftment.

I function at optimal energy. I release natural feel-great bio-chemicals that stimulate and reward my healthy attitudes and action. I'm high on life. Balanced hormone levels bring me joy and comfort. The best high is a natural one that occurs within my own body. Any time I want, I allow the natural, pleasant flow of healthy endorphins and enkaphalins to make me high. I naturally make myself feel terrific.

To get a healthy buzz, I create within my skull an imaginary button that is labeled "PLEASURE." I gently push it and my body releases the perfect flow of feel good hormones. I FEEL GOOD. My endorphin receptor sites lovingly receive each scintillating drop of my natural joy juices. I create within myself intense pleasure any time I want. I'm high on a natural high.

My body is comforted and healed. My mind dances in bliss. I'm high on myself. I generate joy within myself. I'm higher than a kite on joy. I function at optimum levels. I am an optimum-mystic. I'm optimistic. The world has now entered into a conspiracy to do me good. And, even if I try to sabotage it, the world prevails to bring me pleasure, joy and abundance. I choose to flow with a glorious world that brings only good into my life. And so it is.

▲ How Your Mind Works: Manifest A Mirage

☆ *The mind is not a tangible thing; it is a process of producing thoughts. Thoughts are things: they form energy and manifest powerfully in the physical world.*
—Ormond McGill, Ph.D.

☆ *"Oh the realm of your secret mind uncharted and unscathed*
come walk into the golden room do not be afraid."
—Shelley Stockwell, PhD

Think about thinking (take your time).
Notice how it feels to think about thinking.

Challenging isn't it? To think about thinking is like wrapping a mist about a mist. If the mind were simple enough for us to understand, we'd be too simple to understand it.

We do know that your thoughts change brain chemistry, which effects brain function, which in turn effects the structure of your brain. Structural changes, change function which then changes your thoughts; going round and round and round in a circle game.

Structural Change

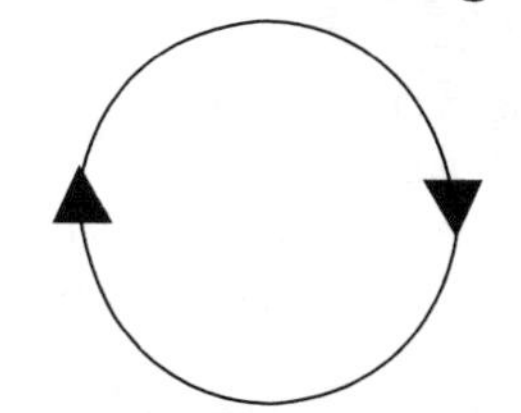

Functional Change

To change your mind, mind your mind. Then you can master your mind and become a mastermind. Pay attention and you'll understand how your mind works and how you influence thoughts. Insanity is when you lose control of your mind.

To change your life, change your mind. The trick to permanent change is to enlist your inner wisdom to assist and empower you to get moving!

A TRUE STORY Shelley

"During a growth Seminar." I was frustrated. Everyone, except me, had created a personal affirmation. All I had was a headache and stabbing pain in my heart. I exploded into tears. Deborah Allen, the facilitator, came to me:

'What's wrong, Shelley?'

'My heart is breaking,' I said.

'No, Shelley, your heart is opening,' she replied.

That was a turning point. My affirmations came easily after that:

'I am Shelley. I am perfect just the way I am. Feeling so glad to be alive. Deeply loving me and deeply loving you.'"

How you think greatly influences your body. Like an organic computer, your perception of life determines what information you let in. Every thought, feeling and attitude affects you and your cells on a very deep level. Your thoughts determine your wellness and whether you grow or defend, relax or stress.

You learn by "wrapping" your inner mind around information, ideas or beliefs. You do this via your senses by intoning sound, envisioning images, feeling sensations and through smell, taste and emotions. You keep behavior patterns alive by the stories you tell yourself with repetitive self-talk and the emotional spin you add to information. No one can see your mind but you. You are the sole witness of thoughts your mind generates. To the world, your mind is private and hidden.

Negative feelings like guilt, anger and depression are not the result of bad things that happen to you, but the way you think about these events. Whether you learn something new or not depends on a decision you make that creates an interaction of receptors, genes and the resulting strengthening or weakening of synapses.

Are You of Two Minds?

☆ *"Because the brain is a physical structure, it exists in space. But the mind operates in time alone."*

—Marcus Raichle
St. Louis University, School of Medicine

Brain and mind are two sides of the same coin. The difference between them is challenging to distinguish and differentiate. Call the brain structure and mind function.

Science attempts to "map" your brain's hemispheres and territories by location and job. But the location of your mind is controversial. Cells within every part of the body appear to hold memory and make decisions; giving us a kind of *thinking body.*

Many paradigms try to explain how our complexly amazing processor of impulses results in thoughts. Scientists correlate mental events and nerve impulse patterns. How do nerves (neurons) interrelate with each other and change with experience? To learn more about the structure of your brain read Chapter 17.

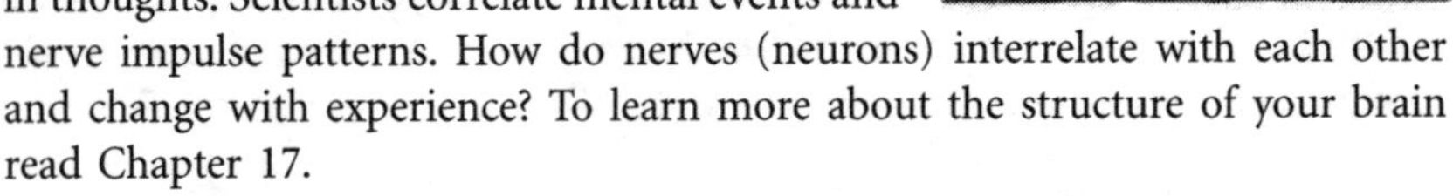

Mind As Well

☆ *"Answers come from the only place real answers ever come. They come from deep inside... Negative thoughts and emotions cause a kind of emotional pollution that kept happiness hidden from me."*

—Lester Levenson

The greatest gift you give yourself is to tune in and be conscious of your own consciousness. Hypnotists arbitrarily categorize mind into three separate areas of function: the conscious, subconscious and super-conscious. When these modes of mind work together we say, you're tuned in and your life becomes a symphony. Here is my paradigm for these three mind modes:

▲ Your Conscious Mind: Ripples On The Nile

☆ Psychiatrist to Parrot: *"So Polly, do you want a cracker or need a cracker?"*

Photo by Nica Lee

Look at your world right now.

Where you are sitting? What is around you? Make note of this place.

Who is the one noticing these things?

Your *here and now* mind; the conscious mind!

Logical and analytical, it keeps you physically aware and lets you shift attention from one thing to another. It protects you from danger by critically judging and weighing one idea at a time. This conscious mind censoring is known as the "conscious critical factor."

Your conscious mind impresses the subconscious with its sensory observations. It makes decisions based upon information from the sub and super-conscious mind and in turn, influences what your deeper mind accepts as truth.

Your conscious mind specializes in, short-term memory and will power. That is why will power works well in the short run here and now but rarely overrides old programs lodged in the sub-conscious. Long-term memory takes place in deeper mind that retrieves and sends these memories *upstairs* to the conscious mind upon request.

Have you tried to change behaviors with conscious will? It's tough! If you ask your conscious mind to change behaviors that live in the subconscious, it's like trying to change a light bulb that's in another room. It doesn't work. Real change only takes place when a decision is made and carried out in the right location, on the subconscious level.

Think of your conscious mind as the mask you use to interface with the world. The word *personality* comes from the Latin word persona and means coming through a mask. Your conscious mind controls the face you present to the world, the stories you tell yourself, others and your personality.

▲ Your Subconscious Mind: Depths of the Nile

☆ *"We are like balloons. When we expand, we are light and fly. If not, we lie on the table thick-skinned."*

—Pro Fylactic

Awareness of your inner self is the realm of the subconscious or unconscious mind. The subconscious mind is a pattern-making and pattern-repeating device that self conducts most brain function. It keeps you active, balanced (in homeostasis) and alive. It's been doing an excellent job or you wouldn't be reading this right now.

Illustration by Shelley Stockwell

Sub•lime

Your subconscious mind keeps your heart beating, lungs inflating; every organ, muscle, nerve and ligament working. And, it fights disease.

The subconscious mind encompasses most of your sub-personalities, emotion, feelings, expression, and instinctive behavior. It drives to survive and fulfill your human potential. Your subconscious mind diligently employs programs that have been planted there with conditioned responses.

Although your unconscious is emotional, it rarely analysis or makes decisions.

Where are Your Thoughts When You're Not Thinking Them?

The subconscious mind! Your subconscious uncritically archives all information about you and from these memories, draws conclusions.

Habits and attitude live here too. These strongly influence your success in peace, love, joy and abundance. Addictions, compulsions and obsessions are bio-chemically patterned and imprinted into your subconscious mind.

Your subconscious mind stubbornly causes you to be who and what it believes you are. If you want to change your behavior, you must change your mind...your subconscious mind.

To listen to your subconscious, listen to your thoughts and babble while you're alone or talking to others. The words you use create your reality and your life.

To change your inner mind, you need to learn how to remove unsatisfactory programs from the active file. A great way to do that is by enlisting the help of your super-conscious mind:

Your super-conscious mind knows your life purpose and lets you discover

▲Your Super-Conscious Mind: Oasis
Higher Self, Expanded Consciousness

☆ *"The perfect pattern, a divine design. A place you are to fill and no one else can fill…Something you are to do, which no one else can do."*
—Plato

☆ *"If prayer is talking to God, meditation is listening."*
—Edgar Casey

Photo by Joann Kelly

and connect with your life force energy. Your super-conscious knows the mystery of all life.

It encompasses and permeates *all* levels of consciousness. It oversees the conscious and subconscious and remembers experiences within and beyond your personality. Super-conscious awareness knows your truth, dreams and the steps you need to take to make life work perfectly. All personal transformation, healing and bliss tap this consciousness.

Have you ever wondered where you go when you pray?

The super-conscious mind! It's the BIG picture.

Here, you enjoy your intuitive, spiritual gifts, have peak experiences and commune with God. Your higher self blesses you with profound wisdom. Your higher self makes you high.

This realm of transcendental joy bypasses the time-space continuum as you easily explore past, future and between-life memory.

Sometimes called the Collective Unconscious, the Akashic Records, the Great Book or the Book of Remembrance, your super conscious mind is your own private genie in a bottle. Learn to listen to it and transform.

The Stockwell Mind Map

Conscious	Subconscious	Super Conscious
Outer Self Physical Awareness	Inner Self Internal Awareness	Higher Self Expanded Awareness
Left brain Stories we tell ourselves	Right brain Attitudes, beliefs, habits	All brain Inspiration, creative imagination
Concrete Analytical Logical, critical, protective, defensive	Emotional Literal Bio-chemical, autonomic response, body function, survival instinct.	Ephemeral Airy-fairy Aura/unconditional love
Co-creates with the subconscious and super conscious	Co-creates with the conscious and super conscious	Brings inner and outer harmony and balance to all parts of self
Some short term memory	Most memory: uncritically accepts, records and stores data from the outside world. Combines stored data into hunches and answers, language	Remembers connection to all, universal wisdom, life purpose, spiritual guidance, God, inner knower, silent witness, light
Honors linear time, aware of now analyzes past might project future	Honors non-linear time, aware of past	Transcends linear time and space, knows all and "future," simultaneous perception
Personality	Most Sub-personalities	Beyond personality Metaphors, archetypes, symbols
Keyboard	Software	Hard drive
Practical	Emotional	Soulful
Waking states	Hypnotic states	Lucid dreams
Body	Mind	Spirit
Son	Father	Holy ghost
Ego	Id	Super Ego
Earth	Sky	Cosmos
Play a record	Record a record	Invent a record
Eros	Shadow	Spirit
Basic self-child	Conscious self-adult	Higher self-parent
Catapillar	Cocoon	Butterfly

☆ BUST LIMITING ATTITUDES

Let's take a step back,
Give the problem some slack.
Look at the picture as a whole
And get the problem under control.

—Janita Mayabb

☆ AWAKE AGAIN

Devoted fully to this moment
Child-like selfless sweet abandon
Without judgment or recrimination
I am caught red-handed and surprised by joy!

—J. Nicholas Graves

Self-hypnosis, affirmations, guided imagery and positive self-talk are simple to learn tools that work. They empower the inner mind to release, reframe and reorder a new attitude. This allows you to discover and replace imprints that no longer serve you well.

Up Your Egypt

Two Worlds as One

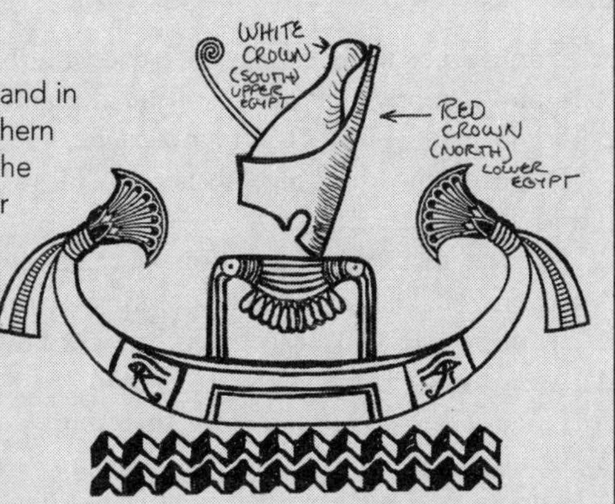

The ancient Egyptians saw their land in two parts, Upper Egypt (the southern delta) and Lower Egypt (the northern part). King Narmer (or King Menes) united the two tribes of Upper and Lower Egypt and made the border town of Memphis the capital. After that, pharaohs wore a combination of two crowns at the same time as symbols of the unity of both peoples.

The white "cone" crown resembled a bowling pin and represented upper Egypt. The red hat with the forward "curl" stood for lower Egypt. Red was the symbolic color of the sand of the Egyptian red land desert and black signified the fertile Nile. There were also two lives: the lives of the people and the lives of the gods. The Pharaoh was the bridge between the two.

When you master your conscious and unconscious mind you wear "two hats" and into-great your mind and soul.

▲ Get Hyp to Hypnosis: Brain Storms

☆ KNOW WELL

Jingle bells, jingle bells, the Christmas season's here
It's time to manifest your dreams and watch them all appear.
—Mary Silva

Illustration by shelley Stockwell

Self-suggestion and resulting neural responses determine how you think, behave and feel. Hypnosis allows you to acknowledge your truth: cause, effect, solutions and choice. Addiction and Compulsion Hypnosis *permanently* disrupts destructive behavior. Solution oriented, guided journeys go for the results rather than dwell on the problem. Results are often immediate. A smoker may quit smoking forever after only one session!

Hypnosis allows you to listen to your profound inner wisdom, keep promises to yourself and honor your progress. The ability to tap the resources of your deepest mind gives you enormous power to be your best! Hypnosis is no mystery. And, it's easy to learn.

Δ Hypnosis positively changes behavior and biochemistry.
Δ Hypnosis motivates you to end hurtful and embrace nourishing behavior.
Δ Hypnosis moves you from ambivalence to commitment.
Δ Hypnosis sends limiting sub-personalities go to the beach and gives you a break.
Δ Hypnosis focuses and emotionally reinforces your inner mind.
Δ Hypnosis helps you discover solutions.
Δ Hypnosis teaches you to push the right buttons.
Δ Hypnosis is a rite of passage.
Δ Hypnosis helps you harness your resources and your bliss.
Δ Hypnosis gets you to the emotional causes to heal physical symptoms.
Δ Hypnosis makes deep, permanent and lasting changes in thought and behavior.
Δ Hypnosis puts you in the driver's seat of your life.
Δ Hypnosis teaches you to get high with your higher self.
Δ Hypnosis works!

Everything is Hypnosis

You hypnotize and emotionally reinforce yourself to be happy, healthy and abundant or to smoke or not smoke, drink or not drink, binge or not binge, obsess or not obsess, rage or not rage, love or fear. Everything you have ever said and done comes from an inner dialogue and program.

Why not reprogram yourself to be free of self-destruction and negative self-talk, to think what and when you want it to think, and to have fun!

Today hypnosis is considered a powerful science and is used by college professors, people in the healing arts and of course, Professional Hypnotists and Hypnotherapists. Past visions of Svengali's "Look into my eyes, you are in my power" and Bela Lugosi swinging his silver watch has been replaced with respect and empowerment.

Every culture uses hypnosis in one form or another. Shamans, witch doctors and healers know the power of suggestion and trance. So, unfortunately, do advertising agencies and PR firms. TV faith healers use a rapid induction technique as we watch those "taken with the spirit" dramatically collapse in trance.

Sigmund Freud, was a hypnotist. Milton Erickson's hypnotic style wove true and fantastic stories as metaphor and trance induction. Grinder and Bandler wrote clear and comprehensive books on the subject and renamed hypnosis *neuro-linguistic programming* or NLP. The Wizard of Oz was a master hypnotist. So was your mother and your teachers.

Defining Hypnosis

"Hypnosis is a natural trance state of heightened awareness where you easily take on suggestions, listen to inner wisdom, and replace limiting imprints with those that serve you better."

"...natural state..."

We say that hypnosis is natural because you go in and out of trance throughout your day. Any time you focus attention from outer to inner awareness, you enter the sacred chambers of your deepest mind. When your attention shifts from actual events around you to the events of thought, you spontaneously self induce a trance.

Hypnosis done by a hypnotist is called a guided trance.

Fantasy is another word for trance. A suspenseful book or movie takes you from conscious thought into the "action" on the screen of the mind. If you weren't in-tranced, your conscious mind would say: "These are only actors and fictionalized characters."

Have you ever been driving and can't remember how you got from here to there? You were in a trance. In trance, your brain waves slow and your analytical mind takes a vacation. Your deepest mind drives the car. If the vehicle in front of you stops, you automatically hit the brakes because your "hypnotic" mind is 100% committed to your survival.

You can actually be in the conscious mind and subconscious mode at the same time. Your conscious mind may carry on a conversation with your passenger while your subconscious mind is driving the car.

When Do You Spontaneously Enter Trance?

Baritone Zone Deep meditation
Big Ba-Zones Fantasizing about sex
Bo-Zone Acting like a clown
Chroma-Zone Polishing your car
Comb Zone At the hairdressers or barbers, eyes closed, relaxing
Couch Potato Zone TV and movie watching
Danger Zone During a traumatic experience
Dis-Zone Arguing and shouting
Fire Zone Staring at a fire or watching ripples on the water
Gramophone Zone Listening to music
Monotone Zone Bored out of your mind
Obsess Zone During compulsive behaviors
Oh! Zone When making love
Ohm Zone Chanting, praying
Personal Inner View Zone Daydreaming, fantasizing
Rub Her Zone During a massage
Speed Zone Driving and not noticing how you got from there to here
Stone Zone While under anesthesia
Tome Zone Absorbed in reading
Tone Zone "Runner's high"
Twilight Zone Between waking and sleeping
Zone During sleep
Zoned Out Spacing out during a boring business meeting or lecture

Hypnosis teaches you to *intentionally* enter trance to control information and behaviors you want to enforce or change. All hypnosis is in fact, self-hypnosis; a hypnotist simply guides you into self-hypnosis. Hypnotists carefully phrase suggestions so that your subconscious mind accepts them easily. This "science of words" uses positive colorful phrases to make a deep impression on your mind. You, of course, are always in charge of your mental state.

"..of heightened awareness.."

In trance you are keenly aware of wherever you focus your energy. Hypnosis harnesses memory. Under hypnosis, witnesses to crime recall, with vivid accuracy, license plate numbers and other details. Subjects of stage hypnosis may appear unaware; yet if *you* are that subject, you're *fully aware.*

"...where you easily accept suggestions..."

Suggestions are pieces of information that you receive and incorporate into your attitudes, behavior and internal data bank. Have you noticed that when you watch someone bite into a lemon or eat salty popcorn, you salivate? If someone tells you that your clothes look peculiar, you may never wear those clothes again. Think about yawning (yawn, yawn, yawn)...and you just might!

These are examples of regular suggestibility; in trance, you're over five times more suggestible than that!

Eighty-five percent or more of what you say to yourself makes a deep impression on the subconscious mind. The power of these suggestions can effect your attitude for the rest of the day. This morning, between wakefulness and sleep (in your natural trance) what did you say to yourself? Was it positive? Did you awaken to depressing news on the clock radio? Did you go to sleep with uncensored TV input?

"...listen to inner wisdom..."

Part of you knows exactly what you need to do to make life work in every way—physically, mentally, spiritually and emotionally. Hypnosis lets you access this wisdom. Mother, father, brother, sister, mate or friends don't know your answers. Your deepest mind knows and intuits what is best.

Hypnosis lets you focus upon your truth. You identify and communicate with your needs so you satisfy them. You re-member experiences, bring forward repressed emotions and put the past where it belongs; in the past.

In trance, you celebrate your gifts of wellness, clarity, joy, tap intuitive and psychic abilities and discover your bigger picture.

"...and replace limiting imprints with those that serve you better."

An imprint is a piece of information programmed into the subconscious mind. These buried thoughts and attitudes strongly influence you.

Your conscious mind completed its development when you were about five years old. Until then you were an open book, tabula rasa, a blank slate to write upon and absorbed as gospel; information the "big people" gave. Some of these thought patterns work well for you. Others limit your health and joy. Most imprints come from the people who reared you.

Imprints evoke unconscious behavior. Think of them as records in a jukebox. Mom's recorded message; "finish everything on your plate" plays automatically and you may make food mountains automatically vanish into the cavern of your mouth!

Childhood messages about self-worth influence adult attitudes. What were you taught about yourself? How do these scripts color your attitude today? If you were taught: "I'm a precious and lovable person. I am smart and talented." These imprints serve you well. If, on the other hand, you were told "You're mean and stupid" or "you'll never amount to anything," these messages can undermine self-worth.

In trance, you easily identify imprints that obstruct or work better for you. Harnessing your mind let's you create what you want for yourself. You can access information for review and understanding and reframe your reactions. Your mind's perfect computer stores every instant of your life. In trance, your mind becomes an open book for self-enlightenment. You can vividly recall details like being in your mother's womb, birth, infancy childhood...every minute of your life. You can even explore where you were before you were you!

So There You Have It!

You naturally enter hypnosis just before going to sleep, upon awakening and many other times throughout the day. Any time you suspend critical thinking, you enter into hypnosis or the subconscious mind. Once you enter this sacred territory of your inner wisdom, you can get a grip on destructive patterns and achieve your dreams and goals. Once again, here is the definition of hypnosis:

"Hypnosis is a natural state of heightened awareness where you easily take on suggestions, listen to inner wisdom, and replace limiting imprints with those that serve you better."

Hypnosis by Definition

Over the past several years, I've asked my hypnosis students: "What is hypnosis?" Here are some replies first from regular awareness and then while in trance: ☆***Hypnosis is...***

Sandi Medearis:

"A tool for a sit down chat with self, a sort of summit conference where you agree on a new way of thinking or behaving that betters your life." (Regular awareness)

"A loving dream state where you know, accept and use everything that helps you most." (Trance state)

Laurel Birch:

"A reality check. A direct path and connection to knowing that puts you where you want to be with your life." (Regular awareness)

"The study of life from an internal point of view." (Trance state)

Meredith Ferguson:

"The most direct way to facilitate change through positive manipulation and the power of suggestion." (Regular awareness)

"In-to-me-see (intimacy)" (Trance state)

Suzy Prudden

"Lets you go inside, heal and create new patterns. Here, you know what you need to function in the world & build trust." (Regular awareness)

"A tool for change and healing." (Trance state)

16 Year Old

"The revelation of the subconscious...Communication with the very limits of imagination and the unknown world." (Trance state)

Rhonda Carpenter
"Taps our universal, vast and unlimited resource to help ourselves and humanity." (Regular awareness)

"A vehicle of change." (Trance state)

Dr. John Goode:
"Living in a new conceptual universe. New power of emotions... new sense of strength." (Trance state)

Phill Wells, Hypnotherapist
"I call Hypnosis the XYZ technique; X to X-out the past, unpleasant experiences, Y because we like you and Z because everyone likes their ZZZ's."

US Department of Labor Definition:
"The bypass of the critical factor of the conscious mind followed by the ability to accept suggestions."

70 Year Old
"I was aware of everything around me and knew that I could open my eyes and walk out, but the process was too interesting. My chair felt like it was rising and my eyes seemed to make a space between me and my eyelids." (Regular Awareness)

Three Deep Breaths: Up, Up and Away

Notice how you are feeling right in this moment. And now...
1. Look up at the top of this page and take a deep breath.
2. Look up at the ceiling and take another deep breath.
3. Finally, look up, all the way up and take a third deep breath.

Notice how you feel now. Better?
What's the difference? You shift your perspective by uplifting your eyes. Chemically you change your brain signals for up-liftment. Any time you consciously move your eyes upward and bathe yourself with more oxygen you feel better.

1. Again, look up at the top of the page and take a deep breath.
2. Look up at the ceiling and take another deep breath.
3. This time, touch your thumb to your forefinger on one hand, making the sign of OK. As you look up, all the way up, take a third deep breath.
This OK symbol serves as your joy anchor.

Think of your mind as a bio computer and you are the programmer. Any time you feel low, take three deep breaths, uplift your focus, and make the OK sign. This changes your brain chemistry, so blast yourself into joy. For an extra blast, straighten your posture, say "yes" to yourself and laugh.

AFFIRM SUCCESS: Commencement Blessing

Read the following affirmation slowly and make these ideas your reality. It's time to start celebrating your life.

I imagine myself in a glorious beautiful setting. I come to this valley of mind to cleanse and renew. I'm ready to love myself and my loved ones completely.

Before me is a flowing brook. I kneel down by its crystal clear, cool waters. With my hands, I splash the water over my face. I cup my hands and drink the water slowly, so slowly. As I do, I am energized, tingling and refreshed.

The sun sends a golden light from the sky.

The temperature of the water is so refreshing! I put my whole body into the brook. Impurities are washed away. I am purified and refreshed.

I leave this cleansing stream and sit beneath a beautiful, strong tree with branches hanging lush with green leaves. I rest and breathe pure oxygen. Pure oxygen from the leaves of this gorgeous tree. I renew. I breathe out carbon dioxide and limiting attitudes or beliefs.

I am a person of integrity and truth. I breathe in a new beginning. The green leaves soak up carbon dioxide and convert it into more oxygen. The oxygen comes through the trunk and enters my body, my pores. I breathe with the tree and we are one.

From earth I draw energy. Like the tree, I have roots. I gather strength from Mother Earth. I'm in control of my life. I am one in the truth of all life.

I bring loved ones to sit with me, the tree, the sun, the earth and the brook. We celebrate a new day.

My life is balanced. I step into my future. I graduate from the school of the past. I give myself an A++ for learning my lessons well. In this moment, I begin a new life. The perfect life for ME. The life God intended me to have.

My life is my gift from God. What I do with it is my gift to God. I practice the golden rule on myself: I do unto myself, as I would like others to do unto me. I pray to the higher power as I know it to be.

'Dear God, Goddess, All that is. Assist me to honor all parts of myself. Help me to listen to my inner wisdom. Teach me to think clearly and take the necessary steps that bring joy, harmony and integration. Help me find right

action, peace, love and joy. Let all I think, say and do be for my highest good. Amen. Awomen. Ah life.'

I expand my awareness in every way. I think my thoughts, feel my feelings and know the bigger picture of each thought and feeling more and more each day.

I am well adjusted in everything I think, say and do. I love solving challenges in positive ways that benefit others as well as myself.

I list what makes me happy (Pause)

I spend time each day doing these things. I focus on small pleasures, like how much I like the color of my sofa or how I enjoy my body moving as I work out.

I enjoy every minute of my life. I feel terrific. I love and respect my body and mind. Joy is my compass. I'm well and I prosper. I am loving and lovable. YES! I am grateful for life.

Up Your Egypt

☥The Cradle of Relaxation

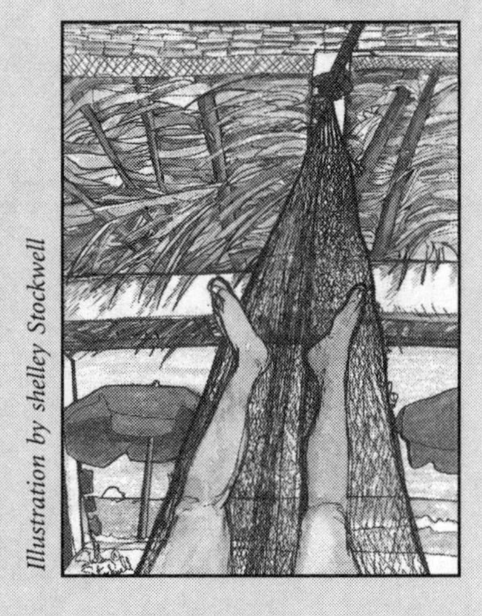

Illustration by shelley Stockwell

Hypnosis was a celebrated tool for healing and enlightenment since earliest recorded Ancient Egyptian history. The "psychiatrist" priest used altered states to rejuvenate others in "sleep temples."

Here, during a one-month stay, Egyptians would renew and regenerate themselves with trance. Engravings from these times show entranced worshippers performing religious rites. Hypnosis was used during surgery.

The word "hypnosis" comes from the Greek root word "hyp" meaning "behind" and "gnosis" meaning knowledge. Ancient Egyptians believed in the blending and separateness of body, mind and spirit. Their paradigm:

Unconscious Mind (haidit, khaibit, or shadow), housing your survival instinct (lower ka), a guardian angel or higher self (higher ka or soul double) and conscience and intellect (ab)

Superconscious Mind Divine intelligence (akh or khu), individual soul essence (sahu), immortal soul (ba).

Photo By Jon Nicholas

Chapter 19
Stockwell's 24 Commandments for Mind:
Brain Storm

To successfully become a mastermind it's important to know the laws that govern the mind.

- ☞ Connecting With Your Profound Wisdom Is Fun and Easy
- ☞ Everything Is Hypnosis
- ☞ Thoughts Are Things
- ☞ Monkey See; Monkey Do
- ☞ Learning and Change Take Place in The Subconscious Mind
- ☞ Change Takes Place in The Present
- ☞ Suggestions Work Best When You Have A Readiness For Change
- ☞ You Are Single Minded
- ☞ The Mind Grasps the Subject of a Sentence: Energy Goes Where Attention Flows
- ☞ What You Affirm You Create
- ☞ What You Anticipate, You Initiate, Create and Exaggerate
- ☞ What You Insist You Resist
- ☞ What You Resist, Persists
- ☞ You Seek Pleasure and Avoid or Ignore Pain
- ☞ You Accept Suggestions Via Dominant Senses
- ☞ Suggestions Are Best When Mated With Heightened Emotion
- ☞ The Harder You Try, The More Difficult It Is
- ☞ Strong Words Work Best
- ☞ Your Mind is Literal
- ☞ Keep It Simple
- ☞ Mind Effects Body and Body Effects Mind
- ☞ Creativity Begets Creativity
- ☞ Repetition Works, Repetition Works, Repetition Works
- ☞ Connecting With Profound Wisdom Is Fun and Easy

☞ Connecting With Your Profound Wisdom Is Fun and Easy

☆ *"Have you been born again?"*
"No I got it right the first time."

Mind explorers have more fun.

Here, you discover and replace imprints and get high with your higher self. It is easy to master your thoughts and your reactions. You can easily learn to talk with your subconscious mind.

My thirty-second zap, puts you into a wonderfully refreshing state of hypnosis in only thirty seconds! A visit to your inner world in this way is beautiful. This is where you live. This is who you are.

To do the Stockwell Zap say the word "blue" three times, each time doing a different thing:

The First Blue Say "blue" to yourself, then close your eyelids. Think and imagine the word blue. Blue as the sky, blue as a deep blue ocean, blue as a warm baby's blanket. Relax your eyelids so that when you test them, they just don't want to open. When you've done a good job of playing this relaxation game, stop testing your eyes and say:

The Second Blue Say "Blue" and then give yourself a positive suggestion, such as "I feel wonderfully refreshed," or "Calm, peaceful and easy."

To deepen your relaxation, tell yourself "With the next five breaths, I go deeper and deeper into the valley of relaxation. Deeper than I've ever gone before. (Five, four, three, two, one)." In the valley, give yourself suggestions and listen to your deepest wisdom.

The Third Blue Say "Blue" and return to room awareness (if you went into the valley count one two, three, four and five). "Wide awake, eyes wide open, feeling terrific."

☞ Everything Is Hypnosis

☆ *"Coming home I drove into the wrong house & collided with a tree I don't have."*
—From a Toronto insurance claim form

Every sensory perception is taken in by your computer mind and incorporated into data as part of the big hologram. You constantly give yourself powerful suggestions that determine what you do, say and believe. These thoughts create moods that change your outlook and behavior.

When you really think about it, whatever you have or don't have, do or don't do, is the result of suggestions you give yourself. Everything you create in your life starts as a conscious or subconscious thought. Life has an element of fate, yet how you talk to yourself about things that happen "out of the blue" has direct impact on the course of your life, too.

The reality tunnels of society, school, parents and friends focus your awareness. If you were repetitively told that the earth is flat, you most likely accept that as truth. It is only when you hypnotize yourself to see things differently that you go outside the limits of such programming.

Up Your Egypt

Backward Water

An Egyptian army invading Syria in 1525 BC had never seen rain and only seen the Nile that flowed north. They couldn't believe it! Water fell from the sky and flowed south!

You literally hypnotize yourself with every thought you accept whether the thought comes from outside or inside. And every thought, real or imagined, creates real biochemical responses within your mind/body.

Ever notice how you talk to yourself or others? Those words create your life. Each time you notice and improve your self-talk, you literally hypnotize yourself for success.

Think how much work it is to hypnotize yourself to smoke: your body hates it, it kills you, and it causes unbelievable problems. You really have to do a number on yourself to prevail in destructive self-hypnosis. You must convince yourself, make excuses and stubbornly persist. Bertrand Russell said it well; "Many people would sooner die than think. In fact they do." Master your thoughts and you master your life.

The work of a professional hypnotherapist is usually to de-hypnotize you. They wake you up from self-destructive hypnosis and teach you to create positive suggestions.

☞ Thoughts Are Things

☆ *"Your Thoughts are the daddies of real.
How much you love equals how much you feel."*
—Shelley Stockwell

What you think consciously and subconsciously manifests as reality. Your thoughts influence your behavior and future behavior.

Thoughts also create the energy between you and others. At any given moment everyone knows the truth about what is going on.

How do you know when someone likes you? How do you know when someone on the other end of the phone stops listening to you? How can you tell if someone's jealous of you? How do you know that someone is staring at you? You intuit energy, and thoughts are energy!

You little mind reader you.

☞ Monkey See; Monkey Do

We imitate what we see around us. As a child you instinctively model big people's behavior. You do this to survive, avoid rejection, abandonment or pain, and to enjoy pleasure, contact and love. If mom was terminally annoyed you may be imitating her harrumphs. If dad popped his cork, you may explode yourself.

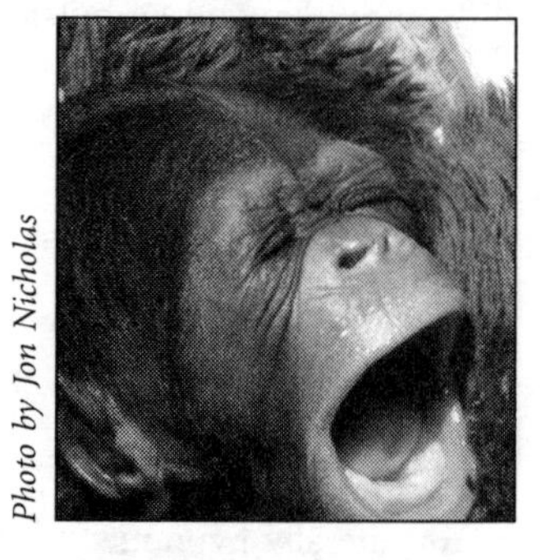

Photo by Jon Nicholas

Teen's dress and talk like their peers. Adults do that too. Even without formal "dress codes" people in the same company dress the same. They often replicate their mentor's behavior. Advertisers set up vivid depictions of behavior to imitate.

Yawn. Yawn. Yawn.

Doesn't that make you just want to...OK, why not YAWN. As an experiment, the next time you're with a group of people, in a classroom, grocery line or business meeting, (or right now if someone is near you) yawn boldly. Notice how others join you. Or whistle a jingle from a popular commercial and notice how others chime in.

If you want to calm someone, try a typical NLP (neuro linguistic programming) technique and synchronize your breath to his or her rhythm, and then, slow your breath down. They will unconsciously join you.

Use this imitative gift to your advantage. Pick as a role model, someone who has behaviors you want for yourself; confidence, grace, success, savvy. Then when faced with a tricky situation, ask yourself: "What would they do right now." Imitate and become like them.

Up Your Egypt

Snake Charming

Snakes don't hear the sound of the snake charmers flute because they are deaf.

Hypnotized, they copy the movement of the flute swaying from side to side.

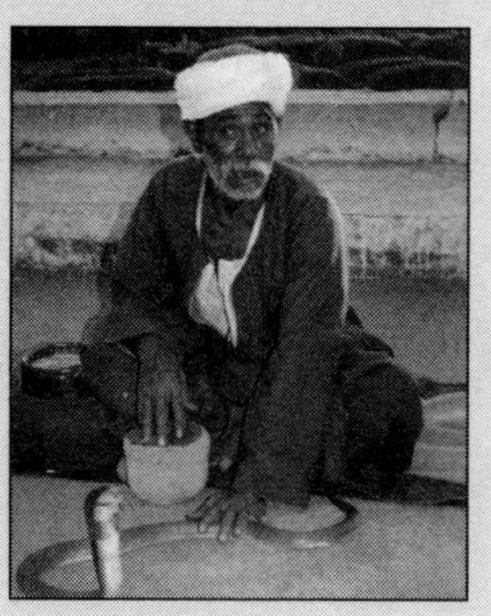

Photo by Jon Nicholas

☞ Learning and Change Takes Place in the Subconscious Mind

☆ *"Your brain uses less power than a 100 watt light bulb and you don't have to get on a chair to change your mind."*

—Wink Martindale

Your subconscious mind initiates and carries out change. That's why you may have tried to change behavior through conscious will—and it was difficult or impossible. Real change *only* takes place when a decision is made and carried out on the deepest level.

Photo by Jon Nicholas

You literally program your subconscious mind. A literal mind; your subconscious literally delivers what you ask of it. *YOU HAVE TO BELIEVE YOU CAN DO SOMETHING TO DO IT.* In 1954 Roger Bannister ran a mile in less than four minutes. No one else had up 'til then. When Roger did it, others said "it can be done" and then many others did it too.

☞ Change Takes Place in the Present

☆ *"It's deja vu all over again."*

—Yogi Berra

Hold a pen between your thumb and forefinger, and think to yourself, "I am going to drop this pen." "I am going to drop this pen."

Because your words reflect a future activity, "I am going to...," nothing happens. Now change the message to "Drop the pen," and notice how you easily release it.

Your deepest mind responds in the present. If you say, "Next week I'll make more money" or "Tomorrow I'll stop smoking," that future time never comes. The subconscious will wait for next week or tomorrow before it carries out your instructions. Phrasing suggestions in the future makes it impossible to carry out the message in the present.

WINNING SUGGESTION	LOSING SUGGESTION
I make $2000 a week.	Next week I'll make money
I have a wonderful full time job	I want a full time job
My lungs are clear and healthy	Tomorrow my lungs will be clear and healthy

DEFINE WHAT YOU WANT AS AN ACCOMPLISHED FACT.

Talk about it and think about it as if it has already happened. Make everything you want fact, in the here and now. Focus on it, repeat and reinforce it, and then just let it go.

Psychotherapy assumes that if you uncover the childhood source of ar problem and understand it, it will be resolved. Not always so! The constant restoking of old pain can reinforce pain. To really be effective, do more than just understand. Extinguish strong reactions, forgive, release and most importantly, return to the present. True change occurs in the here and now with positive reactions and behavior.

☞ Suggestions Work Best When You Have A Readiness for Change

☆ Question: *How many hypnotherapists does it take to change a light bulb?*
Answer: *"One, but the light bulb has to want to change."*

The most important element for successful mind mastery is your readiness for change. Many think about change for years, preparing for our moment of truth, the turning point, the instant when we shift from one point of view to another. If you've been toying with changing something in your life, it starts with a decision. Proclaim the results of your change. Violá, results!

What do you want to change now? Pretend that your goal, what you want has already happened. What's it like having accomplished your results?

☞ You Are Single Minded

☆ Judge: *"Mr. Smith, I find you not guilty of stealing the chicken."*
Mr. Smith: *"Does that mean I get to eat it?"*

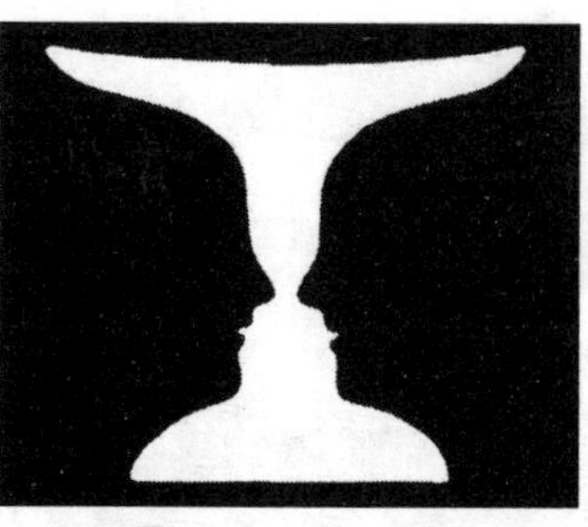

Face or Vase?

As with all figure-ground ambiguity we see one at a time. As much as we try, we can't do two things at once. Behaviors and thoughts are sequential.

Focus your attention on the part of your body that, at this moment, is the most comfortable. Is it your hand or foot? Whatever you decide, notice how good it feels. Pay full attention. Now focus your attention on the part of your body that is the least comfortable. Give that full focus. When you direct your attention to discomfort, do you remember the pleasure place?

All right, now take a deep breath and focus your attention again on the part of you that feels most comfortable; relax.

While test taking, if you repeat to yourself "I can't think of the answer," "I can't think of the answer" that's all you'll think about. These thoughts take up the time and energy that you could use to just think of the answer.

Mothers understand single mindedness when they kiss junior's "owie" and say "all better." The thought of Mommy's kiss is all junior notices. Emotional upsets vanish when mommy hands her little one a new toy.

To take advantage of your one-track mind, train yourself to engage in the mode of thought that serves you best. At any given moment you can focus on the glass half full or half empty. Your subconscious mind does a multiple of things at the same time. Right now it is keeping your heart beating and your lungs inflating and helping you to read these words. Women tend to be more multi tasked than men.

Ormond McGill's Five Modes of the Mind

1. Right Knowledge
2. Wrong Knowledge
3. Imagination
4. Sleep
5. Memory

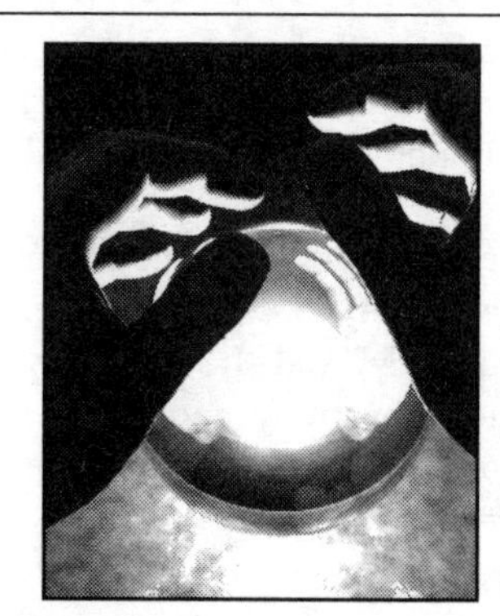

Illustration by Clark Dunbar
(© RF RubberBall Productions)

☞ The Mind Grasps the Subject of a Sentence: Energy Goes Where Attention Flows

☆ *"I really didn't say the things I said."*
—Yogi Berra

☆ *"Any time you don't want anything, you get it."*
—Calvin Coolidge

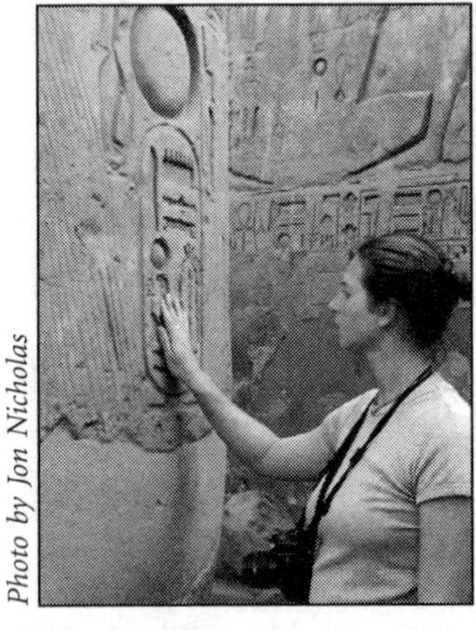

Photo by Jon Nicholas

Many folks mistakenly give themselves poor suggestions, e.g.; "I'm NOT going to eat this bag of cookies. I'm NOT even going to think about these cookies." And, of course, they eat the whole thing. The subconscious mind wraps itself around the subject of the sentence and behavior follows thought.

"I don't smoke anymore" or "I'm a non-smoker" moves the mind to grab the subject of the sentence (smoke) and could motivate you to light up that white scorpion. For positive results, use words that paint positive pictures of the outcome you want. "I choose to feel great," "I breathe with ease," "Breathing well cleanses me. My lungs are born again in this moment," causes your mind to embrace "breathing well."

"I won't be late anymore," won't work. "I'm always early" and 'It's fun to be on time." Get timely results.

If you say "My headache is gone." The word *headache*, the subject of the sentence, is negative and reinforces a negative outcome. Instead say "My head is clear and I feel great."

☞ What You Affirm, You Create

☆ Pharaoh: *"God, please strike down my worst enemy."*
A bolt of lightening kills pharaoh and God greets him at the pearly gates.
Pharaoh: *"Let me rephrase that."*

Keep Affirmations in the affirmative. "I love money, it's good for me." "My lungs are clear." "I choose to live." "I do good kind and loving things for my precious body" And "It's now okay to eat healthy food" will work wonders. State your goal positively and clearly. Positive focus also serves to override the conscious tendency to judge or resist new ideas.

☞ What You Anticipate, You Initiate, Create and Exaggerate

☆ *"You've got to be careful if you don't know where you're going, because you might not get there."*

—Yogi Berra

Let's say you can't sleep, so you worry about not sleeping. Your worry becomes a self-fulfilling prophecy, making sleep more difficult. If you worry about impotence or lack of orgasm, you know how worry self perpetuates the problem. Anticipating anxiety causes more anxiety.

Think about it. Everything in your life started with a thought or a decision. The work you do or don't do, what you love or don't love, what you do for fun, all began with thoughts. Smoking begins with the idea that you *need* to smoke. Smoking continues with expectations like "Smoking calms my nerves" or "It's too hard to stop." Say "No matter how hard I try I can't lose weight," you'll stay correctly plump. You've set it up that way. Anticipate and predict success and you'll be blessed with success.

☞ What You Insist, You Resist

☆ *"If you try to fail, and succeed, which have you done?"*

—George Carlin

Rebellious souls we are. If we insist in dictatorial fashion, saying "Don't tell me what to do." you resist listening to what is said to you. Being right or playing top dog replaces logic. "I did it my way" is the theme we sing as our lungs go black with smoke. Use stubborn determination sparingly until you gather all the facts or all rebellion breaks loose and you lose.

☞ What You Resist Persists

☆ *"I told the police that I was not injured, but on removing my hat, I found that I had a skull fracture."*

—From a Toronto insurance claim form

If you say to yourself, "I'm not going to notice the funny way he moves his mouth" the funny way he moves his mouth becomes your focal point.

Don't think about a pink elephant. Don't think of an elephant. A huge pink elephant. Pink, pink, pink ELEPHANT. What do you think about? Of course, an elephant...a very pink elephant.

The mind embraces the subject of a sentence. "Elephant, not" translates into just plain "Elephant." (schwing).

A negative suggestion like: "I'm not going to think about biting my nails" usually backfires. It suggests the very behavior you want to eliminate. The word "not" is an ignored orphan to the subconscious. Your deepest mind doesn't take "no" for an answer.

The Law of Reverse Effect (L.O.R.E.) Says: *"If you tell me what to do...I'll do the opposite."*

TRY TO FORGET YOU SAW THIS

You can use this reverse reaction to your advantage. Wish you can't sleep, for example and watch yourself drift off. "I affirm that I will not go to sleep. I will not go to sleep. I will not go to sleep." "I will not yawn. I will not yawn. I will not yawn"

To eliminate cookie bingeing try: "Instead of eating a bag of cookies tonight. I'm going to eat twenty bags. If I can eat one, I can eat twenty." With such an absurd suggestion, the inner mind says; "This is ridiculous. I don't want twenty. As a matter of fact I don't want one either." The result is that you eat far less than you did before and this takes the anxiety away.

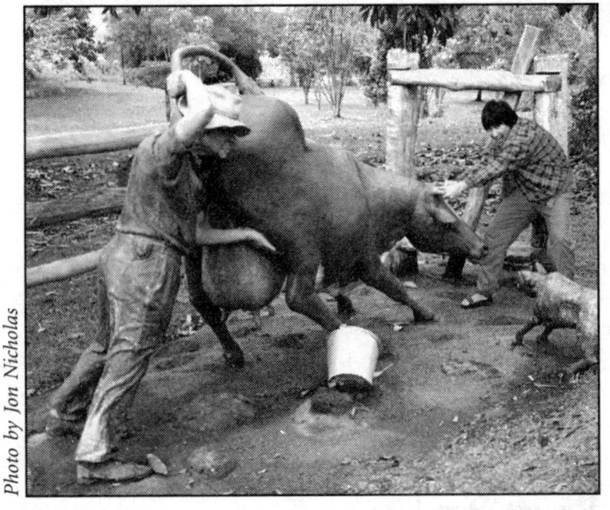

Photo by Jon Nicholas

Milton Erikson, the famous hypnotherapist, discovered this principle when he was a small boy. His father was trying to pull a stubborn calf into the barn by tugging on his ears. The cow wouldn't budge until Milton tugged even harder in the other direction on the calf's tail. The poor mooing soul bolted into the barn.

A hopelessly obese woman visited Milton Erikson:

"I have to lose 150 pounds," she said.

"I will help you only if you promise to do exactly what I tell you. Do I have your word?"

"Yes, whatever you say"

"Very good. See me when you have gained another 35 pounds."

It's said that she forced herself to follow his instructions and was so disgusted with over eating that she easily lost all 185 pounds and then some.

☞ You Seek Pleasure and Avoid or Ignore Pain

☆ *"I never blame myself when I'm not hitting. I just blame the bat and if it keeps it up, I change bats...After all, If I know it isn't my fault that I'm not hitting, how can I get mad at myself?"*

—Yogi Berra

It is your nature to go for the gusto. You want to feel good; we all do.

Pain shows up so we learn. The trick is to get the message and return to pleasure and joy in short order. But if you vehemently deny pain, you may wind up with pain as your bedfellow. Choose joy and you laugh yourself to sleep and to life.

When pain gets too great, we "bottom out" have emotional emergencies or get sick so we get a grip. When we get the consequences of pain, we naturally go for pleasure. To change a behavior, attach pleasure to the positive results you want and pain to unwanted results. Too much energy on pain causes you to lose perspective. Denying pain makes it stick. Moving through it just right, you'll come out the other side.

AFFIRM SUCCESS: Suggestions for Pleasure Seeking
My assignment: become a pleasure seeker, a full-fledged 100% pleasure seeker. From this point forward, I do kind, considerate, nurturing things for myself. I only do things that bring my precious body to radiant health that uplifts me to my higher self. My higher self makes me naturally high. I no longer do anything that harms me in any way.

I am, in this instant, a full-fledged pleasure seeker. Because this is so, I put my hand on my heart and affirm that it is so:

"I choose joy. I choose wellness. I choose peace. I choose life. I find the gift hidden in each life experience. I celebrate my life."

☞ You Accept Suggestions Via Dominant Senses

☆ A duck bought some Chapstick:
"*How do you want to pay?*" asked the clerk.
"*Put it on my bill,*" quacked the duck.
"*Don't duck your bill?* warned the clerk.

To impress a message deeply into the subconscious, use your dominant sense or senses. Smell, taste, feel, see, hear or intuit the result you seek. As you come to your senses, you get results. To communicate well, talk to others using words that match their dominant modes of perception.

What Are Your Dominant Senses?

Close your eyes and go back in your memory to a moment when you felt personal satisfaction. Stay in that memory; notice it from each of your senses. What stands out for you? Is it the way things look?
Smell?
Taste?
Sound?
Feel?
Or something beyond the physical senses all together?

As you journey through each of your senses, notice which one or ones stand out for you.

Words are also clues to your dominant senses. Phrases like "If you see what I mean" means visual focus. If "That doesn't sound right to me," you're sound dominant. "That stinks"...you get a whiff of what I'm saying.

☞ Suggestions Are Best When Mated With Heightened Emotions

☆ *The sky has cracked the morning light.*
The sun is the egg on my plate.
I am going crazy
I hope I'm not too late.

—Shelley Stockwell

Have you ever noticed how you hear bad news first and loudest? The amount of emotion attached to a suggestion, the more passionately it burns in the pathways of the mind. A lover's words spoken in the height of passion sears deep in your memory. So do things that people say in anger.

Photo by Jon Nicholas

How come you remember the phone number of an attractive man or lady more easily than someone who doesn't turn you on? If you want to remember something, attach it to something that brings up feelings.

If you want to remove an old program from the "active file" of your mind, discharge your emotional perception of it. Then attach the lesson to positive emotion.

☞ The Harder You Try The More Difficult It Is

☆ *"Avid pursuit of a goal thwarts it."*
—Victor Frankl

Don't try hard, try soft. Go with the flow. Hang loose and don't sweat the small stuff. When you don't demand solutions, and let solutions unfold, your mind resolves conflicts and solves puzzles.

Make what you want (your goals and dreams) a byproduct of everything and every situation. Let's say you want more love in your life; gently add little loving thoughts at work, on the drive home, during trips to the grocery store and as you drift off to sleep. Let love be part of all you do. Be gently loving with yourself.

☞ Strong Words Work Best

Words like *try*, don't fly. BIG words and phrases get BIG results!

Hold a pen in your hand and *try* to drop it. Try. Most likely, it doesn't go anywhere. Now just drop the pen! Good! It falls easily. Now look at the pen and think to yourself "*Try* to pick up the pen." "*Try* to pick up the pen."

Now tell yourself, "Pick up the pen!" It's a done deal. Try is a weak word in the brain chemistry world. The word, *try* means to fail.

Maybe also means probably not. If someone tells you, "Maybe I'll call..." don't wait home for the call. It won't come.

☞ Your Mind is Literal

☆ *"I'd like a pair of alligator shoes.*
"What size is your alligator?

☆ Meat Pie to Bartender: *I'd like a beer please."*
Bartender to Meat Pie: *"I'm Sorry, we don't serve food here."*

The subconscious mind is a literal mind. If you say "You make me sick;" you may be correct. A "pain in the neck" will manifest as a real pain in your neck. And if someone "gets on your nerves" they will.

☞ Keep It Simple

☆ FLEAS
Adam had 'em.

☆ Mohammed: *"Look up. What do you see?"*
Abdul: *"I see a thousand stars."*
Mohammed: *"What does that mean?"*
Abdul: *"It means that of all the planets in existence, we are so lucky to be here on Earth. We are so small in the vast spectrum of possibilities. Tonight we see a glorious array of stars and tomorrow will be a new sun. We drift in a cosmic sea of forever. What does it mean to you?"*
Mohammed: *"It means that someone has stolen our tent."*

Keep it simple. Boil your suggestion down to its purest form. The subconscious mind may misunderstand words that have a double meaning. Ambiguous words with two meanings like "hire," "tire" and "fly" may be misunderstood by the subconscious mind. Pray for whirred peas.

Ambiguous words are taken the way they are taken. The way you take them might not be your true intention. Pick and choose the words you use carefully.

The subconscious understands sentences the way a five-year-old might. Don't overload or confuse the mind with high fallutin' phrases or long drawn out, confusing, overloaded never-ending sentences that seem to go on and on and on and on and on forever and ever and ever and ever, and ever, ad nauseum.

☞ Mind Effects Body and Body Effects Mind

☆ *"Why do they call ice cream sticks tongue depressors?"*
"Because when the ice cream is gone, your tongue is depressed."

Think about biting into a sour, juicy, yellow lemon. The tart, bitter, juicy drops trickles down your throat. You start to salivate and your mouth tastes the tangy liquid...Are you salivating yet?

This whole lemon thing is just an idea that you are reading in a book, yet when you wrap your thoughts around it, you respond with a physical reaction.

Emotions evoke responses in the body. Depression can cause indigestion and stress a headache. As a matter of fact, an emotion is not felt unless its physical response has been activated. Fear, love, disgust and glee create physical reactions in you and me. The body then creates neurological responses that effect your thoughts. Round and round and round in a circle game.

☞ Creativity Begets Creativity

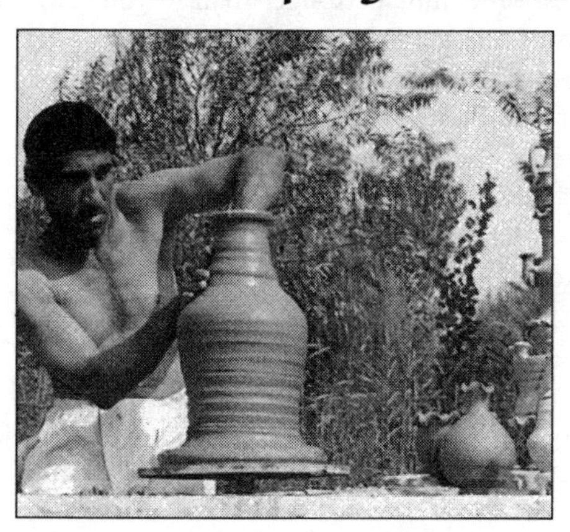

☆ Buddha to hot dog vendor:
"Make me one with everything."

Buddha to hot dog vendor:
"Where's my change?"

Hot dog vendor:
"Change comes from within."

☞ Repetition Works. Repetition Works. Repetition Works.

☆ Pete: *Repetition makes a song stick in your head.*
Repeat: *You can say that again!"*
Pete: *Repetition makes song stick in your head.*

If you've been on the "It's a Small World" ride at Disneyland, you most likely found the words; "*It's a small world after all. It's a small world after all. It's a small world after all. It's a small, small world...*" glued on your singing brain. Are some of your thoughts and behaviors like old stuck records?

Behaviors repeated over and over keep you attached to that way of thinking, acting and reacting. Experience hard wires your brain. If you were soothed by mother when you cried, you learned to sooth yourself to calm down. Repetitive kindness reinforces kindness. Stress and constant threats rewire your emotional circuits too. If you repeatedly stress and threaten yourself you evoke more of the same.

Ask again and again for what you want; what you really, really want. But, be careful what you affirm...you will get it. Make sure it is what you truly want. Repetition conditions the subconscious mind and lets the universe assist. Repetition reinforces. Every time you repeat an old pattern, thought or action, you reinforce it. You can say that again. OK. Every time you repeat an old pattern, thought or action, you reinforce it.

Ask! Ask! Ask! Ask! Ask! Ask yourself and others until you get what you want. Keep asking. The more that you affirm, the deeper the message *thinks-in.*

Repeat the positive affirmations in this book over and over and over. Rephrase them, enlarge them, write them, visualize and imagine them.

Hypnotize yourself and saturate your subconscious mind with the results you want. In hypnosis, the power of suggestion is much stronger than in your day-to-day waking state. Make a tape of your affirmations and then relax as you let the tape repeat for your subconscious mind what it is you want.

Paste up picture and words that symbolize and reinforce your waking suggestions. For example, if you want to be happier, put the word "joy" on stickers and paste them all over your world. Put a "joy" by your computer, on your clock, in front of the toilet, on the refrigerator...You'll see it there often and it will serve as a memory peg and reinforce your suggestion. Then make a joyful noise.

If you want to slow down; paste a heart sticker next to the clock on your car's dash (slow) board.

Repetition reinforces ideas with other people. Others are not mind readers. Make it easy for them to give you what you want. And then impress them with repetition.

JOY

JOY

JOY

JOY

JOY

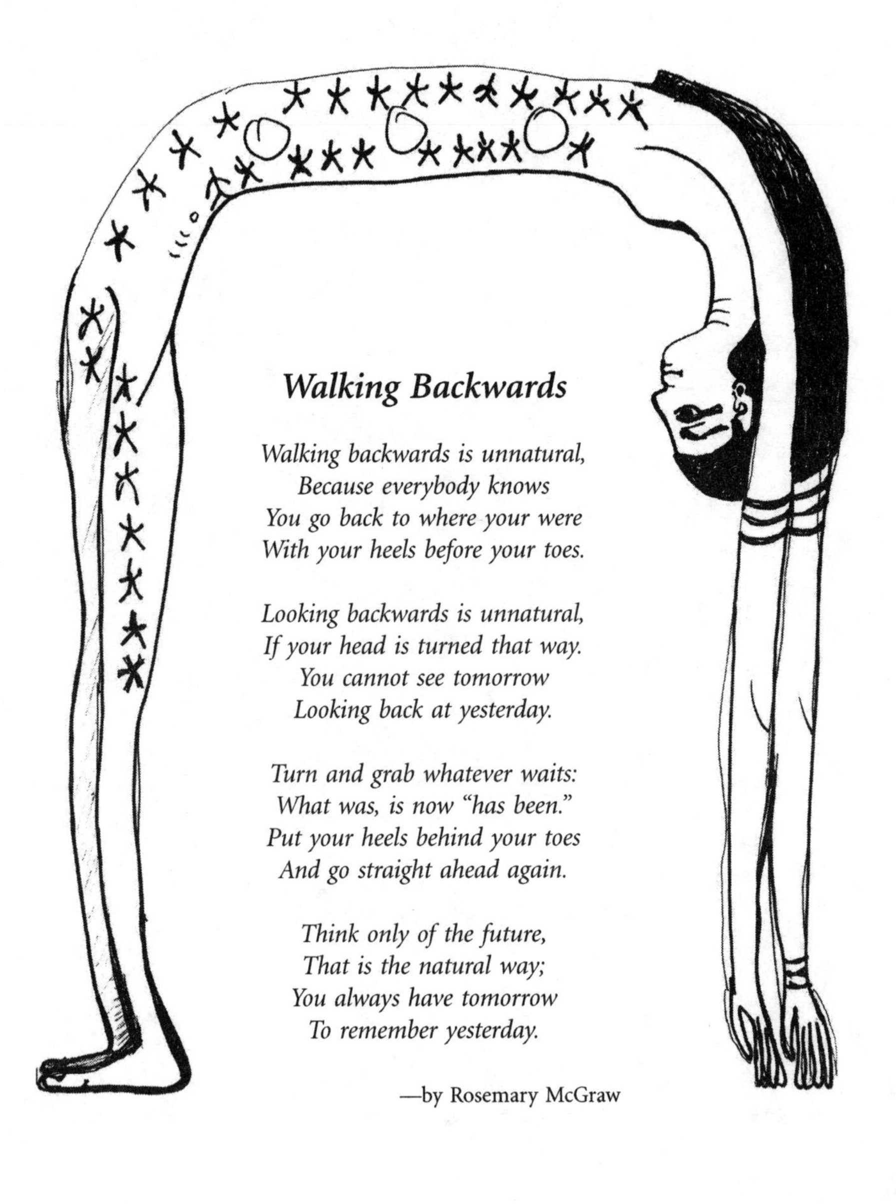

Walking Backwards

Walking backwards is unnatural,
Because everybody knows
You go back to where your were
With your heels before your toes.

Looking backwards is unnatural,
If your head is turned that way.
You cannot see tomorrow
Looking back at yesterday.

Turn and grab whatever waits:
What was, is now "has been."
Put your heels behind your toes
And go straight ahead again.

Think only of the future,
That is the natural way;
You always have tomorrow
To remember yesterday.

—by Rosemary McGraw

Chapter 20

Dig Past Patterns

Archaic/Illogical Remains

☆ *"Life is a game, the object of which is to discover the object of the game."*
—Sanders

☆ *"I'm lost. I'm going back to find myself. If I return before I get back, please ask me to wait."*
—L. Lionel Kendrick

With the best intentions, we indulge in limiting games, patterns, habits and manipulations that undermine peace of mind. Be outstandingly brave, take each test and see if you play any of these games. If you do, use my "Affirm Success Formula" and have fun once again for the very first time!

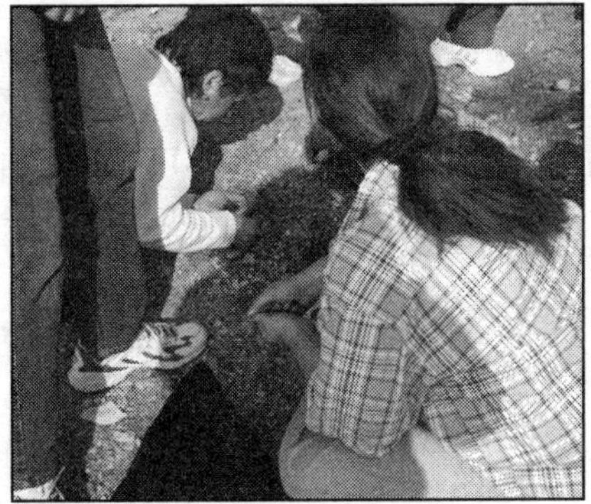

Photo by Jon Nicholas

Dig It: Phran & Tamara

▲ SLAVE DRIVERS
▲ MUMMY-FIED
▲ REVERSE THE CURSE
▲ CONTROL GAMES
▲ GOLD GUILT
▲ SHAME GAME: Nitchy, Nitchy
▲ IN-TURNED
▲ ASHES TO ASSES
▲ DRAMA-DEARIE
▲ MULE
▲ THE GAME OF COMPLAIN: Crab
▲ BLAME GAME
▲ GOSSIP COLUMN
▲ HIPPOPOTAMUS GAME
▲ BIG BANANA GAMES
▲ KNOW-IT-ALL AND BRAGGART
▲ GARBAGE BAG GAME
▲ DISTORTED MIRROR GAME
▲ COULDA/WOULDA/SHOULDA/NEVER/ALWAYS
▲ NEVER-ALWAYS GAME
▲ SALOME GAMES:
▲ WON'T LEAVE ME SALOME ▲ LEAVE ME SALOME ▲ SALOME AGAIN
▲ FLOCK YOU
▲ VAMPIRE GAMES
▲ REMINDS ME OF…GAME
▲ FAN GAME
▲ WORRY WART GAME

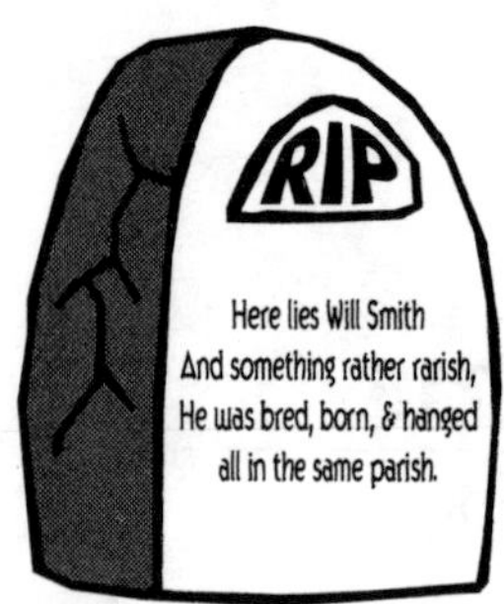

▲ Slave Drivers

Do you recreate situations where you are mistreated, ignored, controlled, or put down? Do negative situations seem familiar? Or, do you find yourself in winning situations where you are loved, supported, cherished and liberated?

Either way you create it.

Long after you leave the home you grew up in, old patterns influence your viewpoint and reactions. Your roles and coping mechanisms from the past often become automatic responses. Some live their whole life from their history. A zombie-like childhood trance can certainly stifle the spontaneity of joy and being self-empowered.

Every moment spent in the past takes away that same amount of time in the present.

> Up Your Egypt
>
> ### Cut the Coprolite
>
> Archaeology is the science of studying things people leave behind. Archaeologists treasure old garbage, which they call midden. They also enjoy studying ancient poop that they call coprolites. Coprolites help them learn about the health and habits of the past.

Painful Past Patterns Pollute Pleasure: A Hard Axe To Follow

☆ Question: *"Have you lived in this town all your life?"*
Answer: *"Not yet."*

Painful and pleasurable patterns are created in childhood to cope with mommy and daddy. Children are eager to learn and receive teachings.

We mimic and imitate the big people's behavior. We try to be like them. "I'm going to be just like my Daddy when I grow up."

Or, we decide to be the opposite. "When I grow up, I'll never be mean to kids like they are."

Each time you re-enact an old response, you "sign an agreement" and re-hypnotize yourself, to keep the past alive in the present and miss the chance for a spontaneous now adventure. Such life traps determine how we think, feel, act, and relate to others. If you are caught in one, you may appear to the outside world like you have everything—status, ideal relationships, and success—but inside you won't believe it. It's almost impossible to savor life or believe in your accomplishments if you're caught in a life game.

Up Your Egypt

Tutankhamun

Pharaoh Akhenaton and his first wife Ti parented Tutankhamun. Akhenaton chose Tutankhamun to inherit the throne. Tut also inherited his dad's genetic disorder, morphan syndrome that gave him a slim face and long fingers and toes and very fat hips. His measurements: 31" chest, 29" waist and 43" hips! When Tut was nine years old, he became pharaoh of Egypt. Tut-Ank-Amun means 'gracious life.'

Young King Tut died in 1327 BC at the age 18 and was most likely murdered by his successor. He was richly adorned and his worldly appointments assured a rich afterlife. He got his afterlife in the Cairo Museum, where you can see his stuff displayed.

Tut's tomb was discovered in 1922 by Howard Carter.

Sweet Spontaneous Spring

☆ *"My mother wanted a perfect child.*
She just didn't realize she got one."

Photo by Jon Nicholas

There are few things written in stone that can't be corrected. Notice habits and reactions that keep negative past patterns in the present. Don't let rigor mortis set into your life! Release limiting patterns and replace them with positive ones. Boldly and bravely cut through limits, alibis, blaming or self pity. Take on a new role in life. When you do, the results are awesome.

Take each of the following life trap quizzes and then decide if it fits. If it does, repeat the affirmation three times, click your heals and celebrate yourself.

AFFIRM SUCCESS: History Mastery
To prepare for your journey, affirm your success:
I take full responsibility for my thoughts and actions. No other person or event is responsible for what I experience in this moment. I create what I experience. If I react in a certain way, I push my own button.

If I don't like the way I think or react, I change my thought or reaction to something I like better. I release limiting patterns. I'm unlimited. Change takes place automatically. It's easy to change. I'm responsible for how I think and feel.

I learn from mistakes. I learn from success. Years of experience allow me to go to capture the wisdom of everything I do, observe and learn. I take these insights forward into my life and they help me make positive choices now. I do things that are good for me.

My behavior is in my control. If my reaction to difficult situations served me well in the past, I use those responses again. If not, I create a new set of responses that serve me better. I am flexible.

I'm a maturing and well-functioning personality. I love growing up. I'm emotionally prepared to deal with life as it unfolds. I flow easily with change, adventure, crisis, stress, joy, love and success.

▲ Mummy-Fied

☆ *"Some mothers don't know when they've done a good job-and when it's finished."*
—Erma Bombeck

Mommy and Daddy are the first and most important relationships of your life and literally spell SURVIVAL. That's why we often model mom and dad...forever.

UP YOUR EGYPT

The Oldest Mummy

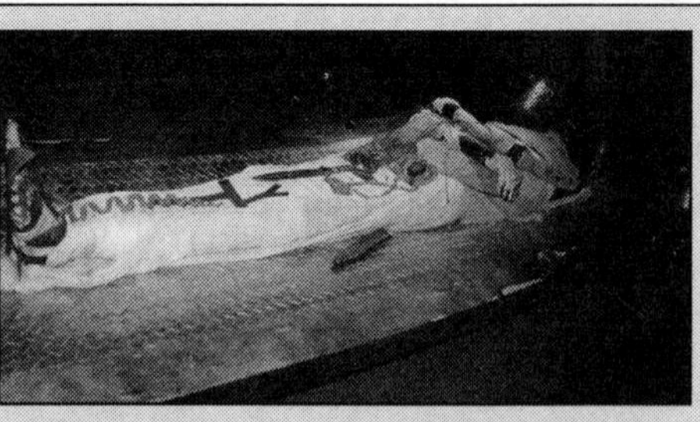

Photo by Jon Nicholas

The word mummification comes from the Persian word mum, which means wax. The Guinness Book of World Records says that the oldest mummy dates back to 2600 BC (about 4600 years ago). She was found at the Great Pyramid of Cheops at Giza and was believed to have lived in the lost kingdom of Ankh Ptah.

Are You Like Mummy?

☆ *"When you arrive at your future will you blame your past?"*
—Robert Half

I often think, say, and/or do:

____ My worst and best traits are suspiciously like Mom, Dad, or my caretakers.
____ They drank and smoked; so do I.
____ They screamed at me, now I scream at my kids.
____ They made me eat everything on my plate. Now I eat the plate, too.
____ Mom/dad was afraid of snakes, so am I.
____ They called me stupid. Now I call myself stupid.
____ They compared me to my sister/brother and I felt inferior. Now I compete with others.
____ My mother/father/caretaker had a lot of rules that ruled out everything in the long run. Now so do I.

If any of the above sound familiar, it means that you choose Mom and Dad's behavior to feel close to them. Take responsibility and choose to be like yourself! Affirm the following and cut the wrap.

AFFIRM SUCCESS: Cut the Wrap
I am like ME! I accept the fact that Mom, Dad, my caretakers and my family were just actors in the movie of my childhood. Their behaviors aren't my behaviors anymore. My thoughts and actions are of my own; I choose them, they are not the same or opposite Mom's or Dad's.

I'm my own perfect Mommy and Daddy, treating myself with respect, encouragement and support. I forgive. I am willing to grow and learn new ways to love myself.

▲ Reverse the Curse

"Reverse the Curse" is the flip side of "Like Mummy" and equally limiting. Not wanting to grow up like them, we do the opposite. To be the same or the opposite of mommy and daddy, still makes life all about mommy and daddy.

Photo by Jon Nicholas

Do You Reverse the Mummy Curse?

☆ *"If you don't stand for something, you'll fall for anything."*

—Bonnie Dean

I often say, think, and/or do:

____ I'll do most anything not to be like Mom, Dad or my caretaker.
____ They drank; I would not go near a drink if you paid me a million dollars.
____ They were never there for me, now I smother with love.
____ They screamed at me. Now, I ignore my kids.
____ They insisted that I eat everything on my plate. I show them, I won't eat at all.
____ They called me stupid. Now, I'm an overboard-super-achiever.
____ They made me feel insignificant. Now, I'm Mr. VIP.
____ They compared me to my sister. Now, I don't compete with anyone.
____ Mom was terrified of snakes, so I'm a rattlesnake trainer.

"Yes" to any of these statements, means you've programmed yourself to be the opposite of Mom and Dad. This is an attempt to feel close to them. Being the opposite keeps you as attached to them as being just like them. It's time to be yourself.

AFFIRM SUCCESS: Rewrap the Past

Affirm the following and rewrap your attitude:

I choose to be like ME. I accept the fact that Mom, Dad, my caretakers and family were just actors in the movie of my childhood. Their behaviors are not my behaviors.

I am perfectly myself. My behaviors are of my own choosing; not the same or opposite of Mom's or Dad's. My behavior is my behavior.

I'm my own perfect Mommy and Daddy. I treat myself with respect, encouragement and support. I forgive. I am willing to grow and learn new ways to love myself.

▲ Control Games

☆ *"Eyes the boss."*

—Dick Tator

☆ *Now I lay me down to sleep,*
a bag of peanuts by my feet.
If I should die before I wake,
Give them to my brother Jake."

Are You A Tie•rant?

☆ *"The only things worth learning are things you learn after you know it all."*
—Harry S. Truman

I often think, say, and/or do:

____ I control my environment and people in it with my systems, rules & beliefs.
____ I starve (or binge) because, finally, I do whatever I want with my body.
____ I go overboard.
____ I control others with an iron fist.
____ To cope with fear, I puppeteer.
____ I wake up surly in the morning; talk to me too soon I'll bite your head off.
____ I keep a tight grip to get a grip.

If you marked any three of these statements, you've learned to cope with uncertainty and out-of-control caretakers by attempting to control yourself and others in your world.

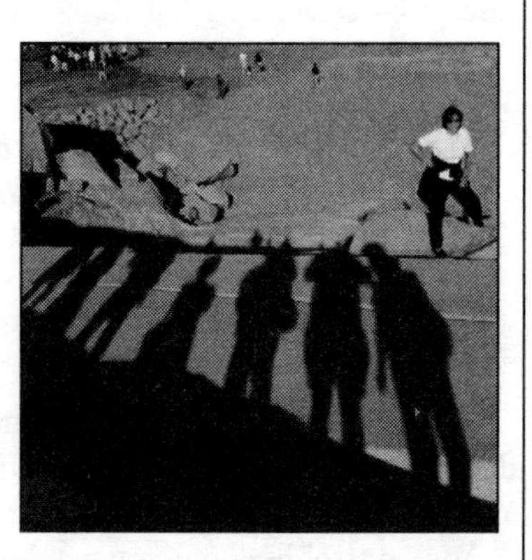

Photo by Jon Nicholas

As human, you try to control as much of your life as possible. The universe will let you know what you can or can't control. The serenity prayer is excellent for this dilemma;

"God grant me the serenity to accept the things I cannot change,
The courage to change the things I can
And the wisdom to know the difference."
Or
"God grant the serenity to accept the person I cannot change
To change the person I can
And the wisdom to know that it's me."

Who is responsible for your peace of mind?
You of course!
Who is responsible for another's peace of mind?
Gotcha!
It's not you again; *They* are!

Assist others when needed, give children well-defined rules and structure, and, for God's sake, stop trying to take their power. That makes them resentful and you lonely.

Almost every game we play attempts to control and exaggerates our instinctive pattern of dominance and submission. It's our attempt to control and cope with uncertainty and out-of-control situations. Controlling yourself is tough enough; controlling others is an impossible and exhausting game.

Say the following affirmation and get a grip on your joy:

AFFIRM SUCCESS: Bee a Honey
I hold everyone (except children) capable to run their own life. I empower myself and take response•ability for running my own life. I allow spontaneous fate to co-create exciting change and adventure.

What Can You Control?

☆ *The problem with living would be no problem at all*
If the brains I possess were possessed by you all.
—Cindy Lee Summerall

You can control *how you react* to others but you can't control others.

What can you control?

You control your thoughts and what you say to yourself. Your self-talk determines your beliefs and behavior. So ultimately, you control your behavior. You decide how you react to your emotions.

You control how old you act. You don't control your actual age, the calendar or the number of hours in the day. You control how your day is spent and how much time you spend on a particular project or activity.

You control what you do. You control your goals. You choose what action you will take or not take.

You can control how you drive your car but you cannot control whether the stoplight turns red or green or how fast the other cars drive. You can't control the spaced out driver in front of you. You can control how your react to the spaced out driver.

You can control whom you choose to hang out with. How do you soar like an eagle when surrounded by turkeys? You choose your friends.

You can control how you treat others and what you say to them. You control the words you use that impact your relationships with others. You control communicating your needs to others. You control how you raise your children.

You choose how much money you make and spend. You are in charge of the job you choose to do. You decide whether you stay or go in that job. (You don't usually choose if you get laid off or not).

You control your health by your diet, habits, sleep and attitudes. You choose whether or not to smoke, drink or take drugs. You control your exercise habits. You control how you react to illness and pain. (You cannot control another's health or death.)

You control how you live your life and fill your time. You choose the activities you do or don't do.

You book your own dance card.

▲ Gold Guilt

Are You Guilt Tripped?

☆ *Real gold does not fear even the hottest fire.*

____ My parents/mate/boss/myself manipulate and control with guilt trips?
____ My parents/mate/boss/myself make me feel ashamed of my actions and thoughts.
____ I often think or say to others "You should be ashamed of yourself."
____ I am and was shamed into doing what they wanted me to do.
____ I please so I won't disappoint or let them down?
____ "Shame on you" is an old familiar phrase.
____ I feel guilty for not doing a better job (not calling...)
____ I am a relentless judge, jury and jail warden who punishes myself for crimes I've committed?

If you answered yes to these questions you may suffer from feelings of guilt and shame. Well shame on you. *(See, it's contagious)*

You may feel guilt or shame for something you've done or not done.

Guilt and shame are based on rule breaking. If you go against rules laid upon you by somebody trying to control you, you may feel guilty. If you break your own rule and do something that goes against your conscience, (your innate ability to distinguish right from wrong) guilt follows also.

Shyness for example can be an outward sign of feeling bulldozed by someone's rules. A shy person may believe that asking for what they want is risky and too aggressive. They may "hold their tongue" for fear of saying the wrong thing.

If you do something you should not have done and fear being found out; your fear, turned inward, may change to guilt. Unexpressed guilt often leads to sadness and depression and, according to Louise Hay, cellulite. Sadness and depression often hide under the guise of guilt. If you want to bust this pattern affirm the following golden rules:

Photo by Jon Nicholas

AFFIRM SUCCESS: Golden Rules

I speak kindly to myself. I listen more to my heart than to rules. I live in the present. I live in the moment. I live honestly from my truth, ethics and heart. I am sensitive to my own feelings. I am in charge of my actions and reactions. I do not allow others to take responsibility for what I do or don't do. I listen to what others want for me and I MAKE MY OWN DECISIONS. I do what is best for my own growth and maturity.

I release all guilt trips from the past and present. I forgive those who guilt trip me. They are only trying to control me. God bless them. I forgive anyone who has been insensitive to me. What others think about me is none of my business. If I think I have been insensitive to another, I ask them. If I've hurt their feelings, I apologize and forgive myself. I NEVER guilt trip others. I am neutral about others. I am in charge of my emotions.

Ain't That A Shame Quiz

Are these phrases familiar?

____ "You're bad."
____ "It's all your fault."
____ "You little brat. You don't clean your room."
____ If only I got better grades.
____ "You act like nasty Uncle Fred."
____ "It's all your fault we have no money."
____ It might upset Mom/Dad.
____ "You could give Dad a heart attack."

Guilt is usually a response taught by someone who tries to control you. If these phrases are familiar, you have been manipulated by guilt and shame.

▲ The Shame Game: Nitchy, Nitchy.

Guilt is a control game that shackles you to the past. It is often a family tradition. Manipulators and guilt trippers put you to shame...and guilt…and try to make you responsible for another's consequences. Weak, easily hurt folks control with sighs.

Children shamed into doing what they don't want to do, are often depressed and angry. They learn to shut up and take responsibility for the craziness of the guilt tripper: "I love my Mommy. It must be my fault." "If only I got 100." "I'm bad that's why daddy hits me."

Over time, guilt-ridden children believe they are an awful person and punish themselves to feel better. A tip-off that you are under a guilt "spell" is if you think or use the words "guilt" or "shame" and/or beat yourself up with hostile self-talk, recriminations and self destructive action. If so, read the Pride Stride affirmation and take a giant stride into self-pride.

What To Do If Someone Guilt Trips You

Smile sweetly and say to the guilt tripper; "You are not trying to make me feel guilty are you?" And if they continue; "You're still not trying to make me feel guilty are you?"

AFFIRM SUCCESS: Pride Stride

I'm responsible for my joy. I chose to feel great. I free myself, I return to the present and who I am.

I ask myself "Whose problem is this anyway." I give any guilt trip back to the person who laid it on me. It's their problem, not mine. I forgive the insensitive. I forgive for my sake, so I feel better. I set them free, even if they abuse that freedom beyond exasperation. God bless the guilt tripper, they have to live with themselves.

If I have guilt tripped another, I forgive myself and ask them to forgive me. I speak my truth. I speak kindly to myself. I'm proud to be me.

▲ In•Turned

☆ Receptionist to Hypnotherapist: *"There is a man out here who says he's invisible."*
Hypnotherapist to Receptionist: *"Tell him I can't see him."*

Rather than cope with impossible situations outside of self, we save our life by withdrawing. This works well, until life seems stagnant. Anger feelings, TMJ, constipation, and ulcers are often internalized hurt needing to be released. Be keenly aware of your inner dialog and change limiting self-talk and behavior into positive affirmations and action. Read the following affirmation and express yourself:

Do You Shut Up?

☆ *"Who is it that is dragging this corpse around?"*
— Zen Koan

I often think, say, and/or do:

____ "If I get fat, he won't molest me again."
____ "If I go inside (lay low, shut up, be ideal, work hard), I won't get hurt again."
____ "If I stay helpless, maybe I'll be rescued."
____ "If I disassociate from my body and life, maybe I won't feel the pain again."
____ "If I have panic attacks, I won't have to go to work and fail."
____ Secretly, I'm very angry.
____ I shut up and shut down.
____ I started out with nothing and I still have most of it.
____ Mr. Cellophane, you can walk right by me, see right through me & never know my name.

Yes to any of these, means you've given up personal power to be close to the past. You've tried to make yourself disappear by withholding yourself from you and others. Be here now. The opposite of depression is expression.

AFFIRM SUCCESS: Dig It
I choose positive behavior. I claim joy and vitality in my life. I easily change any negative to positive. I stay aware. I express my truth and myself easily.

I do good, positive things for myself. I am awake. I seek out and enjoy others. I choose healthy people who are safe to talk with. I am natural, outgoing and spontaneous. I always tell myself the truth.

▲ Ashes to Asses

To right old wrongs and release trapped pain we sometimes turn our anger inward or strike out. Do you show them, or hurt and insult yourself? If so, you most likely insult, smack, rage and abuse others and yourself. Getting even or venting frustration, hurts you terribly. If you would like to break this gotcha game, rise from the ashes and affirm success.

AFFIRM SUCCESS: Phoenix
I now release behaviors that harm others. I now release me. I find positive ways to release buried frustration. I bash the heck out of a tennis ball, punch a pillow or sing at the top of my lungs. I know that all behavior is simply energy wishing to be released. I release energy in healthy ways.

Do You Show Them?

☆ Question: *"Did you come here to die?"*
Answer: *"No, I came here yester•die."*

I often think, say, and/or do:
____ "If I get sick, they'll be sorry."
____ "If I hurt myself, I'll show them."
____ "If I insult all women, I get even with Mom."
____ "If I insult all men, I get even with Dad."
____ "If I'm a nervous wreck, she'll know it's her fault."
____ "If I kill myself, she'll blame herself."
____ "I throw a tizzy and rage to get their attention.
____ "I can be very sarcastic."
____ "I am hard on myself and/or others."

Yes to any of these is your attempt to fill your needs that were not met long ago or to avenge a deep hurt.

▲ Drama-Deary

☆ Captain: *"What would you do if a sudden storm came on starboard?"*
Sailor: *"I'd throw out an anchor, Sir."*
Captain: *"What would you do if another storm sprang up aft?"*
Sailor: *"I'd throw out another anchor, Sir."*
Captain: *"What if a third storm sprang up forward?"*
Sailor: *"I'd throw out another anchor, Sir."*
Captain: *"Where are you getting all those anchors?*
Sailor: *"From the same place your getting all your storms, Sir."*

We re-create an original trauma that caused pain and despair, in a futile attempt to re-solve it. Unfortunately, repeating a past trauma in a present drama creates the same outcome. Oh, the frustration of repeating the same behavior, hoping that this time it will have a different outcome.

If you do that, in some crazy way, you're hoping to resolve problems. "Maybe this time, it will turn out right." Great idea…it just doesn't work.

Photo by Jon Nicholas

Is It Old Home Week, Again?

☆ *"If you always do what you've always done, you'll always get what you've always gotten."*

—Bernie Seigel

I often think, say, and do:

____ "Dad/Mom beat me, now my husband/wife does."
____ "Mom/Dad abandoned me, now everyone does."
____ "They put me down, now __________ does and I do.
____ "Mom/Dad made me eat everything on my plate, now my boss forces me to keep my desk clean."
____ "They didn't love me; nobody ever will."
____ I obsess about what happened before.
____ I relive old hurts, again and again.

If you marked any of these statements, you recreate an original trauma that caused pain and despair. You relive old hurts again and again, hoping that in some crazy way they'll get resolved this time. ("Maybe this time they'll change and love me.")

To quit the rerun of the same boring movie, affirm success and say yes:

AFFIRM SUCCESS: Yes-To-Day

I want to feel good all of the time. Others do themselves perfectly. I give up the myth that others will change. They are never going to change. No matter how many times I replay the scene, if I play my old part, 'they' will always play the flip side of my part. I stop playing the game.

I create a new movie. In it, I am my own perfect mommy, daddy, best friend, lover and cheering section. I am one hundred percent responsible for everything I create in my world. I choose joy. Joy is my compass. I live my life joyously in the here and now.

▲ Mule

One thing about being stubborn, you always know what you'll be thinking tomorrow. It's a lot more fun however to relax your death grip and enjoy new possibilities.

Are You A Stub-Born Mule?

☆ *"Unless you change your direction, you might wind up where you are going."* —Old Chinese proverb

I often hear myself saying or thinking: *(fill in the blanks)*

____ It's my way or the highway.
____ You can't teach an old dog new tricks.
____ I'm not stubborn. And that's final. I won't budge an inch on that one.
____ I must control the process to make it come out right.
____ Everyone wants to have it their way, when I know that my way is best.
____ Secretly, I'm stubborn and make sure that I get my way.
____ I ain't gonna do it and you cain't make me.

If any of these sounds like you, you've learned to cope with uncertainty by digging in your heels and not budging.

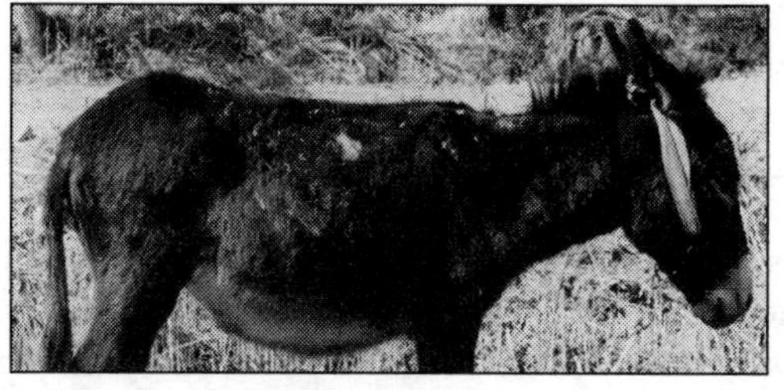

Photo by Joann Kelley

Read the following affirmation and you will get a fresh start:

AFFIRM SUCCESS: Re-Born
I gently ease up. I open my mind to new possibilities. The change is gonna do me good. I lighten up. I'm always learning new and better ways to think, act and react. Change is exciting. Life is dynamic. I'm an unfolding, developing personality. Each day is a new day. Each experience is a new experience. I am flexible. I have fun. I enjoy my tenacity. I am well balanced.

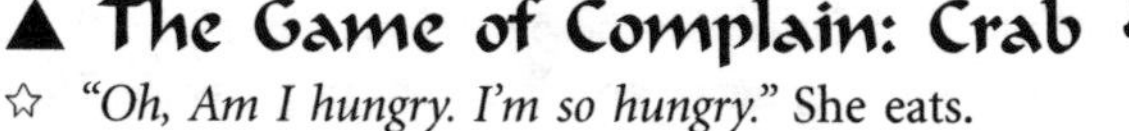

▲ The Game of Complain: Crab

☆ *"Oh, Am I hungry. I'm so hungry."* She eats.
"Oh, was I hungry, I was so hungry."

Complaining often engages people in conversation…for a while. Then it becomes boring. We usually learn to complain from our caretakers. If you get stuck in this trap your whole life can be a never-ending saga of doctor visits, "woe is me" and "ain't it awful."

Do You Play the Complain Game?

I often hear myself saying or thinking:

____ Every silver lining has a cloud.
____ Ain't it awful.
____ I'm so tired.
____ 'm so sleepy.
____ My hair is coming out by the handfuls, what should I do?
____ He never comes home on time.
____ School sucks.
____ Work sucks.
____ Life sucks.
____ I've got troubles, I've got worries, I've got my gal who could ask for anything more.
____ Oh, my aching bones.
____ Poor me.

Illustration by Shelley Stockwell

Sufferin' succotash! If you've heard these kinds of messages from yourself you've tuned into a painful victim game.

If Another Plays the Game of Complain

Don't get engaged in the game. Give them a hug. Say only once:

"It sounds like you're having a rough time," or offer a helping hand solution. Then notice their response. If they discount your ideas and continue playing *ain't it awful say*:

"You're wise. I'm sure you'll figure out what you need to do to be happy."

If they appear eager to negotiate a solution, jump right in, the game is over. If not, disengage from the downer; they are boring and depressing.

Here's how to break this negative pattern:

AFFIRM SUCCESS: Cut the Crab

I'm thankful that I have been able to complain. It proves I'm alive. Indeed everything in my life is miraculous. The fact, that I think, see, hear and speak are all part of the miracle of me. As I reflect on these precious gifts, I am filled with pleasure. I submerge every muscle, nerve and ligament in pleasure. How fortunate I am to be alive. I experience pleasure. I enjoy pleasing myself. I enjoy of celebrating my life.

It's a lot of fun to have positive exchanges. I now enjoy getting attention in more positive ways.

If something bothers me, I enjoy discovering why and enjoy creating positive solutions. I find creative solutions. I enjoy telling others what's on my mind so we can brainstorm solutions together. I listen to the ideas of others. If their advice is good for me, I take it.

My problems belong to me. My solutions belong to me. I don't wear others out with my problems. I enjoy overcoming challenges. I get attention from others and myself in positive ways.

▲ Blame Game ☞☞☞

☆ Question: *"Did you get the job as the radio announcer?"*
Answer: *"H-h-h-heck, n-n-n-o, th-th-th-ey wou-wou-wou-ldn't h-h-h-hire s-ss-someone f-f-f-f-rom Co-Co-Com-m-m-pton.*

☆ *"A specialist is someone brought in at the last minute to share the blame."*

Do You Palm it Off?

☆ *"Nobody can write your autobiography but you."*
—Helen Shaw

I often hear myself saying or thinking:

____ It's not my fault. (It's the computer, car, bus, etc.)
____ My secretary (boss, mate, kids...) screwed up.
____ I drink (eat, smoke, cry) because of...
____ If it wasn't for _______ I would have what I want.
____ I'm depraved because I was deprived.
____ I blame that SOB, but secretly blame myself.
____ "My darn shoe slipped on the step."
____ "I'm not late, the freeway was crowded."
____ "I yelled at you because I have a stomach ache..."
____ "It's not the kids fault, they "act out" because of the divorce.
____ "It's the fault of the Republicans (Democrats)."
____ "If it wasn't for you, I would have divorced your father/mother long ago."
____ "Because of you I had to divorce your father/mother."
____ "We'd get a divorce but no one wants the kids."
____ "It's the fault of evil spirits."
____ It's their fault I answered 'yes' on this quiz.
____ I have bad Karma.
____ I beat my kids because I was beaten.
____ God has forsaken me.

If you marked any of these statements, you've let the fickle finger of fate focus fallaciously. This kept the heat off of you.

Most people live life by default: "de fault ain't mine." Blame shifting is a cultural pastime. Drunks aren't drunks they have a "disease." Criminals aren't bad they have dysfunctional families.

The blame game takes the heat off us and holds others responsible for our attitudes and behaviors. We make others wrong to feel right. We make excuses. We point fingers.

Blame shifters have a harder time learning from their mistakes.

To be healthy, happy and centered, we need to take responsibility for what we do in our lives. True, some things are beyond our control. But how we react is within our power. Let the buck stop here and buck the blame game.

EXPLORE PAYOFFS

Use this exercise; shift happens:

1. Replay the scene where you blame another but this time pretend that you are the only one in power.

2. Ask yourself, "How did I create or contribute to the situation?"

3. Ask yourself, "What was my payoff in blaming them or circumstances?"

4. If you hadn't blamed, how would you tell yourself the same story? Then tell the story again without blame.

5. What did you learn from this scene?

6. Situations from the past gave you a gift. What is the gift? An insight? A strength? An awareness?

7. If the same circumstances happen again, what would you do differently?

AFFIRM SUCCESS: Response-Ability

I play 'The Game of Gift' and learn from every situation in my life. I take full responsibility for my behavior and actions. If I make a mistake, I honestly admit it. I notice what I learn and congratulate myself for taking charge of my life. If necessary, I apologize. I right wrongs. I honestly own up to the situation as my responsibility. I forgive myself. I am sensitive to others. I am sensitive to myself. I congratulate myself for growing in wisdom and responsibility.

▲ Gossip Column

☆ *They hover like flies as you tell them the scoop.*
Flies don't smell the stench when surrounding fresh poop.
With the skill of a surgeon you dissect each act:
Her demeanor, her boyfriend her complete lack of tact.
You're the most charged, the loudest, animated as hell
And they cluster and listen to the tales that you tell
You're the star of the show. Their ears stick like glue.
Until you're not around and they talk about you.

—Shelley Stockwell

Photo by Janus Welton

If your inner thoughts regularly criticize, judge yourself and others, or openly finger inadequacies, you may be a gossip addict.

Gossiping is a time consuming pastime. Like any addiction, gossip addicts get excited and may suffer withdrawal when no one wants to play anymore.

Do You Cluck?

☆ *"Flattery is like perfume. Smell it but never swallow it.*

—May Schwartz

I often think, say or do

____ I'm angry with you, so I'll tell everyone else rather than work it out.
____ Talk a little, pick a little, pick, pick, pick...
____ As I learn someone's inner most secrets they reward me to keep me quiet.
____ My sharp tongue sometimes cuts my own throat.
____ I bash men or women "They're all alike..."
____ I have special friends I gossip with.
____ I can't wait to call with the latest poop.
____ I spread rumors about other people.
____ I love scandals and digging the dirt.
____ I can be petty, punitive and unforgiving toward others.
____ I can be petty, punitive and unforgiving toward myself.
____ I feel guilty about some of the things I have said about others.
____ I can't keep confidential information confidential.
____ I start a sentence with "don't tell anybody..."
____ Let's have a family dinner and talk about those who didn't come.
____ I gossip about myself.

Do the faults of others seem like bright headlights on a passing car and more glaring than your own? If so, ask yourself, what is it about them that you dislike? Do their faults reflect an uncomfortable quality in yourself? Gossip is generally an unconscious, passive aggressive, attempt to distract yourself from handling your own limits. We project negativity outward in snipes and criticisms so we don't have to deal with our own stuff. The world is our mirror.

Some hide gossip behind humor, but no matter the style, gossip is generally another version of top dog/bottom dog and the Blame Game. Its payoffs make you a victim, bring sympathy and support and give a feeling of being powerful.

Some friendships are fault-finding based but usually, fatal flaw finding keeps you separate and alone. An acid tongue hurts or rejects before someone else hurts or rejects you.

Gossip not only reflects insecurities it makes you look bad. Researchers at Ohio State, Purdue and Indiana Universities say that ultimately, the characteristics you point out in another is spontaneously transferred back to you by the listener. If you call others cheap, you become thought of as cheap.

How do you feel when someone gossips about you?

When you give up gossip, life is much happier.

AFFIRM SUCCESS: Chicken Out
I hold my tongue. I'm secure. I speak kindly. Anything that is said, is said by my heart. I speak from the heart. I keep confidential information confidential. I say good things about myself and others. I celebrate the gifts of others. Here is a ditty to the pretty: "Wherever you are and what ever you do, I always love the look of you."

▲ Hippopotamus Game

☆ *"My little girl is so smart she walked when she was eight months old."*
"You call that intelligent? When my baby was eight months old, she let us carry her."
—Ard-Jan Dannenberg

Hippo game sounds like this:

"I've got a hippo in my backyard."

"I've got a hippo in my backyard and it weighs two tons."

"Mine weighs four tons and is green."

"Well mine won an Olympic gold medal...."

"Well my hippo can recite the Gettysburg Address."

This never-ending game of one-upsmanship is an unsuccessful attempt to feel "better than."

Do You Have A Hippo Hang Up?

☆ *"What do you get if you cross an elephant with a rhino?"*
"El-if-I-know"

I often think and say:
___ I'm big, you're little.
___ Mine's bigger than yours.
___ Mine's better than yours.
___ I am, you are not.
___ Anything you can do, I can do better.
___ I've upped mine, up yours.

If so, Hippo's got to go.

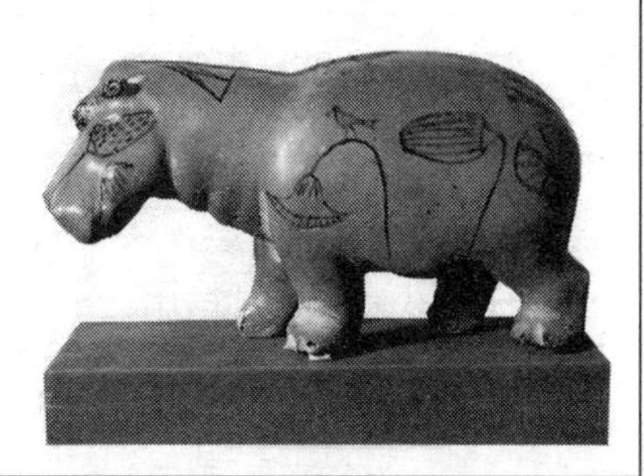

The Last-Worder

Another version of the hippo game in which the players engage in oral combat with "yeah-but..." with their last word signifying "Boy, did I show them."

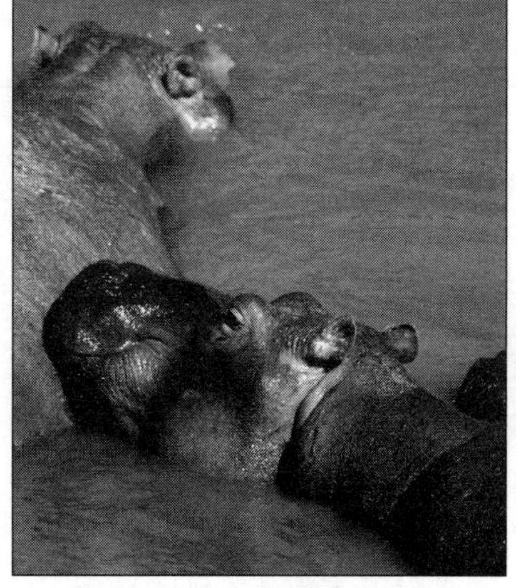

Photo by Neredah Bradstreet

If Another Plays Hippo:

Let them have the last word. Your response can simply be: "How nice, you have a hippo in your backyard!" "You may be right." Or say NOTHING and let them have the last word.

If you play these games use the following affirmation and you'll have the last word to let it go:

AFFIRM SUCCESS: Hip to Hippo
I value myself. I'm perfect just the way I am. I have nothing to prove. I am a growing and maturing person. Everyday in every way I find new ways to respect and honor my gifts, growth and potentials. I like it when I shine. I like it when other people shine.

▲ Big Banana Games: Top Banana, Bottom Banana

☆ *"It's not whether the glass is 1/2 full or 1/2 empty, It's that you got the biggest glass."*

—Jon Nicholas

Do You Play Top Banana?

I often think or say:
___ I know, you don't.
___ I'm right, you're wrong.
___ I'm smart, you are stupid.
___ I am king of the mountain.
___ I am, you're not.
___ I am not as judgmental as all you self-righteous sons of bitches.

If so, this trip has limited a-peel. It is an unsuccessful attempt to feel OK by making others less than. Slip out the back, Jack. Make a new plan, Man. No need to be coy, Roy, peel out of this game.

Top Banana

The top banana game can be played silently or out loud. Aloud it becomes the gossip game.

Bottom Banana

Do You Play Bottom Banana?

I often think, say or do:
___ Most people are much better than I am.
___ I'm just not good enough.
___ I won't win so why bother?
___ She's better looking, so I won't bother trying to get his attention.
___ There is too much competition to succeed.
___ I have an inferiority complex and low self-esteem.
___ I have been diagnosed with depression so I can't do it.
___ I can't be hypnotized, so why try?
___ I put myself down in my head or out loud
___ I'm a little person surrounded by all powerful big people.

Illustration by Shelley Stockwell

JUDGE-MENTAL

If you recognize yourself here, you are trying to prove to someone that they are right by making yourself wrong.

Such a game is a great way to lay back and not take responsibility for action. Often this game comes from the family trance that convinced us that everything in life is being taken care of by the all-knowing big people, parents, teachers, pastors, doctors, therapists, the mayor, the president, the government, scientists, movie stars, therapists and the ultimate big guy, God. Such a trance enables you to function in your social world, until "the pain is so great you feel nothing at all." Down trodden games becomes a tattered banner that keeps us lazy and not responsible. Competition (by not competing) is another reason for this game.

To give up banana games, read the following affirmation and let the words sink in:

AFFIRM SUCCESS: Re-Peel of the Top Banana Act
Slip into this affirmation. Take a deep breath and ask yourself,
"What is it that I want or need right now?"
"What is it that I'm not getting?" I now find a healthy way to get it.

I ask for what I really want. I give myself what I want. I love to give myself what I want.

I forgive others for mistakes they've made and I say good, kind and loving things to and about them. I look upon them with "soft eyes." I forgive them for me. It makes me feel so relieved not to release resentment. I forgive myself for any mistakes I've made and I say good, kind, and loving things to and about myself. I look upon myself with soft eyes.

I am my best; no contest. I am a perfect, brilliant, beautiful/handsome, magnificent being of light. I am learning and maturing. I'm my best.

▲ Know-It-All and Braggart

☆ *"Do you think I'm conceited?"*
"No, why do you ask?"
"Because most people as gorgeous as I am usually are."

Know-it-alls and braggarts try to impress you with their knowledge and accomplishments. These characters want recognition to help them deal with a need to be recognized.

Lost in the shuffle at home, school or life, they starve for

Photo by Jon Nicholas

attention. They usually say things like: "Enough about me. Tell me what do you think about the nice job I did building this house (playing the game, choosing my clothes…)"

If You Play Know-It-All: Write a book, take up public speaking, join a discussion group, go into counseling or take up singing. Toot your horn where people are interested in your music; you'll feel much better.

If Another Plays Know-It-All: Let them bring and brag, share and spout off…if you can. Many know-it-alls just need to be heard so that they can get off it. If the game is chronic and doesn't stop, it's so boring!

▲ Garbage Bag Game

This game is a silent victim game until the end.

In your head you say: "You did this bad thing to me, but I won't say anything, I'll just take it and throw it here in my gunny sack."

"Oh, oh, you just did another bad thing, but I won't say anything again. I'll just throw it in my gunny sack... etc."

Sacked and Trashed

It's in the bag. Somewhere down the line, when the sack is full, you dump your resentment bag on your offender's head and say, "You SOB!" Then you bring up out of the bag all the past hurts, wounds and violations.

Communicate before your garbage bag builds and bulges. Or bring it to the curb for the trash truck to carry off and recycle.

To clean up your act, read the following Affirmation:

AFFIRM SUCCESS: Daily Clean Up for Gunny Sackers
I speak my truth. I communicate what bothers me as it happens. I notice what I think and feel. I communicate clearly and kindly about how I feel or what I think, as soon as I notice. I'm direct. I tell others if what they did hurt. I am willing to hear what they have to say. When I say how I feel, I feel better. I express my feelings with ease and honesty. I say, "When you did _______, I felt ________."

If it's not appropriate to express my truth out loud, I pretend I'm looking through the back end of a pair of binoculars. I see the obnoxious person several thousand miles away. I detach, take a deep breath and do something else. I am friendly and frank.

▲ Distorted Mirror Game

We create self-fulfilling prophecies by projecting our beliefs upon the world. If you tell someone: "You don't love me (anymore)," eventually, you'll be correct. If you tell another: "You can't be trusted," eventually, you'll be correct. If you tell them: "You're going to leave me. You're glad we're apart." Eventually, you'll be right. If you tell yourself: "People hurt me," you're correct. If you tell yourself, "Men/women are impossible to get along with," you'll be right. Here is the way to make your world a happier place:

AFFIRM SUCCESS: Positive Reflection
I allow the world to mirror my beauty, love and kindness. I see the beauty in others. I ask for positive results in all situations. I trust the goodness in others and myself."

▲ Coulda, Woulda, Shoulda Game

Do You Should On Yourself?

___ I should have studied more (tried harder.)
___ I'll try to come.
___ If I could make more money then I would save more money.
___ I would if I could. I could if I would.
___ I can't do it. It's too heavy. I'm too tired.
___ If I coulda slept more
___ I could have done it.
___ If only there was less traffic; I would have been on time.
___ I'm fixin' to do it.

Words like "kind of," "sort of," "I'm not sure," "I'll try," and "would of," "could of," should of," are nonproductive and make you feel terrible. Change your words and you positively change your mind.

Take back your power and affirm success:

AFFIRM SUCCESS: No "Should"Game, No Pain
I stop "shoulding" on myself. As I change my words, I change my mind.
I change "I'll try" to "I will" or "I won't." "I choose" to "I choose not to." I change "Woulda, coulda, shoulda" to "I did," "It was," and "Oh well." The change is a relief.

▲ Never-Always Game

Players of this game use sweeping generalities. Does someone you know always do that? Never!

This game limits possibilities. Of course, we don't want to make the same mistakes twice, so often we vow "never again." Often used as an excuse, the never/always game disempowers your freedom of choice.

The problem with narrowing your scope with such finalities is that you assume that there is only one potential outcome. When you widen your scope, you discover an unlimited range of possibilities, choices and outcomes.

Do You Play Never/Always

☆ *"I've told you a million times not to exaggerate."*

___ I'll never get married (again).
___ Nobody ever cares about me.
___ I'll never fall in love again.
___ I'll never get into a long distance relationship again.
___ I'm always going to be fat.
___ You're always late.
___ I never get it right.
___ I've always been terrible at math.
___ I always get the short end of the stick.
___ I never get what I need.
___ Nice guys always finish last.
___ "How come you never?"
___ "How Come You Always?"

AFFIRM SUCCESS: Shades of Gray
I enjoy the subtleties of life. I open to unlimited possibilities. I enjoy and experience each moment as a new moment. I am open to the now and all its surprises. I am an artist of life. Because I'm aware of my thoughts and self-talk, I say "Cancel, Cancel" to any limiting word. I immediately replace limits with unlimited possibilities. I am an unlimited human in unlimited moments of now.

▲ Won't Leave Me Salome: They All Come On To Me

☆ *"Did you tell them how pretty I was?"*
"No, how pretty were you?"

—Linda Eisenbart

Do You Play "Come Here, Go Way?

___ Everyone comes on to me.
___ I do one to others before they do one to me.
___ I'm the babe/hunk, gotta love me.
___ They can't keep their eyes off of me.
___ Come here, go away.
___ My lips tell you "yes, yes" but there is "no, no" in my mind.

If you do, manipulation is true, and is happening to you. Your double message is a hurtful way to get attention and vent hurt...usually at a parent who hurt you long ago.

Do you wear fetching clothes, stick out your chest, swing your rump, use sexual innuendoes, dirty jokes, pat or rub or touch others excessively? And then, when they come on to you, say to your friends or yourself:

"I'm amazed. Men/women always come on to me. I can't understand it."

"Men/women are like fleas. I just have to slap them off."

The seduction game is a power trip that veils anger, insecurity and a desire to control others. It hurts you and others. The temporary ego rush is always burdened by an awful feeling that you are lying to yourself and others. Here's the affirmation to change this game:

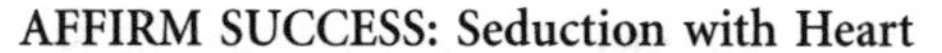

AFFIRM SUCCESS: Seduction with Heart

I only play the seduction game if I mean business. Seducing just to notch my bedpost or count my conquests isn't any fun. I'm comfortable with myself. I'm attractive and desirable. I no longer hurt myself and others. I enjoy feeling well. I now carefully select who and what I draw to my life. I put out my sexual beam when I'm interested and available for real relationships. Otherwise, I put my energy into more rewarding and productive efforts. I get attention in positive ways. Joy and peace turn me on.

▲ Leave Me Salome: No One Comes On To Me

☆ Question: *"Why did the raisin go out with the prune?"*
Answer: *"He couldn't find a date."*

An upside down seduction game is a control trip that says: "Off with my head!"

If anyone shows interest in you, you immediately turn them off. If you don't bother to groom yourself, make no eye contact, your posture is pathetic and you hold yourself away from others, you may be playing this game. Its purpose is to avoid the very thing it creates; loneliness, hurt and rejection.

Use this affirmation to change the game:

AFFIRM SUCCESS: Attracting Love

I enjoy the company of my brothers and sisters. I stop playing "them and us," and view every human being as a precious individual with feelings and needs just like my own. I am proud to be me. I like looking and feeling my best. I stand tall. I am open to receive a lot. I like others and they like me. I enjoy looking at myself in the mirror. I love being clean and well groomed. It shows me how proud I am to be alive. I easily attract into my life a loving mate.

▲ Salome Again Game

☆ *As I was letting down my hair,*
I met a guy who didn't care;
He didn't care again today—
I love 'em when they get that way!
—Hughes Mearns

☆ She: *"Does everyone here hate me?"*
He: *"No. There are people here who don't even know you."*
—Steve Bhaerman

Photo by Jon Nicholas

If you think you are destined to always be alone; you're correct. The Alone Again Game is played to re-experience disappointment and abandonment. Set 'em up, so they can let you down. When playing "Alone Again" we choose unavailable people and are shattered because they let us down.

"I'll reject you before you reject me" is another form of this game.

Of course you want love in your life! Use this affirmation and you will manifest love:

Are You a Lonesome Dove?

☆ *"Suppose they threw a war*
and nobody came?"
—Unknown Soldier

Photo by Jon Nicholas

I often think, feel and do.
___ What's wrong with me?
___ I guess I was meant to be alone.
___ Guys/Gals always dump on you.
___ Dumped and dumped on again.
___ I was used and abused.
___ Nice guys finish last.
___ Nobody likes me. Everybody hates me. Guess I'll eat some worms.
___ There is always something wrong with guys/gals.

If this sounds like you, change the "victim" written on your forehead to "victor."

AFFIRM SUCCESS: I'm Open to Love
I actively pursue loving relationships with others. If I don't know what a healthy loving relationship is, I find out. I am loveable. Everyday, in every way, I learn better ways to love myself and others.

▲ Flock You

Are Your Decisions Majority Ruled?

☆ Judge to jury: *"If that be your verdict, so say you all."*
Jury: *"You all."*

I often think, say or do:
___ "Don't you think she is boring?"
___ "Do you think I should call my sister today after she did that to me?"
___ "Should I stay with my husband or leave?"
___ "Let me ask your opinion. And yours and yours..."
___ "My friends think that I should move to _______. What do you think?"
Yes to these means that you may take votes rather than responsibility for your own behavior, attitude, decision or feelings.

Any decision is ultimately your own. God invented counselors and best friends to assist you to embrace different, helpful, perspectives. Hearing their ideas helps us.

Yet, most chronic vote takers don't usually gather opinions to honor advice. For them, votes let them off the hook if their decisions don't pan out. Vote gathering can be a way to initiate a co-dependent relationship. Some collect votes as a passive/aggressive way to gossip, berate and make someone wrong so they can be right.

Photo by Stan Hillis

If your decisions are solely based on votes, use this strategy instead:
1. Write down your choices and options.
2. What are the positive and negatives attributes from each one?
3. Weigh these attributes.
4. If you're still stuck, go to someone you respect and tell them what you've been thinking. If you ask advice always consider the source. Like the song says: "He can't even run his own life, I'll be damned if he runs mine."
5. Listen to what they have to say and then...
6. YOU decide. It is YOUR life.

AFFIRM SUCCESS: Trust Builder
I'm confident in my decision-making and happy with the outcome. I'm grown up. I play "mother may I" with myself. I tell myself YES. I'm responsible for my feelings, responses, decisions and behavior. I accept the consequences of my feelings, responses, decisions and behavior. I ask for other's opinions if they are a good role model. I consider the source. I make my own decisions. I take responsibility for my behavior, attitudes and feelings. I am in charge of my life and my choices. Once I decide, I only look forward.

▲ Vampire Games

☆ *Psychic vampires talk to themselves*
And hook you in their game
Of "poor me," "gotcha," "gimme some"
And it's really quite a shame.
For underneath their record stuck
Dwells a sacred soul
But I will not be suck-ered in.
I'm in charge, I'm in control.

—Shelley Stockwell

Are You an Energy Suck?

☆ *"A gossip talks to you about others, a bore talks to you about himself and a brilliant conversationalist talks to you about yourself and then listens to your reply."* —John L Mason

___ I talk just to talk?
___ I talk to myself while someone else is supposedly talking with me?
___ I always think about how I'll answer rather than listen.
___ I compulsively interrupt.
___ Sometimes I don't hear a word I say.
___ Sometimes I do not hear a word you say.
___ I tend to be blunt and critical.
___ I am self absorbed and needy.
___ I have difficulty keeping friends.
___ I take more from my friends than I give.
___ I tend to wear friends out.
___ I sometimes get obsessed over someone and just can't leave them alone.

If you answered yes to any of these you need to come out of your self absorption and listen to the words and needs of others.

Are You Being Eaten by a Psychic Vampire?

Vampire relationships are based on your giving and their taking. Is someone's slicing tongue or motor mouth sucking you dry? You may not notice you've been vampired at the time but afterwards, you feel drained, headachy, with a vague feeling, "I've been had."

If you work hard emotionally and nothing comes back, you've been vamped. If the kinder you are, the greedier the suck becomes, watch out! There lurks a psychic vampire. Psychic Vampires play variations on the theme: Crisis Criers, Broken Record, Sniper, Stalker and Yada, Yada, Yada.

Avoid vampires unless they change their tune; they are too exhausting and hurtful. If you are enjoying being vamped beware of your own co-dependency.

If you are trapped with a Vamp, tell them the truth, the whole truth and nothing but the truth. Say something like: "When you obsess, I get bored/exhausted/lonely and my mind drifts off. You wear me out."

If you want to encourage them and continue in relationship say: "If you want to have a relationship with me, you need to be sensitive to my needs. My needs are just as important as yours. Otherwise, I won't hang out with you any more."

Make sure that you always have a fast escape route. The last thing you want is a three-day car trip with a vampire. If you are trapped by a suck, remove yourself mentally from their auric field. Think about a beautiful place or a beautiful moment in time.

If one corners you at a party, try these exit lines:

"Bye for now, I need to circulate (or talk to my friend Suzie) now,"

"Look a fox (and walk away)!"

"Excuse me, I have to call my husband (wife, stockbroker, babysitter)"

"Bless you."

"Gotta move on, I think you'd enjoy talking with Joe (point out some other victim) over there."

Crisis Crier

☆ *"Help, I can't swim."*
"Why?"
"I'm not in the water."

Ask a Crisis Crier: "How are you?" and you'll hear an hour-long dissertation about their latest drama, capped off with: "To make a long story short" or "Enough about me, how are you?" And "What do you think about that?" And before you can answer: "What you just said reminds me of this terrible thing that happened to me..."

A sneaky version of the Crisis Crier is the whiner.

Broken Record

No matter what the situation or conversation, the broken-record suck comes back to the same old story, played it in three-part disharmony.

How many times have you heard the story of that "Son-Of-A-Bitch?" or what "So-in-So did!" or "Oh, my papa?"

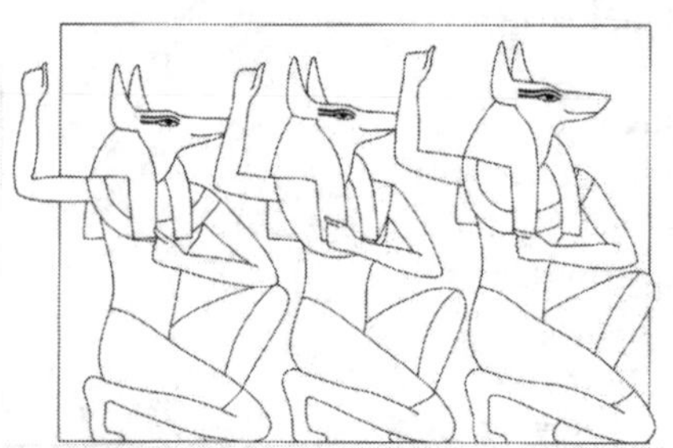

With someone like this, you need to set limits by saying: "I don't want to hear about your ______ story today. If you'd like to talk about something pleasant, I'll meet you for lunch."

If you are a broken record player, set limits for yourself. Limit your comments to one minute or don't bring it up at all.

Sniper

Sniper-Vampires criticize, so you agonize. They know exactly which buttons to push to create resentment. They love pointing out how you don't give them what they need. Give one a lovely blue shirt for their birthday, they might say: "You were a week late for my birthday, your wrapping paper looked recycled and you know I don't like blue;" leaving you to apologize for your insensitivity.

Try this response: "It's not OK for you to talk to me that way." Or "I'll show you how insensitive I am, take a hike." or "I went to a lot of trouble to do this for you and a nice person would say thank you and appreciated it."

Some snipes love to get you in public to let you have it. The pit bull at work that waits to nail you in a board meeting with: "Well, Miss Three-Hour Lunch, what makes you an authority?" This can be devastating if you let it. Try this response: "You appear to be upset and that may be clouding your perspective on this subject."

If you are the sniper, stop it. Graciously say "thank you" and turn in your sharp tongue.

Stalker

Someone tailing another is obsessed and will go to all lengths to hound and surround. The one they stalk fits into their movie as a key player.

Stalkers may bombard you with gifts or hatefully attack and troublemaking. They can be blatant or anonymous.

A True Story: Terri

Terri is an attractive woman in her mid forties who works for her city.

She confided in a neighbor the details of her nasty break-up with her boyfriend. She reported the words that they had said and how they had broken up.

When Terri made up with her beau, the neighbor began an anonymous poisonous letter writing campaign and a barrage of telephone calls. "How can you take back that horrible foul man after he called you a c—t." She called Terri's relatives, friends and neighbors to rant and rave.

After 2 months of harassment, the police put a tap on Terri's phone line and identified the culprit. She was prosecuted and charged with stalking and fined $1000.

If you are being stalked tell them in no uncertain terms to leave you alone. Call the police and ask them how to get a restraining order if they don't back off. Drugs and alcohol can exacerbate a stalkers fear, aggression and paranoia. This case study of Skip tells a typical stalker story:

A True Story: Skip

Skip age 25 and his 23-year-old girlfriend used crack and hash together. His girlfriend's father intervened and insisted that she stay home and not see Skip anymore.

Skip went bonkers and stalked her day and night. He broke into her office at work and drove his car across her lawn into her bedroom wall. He was arrested, sent to jail for two weeks and then into a rehab program. After 9 months, he was released clean and sober.

Bets was Skip's next lady friend. She was a quiet girl who looked like Doris Day. They lived together for 5 months. He got violent and broke her jaw. She filed a police report that was dismissed because she had hit him also. He moved out and then followed her everywhere. She got a restraining order against him.

He then met Libby. They used drugs together for a year. During that time, they had hitting fights. He want to jail again for domestic violence. When they broke up she followed him, broke into his car to sleep and kicked down the front door to his house. He now attends weekly Domestic Violence and Narcotics Anonymous meetings and got a restraining order against Libby's harassment.

Yada, Yada, Yada

Do You Play Yada Yada?

Yada, Yada, Yada Version #1:
"What do you think I should do?"
"Whatever."
"Oh thank you, thank you, thank you."

Yada, Yada, Yada Version #2:
"What do you think I should do?"
"Whatever."
"That's not true, it's this way. What do you think I should do?"

Yada, Yada, Yada Version #3:
"What do you think I should do?"
"Whatever."
(They ignore whatever you say and keep talking.) Yada, Yada, Yada."

If these games sound familiar, you are a non-communicator, on a one way street that echoes only the sound of your own voice.

If you obsess about the past, you bore others and bore yourself. Practice listening more. Otherwise you'll be as lonely as a pork chop at a Jewish wedding.

Your job is to fill your own needs. No one else can do that for you.

Read the following affirmation and end the game of energy taker:

AFFIRM SUCCESS: Silence Is Golden

I live my life in each moment of now. I do whatever it takes to change limiting, boring habits into new habits that are fun and exciting. I talk about pleasant things. It's fun to be around me because I'm having fun. I keep clear and defined boundaries between myself and others. I enjoy my own company. And, I enjoy listening to my friends."

I give myself time to think, to listen and to learn. I am a keen observer of myself and others. If I need to express myself, I get involved in Toastmasters or discussion groups. I write down my thoughts. I take a writing class. I spend 90% of my conversation listening and 10% talking. Communication is a give and take experience. I listen from the heart.

I choose to be nourishing. I commit to hang around only with nourishing people. Sucks, are toxic and only talk to themselves. The best advice I can give myself is that if a relationship is not fun, I cut bait and find a better one. I'm no longer the sucker at the end of the line.

I chose to have a relationship with someone other than myself. I am supportive. I am a nourishing listener. I enjoy the give and take of conversation. I am a great listener. I listen and hear. I listen to what I say. Is what I say nourishing, valuable and loving? I enjoy and allow silence in conversation.

▲ Reminds Me Of...Game

Once Again for the Very First Time

___ Everything I see remind me of something else I once saw.
___ Everything I hear reminds me of the past.
___ When you talk I take out my to do list and think about what I have to do next.
___ "You remind me of..."
___ "You look just like..."
___ "Tomorrow, I'll..."

If you play this game, you never live in the now, everything is either past or future-tense.

AFFIRM SUCCESS: Here, Here
I am present. I enjoy the now. I stay conscious, awake and alert. I easily listen to others without adding my story. It is safe in my world.

▲ Fan Game

In the Fan Game, the victim stands below a spinning fan. When the sh__ hits the fan and they are well splattered, they point to a clean place on themselves and say: "You missed a spot."

Fan folks rush around being all things to all people. They meet everyone else's needs but their own. Usually, this results in their feeling like a doormat and resenting it. Those they wait on hand and foot usually feel uncomfortable and smothered.

AFFIRM SUCCESS: Clean Up Your Act
I choose joy. I create healthy relationships. I know when to get away from icky situations. I support others to solve their own problems.

▲ Worry Wart Game

☆ THE GHOST

Listen—there it goes again! Hear it?
Should I investigate, or not go near it?
The bumps, the knocks, the squeaks. What's the source?
My imagination's running wild, of course.
Under covers, I am shaking
Eyes are closed, but I am faking
How I want to slumber sweet.
If only I could move my feet!
But I lay frozen heart skipping beats
'til early light in the window creeps
Then cautiously I go,
Ready to confront my foe
The apparition disappeared
The only "spirit"- my own fear.

—Charmaine Bice

What Me Worry?

___ I'm afraid something bad is going to happen.
___ A catastrophe can strike at any time.
___ I worry a lot about being assaulted
___ I worry that I am sick and don't know it.
___ I have anxiety attacks.
___ I'm afraid I'll lose control.
___ I feel helpless.
___ I worry a lot about __________.
___ I worry when I'm having fun that the "other shoe will drop.'
___ I worry about worrying.
___ I worry that I am fat/thin.
___ Poor Me, I worry about money.
___ I'm depressed about money.
___ Why waste time reliving the past, I can spend it worrying about the future.
___ Why waste time worrying about the future, I can fret about the past.
___ If I lose my grip on money, I lose my grip on my only security.
___ I worry about others.
___ I worry about the past or the new millennium.
___ I worry about sin and sinners.
___ I worry about spirit attachments/ germs/ pollution/aliens…
___ I worry out loud so others can console me.
___ I worry about what I should or shouldn't do.

Queen Tyi

If you play the worry game, you never live in the now, you are creating negative self-fulfilling reality.

Is worrying a full-time recreational activity for you?

If so, what you worry about is not the least bit important. Worry always derives from misreading reality. When you worry, your distorted perception makes you jump to the worst possible conclusion.

You dream up any situation to ruminate about. Worrying exaggerates the likelihood of catastrophe. What are the odds of a bad thing happening? Really?

Worrywarts are highly creative people or they wouldn't find such a myriad of things to worry about: being too fat, too slim, too poor, what others are doing or not doing. The list goes on and on.

Why Worry?

☆ *"Worry is a thin stream of fear trickling through the mind. If encouraged, it cuts a channel into which all other thoughts are drained."*

—Arthur Somers Roche

Worry creates an arousal that many find comforting or pleasant. Then it becomes a habit. Like any habit, you can change it for a better habit.

Worry attempts to make things come out your way. You behave as if you had control over something you cannot control. But as much as you worry, fretting never solves problems. If anything, it creates problems. The only thing you can control are your thoughts.

Worry gives you the illusion that you are doing *something*. It's a time filler that takes up mental energy.

If you worry about yourself, you get to prove that you are a weak and powerless victim. If you worry about others, it becomes a diversionary tactic that takes the heat off yourself. If you worry out loud to another, it becomes a way to get attention. Some relationships are entirely based on "helping" a worrier not to worry.

Far from a release, worry causes and builds tension in the body and robs you of living your life in the present. If you take the same energy and put it towards positive action, you feel great. Worry certainly doesn't solve problems. It creates problems. Don't worry. I've tried it many times and it doesn't work. You can't worry about life forever.

Pray Tell

Some worrywarts specialize in worry prayer. Praying constantly to protect themselves from some unknown catastrophe or cutting the "cords" of mythical negative forces.

Money Worries

The way you think about money is symbolic about the way you think about yourself. Abundance begins with an abundance mentality expressed in positive action.

Where Do We Learn to Worry?

Most worriers are schooled in the art of fretting. Were you trained to fret?

Does worry remind you of someone you grew up with? Did one of your parents worry? Some worry is an attempt to be close to worried parents.

Have you trained your children to worry? Excessive “Be careful, Dear” translates into “Life is dangerous.” Why not send children into the day with a “Be careFREE, Dear?”

Stop Worrying

If you begin to fret, rank the events that bother you in order of severity and assess their probability of happening. Review your list a few weeks later for a reality check. You’ll see that most worries are imagined, hypothetical thoughts only. Stop asking friends and family for reassurance, you wear them out.

AFFIRM SUCCESS: **Don’t Worry. Be Happy.**

I am realistic. This moment is the only truth. I live in this moment and make positive choices about what and how I think. The future is made up of possibilities that change instantly with my positive thoughts. I deliberately direct my mind to pleasant activity. I get out of my chair and walk around, pet the cat, hug someone, wash the dishes, talk with a friend or think of something else to do besides worry. Sing “pack up your troubles in your old kit bag and smile, smile, smile.” Or sing “Don’t worry, be happy.”

Worry shows a creative mind. I now turn my creative mind toward interesting pursuits. Drawing, painting, building, designing, writing, sculpting or making positive plans put me in the driver’s seat. I thoroughly engage myself in things that I enjoy.

If my mind goes back to an old pattern, I say to myself “enough!’ and I think of new ways to move forward in my life. I move my body, make new plans and get a life. If I learned to worry from someone else, I give this pattern back to him or her. It’s theirs. I don’t want it and I don’t need it.

I choose to enjoy my life. Nix on the News. I only listen to, read and watch pleasant things.

Illustration by Shelley Stockwell

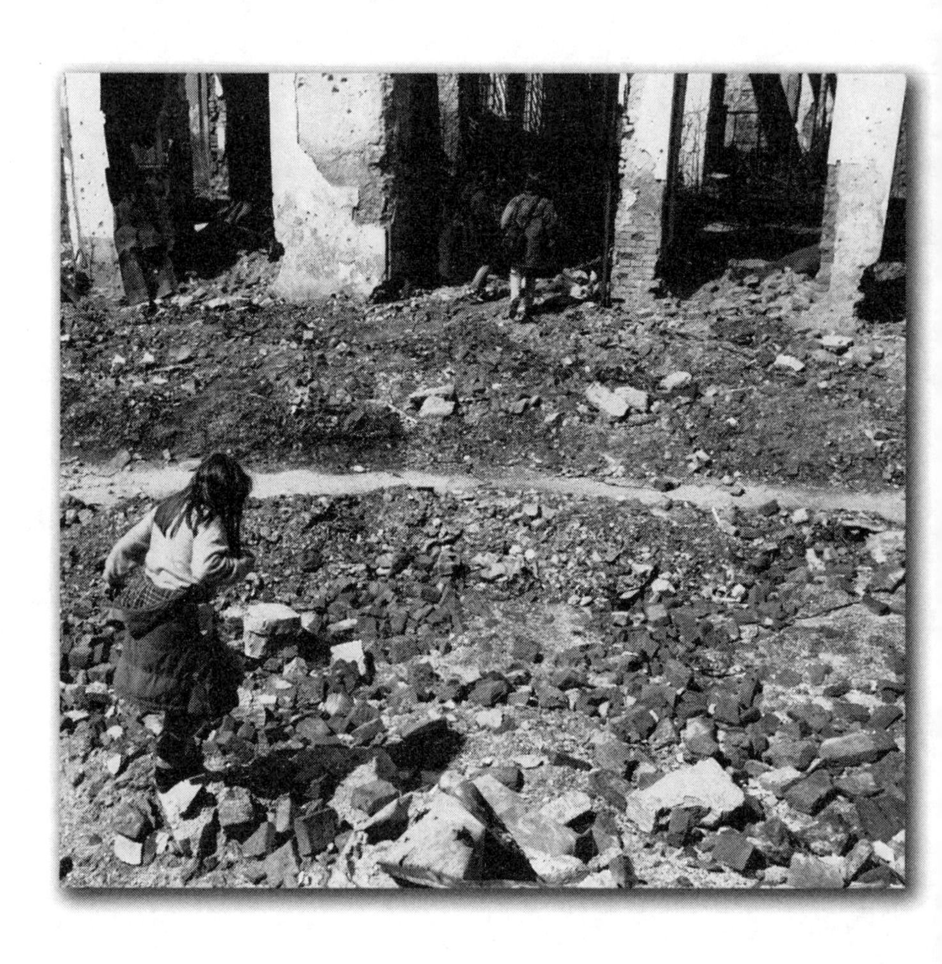

Step Five

Down & Dirty:

Nitty Gritty City

How to Conquer Specific Problems

☆ Question: *"What makes your problems worse than everyone else's?*
Answer: *"They're MINE."*

The Following chapters deal with specific problems and their solutions:

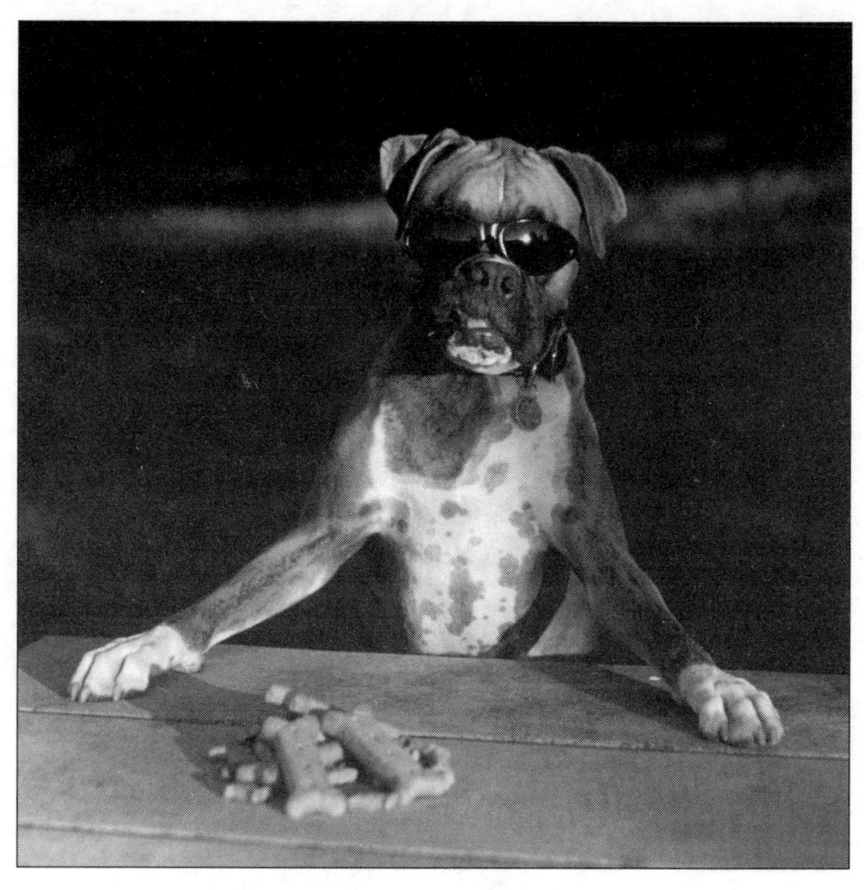

Chow Hound

Chapter 21

Eating Disorders:

Feast or Famine

You need food to live. Food is fuel that gives energy to do the things you enjoy; breathing, playing, sex, creativity, and being successful. This chapter explores eating patterns and how to get a grip on your patterns. Being your perfect shape gives you confidence and more energy.

My book Stockwell's Hypnosis For Weight Control: Ten Easy Steps To a New You and related audio tapes found in the resources section of this book offer more helpful tools.

▲ Modern Mandates
▲ What You Weigh Is BIG Business
▲ The Plot Thickens: Stress, Drugs and Alcohol
▲ There Are Reasons and Results
▲ What's Wrong with "Diets" Anyway
▲ Body Image
▲ Eating Is Done In Your Head
▲ How Do You Get Fat, Anyway?
▲ Overstuffed or Starving: Both Ends of the Scale
▲ How to Get a Grip on Yourself
▲ Oil of Old Age

☆ *Mary had a little lamb*
Some lobster and some prunes
A glass of milk, a piece of pie
And, then some macaroons.
It made the naughty waiters grin
To see her order so
And when they carried Mary out
Her face was white as snow.

Eating Patterns: Feast or Famine

Are You Starving At Life's Banquet Table?

Snack Brigade:
Eat and run. No time to sit
Grab and chomp. I munch a bit.

Emotional Eater:
I eat or starve when I'm upset.
That's my consolation.
for the ways you've hurt me,
I soothe aggravation.

Lay Away Plan:
I didn't eat all day,
And gorge the night away.

Party Animal:
I'm a human vacuum cleaner,
I suck up petit fours,
and always drink another beer,
that my buddy pours.
I like to order lavish.
Seconds are my thing.
Aunt Tilly has me over,
'cause I eat everything.

Rapid Transit
Food enters like a high speed train
Run by patterns in my brain.
I taste nothing, in a fog
And I become a travel log.

Clean Plate Brigade:
For all the kids in China,
I lick my platter clean.
Wasting not goes to my waist.
I'm on the good boy team.

Sneak Attack:
What they don't see can't hurt me.
Happened? It never did.
That little bite,
in the middle of the night,
Or the candy wrappers I hid.

Gourmand:
The world's a lazy Susan.
My palette is refined.
My self worth is determined
By truffles and fine wine.

Model Citizen:
Twiggy puts me on a limb
How I'm dying to be thin.

Roman Holiday:
I look good in public,
while dining I'm refined,
then pad off to the restroom,
Or barf until I'm blind.

Consolation Prize
I deserve a little fun
Eating makes me giddy.
When I receive my just rewards
I pork up, what a pity.

INNER•VIEW QUIZ

Are You Consumed by Eating?

☆ *"If food is the answer, what is the question?"* —Adele Boreman

Honestly mark the statements that are true for you.

___I'm living beyond my seams. I hang something in the closet and it shrinks two sizes.
___I'm on a see-food diet: I see it, I eat it. Then, I can't believe I ate the whole thing.
___I'm out-of-control with eating or not eating.
___Eating or not eating makes me high.
___I eat half of what I prepare before I serve it.
___I eat until I feel uncomfortable and I have food hangovers.
___I'm an emotional eater.
___I eat when I'm not hungry.
___I use food as a reward.
___Certain foods send me off into the wild blue yonder of eating.
___Celebrations are food orgies where I'm more stuffed than the turkey.
___I eat when I'm blue, and hate myself when I'm through?
___I trick myself by buying "lite" food and then eat twice as much?
___To lose weight, I might skip meat and eat salad drowned in dressing?
___As a snack, I order the Godzilla size from the fast food take-out window?
___I throw out the apple and eat the dessert.
___I dine on packaged snacks from vending machines.
___I lie, sneak-eat and hide food: If no one else sees or knows, it didn't happen.
___I eat sensibly in front of others, then make up for it alone.
___I eat faster than other people.
___I say, "I'm in control, because I pour the fat off my pork chops."
___Soft drinks are my "thirst quencher" and I ignore their caloric blitz?
___I call myself "pleasantly plump," then avoid seeing myself in a mirror."
___"Why walk, if you can drive?" "Why get up to change the TV channel when you can push the remote?"
___I avoid sex to hide my body and only do it with the lights out.
___I go on and off diets to lose pounds, only to gain them all back and more.
___I've tried fasting, restrictive diets, laxatives, diuretics, pills, throwing up...
___I don't eat when I'm starving, saying, "I can never be too thin or too rich"?
___I constantly feel fat and am deathly afraid of getting fat or gaining weight.
___My ideal weight is much less than what standard weight charts show.
___I don't want to know how much I weigh.
___I focus on one particular body flaw, demanding perfection.
___I get mad if someone watches me eat or tells me what to eat.
___I feel guilty, ashamed, disgusted and/or embarrassed about my eating behavior.
___I feel empty inside.
___I'm obsessed with exercise.
___I believe that love is based only on performance.
___All my relationships are superficial.
___I never know what I want except when bingeing.
___I eat or don't eat to "show them.'
___I think of committing suicide to punish someone.

If you answered this quiz honestly, congratulate yourself. If you weren't honest, truthfully take this quiz again and then congratulate yourself. If any of the above statements sound like you, you are using food to numb pain and emptiness. Let's get you back in control so you feel full, happy, healthy and gorgeous!

For billions and billions of years humans have thrived by eating, drinking water and moving their body. Thank heavens for that or you wouldn't be reading this right now. Food was, and still is, the cornerstone of socializing, care-taking, pleasure and survival. Culture influences girth. If you live in the Midwest, you may not be as motivated to lose weight as if you lived in California.

Tongans and Hawaiians like extra meat on their bones. So do Arabian cultures. Egyptian belly dancers are meaty. American actresses, dancers and models, on the other hand, are generally skinny wisps.

I recently saw a television show featuring Nigerian tribesmen competing for who could gain the most weight in a short time. The winner of the competition did such a splendid job of fattening, that his stomach literally burst. His burial mound was the sacred centerpiece for his first place awards celebration.

A Word to the Wide

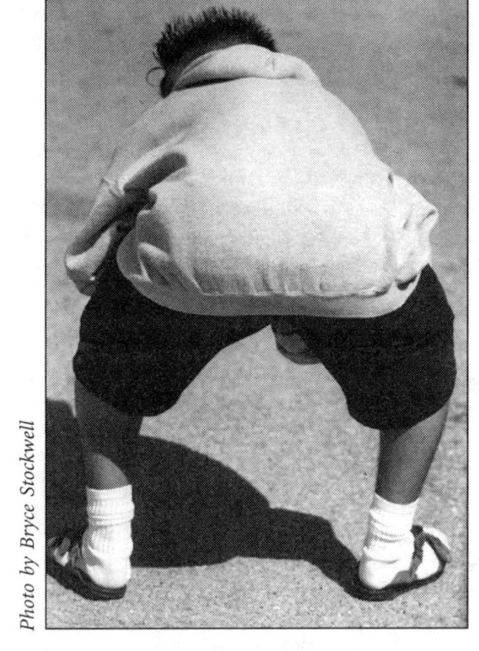

Photo by Bryce Stockwell

☆ *"Obese people and those desiring to lose weight, ... should eat only once a day and take no baths and sleep on a hard bed and walk naked as long as possible."*
—Hypocrites, 400 BC

☆ *"Dancing 'til dawn makes one lose weight."*
—Socrates

In the Middle Ages, 400 to 1500 AD, it was mandated by the church that folks could only eat two meals a day. Exceptions were made for the sick, infants, old folks and laborers who were allowed to have a third meal, which was the breaking of the fast or breakfast.

17th Century French King Louis XIV topped off 400 course banquets with a midnight snack of peas mixed with flour, cream, butter and eggs. If food didn't smell right to him, he sprayed it with perfume.

▲ Modern Mandates

☆ *"The best way to lose weight is to eat naked in front of a mirror...because the restaurant will throw you out before you can eat too much."*
—Jay Trachman

Modern life affords us less time to gather and prepare whole foods. The demise of home cooking, and a stay-at-home caretaker, results in nutritional starvation and high-fat and hollow calories stuffing.

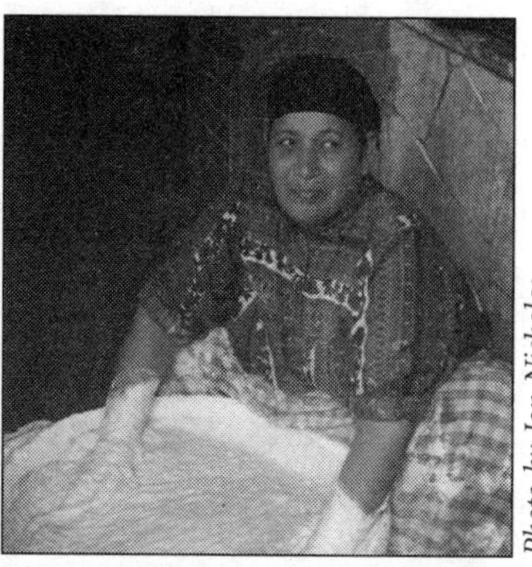

Photo by Jon Nicholas

Fast food, eating out, pot lucks, processed snacks, sweet treats, party feasts, holiday smorgasbords and parental conditioning, contribute to our diet dilemma. Long working hours, commuting in cars, trains and planes, and then sitting, sitting, sitting in front of computers, video games and TV, leave us grabbing quick unconscious amounts of processed foods and snacks. Gas stations, shopping malls, convenience stores, vending machines, ballparks, movie theaters and restaurants tempt us to eat junk. Size zero models advertise processed foods as the healthy way to eat and we buy bigger and bigger sized clothing.

Happy, slim television families and friends bond during fast-food and soft drink orgies, while millions of us cruise the same fast food windows and grow obese on hamburgers, french fries, colas, cookies and fried apple turnovers.

Movie ads show luscious boxes of popcorn, candy and soda and we unconsciously glut ourselves with impossible to digest fats and calories.

The cover of ladies magazines (women are the diet industries greatest consumers) show sugary, gooey desserts with lead articles on how to lose weight. A recent study found that fifty-four percent of American adults are overweight and one out of eight school age kids are obese.

Go to Las Vegas and see the showgirls. Many look like concentration camp victims. Then go into the casino and watch the vast sea of overweight bodies roll past.

Many of us have misconceptions, emotional attachments and resulting compulsions around what we put into our mouth. Food patterns bring you home to your childhood and survival. We substitute cookies for love, and use food to "medicate" hurt feelings.

It's fun to dine with friends or cook up luscious plentiful high calorie creations. It's painful to be heavy, exhausted and ill. Food can seem baffling because it brings pleasure and pain.

▲ What You Weigh is BIG Business

☆ *"Buy my product, drink this brew,*
We like to see a lot of you."

—Root Beer (Shakespeare's brother)

Little Spuds Have Big Eyes

☆ *"Think how you'd feel if on Saturday morning television, your children saw 10,000 commercials for alcohol. Then you'll understand why we need to change the child's television environment."*

—Kelly Brownell, Yale University

$34 million a year is spent on obesity research.

The American food industry pays $36 *billion* a year to promote its products. Kellogg's for example spends $32 million a year just to advertise Frosted Flakes.

A typical American child, watching more than two and one-half hours of TV daily, can see as many as 10,000 food commercials a year. Nearly all the food commercials on Saturday morning kids' programs highlight sugary, fatty or salty foods.

It's no wonder that a national survey found that most 7th and 8th graders said their favorite food was pizza, with hamburgers and ice cream second and third.

The food industry grows fat making us fat, and the diet industry grows fat selling "thin." One out of every four people in the US is on a diet and consumes $30 billion a year in diet related products, like books, videos, wired jaws, and diet pills.

Some take drastic gastric action; surgery: gastric stapling, gastric bypass, intestinal bypass or liposuction. Jeanine is a good example of what happens when such drastic measures are taken. She weighed three hundred pounds and her mother talked her into having bypass surgery.

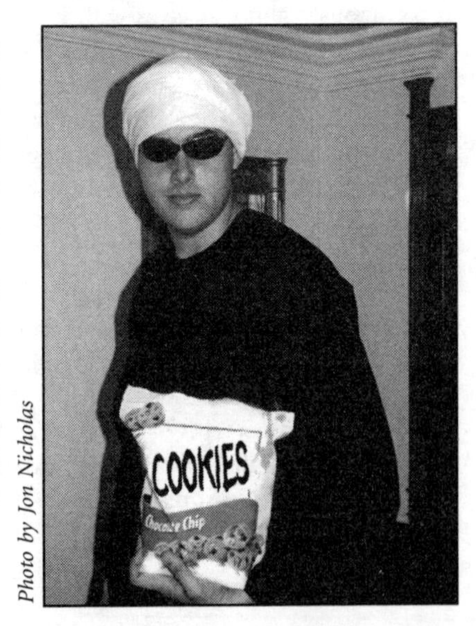

Photo by Jon Nicholas

A True Story: Jeanine

"When I had my bypass surgery, I thought that my troubles would be over...they were just beginning. I threw up for a year after that and was hospitalized. I almost died. The kind of surgery I had kills most people who have it.

I did lose the weight but since, I have had eight more surgeries to correct the damage from the bypass and plastic surgery to sculpt away my hanging flesh. The incisions on my legs got infected and I had to go to the hospital three times a week for months to keep from going toxic. Finally, I healed. But I am severely scarred from all the ways that I have mutilated my body.

The worst part was my mental anguish. I pummeled myself repeatedly for what I did to myself. I blamed myself, the doctor and my mother. Hypnosis has helped me accept the past as a gigantic lesson I gave myself. I have learned so much about what matters in life. I am dedicated now to celebrating myself and my life."

▲ The Plot Thickens: Stress, Drugs and Alcohol

☆ *"The more extreme the diet, the greater the risk of developing drug or drinking problems."*

—Dr. Dean Krahn, M.D., University of Wisconsin

Poor eating weakens your immune reserves. Junk food and starvation steal needed resources, and often leads to disease.

Radical eating may eliminate essential balanced food groups. Yo-yo dieting, obesity and starvation cause ailments like digestive problems, heart disease, stroke, high blood pressure, high cholesterol, gallstones and gall bladder disease, infertility, diabetes, gout, arthritis, ovarian and endometrial cancer.

Crazy eating makes you feel crazy. Depression, low self esteem, anxiety, loss of concentration and isolation are typical by-products of out-of-control patterns. In one study, seventy percent of women who looked at pictures of high fashion magazine models for three minutes felt depressed, guilty and shamed.

Elevated insulin levels and fatigue, anemia, depression, headaches, muscle aches, nausea and HUNGER are the result of eating patterns gone askew.

Studies say that one-third of women in eating disorder programs are substance abusers and one-third of the substance abusers have eating disorders. In a survey of two-thousand female college freshman, 87% said they "diet" regularly and during a diet they were more likely to drink heavily, experience alcohol blackouts and have unintended sex.

When your system is out of whack, you may self medicate with caffeine, sugar and other socially acceptable drugs. Over-the-counter drugs are often used to relieve biochemical side effects. Resulting symptoms of ill health may move you to take prescription medicine. More drugs are then needed to override their side effects. Diet remedies and antidepressants are typical drugs that result from body imbalance.

Breathtaking Implications Harvard Medical School's Dr. Carlos Camargo, studied women ages 27-44 and found that the most obese were three times more likely to develop adult onset asthma. Asthma medicine most certainly must have its own biochemical ramifications.

Adding Insulin to Injury If diabetes results from poor eating, insulin is given. Some diabetics on insulin decrease or omit their insulin after over eating or bingeing, to avoid gaining or to lose weight. This "trick" increases micro-vascular problems that result in blindness, protein albumin in the urine with risks of diabetic kidney disease.

Drugs Compulsive eaters also can be compulsive about medication. As one of my clients said; "First I was addicted to over-eating. Now I'm addicted to the drugs I use to stop the overeating."

Prescription and over-the-counter appetite suppressants raise metabolism and can cause high blood pressure, dehydration, poor nutrition and addiction. We all remember how Fen-Phen (dexfenfluramine-Redux and fenfluramine-Pondimin) was yanked from the market in 1997 because it caused irreversible lung and heart valve damage in some users. Use of Phentermine (Apidex-P, Festin, and Ionamin) is hyped as being safe; but there is no current data on potential dangers. Herbs that contain ephedrine vary in the amount of active ingredients so it's hard to know how much you are taking and we don't know what they do to you in the long run.

Health problems that over or under-eating cause, lead many to prescription drugs. Do you take antidepressants because your weight gets you down? Do you take painkillers to numb weighty aches and pains? Do you chemically curb high blood pressure caused by excess pounds?

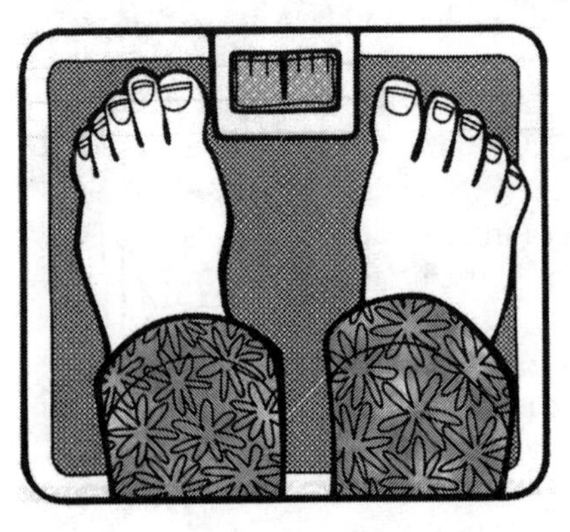

Meds may seem fine until they bring side effects and more or different drugs to override those side effects. According to the U.S. Surgeon General, 66% of all deaths in the U.S. are diet related. Most doctors, well trained in medical procedures and drug disbursement, know little about nutrition. Susan Lark, M.D. reports that she received *less than three hours* of nutritional training in medical school!

▲ There Are Reasons and Results

☆ *"If you always think what you've always thought; you'll always get what you've always gotten."*

Reasons we give ourselves for crazy eating are respectable enough: an ideal figure, to be happy, look and feel great, and of course, to be loved. Great idea if you get these results. But, if you are controlled by food, whatever reason you give yourself is not good enough. No matter how you slice it, crazy eating is crazy.

Problem eaters feel like a victim and persecutor and are downright hostile in their self-talk. They feel disgusted, depressed, guilty and angry with themselves.

Were you controlled or do you control with what is eaten or not eaten? Out-of-control patterns are an unconscious attempt to be in control. Have you used eating or not eating to assert your power?

Did your eating divert your parents' attention away from their problems and onto you, their "problem" child? Eating disorders are often born from fears of intimacy and emotions. They may result from superficial conversations, dogmatic rules and talking through, not to, each other. Eating issues also arise in families that have unrealistic and perfectionistic expectations of each other.

▲ What's Wrong with "Diets" Anyway?

☆ *"Some diets really don't make you live longer; they only make you feel like you are living longer."*

—Dean Ornish

Reasons we give ourselves for dieting are respectable enough:

"I want to have an ideal figure," and "I want to look and feel great."

But how many times have you lost the same twenty pounds only to put them on again and then some? How much of your time has been stolen by nagging thoughts, guilt, worry and obsessing about your weight? What would it be like if you had that time back?

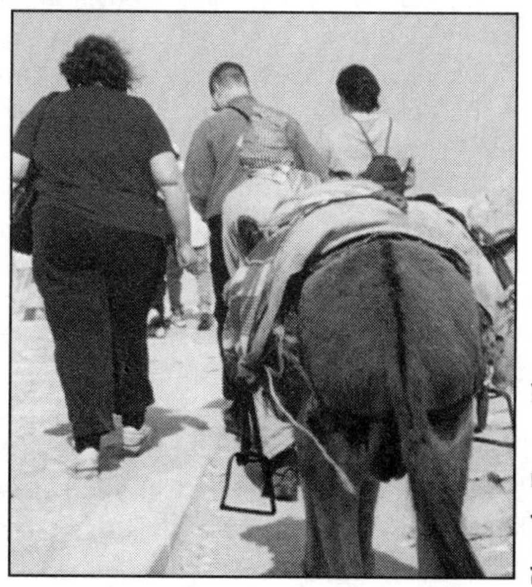

Photo by Tamara Thomas

Photo by Jon Nicholas

Are You the Yo-Yo at the End of A Diet?

☆ Man with a banana up his nose:
"What's wrong with me?"
Hypnotherapist: *"You're not eating properly."*

The word diet starts with "die" and ends with "et."

"Diets" usually increase weight because you feel deprived and rebel by eating twice as much. Chronic dieting creates a binge/starve cycle. If you under-eat, your body shouts "famine" and saves fat so you won't starve later. Bingeing and/or starving keeps a death grip on fat reserves. To lose weight once and for good, eat when you need fuel and stop when you are physically nourished. Make healthy choices and stop dieting! Diets aren't the solution. Healthy eating habits are.

If you overeat, your body finds and creates amazing places to deposit excess fat and you feel icky, irritable, lethargic, guilty, disconnected and frustrated.

If you don't eat when you need fuel, your body grabs and holds fat with a death grip and you feel icky, irritable, lethargic, guilty, disconnected and frustrated.

If you beat yourself up with guilt and remorse, you add insult to injury.

A TRUE STORY Solan

Solan has eating patterns of bingeing and starving. During hypnosis she explored the source of her eating patterns. Once she discovered and reframed these patterns, she lost 40 pounds.

I'm five years old and my mom is yelling at me, 'Go to your room.' I hide in my closet. Daddy is yelling at Mommy, 'Why do you spend all my money on this kid and I can't get a decent meal?'

My eating makes Daddy mad. I'm not going to eat, so he won't yell and get so mad. But it makes Mommy mad if I don't eat. She is always stuffing me full of food. Mom gets mad if I'm not hungry. And I'm not always hungry. Eating makes me too full.

They don't love me. I'm a big pain. I make them fight. It is my entire fault.

Now that I look at my life as a grown-up, I realize that it didn't matter to my parents whether I ate or not. My mother had issues about eating and my father had issues about money. I've lived my whole life bingeing and starving because of their issues. I now eat food to sustain my life.

How do I change my eating? I toughed it out. I wasn't sure I could succeed, but I did. I became as stubborn about feeling good as I was about trying to be close to, or get even, with Mom and Dad. What a relief to leave them in the past "slipping into an oily grave."

HARD TO SWALLOW MENU

Pure Baloney

Calendar dates, traffic jam,
A roll in bed with honey.
Drink from the bedspring, tees from golf;
Would a two-carrot diamond taste funny?

Scallops from curtains, a toolbox plumb
Leeks from the faucet, eraser gum.
The toast of the town, a corny joke
Cauliflower ears make Arty choke.

Basic staples can clog up the works.
Would you throw up the window for a soda jerk?

—Shelley Stockwell

▲ Body Image

☆ *"The waist is a terrible thing to mind."*

—Ziggy

What Does Thin Mean to You?

☆ *"I'm trying to get down to my original weight."*
"Why would you want to weigh seven pounds, six ounces again?"

Do you eat to live or live to eat? Is "thin" an arbitrary number on the scale? Do you judge yourself by a number you made up in your head? How old were you when you made up that number?

Body image is the way you see your own body. How you think you look, walk, stand, smile or talk is mostly about *how you feel about your body and yourself.* The bottom line: how you think you look is a completely subjective experience. The mental environment you create for yourself influences your thoughts, behavior, your shape and how you present yourself.

A TRUE STORY" Jennie

Mighty Bulk from Little Acorns Grow"

"I once weighed 250 pounds and as you can see I'm short. My doctor refused to give me stomach by-pass surgery, because I had regular heart pains. My best friends were with me and told the doctor they loved me. I realized then that they thought I was going to die a young and miserable death. That was the day I realized I had a choice and I decided to live.

I was successful at work and because of my determination, I won an Emmy for my work in the movies. Therefor, I decided to be successful at weight loss. I made that my job. I got up every morning and walked. I thumbed my nose at the restaurants as I walked past them. After a while, I began getting excruciating headaches. That's when I discovered my acorn theory. It goes like this:

Children see life's contradictions and want to express their truth. Yet, they are too young to verbalize, so they place an acorn in their belly. Over time, it grows into expansive foliage.

When I recognized my acorn, I did a mental acorn transplant. I said good-bye to it and started my life anew. I lost 100 pounds and have kept it off for three years and I believe for the rest of my life."

Note: Two things are striking about Jennie's acorn theory. She puts her "unexpressed truth" in her belly, her third chakra, where gut truth lives. And two, the word "acorn" begins with "ache."

▲ Eating Is Done In Your Head

☆ *"Thank goodness we don't have to consciously direct the thousands of chemical processes that take place just to process one meal. I enjoy the responsibility that was given to me of putting food into my mouth, chewing it up, and swallowing it. I can handle that just fine."*

—Mick Hall,
Five Principles of Balanced Health

Of course, how you think about food results in how you behave toward food. Action follows thought. If your subconscious tells you to "always finish everything on your plate," you will. If you reprogram your subconscious to "always leave something on your plate," you will. Think about your life script messages about eating. Were you hypnotized by these sentences?

"Manga, manga. Have some more spaghetti."

"You're so skinny! Eat your pastrami sandwich."

"Fat and happy...skinny and miserable"

Were the rich; "lean machines," and peons; "poor, fat schleps?"

"Put some meat on your bones in case you get sick."

If you believe you should have extra girth "In case I get sick," most likely you'll stay overweight and get sick.

Better to get a new attitude.

Train Your Subconscious Mind When you train your subconscious mind, you get the results you want. Start by monitoring your self-talk.

What you say to yourself literally hypnotizes you. Demand that you say positive things to yourself about eating and drinking. Without effort you'll eat properly, make good choices and feel great. You won't even have to think about it consciously; your inner mind takes any stress away. You have more important things to think about.

But you needn't go nuts on the subject. Replace junk food and junk attitudes with better food and attitudes. De-emphasize food, eating, diet and weight so they take their rightful place in your life, as fuel to follow your true bliss.

It's Not What You Eat, It's What's Eating You: Food as A Drug

☆ MY MOM WAS FAT

My Mom was fat.
She'd hide her flabby belly in corsets and flowered muumuus
And fly jet propelled, on diet pills.
At night, pumping ice cream heaps into her ori-face;
Like high-speed trains through a tunnel:
She sat alone at the kitchen table.
The house creaked.
My father snored loudly in the bed, and the cat stalked the night yard.
My mom was fat, No doubt about that.

—Shelley Stockwell

A compulsive relationship with food stresses us out. Do you substitute eating or not eating for love? If you use food to stuff feelings or thoughts, fight depression, tranquilize, override insecurity, go home again or for a high, food consumes you.

Over time, out-of-control overeating or not eating really depresses. All the food in the kingdom can never fill emptiness.

Food comforts, and satisfies…for a while.

Vicious Circle

Who rewarded you with food?

If you use food to numb emotions, over time, you'll need more and more food to stay numb. Hiding behind protective walls of flesh is a child. If you were abused, eating or not eating is a clever survival technique that numbs underlying pain.

"If I look terrible, nobody will bother me again."

"When I'm numb (with weight, food, starvation and compulsion), I blot out my anger, guilt and shame."

"If I starve, I'll show them."

▲ How Do You Get Fat, Anyway?

You were born with about five billion fat cells. From birth to age two. Teenagers and pregnant moms, create additional fat cells needed for health.

A healthy-sized person has some thirty billion fat cells in their body. An obese person can have 300 billion fat cells, and each one is often hundreds of times larger than slim people have!

Large quantities of ingested fat, extra protein and carbohydrates create more fat cells than necessary.

Extra calories not burned off as fuel for resting or metabolism, are stored as fat in cells. 3500 extra calories can produce one pound of body fat or puff up other fat cells to almost unlimited proportions.

Once your body makes a fat cell, you have it for life. It may shrink when you use its stored triglycerides for energy, but it never goes away.

There are two kinds of fat cells: white fat cells, which hold one drop of fat and brown fat cells, which hold several droplets of fat and a small society of mitochondria whose job it is to burn the fat.

Converting protein and carbohydrates to fat requires more energy than storing plain old fat. When your body does turn fat into energy, it uses the most recently stored fat first. So if you first gain fat around your buttocks, then thighs and waist, you'll start burning it off the waist first, then your thighs, and buttocks.

Exercise allows fat and calories to convert into energy. But, when you don't move your body for a long time, it returns to fat.

A TRUE STORY Fred

"I've been 100 pounds overweight for 20 years and have suffered with low energy, exhaustion and fatigue. I've tried to lose weight many times by not eating. Then I get depressed and bored. Life sucks. I'm just killing time, so I go to the grocery store.

When I walk into the store, I get excited. I feel sexually aroused. It's wonderful. 'I can have anything I want in the store,' I say to myself. I'm excited all the way home. At home, as I begin eating, I lose consciousness. When I come back, there's no food left in the house.

Hypnosis helped me change my behavior. During hypnosis, I thought of my alcoholic father beating me. When I was ten, he died and I felt relief and terrible disappointment. My mother remarried and ignored me after that.

My own marriage fell apart because I drank and beat my children. I'm so disappointed in myself. I pretend to be a nice guy but that's a joke. I always push other peoples' buttons and they either leave me or get angry with me. Whenever I'm needy, something worse happens to me. I never get anything I want. No sex. No family. No relationships. I realized with hypnosis that I was in a terrible mental and negative rut. I had to do something that brought me real happiness.

Under hypnosis I realized that the happiest I ever feel is when I volunteer to do something for others. Six months ago, I became a driver for the elderly. That feels good. I'm taking evening walks and the grocery store seems to be less of a turn-on when I get exercise. I'm finally losing weight now, because I'm leaving the past where it belongs; in the past."

▲ Overstuffed or Starving: Both Ends of the Scale

☆ *"It's not the food's fault. It's how much of it you eat and what you do with it after you've eaten it."*

—Margo Lemis and Mark Berlin

Overstuffed

Three hundred thousand people in the United States die every year from being overweight. Over stuffed is overstressed. It is often even difficult to breathe.

Bulk stresses joints and ligaments and causes injury. If you're over weight you most likely have aches and pains. It's a lot of work carrying a lot of weight around.

Starving

☆ Question: *"Why didn't the skeleton cross the road?"*
Answer: *"Because she doesn't have the guts."*

Do you stubbornly refuse to weigh what society says are minimal, normal standards?

Do you constantly evaluate yourself by your weight or shape?

Do you put yourself on severely restrictive diets or excessive exercise?

Are your thoughts and behavior obsessed with weight?

Do you go unconscious at mealtime?

Are you self-absorbed by your fear of being fat or gaining weight?

Anorexia or anorexia nervosa is the label used for self-imposed starvation. Such abstinence is sometimes sprinkled with binges and/or purging and a distorted image of yourself in the mirror.

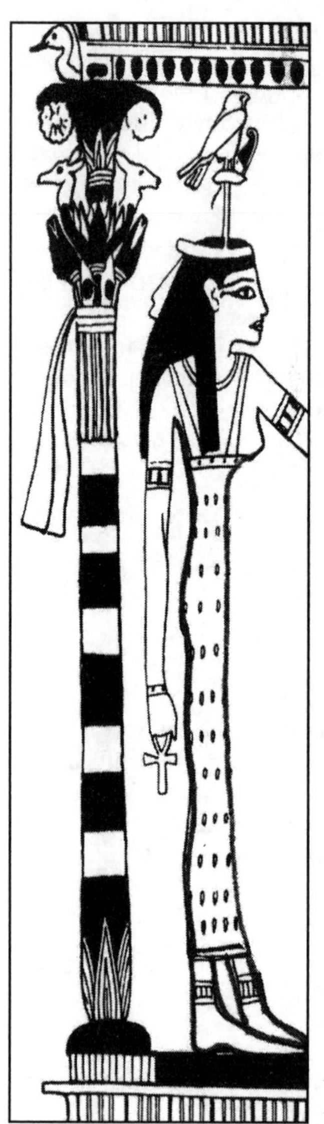

Stick thin models used to be the domain of fashion magazines. Now it's estimated that seven million women and one million men in the United States suffer from eating disorders. Many wrestlers vomit before weigh-in and gorge before the actual meet. Karen Carpenter was anorexic. Sandra Dee and other famous actors admit that they are too.

If you starve yourself, you risk serious illness like high blood pressure, heart and gallbladder disease. Depravation, vomiting, laxatives, diuretics or enemas damage your teeth, gums, intestinal tract and reproductive system. That's why many anorexics and bulimics don't have periods, erections or teeth. Sick people don't look good no matter how they trick themselves.

Starvation is devastating: chemical imbalances, osteoporosis, dehydration, irregular heart rate, tears in the lining of the esophagus and stomach, constipation, tooth cavities, swollen salivary glands (parotid) and serious cardiovascular problems. Eighteen percent of people with a severe eating disorder will die from that disorder.

Starving long enough, can be fatal. If you are female, be alarmed if menstrual periods stop (amenorrhea) unless, of course, you're menopausal. Your body's hormonal regulating system shuts down when you are starving or over exercising.

Throw up or take laxatives to lose weight and soon, your whole life is about throwing up and eliminating.

If you are too thin and need to gain weight, you simply must eat when you need fuel whether you feel the hunger or not. Wake up sweet one. Let food do its good work of nourishing you.

A TRUE STORY Carl

"At fifteen, I got suspended from school for smoking pot and they sent me to a rehabilitation center where others taught me 'the art of compulsive eating, purging and exercise.' I fluctuated between starvation and bingeing.

I always knew I was fat. Somehow I did not see the truth in the mirror. When I was twenty, I weighed 120 and was 5' 10". I spent over a hundred dollars a day on food and threw up 30-40 times. I stole food to support my habit. What added to my shame was the fact that I had a 'girl's disease.'

One morning I was listening to a radio talk show and a hypnotist talked about helping people stop smoking. Former smokers said that they no longer thought about their problem. 'I want to forget about my problems!' I said out loud. Finally, I got help. The very first time I was hypnotized I felt relaxed, something I had not felt for a long, long time.

I discovered the source of my problem. My parents were control freaks and my habit gave me some power by controlling the destiny of my own body. Of course, it was crazy, because I was totally out-of-control. After eight months with the hypnotist, I progressively got better. I'm now twenty-seven, I weight 168 pounds, and I feel great. It's good to eat and enjoy my food. Most importantly, I like living in this body."

☆ *The cure for anorexia is to eat.*

—Jon Nicholas

Binge, Guilt, and Purge

☆ *Mary had a lot of lamb*
She also had some steak and ham.
Her cholesterol zoomed
From the fat she consumed
And she went for a cardiogram.

—Pat Cotterell

☆ *Do you go unconscious: feeling ugly, heavy, fat?*
Is your stomach tied into a knot? It's hard to live like that!
Have you make yourself an orifice: wide open or tightly shut?
Do you heave, starve or take laxatives and hide your truth with "buts?"
Then ask yourself these questions and take an honest look
At all your patterned attitudes and measures that you took
If you starve or regurgitate who do you manipulate?
Who do you hurt? Who do you hate? What causes you to numb- stagnate?
And why is your focus all about weight?
You came here as a perfect child right from the hand of God.
You were given a mind that's clever and a functioning healthy bod.
You may not come around again; this may be your only chance.
Stop pretending, get a grip, make your life a joyous dance.
You're valued as a person; not just by your looks,
Heal your hurt, start anew, follow the words in this book.
Your value is your kindness to your body and your health
And the precious life God gave to you and honoring yourself.
So if you feel embarrassed, guilty, empty, low.
Leave the past behind you: love yourself and grow.

—Shelley Stockwell

Out-of-control eating follows a binge-guilt-purge-guilt cycle. Even the starvation high or a sense of false pride can't hide the terrible hurt inside. The voice of inner wisdom always says, "Stop hurting me."

Binge - Guilt

The Binge-Guilt-Purge Cycle: Guilting A Lily (or Debby or Steve)

Purge - Starve - Guilt

Are you hurting yourself with your behavior?

Take a moment right now and check in with yourself. Give your inner voice a chance to tell the truth.

Listen.

If you are out-of-control and hurting yourself, you know it. A full-fledged eating disorder is serious and potentially life threatening.

Who are Prime Candidates For Eating Disorders?

- Male and Female Actors
- Body-fat percentage watchers
- Teenage girls
- The elderly
- Minorities and the affluent
- Models
- Athletes: Gymnasts, Jockeys
- Older men driven to extreme dieting by fear of heart disease
- Older women obsessed with looking youthful
- Wrestlers often vomit before weigh-in and gorge before the actual meet.

A TRUE STORY Stella

"I was so ashamed. I had to keep an image in the world but underneath it all my life was a chaos of sneaking, stuffing and regurgitating. My teeth were starting to loosen and I hadn't had a period for three years—and no one knew. I remember the first time I purged. I was at a girl's boarding school and we ordered pizza. One of the girls said, 'I know the best diet in the world. You can eat as much as you want, as long as you throw up afterwards.' We all thought it was a great idea, so we threw up together. The problem was that I continued this pattern for years. After all, I'm supposed to be a movie goddess.

During hypnotherapy, I had a remarkable rebirthing experience. And as painful as it was to remember, I recall my mother trying to abort me. She threw up while I was inside of her. When I was small, my mother wanted to get her figure back because she was having an affair with a famous political figure. I remember hearing her throw up in the bathroom.

I've toughed out six months of Overeaters Anonymous meetings, hypnosis regressions and hungry news reporters. I'm well now. It was the combination of remembering, being around others with the same problem and my determination to stop being like my Mom. That made me well. My relief is immeasurable."

Binge Eating

☆ *Chubby Jack Horner sat in the corner*
Eating his diet gruel.
He hopped on the scale, turned very pale,
And said, "Why is my life so cruel?"

—Pat Cotterell

Bingeing or rapid eating in a relatively short time (usually 2 hours) brings discomfort. It is often done in solitude, to avoid embarrassment. Bingeing is bulimia without the purging.

A TRUE STORY Hal

"It all began when I was 19. I was a New York model who loved to eat. I'd get out of work and spend $100 to $200 on pastries. My eating had a numbing effect, like taking Novocain. Then I'd throw up. The way I sopped bingeing and purging was to stop eating. Then I vomited my water.

I tried everything. I had lost everything. It was do or die. Now I eat well and attend AA meetings. Every day I remember how terrible it was and I never want to go back."

Bulimia

Those who binge and purge are tagged "bulimics" by doctors. Some compulsively and uncontrollably stuff and then vomit. Others use enemas, diuretics, laxatives or drugs. Their weight may be normal, overweight or underweight.

A siege of stuffing or eliminating may last months or years. It may go on all day, once a day or episodically. Fasting, severely restrictive diets or excessive exercising usually go along with these patterns as the person tries to make up for "all that eating."

Resist the Urge to Purge Chronic vomiting causes acidity that damages your gums and tooth enamel. Pancreas and kidney problems and holes in the stomach or esophagus result. So do temperature and blood problems. Over time, body metabolism and electrolyte balance is disturbed. Vomiting strains the heart and causes cardiovascular problems. Reproductive systems may be damaged, in both males and females.

Laxatives: The Straight Poop

Many get hung up on laxatives because they think that they are constipated or not "regular." Many think that if they don't have a bowel movement everyday something is wrong. What they don't realize is that having a bowel movement only three times a week is healthy for some.

Over-reliance on laxatives often causes the very constipation you try to prevent. Constipation is when the stool is hard and you strain more than one out of four times you go. Constipation is the result of improper diet, not enough fluids or intestinal muscles that aren't working well together. The result: sluggish stool that moves slowly through the intestines.

Laxatives: Did They Get You in the End?

Answer Honestly:

__I regularly use laxatives.

__I regularly use laxatives and I'm still constipated.

__I need to take a laxative to have a bowel movement

__I have abdominal cramping.

__I get bloated.

__I have nausea and vomiting.

__I use laxatives for weight control.

If you answered "yes" to any of these questions, watch out. Continued laxative use causes dehydration, diarrhea, weakened intestinal muscles and lack of nutrient absorption, damage to the colon and gastrointestinal bleeding.

Up Your Egypt

Slip Sliding Away

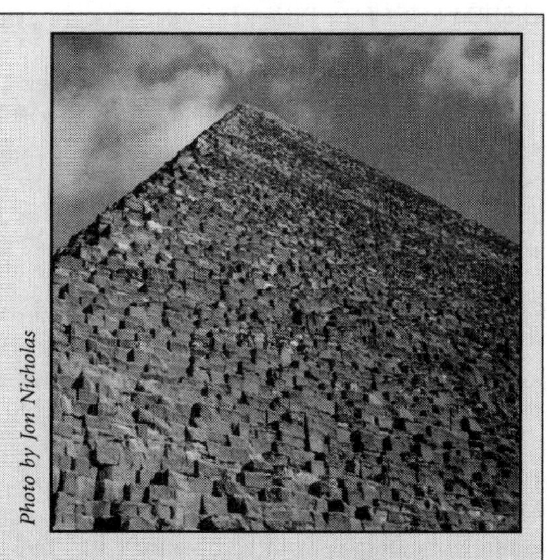
Photo by Jon Nicholas

Castor oil was often used for sliding the big stone blocks along wooden rollers to construct the pyramids. Some wise person thought; "Hum, (use your own words).

By 1500 BC, laxatives became an obsession.

In 1905, Max Kiss combined chocolate with phenolphthalein, a chemical used in wine production, greasing the way for Exlax. A clever colon combination, because chocolate irritates and phenolphthalein releases. Besides, kids liked chocolate better than castor oil.

Over-the-counter laxatives are now a half-billion-dollar industry in America.

Pass on Laxatives You need high-fiber intake, some fat (fish oil is super), water, water, water and regular meals and exercise to keep things moving naturally.

Repeated laxatives, enemas, diuretics and colonics irritate and change the way your intestines work, weaken your body's natural ability for peristalsis, and interfere with your body's ability to absorb nutrients and calories. Laxatives can cause you to lose your electrolyte balance and fluids which can be life threatening. Using laxatives while aggressively exercising increases your possibility of adverse effects.

Rolls In Life

Some 68% of adults roll their toilet paper over the top of the spool; the other 32% roll it under. And 50% will "switch it" if it's wrong for them. Women tend to scrunch tissue up, while men usually fold it neatly.

AFFIRM SUCCESS: Eating Disorder Straight Self-Talk
I say positive and healthy things to myself and take an honest evaluation of my health. I put my priorities in proper order. I choose to live. The words I choose when I talk or think about food determine my behavior. I mentally replace limiting or critical self-talk with loving, positive and healthy thoughts. I say positive things about myself. I have healthy thoughts and healthy actions. If I need tough love from myself; I give it. I'm in control of my mind and body in positive, realistic and healthy ways.

I now release unwanted weight or receive necessary weight. I permanently change my eating attitudes for my highest good. I remember to eat when I need fuel. I am conscientious, healthy and honest.

I take back the reins of my actions, enjoy life and stay conscious. Because of this, excess pounds slip away or needed pounds show up. My healthy weight stabilizes slowly, easily and effortlessly. Permanently. My body's natural, self-regulating system is restored because I stop overriding it. My body loves me. I love my body. I am proud of my body. My body is my gift from God. What I do with it is my gift TO God.

I eat regular healthy meals that include high fiber. I enjoy whole grains, fruits and vegetables. I enjoy moving my body. Movement is living. I love to exercise. I exercise regularly and in moderation. A twenty-minute workout or a walk three times a week makes me feel great. I drink 8-10 glasses of water. Since caffeine and alcohol hurt me and dehydrate me I avoid such poison like the plague. If I have a challenge I deal with it directly so I easily return to peace and harmony. I get my pleasure out of so many other things. I eat regularly for fuel and I stop eating when I am pleasantly full and physically fueled. I am 100% committed to loving my healthy body.

▲ How to Get a Grip on Yourself

☆ LAUGH, CRY, SING, HEAL

I am beautiful just being me
It's time my eyes this beauty see.
I make a pact to be my best
And know that I am truly blest.
My heart once broken, now is healed,
I eat with reverence every meal.
For I am perfect as I am
Because I choose to give a damn.
I eat for fuel. My body burns fat.
I read this section and learn to do that.

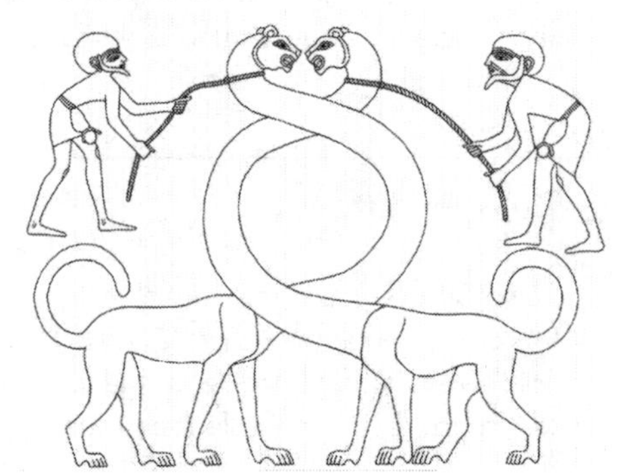

—Shelley Stockwell

It takes only *four* weeks to entrench a new "get with it" attitude in the subconscious mind. After that, you have a healthier pattern automatically. Behavior patterns are just that; patterns. You get a grip on your actions when you make a SINCERE commitment to do that.

Start with a good honest evaluation of what you are doing to your body. Get real so you can heal. If you are hurting yourself, you know it is literally a matter of life and death; your life. Get tough with yourself and do whatever it takes to get a grip.

Only Habits Everything you do begins as a pattern you create in your mind. To reach and maintain a healthy size, you need to acknowledge patterns that make you out-of-control, ill, overweight and/or undernourished. Then create new patterns to balance yourself to the beautiful, healthy you. Identify your thoughts and emotions, stay connected to your body and your behavior, accept yourself as you are, and stubbornly demand wellness and joy. Require intelligent attitudes, action and tough love.

Sensible Steps for a Shapely You

1. Move it To Lose It

Moving your body makes huge differences. The kind of exercise, how much and when you do it creates dramatic weight differences. For example, morning aerobic exercise before you eat seems to burn more fat than the same exercise later in the day. No other exercise rejuvenates and redistributes as well as weight lifting. Weight bearing exercise rebuilds muscles that you lose as you age and changes the fat to muscle ratio.

Photo by Jon Nicholas

Do or Die According to Neil Gordon, M.D., Director of Physiology at Cooper Institute, exercise lowers elevated blood pressure by an average of ten points. "That's enough to keep some people from ever having to take hypertensive drugs." Only thirty to forty-five minutes of exercise reduces your risk of heart disease.

AFFIRM SUCCESS: Move to Lose It

I love to move my body. Exercise at least three times a week for at least thirty minutes tones me and lets me easily maintain my perfect body. I use my peak energy times to move and that makes me more energetic for the rest of the day.

Calories to Burn

ACTIVITY	CALORIES BURNED PER MINUTE (130 pound woman)
Climbing stairs	18.0
Taking an elevator or standing	1.8
Grocery shopping	3.5
Ordering groceries on line	1.5
Washing dishes	2.5
Watching TV and using the dishwasher	0.9
Chopping wood for fire	6.0
Turning up the thermostat	1.0
Hand mowing the lawn	6.0
Riding a power lawn mower	2.5
Washing the car	4.5

Photo by Jon Nicholas

2. Get Real

REALITY CHECK! Get on the scale, look in the mirror and stop games. What weight lets you feel your best physically as well as emotionally? What is healthy for you? BE HONEST with yourself. There is no room for self-deceit or denial when it comes to your health and joy.

Take a good, hard and loving look at how you pull the wool (or fat) over your eyes. If you hear yourself rationalizing, STOP and tell yourself the truth. Stay awake.

Bust these myths and come out of denial:

1. If you drink a diet soda and a candy bar, they cancel each other out.
2. If you eat food off of someone else's plate, it doesn't count.
3. What you eat while cooking doesn't count.
4. What you eat while cleaning up doesn't count.
5. If no one sees you eat it, it doesn't count.
6. If you eat the same as someone else, it doesn't count.
7. If you eat while in a movie, it is just a snack and it doesn't count.
8. Cookie pieces and crumbs contain no calories because the process of breakage causes a calorie leak.
9. If you eat while standing up, the calories go out your feet and get walked off.
10. Foods eaten for medicinal purposes (diet shakes, power bars, ice cream, brandy, chocolate, Sara Lee) don't count.

11. If you buy it at a health food store or gourmet shop, all the sugar, fat and calories don't count.
12. Girl Scout Cookies, charity candy or baked goods, are good deeds, so the sugar, fat and calories don't count.
13. If a fat person made it or you buy it from a fat person, it counts double.
14. Fat free dressing on your organic salad cancels out the pie a la mode for dessert.
15. Birthday lunches, cake and treats are a celebration and don't count.
16. Free samples from the market or Costco don't count.
17. Free snacks while on duty (like donuts for police and candy for nurses) don't count.
18. If you eat it with your fingers, it doesn't count.
19. If it is a good buy and has a happy name it must be fun and therefor doesn't count.
20. If you eat candy while exercising it gives you energy and therefor doesn't count.

Fast food places love to trick you with "super size" bargains. Instead think water. Instead of a huge "value meals" which bump up your caloric intake 40 to 50 percent!

Order la carte, bring along carrot sticks or an apple and eat it instead of french fries. Better yet, eat out in a sit down restaurant that offers healthy choices.

Photo by Jon Nicholas

3. Become Well Balanced

A moderate WELL BALANCED diet is your ticket to health and slimness. Make good food choices and you will see yourself transform into your most perfect healthy shape. Here is a terrific formula:

In the morning I eat like a pharaoh.
In the afternoon I eat like a pharaoh's daughter.
In the evening I eat like a slave.

4. Drink Water

Water is the solution.

5. Honor Fluctuations

Ever notice how slim, trim people maintain a great shape? They pay attention, and if their weight goes up more than five pounds, they give up treats or snacks until it goes down again.

Metabolism rates fluctuate. Women need to honor changing appetites because of their monthly cycle. Men's metabolism seems to operate on a three-month pattern. Your weight too may fluctuate on the time of the day and what you've eaten.

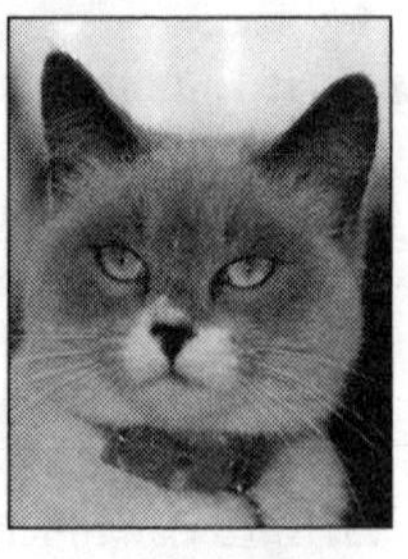

6. Chill Off

Keep your mouth cool with ice water or freeze some fresh juice for a Popsicle (with no sugar added) or cool off with natural yogurt (without fruit or sweeteners) instead of ice cream. Melting an ice cube in your mouth burns 2.3 calories.

7. Make Good Choices

Read Labels Package labels truly educate you. Avoid processed foods as much as possible. If comparing two products, take the one with fewer grams of sugar, fat and salt. One cup of coffee, vanilla and lemon flavored yogurt has 35 grams of sugar, plain yogurt only 17. (50 grams of sugar is 12 tablespoons and 200 calories). Let no more than ten percent of your calories come from refined sugar.

Play to Your Psychology

Photo by Shelley Stockwell

Studies show that people eat 70% more M&M's if they are served in a larger bowl and 44% more popcorn if eating from an extra large tub or bowl. Eating out of a package or carton causes us to eat more. The best strategy is to eat from a small bowl or on a small plate. Psychologically you feel like you ate more that way.

Monitor your portions. If you have hypnotized yourself to take monstrous servings, readjust your thinking. Here is the American Dietetic Association "standard portion" size list:

FOOD	QUANTITY	SIZE
Fruit or vegetable	1/2 cup	Clenched hand
Juice	6 ounces	Small juice glass
Meat	3 ounces	Computer mouse
Rice/spaghetti/ice cream	1/2 cup	Cupped handful
Yogurt/milk	1 cup	Baseball
Cheese	1 ounce	Thumb

Eating Out? Steak sauce, lemon or salsa are delicious on a baked potato. So is cottage cheese. If you have a choice between butter or sour cream take the sour cream. A teaspoon of butter has the same amount of calories and fat as two tablespoons of real sour cream.

Eating Junk at Work? Plan your food by bringing lunch, a nourishing snack, like an apple, and lots of water. This keeps your energy up. Instead of buying eats from the garbage truck or the machines at work, go to a grocery store that has a salad bar and load up with fresh veggies. Avoid the salads loaded with mayonnaise, pasta and marshmallows. Instead of gobs of dressing, use lemon juice, pepper or hot sauce.

If you have to buy a snack, choose the smallest package or opt for dried fruit or an apple.

If your office pals think that cake, cookies and candies are part of every occasion maybe you can enlist them to think healthier. If they won't budge tell them that you choose to celebrate a birthday with a healthy smile, then pour yourself a hefty glass of water and toast the celebrants.

If someone puts a box of candy at your nursing station or desk...give away quick. Keep something healthy in the company refrigerator when you need a snack. A fresh orange, for example, can work miracles.

If you are dying for chocolate, add a little cocoa to your hot cereal and skip the butter. You'll get less fat while you give yourself a taste treat.

Italian Food? Choose red sauce instead of white. Make your salad dressing with olive oil and a lemon squeeze.

Mexican Food? Ask for vera cruz (tomato and vegetable style) instead of cheese and sour cream topping. Or better yet, take it dry. Have cream sauces and salad dressing put on the side. Ask your waiter to put half of your entrée in a to go box and bring it to you with the bill. Eat an appetizer instead of a meal. Seek moderation, not deprivation, Choose a meal you enjoy and ask for a small portion or eat half and push it away. All calories are not created equal. Some calories break down and quickly metabolize into usable fuel while others store it as fat.

8. Eat More Protein

Your energy-efficient body would rather use proteins than waste energy storing them as fat. Protein takes more calories (energy) to process than carbohydrates or fat.

If you eat 100 calories of carbohydrates or protein it takes about 23 calories for your body to process it. If you eat 100 calories of fat, it takes only 3 calories for your body to process and store it. Protein uses much more. The solution...Count portions and not calories and eat protein foods more often.

Protein is necessary to help repair your cells. It influences how your body reacts to carbohydrates. Chicken, turkey, fish, whey, eggs, lean red meats, soy and firm tofu are excellent sources of proteins.

9. Enjoy Carbohydrates

Carbohydrates are high fiber foods and are essential for roughage that cleanses you. A cleansed body holds a clear thinking mind. Enjoy fresh fruits, vegetables, potatoes, whole grains and beans every day. Avoid excessive bananas and avocados if want to lose weight. An apple or an orange a day really does keep the doctor away. A recent report published in the British medical journal *Thrax* found that 2,500 men who ate an apple a day over a five-year period had more unobstructed, healthier lungpower than those who didn't.

10. In a Nutshell

Feed yourself healthy fuel food and water, move around and keep your mind positively occupied and your body will function perfectly. Say positive things to yourself, stay awake and make healthy choices and you feel terrific.

Avoid fat, especially saturated ones, and treat sugary sweets, alcohol and processed foods like the plague. They unbalance your insulin and rob you of vitamins and minerals.

▲ Oil Of Old Age

Render Me Cured Eat simple, natural, whole foods, and stop eating when you are fueled. You'll look and feel great.

If you eliminate one pat of butter, margarine or solid fat a day, over a year, you'll drop ten pounds. Delete two tablespoons of oil a day, and you can drop 21 pounds in a year! Just eliminating the slabs of butter between each pancake or the cheese melted on vegetables or pizza, can make a terrific difference.

A potato is a low fat food with a modest 70 calories. Add a chunk of butter or margarine and you add saturated fat that clogs arteries and puts on weight. French fry the potato and its fat content soars up forty percent; doubling or tripling its calorie content to 440 calories.

Donut Disturb

Instead of crunching on potato chips, crunch on an apple.

One Tablespoon of salad dressing has four to five times the calories of a salad with lemon juice or no dressing on it.

Think of a 1.4 ounce bar of milk chocolate as one tablespoon of mayonnaise or 2 tablespoons of salad dressing. That is 1/5 of a healthy fat allowance. Skip the chocolate.

Instead of cooking with oil or fat, use water and lemon juice. A little bit of olive oil and lots of vegetables and whole grains will make you healthy and slim.

Don't get too excited about fake fats like Olestra. A study conducted by the manufacturer, Proctor and Gamble, showed that people who ate one or two serving of Olestra snacks for a year instead of snacks with the other fats, lost only 1 pound.

Suicide note written by 2 million Americans last year.

—Physician's Committee for Responsible Medicine

The Frosting on the Cake

☆ *"They called her shortening because she was fat in the can."*

I took a class in cake decorating. Frosting is made of hydrogenated fat with a little powdered sugar and artificial flavor and color. Might as well spoon lard directly from the can into your mouth. Read the prepared frosting label: monoglycerides, diglycerides, cellulose gel, polysorbate 80 and sodium acid pyrophosphate. You can almost feel the fat and chemicals globbing your arteries.

Script #1
AFFIRM SUCCESS: Fats Enough Already

The right amount of nourishing fat supports growth, maintains a healthy weight, cushions internal organs and gives me fuel. I get what I need from simple, natural, whole foods. Whole foods are holy.

I eat for fuel and I stop eating when I'm fueled. My weight is lean. I feel great. I avoid slimy fats, oils and fatty foods. Globs of hydrogenated fat clog my body. No more white globs swimming round in my blood stream! No more globs of goo gumming my arteries. I am cleansing. I make healthy food choices: a little olive oil or rapeseed oil is good for me.

Salmon, sardines, mackerel, almonds, peanuts, avocados, sesame seeds, tahini, whole grains, legumes and vegetables supply me with healthy fat. I enjoy new tastes and am satisfied with new textures. I find exciting and new healthy ways to pleasure my mind. I eat healthy nutritious whole grains and whole foods.

Script #2
AFFIRM SUCCESS: I'm My Perfect Weight
I use mind over matter: I mind/I matter. Those who don't mind, don't think that they matter. I use my mind over platter.

It's fun to look and feel my very best. I feel great about myself. I lovingly accept myself as I am and as I am becoming. I am a growing and maturing personality. I now return to my perfect, most healthy weight. My body brings me pride.

I get high doing all the things I really love. I'm high on my many hobbies, interests and talents. I'm high on life.

I accept healthful habits and myself. I eat only what I need for abundant energy. I have the energy to do the many things I enjoy. I am slim and trim. I enjoy life and stay conscious. Excess pounds slip away or needed pounds show up, slowly, easily and effortlessly. Permanently. I am in charge of what I do.

My body naturally releases unnecessary bulk (or puts on necessary nourishment). I enjoy good healthy behavior. My behavior is in my control. I'm in control of what I do or don't do. I am kind and loving to myself.

I am realistic. I am just right. I think about the wonderful clothes I get to wear. I fill out my clothes perfectly. I am perfect. I am my perfect HEALTHY size. I am radiantly healthy. No more "food-hangovers!" I feel great all the time. My body feels terrific. It feels great to move my body. My health is radiant. Food, eating and weight take their rightful place in my life. I give myself permission to eat whatever I want. I want healthy food and water. I put my energy to fun, love, creativity, learning and joy. I'm high on life.

Because I accept myself, society accepts me, too. I love to be seen in public. Others are friendly to me and I am friendly towards them. I'm proud of my shopping cart at the checkout line. I make healthy food and drink choices. I love going places, doing things, meeting new people and following my dreams and goals.

I'm proud of myself. Those who care about me are proud too. My children, mate, family and true friends are proud of me. I attract to me other healthy and well-adjusted people to love. I chose people who are kind to me and kind to themselves. Because I look and feel my best, others like and respect me.

I take charge of my life. I tell the truth about what I do, including what I eat or don't eat. My self-regulating system is restored. I naturally embrace healthy eating.

I have lots of extra time. Time wasted on obsessing is now a gift. I am relaxed. I have so much time to enjoy my life. I turn my time and energy into new exciting activities. I schedule time for fun. I get a life. It's fun to feel terrific.

I choose to eat protein and avoid fatty, processed foods. My eating is well balanced. I eat for fuel when I need to. I eat regularly and am biologically balanced. I stop eating when I am physically fueled. I up my energy and metabolism. I make healthy choices and eat fresh, lean and green.

I savor the flavor of each bite. I eat with reverence. Healthful eating fuels me. I make wise choices about what I eat. I have lots of time to do good and kind things for myself. I'm proud to be me.

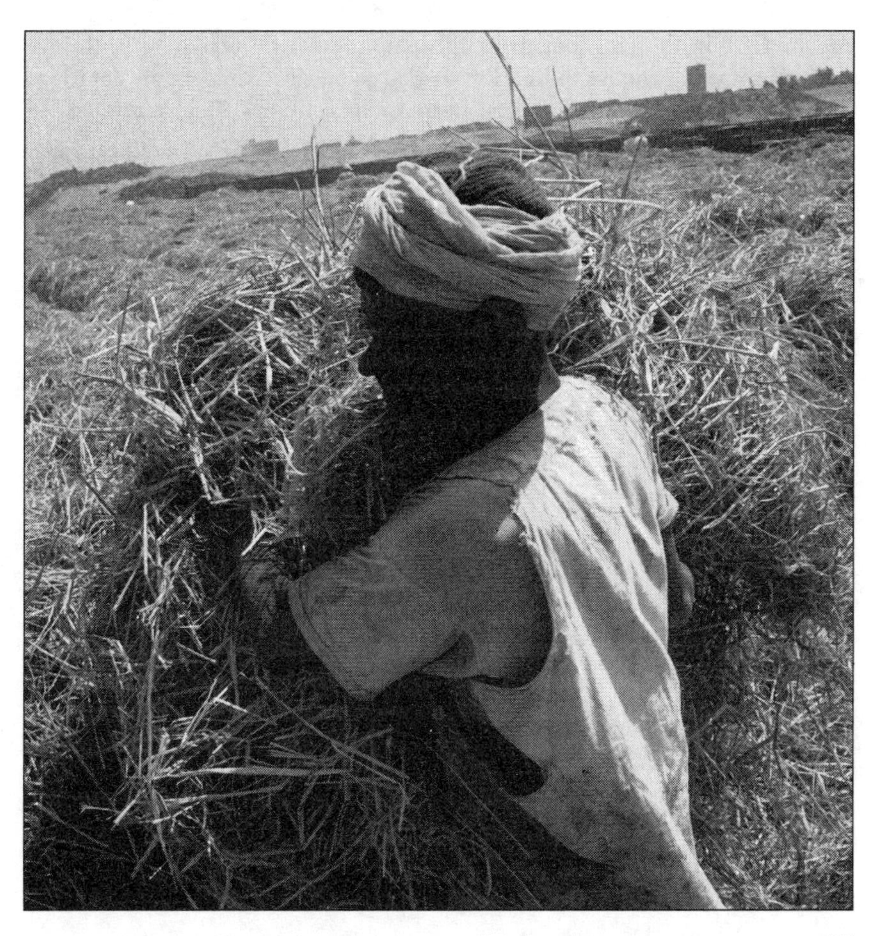

Script #3
AFFIRM SUCCESS: I'm My Perfect Shape

I am my comfortable healthy shape. I make an honest inventory of my attitudes and behaviors. I use proper nutrition and exercise to easily reach and maintain my perfect shape. I am comfortable being me.

The past is just a memory; the future is a fantasy. I am bigger (or smaller) than my history. My life is now. I make in-control choices that give me fuel for life and fun. My body becomes its perfect shape.

I look beautiful and I feel beautiful. I now become and maintain my healthy, appropriate weight. I'm conscious of what and how I eat. I eat when I need fuel. I stop when I am comfortably fueled. Eating fuels me. I make wise choices about what I eat.

All the food in the kingdom never fills emptiness. I fill myself up with love and self-respect. I choose to live. I'm so glad to be alive. I satisfy my emotions with my many interests, hobbies, talents and activities. I'm committed to feeling great. I have fun.

I manifest the perfect job, the perfect challenges, the perfect friends and loves. I have a perfect body. I tell the truth about everything I do. I tell the truth about what I eat or don't eat. I savor the flavor of each bite. I eat with reverence.

I am in perfect health. Because I no longer suffer from "food-overs" I feel great all the time. My body feels terrific. It feels great to move my body. I am radiant.

I'm comfortable being me. I enjoy parading my body in front of my loved one. I enjoy my sexuality. I love the ME I see in the mirror. "Hello beautiful/handsome one."

I am my body.
My body is me.
I love my body,
Unconditionally

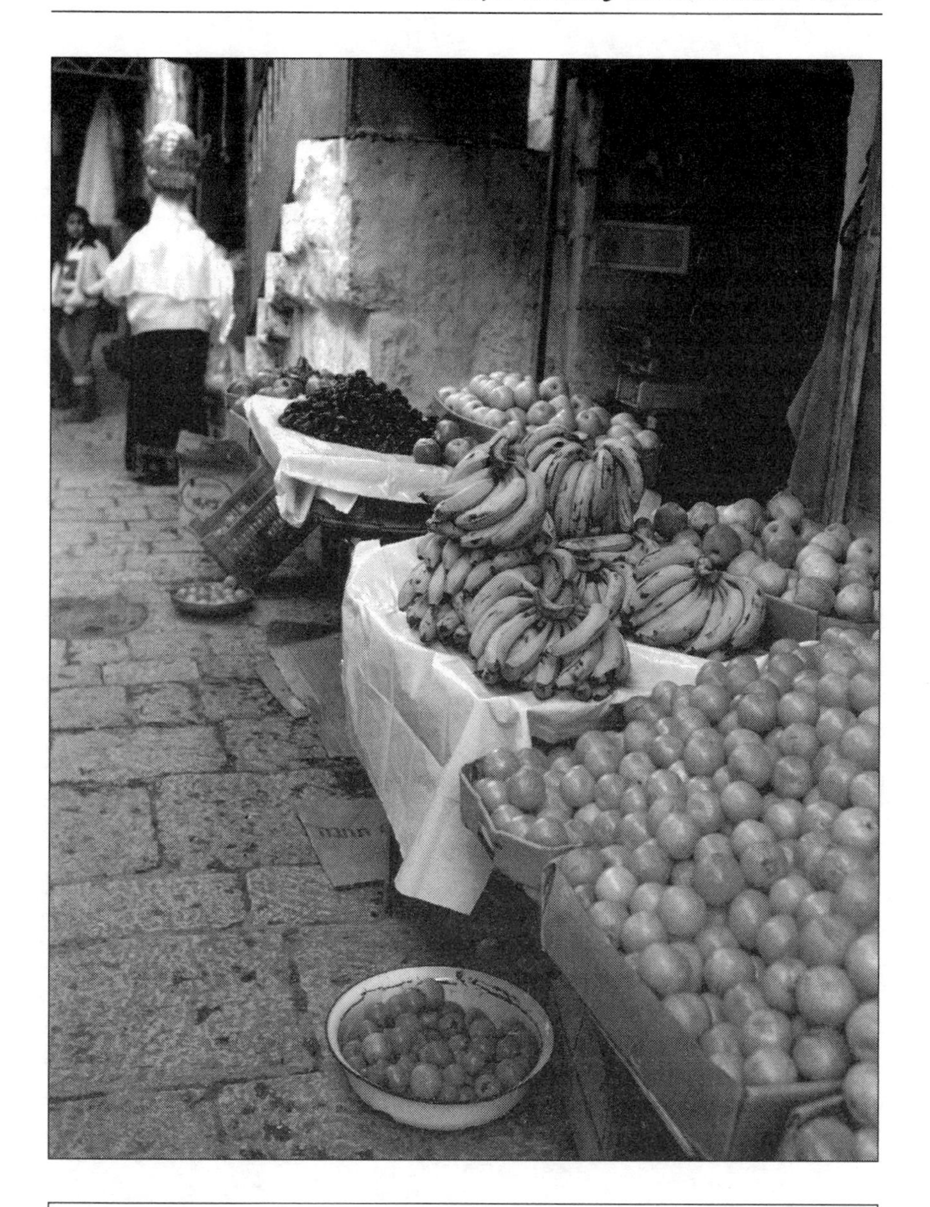

Hypno-Helper

To get fabulous shapely results, order Stockwell's Hypnosis for Weight Loss Program. It includes the Book: Stockwell's Hypnosis For Weight Loss: Ten Easy Steps to a New You, the video Stockwell's Weight Loss Seminar and the audio tapes Lose weight, No More Sugar Junkie, I Love Exercise, and Peace and Calm for only $99. You can order it at the back of this book.

Harem of the Dog That Bit You.

Chapter 22
Alcohol:
Embalming Fluid

Because alcohol is legal, readily available and popular, you may think it is safe. Think again. This chapter explores the joys and pitfalls of a real troublemaker. If you choose to get off the sauce, I recommend my audiotape No More Alcohol.

- **Mud in Your Eye From Days Gone By**
- **Why Do We Drink?**
- **What's the Problem?**
- **What Happens When You Are Drunk?**
- **What Causes a Hangover?**
- **Nine Truths: We All Have Our Axioms to Grind**
- **Step To Heaven On Earth**

Addled, besotted, binge, blind drunk, blitzed, blottoed, bombed, boozed, boozy, buzzed, canned, doped, drunk, drunk as a lord, ebriosity, far-gone, hammered, high, fried, hooked, inebriated, intoxicated (from the word toxic), loaded, pickled, pie-eyed, pissed, plastered, potted, ripped, see double, shellacked, shikker, slammed, smashed, snookered, sotted, stinko, stoned, swacked, three sheets to the wind, tight, tipsy, trashed, and wasted, describe the effects of alcohol.

Bibe, bolt, booze, chig, chug, down, drink, go on a spree, guzzle, hit the bottle, imbibe, knock back, kick back, make merry, nip, party, pull, quaff, suck up, sip, sup, swig, swill, slug 'em down, snort, slurp, tot, toast, tie one on, tipple, toss off, wet the whistle, and wolf, all describe the act of drinking.

Alcohol, antifreeze, barley-pop, barleycorn, brew, bubbly, cheer, draft, dram, embalming fluid, fire water, formaldehyde, grog, hooch, libation, liquor, medicine, panther piss, potation, poison, ruddy cup, reviver, rotgut, sauce, shine, social lubricant, snake medicine, snake oil, spirits, suds, tiger milk, tonic and vintage, are words used to describe alcoholic beverages.

A hangover is retribution for heavy drinking. A gin blossom describes the capillaries that burst on the nose and face because of excessive drinking.

Inner View Quiz

Do You Have A Drinking Problem?

Take this quiz and find out. Congratulate yourself for telling the truth.

___ My drinking and other habits have gotten out of hand.
If this is so, you already know that you are ready to change for the best.

One Tequila, Two Tequila, Three Tequila, Floor!

___ I'm sensitive and defensive about my drinking.
___ The amount of alcohol I consume is a secret.
___ I've decided to give up drinking several times.
___ I've switched drinks to reduce my alcoholic intake.
___ Life leaves me with no choice but to drink.
___ I can drink anyone under the table.
___ I'm the life of the party when I drink.
If any of these apply to you, you've been lying to yourself.

Ti Martunies and You Fool So Feelish

___ I use alcohol to escape or change moods or feeling.
___ I go out of control when drinking.
___ Alcohol controls me; I do not control it.
___ I try to tell myself that it's not a problem when I secretly know it is.
___ When I drink, my personality or behavior seems to change.
___ When I don't feel well, I drink.
___ When I drink, I don't feel well.
If any of these are true, alcohol is adding pain and stress to your life.

I'll Drink to Your Health Until I Lose Mine

___ I've awakened with a hangover.
___ Sometimes I drink in the morning.
___ Sometimes I drink before going to bed.
___ There are times when I feel I must have a drink.
___ There are times I say I won't drink, but I do anyway.
___ I drink when I take medications (for sleeping, pain...)
___ I frequently wind up drunk.
If any of these apply to you, your body is trying to get your attention. Alcohol poisons the body and lowers immunity. That's why you feel ill or hung over when you drink. Congratulate yourself for noticing. A healthy mind lives in a healthy body.

Use a Church Key and You Haven't Got a Prayer

___ It's not a social event without alcohol.
___ My drinking causes problems or hassles with others.
___ I've lost friends after a drinking incident.
___ I drink alone.

Drinking is a lonely habit. You can't be a good friend to another unless you are a good friend to yourself. If you checked any of these statements, you get the message.

Drinking Problem?

___ Social drinking at lunch is causing me problems.
___ I have missed work or school because of drinking.
___ I drink while at work or school.
___ I have been drunk at work or school.
___ I leave early to not miss the cheaper drinks at happy hour.
___ My work suffers because I drink.

If yes to these questions, drinking is interfering with your daily life. In truth there isn't any problem that alcohol can't worsen.

Blackout

___ I experience gaps in memory while drinking.

Blackouts are proof positive that your body is unable to process alcohol in a healthy fashion. That's what being an alcoholic means. A healthy central nervous system will pass out. An alcohol addict continues walking, talking, behaving and "functioning" while the impulse controlling brain "passes out."

Simple steps for a new life, clean and sober:

Responsible Social Drinker	**Out Of Control Drinker**
A pleasant social activity	The main focus of a social activity
Maintains personal drinking limit	Doesn't know when to stop Or can't stop
Switches to non-alcoholic drink	Keeps drinking when they've had enough
Never drinks and drives	Drinks and drives
Never takes alcohol with drugs	Combines alcohol & drugs
Eats while drinking; avoids salt	Doesn't eat when drinking excepts salty snacks & carbonated mixers or drinks alcohol straight to enhance its effect.
Has a drink at the party	Drinks before the party to get in the mood, during the party to stay high, and after the party for the "hair of the dog"

▲ Mud in Your Eye From Days Gone By

☆ *An Egyptian by name of Heroun*
Ate whisky by means of a spoon.
To one who asked, "why?"
Heroun made reply:
"To drink is forbidden, you loon."

Fruit juice, exposed to air, ferments. Alcohol was probably the hit of the ice age. Since then, it has been used socially, medically and religiously. In the first millennium BC, the Denizens of the Near East used wine as their principle commercial product, as did the later Minoans, Greeks and Romans. George Washington soaked his wooden dentures in port to "improve their flavor." In 1980, on an obscure finger of the Peruvian Amazon, untouched by the modern world, I was offered sugar cane wine.

Up Your Egypt

Early Cask It

The god Osiris was said to be the first man to drink wine and plant grapevines.

Six thousand-year-old hieroglyphics show grape growing and wine making in the Nile valley to the far side of the Mediterranean. Winemakers crushed the grapes with their feet but treaders kept slipping, falling in and drowning. So the Ancient Egyptians created a grid of overhead bars for them to hold on to.

Another popular Ancient Egyptian cocktail was made by cutting a hole in a ripe cucumber, slitting the insides with a stick, plugging it up and burying it in the ground for a few days. The fermented pulp made one high in a gulp.

Bread and Beer were important to the Ancient Egyptians. They used the foam from beer to make the bread rise. Beer foam is full of yeast, which we use today to make our bread rise. Their bread was used for money before coins were invented. Maybe that is why we call money "bread."

Parties, particularly funerary feasts, encouraged guests to drink to drunkenness. One tomb inscription shows a woman calling to a servant "Bring me eight more goblets of wine! Can't you see I am trying to get drunk! My throat is as dry as dust."

▲ Why Do We Drink?

☆ *"Why do you drink?"*
"I drink to forget."
"What are you trying to forget?"
"I can't remember."

A drink helps people relax, escape tension, fit in and have fun. Occasionally, and in small amounts, drinking does these things well.

A few drinks make you high by numbing the control centers of your brain and fatiguing your central nervous system. You don't consciously notice the fatigue since it bypasses your feedback mechanism. That's why, while you are drinking, you think you feel OK.

▲ What's the Problem?

☆ *"Why did you take up the piano?"*
"My beer kept slipping off the violin."

Alcohol ruins your looks, gives you bad breath, and makes you gain weight. Alcohol affects your brain, mind and behavior. With alcohol, you do things that create a lot to worry about. Alcohol causes depression, dullness and guilt.

Even the smallest amount, significantly impairs judgment and coordination. One or two beers puts your brain to sleep and can mean the difference between an accident and a near miss.

Drugs and alcohol distort your body's healthy ability to mentally map your body parts in relation to each other. That's why police use the "nose touching sobriety test."

Alcohol is a Diuretic that Dehydrates

☆ *"A drinkers is a middleman between the beer and the outhouse."*

Alcohol and its byproducts suppress hormones that regulate urinary output and pull water out of cells, causing dehydration. Not only does a drinker lose water, they lose precious reserves of salts, vitamins and minerals.

Alcohol removes magnesium, which is the memory mineral. That's one of the reasons drinkers forget. Tremors and cramps result from the loss of magnesium and also B vitamins. When alcohol robs your body of magnesium, B vitamins (particularly B6, B1) thiamin, potassium, calcium, C and others, your nerves are not nourished and you feel nervous. Depletion of resources also makes you more susceptible to virus, bacteria and illness.

Alcohol Upsets Your Stomach

Irritated stomach lining and increases gastric acids back up causing heartburn.

Alcohol is Polluted

Most alcohol contains contaminants, which result from the additives of the fermentation process. Red wine uses an aspirin derivative, causing a severe allergic reaction for many.

Have you noticed the sulfites warning on wine? Sulfites are added as a preservative to prevent discoloration, bacterial growth and fermentation. Sulfites are the only additives publicly proclaimed to kill people. That is why wine has the warning label says that it is dangerous for pregnant women to drink.

Alcohol is Fattening

Alcohol has 7 calories per gram.
Spiked eggnog (4oz + 1.5 oz rum)= 268 calories.
12 oz beer= 146 calories.
12 oz ginger ale= 124 calories
5 oz red wine= 106 calories
5 oz white wine= 100 calories
5 oz champagne= 116 calories
1.5 oz vodka, 80 proof= 97 calories

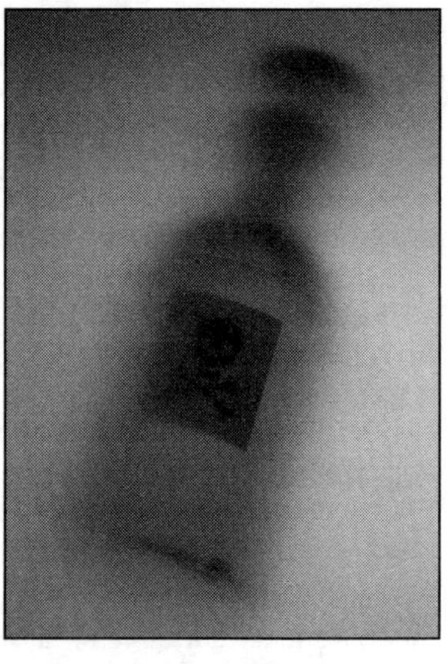

Alcohol is a Nightmare

Because a drink makes it easier to drift off to sleep, some think that it is a good sleep aid. Actually, the metabolization of alcohol usually wakes you up. The sugar in the alcohol further interrupts sleeping patterns.

Alcohol inhibits REM (rapid eye movement) dream sleep and disrupts sleep patterns. When this happens, you cannot process and balance yourself psychologically. You awaken feeling irritable, fatigued and depressed. People don't always connect daytime fatigue with a nightcap.

Your body takes about five hours to absorb a "night nip." At which time you go through withdrawal. This fragments, lightens and disrupts sleep even more, activating troubled dreams.

Alcohol aggravates sleep apnea, by causing mouth and throat muscles to relax and represses the breathing mechanism. That's why drinkers sometimes die of asphyxiation. The more sleep apnea, the less oxygen enters the blood and the more your brain is damaged. That's another reason why long time drinkers get weird.

Alcohol Fatigues and Depresses

☆ *"Chronic Drinkers Get Stiff in the Joints."*

—Shelley Stockwell

Because alcohol lowers inhibitions and creates feelings of euphoria, it is sometimes thought of as a stimulant. It's not, it's a depressant. When the buzz subsides, fatigue and lethargy are usually left over. Alcohol is a main contributor to chronic fatigue. It clouds thoughts and depresses. This mental fog gets worse if alcohol is taken with tranquilizers and antihistamines.

As the blood alcohol levels rise, more internal senses are suffocated and blotted out; social control, muscular coordination, emotional stability and clear judgment are impaired.

Over Time, Alcohol Kills Sexual Desire and Performance

Since alcohol affects your hormones, it eventually harms sexual functioning.

Brain Drain

Your blood-brain barrier, filters and prevents harmful chemicals from reaching your brain. It cannot stop alcohol. Five percent is *instantly* absorbed into your mouth and tongue and sent to your brain within five seconds. There it kills and distorts brain cells. Alcohol's fatty acids clog neurons and effect your reaction time. Emotional dullness spins you out on an up and down emotional roller coaster and results in *stinkin' thinkin'*.

The numbing quality of alcohol takes the guts out of joy. That's why some drinkers feel and look dull. For others, brain and organ damage causes exaggerated and hysterical behavior, which also kills joy.

Remaining alcohol goes to the stomach, where it irritates stomach lining and increases gastric acids. It's so irritating that if you put a drop of whiskey on the back of a scorpion, it will sting itself to death. Your stomach gets rid of alcohol as fast as possible by sending one-fourth of it through the blood vessels of the stomach lining. The blood flows more alcohol to the brain.

Infants born marinated in alcohol suffer from fetal alcohol syndrome, with mental retardation and physical abnormalities. Depending on when and how much drug was introduced in their development, they can have deformed lips and joint problems, epilepsy, seizures and low IQ's.

Let Me Go Liver

☆ *"The last time I gave a urine sample there was an olive in it."*

—Rodney Dangerfield

Remaining alcohol goes to your small intestines and then the liver, and pancreas, where it is broken into sugar, water, carbon dioxide, alcohol and contaminants like poisonous histamines, acetaldehyde, acetylcholine and then

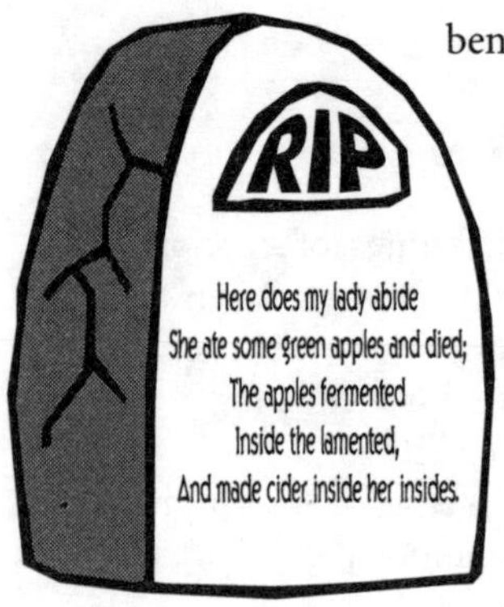

benign acetate. Contaminants are stored in fatty tissue.

Have you ever noticed a flush red color on a drinker's face? It's caused from the poisonous acetaldehyde and acetylcholine. Over time, these poisons also cause poor reflexes and slurred speech.

Chronic and binge drinkers permanently alter their liver so that it no longer metabolizes alcohol. A healthy liver breaks down only one and one-half ounces of alcohol per hour. Your precious liver is like a rubbish dump. More than one drink per hour seriously overtaxes your liver. Over time, an abused liver becomes spongy, less permeable to health-giving water and suffers irreversibly damaged.

Yellowed or muddyish skin color and a dry morning mouth, are symptoms that an overloaded liver is storing toxins in your skin, bones, tonsils, tissue and organs.

Has drinking or other toxic habits make you irritable, allergic and your vision less clear? If so, these are signs that an overloaded, malfunctioning liver is being harmed.

Have You Ever Had a Lapse of Memory While Drinking?

If so, it is *proof* that liver damage has begun. If your liver were perfectly healthy, you would have passed out long before your memory blacked out.

Allergies are a result of an over taxed or polluted liver. The more toxins a liver's exposed to, the more sensitive and reactive you become to other toxins and drugs.

▲ What Happens When You Are Drunk?

☆ *"I don't jog. It makes the ice jump out of my glass."*
—Martin Mull

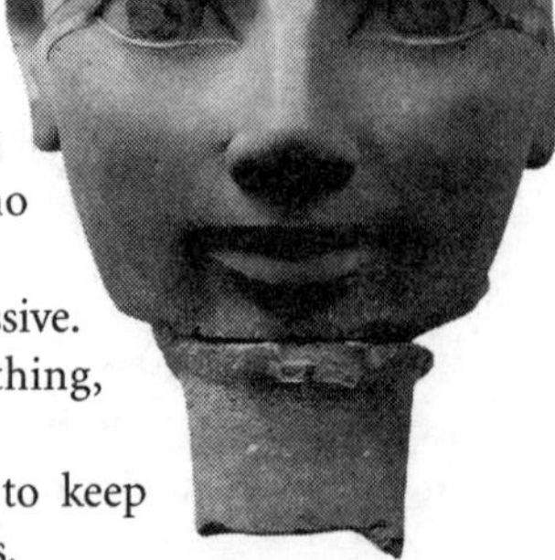

Alcohol affects brain chemistry. One ounce of alcohol can kill thousands of brain cells. Over eight neurotransmitters, the chemical messengers of the brain, are profoundly affected. This alters your senses, thinking, memory, concentration and actions and eventually causes hallucinations. There is no glamour or adventure in being a drunk.

Altered *seratonin* levels make you sleepy or aggressive.

Norepinephrine interference effects breathing, temperature, and raises blood pressure.

Lowered production of *GABA* causes a drinker to keep drinking, get depressed and sometimes have seizures.

Endorphins and *enkephalins* are replaced by THIQ, which is similar to morphine. This is what creates cravings, anxiety, depression and pain when you stop drinking.

Imbalanced neuro transmitters dehydrate and deplete vitamins like B and minerals like salt, potassium and amino acids. This lowers your body's ability to fight illness.

▲ What Causes a Hangover?

When all alcohol is burned up in the body and no more follows, alcohol-altered brain cells go into withdrawal. Blood vessels in the head swell and cause headaches, dizzy spells and nausea.

Alcohol upsets the balance in your inner ear, which sometimes causes nausea.

The depletion of minerals that result from alcohol contribute to the headache, aches, stomach disorders and fatigue that come along with hangovers.

Many cures abound for "helping" a hangover, raw eggs in tomato juice, coffee, and more booze. If you drink coffee or more alcohol, you simply prolong and intensify an inevitable hangover.

Your best bet is to not drink in the first place, or if it's too late for that, drink water, eat a mild meal, have some fruit juice, take a vitamin, put an ice bag on your head and then sleep it off.

▲ Nine Truths: We All Have Our Axioms to Grind

☆ AS A REMOVER OF THINGS, ALCOHOL HAS NO EQUAL

Alcohol removes stains from clothes, clothes off your back, food from the table, the lining from your stomach, vision from your eyes and judgment from your mind. It also removes good reputations, jobs, friends, happiness from children's hearts, freedom, love and life itself.

—by Jennifer and Kelly

Here is the skinny on what really happens when you drink:

Axiom #1: You Must Lie & Deny to Poison Your Body

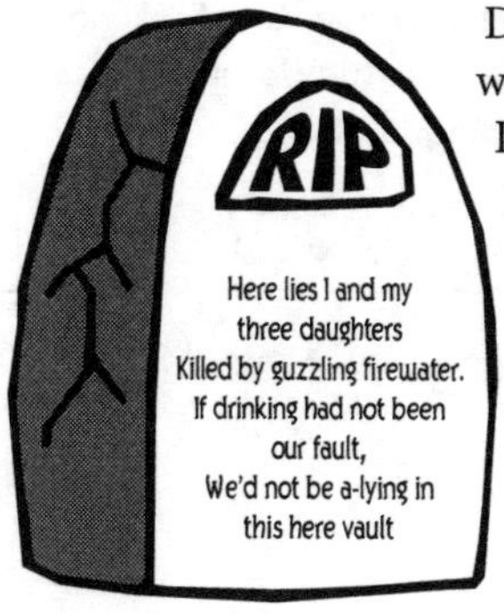

Denial is when you refuse to believe that you are doing what you are doing...harming your body and life. Drinkers drink to numb out pain and discomfort, and pretend they are doing just fine.

Hurting yourself, requires denial, manipulation and games. Without lies no one would continue drinking. Self-deception compromises integrity and self-esteem. Even if a drinker acts OK or behaves like a "know-it-all," inside they feel grief, sorrow and guilt.

Are You In Denial?

☆ *"I always keep a supply of liquor handy, in case I see a snake. Which I also keep handy."*

—W.C. Fields

Cross your heart and hope to die, do you buy these Alibis?

It's not me:

___ "I don't have a problem with alcohol."
___ "I can stop any time I want."
___ "I didn't act that badly."
___ "People who judge me are prudes."

It's not my fault:

___ "I work hard; I deserve a drink."
___ "The children (my boss, my mate) are impossible."
___ "I'm a wreck. I need a drink."
___ "I had a terrible childhood. Drinking helps me put the past behind me."

It's your fault:

___ "No one understands me. Guess I'll have a drink."
___ "If you weren't so hard to get along with, I wouldn't drink."
___ "I had a terrible childhood; down the hatch."

I'm Super Man/Woman:

___ "I can't leave my job and family to go into a rehab program."
TRUTH: You leave your family and job every time you take a drink, because you are not there any more.

___ "I'll detoxify myself."
TRUTH: If you do it, terrific. The problem is, you may only stop drinking and not heal the underlying cause. Quitting that way usually doesn't last long. Help helps you change patterns. People who stop often develop the "I'm not drinking, that's enough, don't ask anything more of me" attitude and find a great many excuses to just "tip a few." Stop pretending. Get help.

___ "I couldn't bear going through detoxification: DTs, convulsions and moods swings are horrible."
TRUTH: Believe these alibis and you convince yourself to keep drinking. Underlying pain worsens pain.

___ "I can stop any time I want to"
TRUTH: If that were true, your drinking would have stopped long ago.
___ I'm responsible. I don't drink and drive. I always have a designated driver.
If you depend on the alcohol "to relax," "have fun," "numb," or "kill emotional or physical pain." Get real and

GET LIVING!
All drinking alcoholics believe they are not.
They lie to themselves and say; "I'm just fine."
If you pretend that drinking is OK, and continue to drink, guaranteed you'll cause yourself great mental and physical damage.
Alcohol does not discriminate. It is an equal opportunity compulsion that cuts through all financial levels, ethnic groups and ages. Contrary to popular myth, only about 3-5% of alcoholics are skid row bums; the rest are good, kind, lovable folks just like you. Over time, no matter who you are, alcohol will screw you up. All the lying, denying and convincing others will not change the truth. Alcoholism is a compulsion. It runs you, you don't run it.

All in the Family

Not only do you have to lie to harm yourself, others around you mollify you by lying to and about you.

In truth, if you, or someone you love, are in trouble with booze, you know the problems it causes.

Drinkers are unavailable. You never talk to a drinker; you talk to their drink. A "relationship" with a drinker leaves you emotionally alone and angry about being abused, abandoned and/or mistreated. Promises not kept, meals not eaten, functions not attended, holidays ruined and time wasted on stupidity, are very frustrating to deal with.

Mates and children "walk on eggs," carefully avoiding the drinkers out-of-control behavior. Because alcohol lowers impulse control, drinkers are often physically, sexually and verbally abusive with family members. Fear and self-preservation motivates some to pretend.

The drinker constantly focuses on drinking, while the spouse and children constantly focus on the drinker. Watching another human slowly kill them self is painful. Drinking harms loved ones so severely they often go away for self-preservation.

Drinkers who pretend or believe that they really don't have a problem often have the whole family pretend right along with them. Family members, who rationalize drinking, (called enablers) live in fear, anger and depression.

Excuses drinkers give often become accepted rationales by the whole family: "Poor Dad (Mom, Sis, Bro, Daughter, Son), they have such a hard time because of ________. It's no wonder they drink."

Family members pretend in order to protect. "They can't help themselves." Co-dependents think that they can rescue someone else.

Drinkers often blame others for their drinking problem and family members may accept responsibility. "I can help them to stop hurting themselves if I try a little harder."

"If I'd stop nagging, he'll stop drinking."

"If I had the meal cooked on time, she'd be sweet."

"Daddy says I'm not cooperative enough."

Some protect out of embarrassment; "What would the neighbors think?"

Some protect for fear it might hurt the family income. They call in sick for the drinker, make excuses and stomp out the fires.

Family members with drinking issues themselves deny others have a problem for fear they will have to deal with their own issues.

Children of out-of-control people suffer because their emotional needs are overlooked. They shut down physically or emotionally. Children erroneously believe that if they just keep their room cleaner, get better grades, or are better people, the drinker will stop.

Children of drinkers, drug takers and even smokers live in fear, and uncertainty. They never know how the self-destructive one will behave. Arguments, abuse and lack of impulse control may become role models for children who grow up and become just like Mom or Dad.

Drinking is often a family secret. Enablers clean up after the drinker. Make up stories or withdraw from social situations. Such family "support" makes problems worse. The abuser avoids owning the consequences of their self-destruction.

Elephant? What Elephant?

☆ *I think you'd better stop drinking now, you're getting blurry.*

Where there is a self-destructive family member, there is an enormous elephant under the living room carpet. Everyone knows it's there and no one talks about it. They simply walk or talk around it. If the truth was told, and everyone refused to play, the responsibility would shift to the drinker. Drinkers who wake up from the trance of self-destruction get to grow up, get a grip on life and stop pretending. The family who honestly reports the elephant under the rug gets a chance to heal and get real.

When victims of a drinker stand up and speak their piece, they experience great relief, for they have now put the ball in the drinker's court. The drinker, also feels a great sense of release, because they don't have to hide a secret life any more. Only raw truth evokes positive change.

A TRUE STORY K.D. Dillon, professional interventionist

(Edited excerpt Lear's Magazine April 1993)

"We had a typical family; never talked about it, never mentioned it." "When my father died of alcoholism in 1942, his death certificate read, "Cause of death: exhaustion."

"My family denied his alcoholism so deeply that they did not even question this improbably cause of death."

"There was so much stigma around the term alcoholism that no one talked about it. The first time my mother ever mentioned my Father's alcoholism was twenty years later."

12 Things You Can Do for Yourself If a Loved One Drinks

Don't do an alcoholic loved one more harm than good. You are not responsible or in control of another's drinking. Avoid the following co-dependent behaviors at all costs.

1. Don't regard alcoholism as a family disgrace

Another person's habit is their habit. It is not your problem. Tell the truth in the world, and you will be pleasantly surprised how others will support you in taking good care of yourself.

2. Don't nag, preach, or lecture

Chances are they have already told themselves everything that you can tell them. Nagging only increases their need to lie or make promises they can't possibly keep.

3. Give up "holier-than-thou" or martyr

You create this impression without saying a word. Alcoholics judge another's attitudes by small things rather just the spoken words.

4. Don't use the "...If you loved me" appeal

This only increases their guilt. Love of home and family is not enough incentive to seek recovery. The motivation to regain self-respect is more compelling than a demand to respect you.

5. Avoid threats unless thought out carefully and you definitely intend to carry it out

Idle threats mean that you don't mean what you say.

6. Don't hide or dispose of liquor
This makes the drinker desperate. In the end, they will simply find new ways of getting more.
7. Don't play the "drink with me and you'll drink less" game
It doesn't work. When you condone drinking, the problem drinker puts off getting help.
8. Don't be jealous of the recovery method they choose
If you feel left out when the alcoholic turns to others for help, get over it. You wouldn't be jealous of the doctor if someone needed medical care, would you?
9. Don't expect an immediate 100% recovery
In any destructive pattern, there is a period of convalescence. Relapses, tension and resentment may show their ugly face while behaviors change.
10. Don't do for alcoholics what they can do for themselves
You cannot take someone's medicine for them. A rescuer deprives the drinker of facing, solving and taking the consequences of their drinking. Rescue yourself instead.
11. Don't treat the alcoholic like a child.
Infantalizing anyone (except an infant) is insulting. It undermines self-confidence and another feels weak and helpless.
12. Support sobriety.
Love and respect the human underneath the alcohol. Love and respect your children and yourself.

Source: Care Unit Hospital

Axiom #2: Drinking's a Solution that Always Turns into a Bigger Problem

The Circle of Addiction

Addiction and compulsion create infinitely more problems and than any problem you attempt to numb.

Dependency can occur on the first drink or from drinking too much for too long. Problem drinkers are often cross-addicted and tend to replace drinking with other destructive behavior. It's not unusual at an AA meeting to see a volcano in the ashtray, bowls of candy and copious amounts of coffee and soft drinks. So long alcohol, hello sugar, caffeine and nicotine.

Drinkers build up a tolerance to the effects of alcohol and simultaneously develop a tolerance for other drugs like barbiturates. That's why they can survive an enormous dose of barbiturates the first time.

Extra, Extra, Read All About It

The father of Siamese twins born in Lakesburg, spent donations given for his children's surgery on a three-day cocaine and alcohol binge. "I need help, I don't want to lose my family." He said later.

Rodney King sparked Los Angeles riots while driving under the influence.

"I look for ways to calm down," says a police captain. "Drug and alcohol abuse are major problems among law enforcement officers. Our stress is enormous...Undercover cops sample the wares."

Airline pilots share "barley pop" beer (and hard liquor) in hotel rooms to "de-brief."

The Valdez oil spill was caused by a drunken captain.

Axiom #3: Alcoholics Never Remember or Forget Statements About Drinking

If you're touchy about your drinking, you're troubled inside. The part of you that knows the truth, gets upset when you deceive yourself or when someone points out your denial. Even if you never remember anything when drinking, guaranteed you never forget what others say about your drinking.

Why is it that people who drink to forget never forget to drink?

Axiom #4: The Pain You Try to Numb is Directly Proportional to How Addictive and Compulsive You Are

Axiom #5: Alcohol is an Acquired Pattern, Therefore You Can Change It

☆ *"Son, when you participate in sporting events, it's not whether you win or lose, it's how drunk you get."*

—Homer Simpson

Some say that there is a genetic reason for alcoholism. It's true that a drinker has more THIQ, the morphine like chemical disrupter. It's also true that the biological children of heavy drinkers are born with more THIQ than others. But no one is born an alcohol drinker. Alcohol drinking is an acquired pattern and therefore, can be changed.

Axiom #6: Alcohol is a Caustic Killer

Alcohol is a one-way street ending in a miserable death—your own. It is now considered the Number three killing disease behind heart disease and cancer.

According to law enforcement authorities, alcohol is responsible for over sixty-percent of all traffic deaths, fifty-percent of all drowning and fire deaths, seventy-five percent of all people in jails, and twenty-five percent of all suicides.

In fifteen to twenty-four year-olds, alcohol is linked as the number one cause of car wrecks, suicides and homicides deaths.

Putting the Quart Before the Hearse

In 1987, 2,754 persons died in accidents in California caused by someone drinking. That averages out to about eight people a day. Some 68,816 were injured in alcohol-related accidents, which averages out to 188 a day, in California alone.

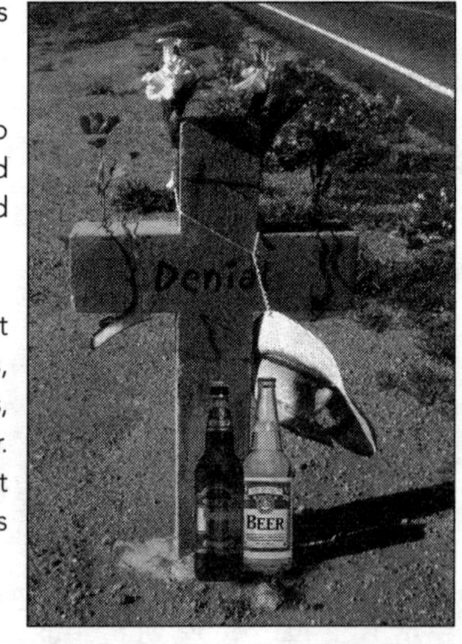

Even though young people—ages 15 to 24—represent only 16.2% of the licensed drivers, they represent 31.6% of drivers killed or injured in alcohol-related crashes.

Alcohol-related automobile accidents cost our society (including productivity losses, insurance, the cost of government programs, etc.) approximately $642 million each year. While the cost to a defendant of a first conviction for driving under the influence is approximately $2,000.

(from California Office of Criminal Justice Planning)

Axiom #7: You Can Never Control Alcohol

☆ *"Lose ways that make you be*
What you really don't want to be
Lose ways that make you love
What you really don't want to love"

—Nick Drake

You honestly know if alcohol has been an issue. If it is, stop drinking immediately. The only method of arresting alcoholism is total abstinence. To control your life, stop drinking alcohol. If you continue to drink, your compulsion to drink gets worse.

Will power is not the answer, "won't power" is. Hypnosis makes change easier by creating new patterns of behavior.

A TRUE STORY: Rafaela

"I was the youngest of five children. After I was born, my father left my mother, and she left me with my grandmother. She was too busy to watch over me. When I was five, I had a nosebleed. I was all-alone. I was sure I was dying. I didn't tell Grandmother. I thought she'd get mad.

I rarely saw my mother. I was frightened of my older sister and brothers, and I learned to keep quiet. When I was seven, my older sister and my uncle Juan taught me to play a game called sex. I would be the star.

When I was sixteen, I married a man twice my age. He took me to America. I thought I could start all over again, leaving my lonely life behind. I didn't love my husband but he was kind to me. I started to drink a little.

Then, I fell in love with another man and told my husband. He was very understanding and I drank more. Eventually, I left him and moved in with my boyfriend. We ran a nightclub where I became a topless dancer. The only way I could dance was to drink. My boyfriend and I had two children. My children don't know what I do for a living and I've hidden my alcohol. "What kind of an example am I for my children?"

One night, a voice spoke to me. It said, 'Find spirit.' I started seeing Shelley for hypnosis. I joined a yoga class. Thanks to these two things, I stopped drinking and I've gone back to school. I've left my boyfriend and my life is beginning all over again—for real. The one piece of advice I'd give anyone with a serious drinking problem is: ask for spiritual guidance and realize that the past is truly past. Life begins now."

Axiom #8: Regardless of What You Drink, Alcohol Damages Your Body in the Same Way.

There are lots of old wives or husband tales about how to handle your booze, like:

Beer before whiskey; pretty risky
Whiskey before beer; never fear

It makes no difference if you drink beer, wine, a cocktail or alcohol hidden in mouth wash; the results are the same. Fermented fruits and grains destroy organs and brain cells. One and a half ounces of whiskey has as much alcohol as 5-ounces of wine, a 12-ounce beer or a wine cooler.

Alcohol is hidden in over-the-counter remedies. Most mouth washes have as much as 15 to 25% alcohol. Robitussin has *benso* alcohol, a powdered form of alcohol. Vanilla, herbal remedies, tinctures and perfume often are alcohol laden.

Alcoholic Guide

Item	% Alcohol	Added Sugar	Calories
Beer, 12 oz			
Lite beer	5%		70+
Regular			150
Wine, 4 oz:			
Dry white, Rose, Red	12%		80
Champagne/ sparking			80
Wine cooler	5%		100
Sherry, 2 oz.			
	81		
Dessert Wine		3.4 tsp.	100
Hard liquor, 2 oz.			
Manhattan			175
Martini			160
Old fashioned			150
Gin and tonic			180
Average shot of hard liquor			140
Average shot with fruit juice or soft drink (6 oz)189			
Average shot with regular tonic water			176
Rum with egg nog, 4 oz			300+
Liqueurs and cordials, .07 oz		1.5 tsp.	
Brandy or cognac, 1 oz		1.7 tsp.	
Over-the-Counter Remedies			
Most Mouth Washes	15-25%		
Nyquil	25%		
Tylenol Drops w/codeine	5%		

Axiom #9: The Destructive Effects of Alcohol Are Cumulative.

☆ *"Ale has too often been praised by poets. The longer you drink the less sense your mind makes of things."*

—1000-Year-Old Viking saying from Havamal

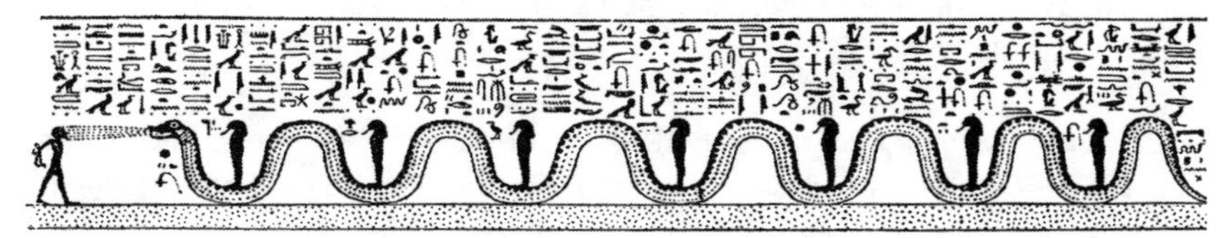

Each year you drink, permanently destroys your internal organs, nervous system and brain cells. You damage your social relationships and eventually become incapacitated and die.

Slow Suicide

☆ *Studies in France say that wine every day*
lessens the risk of heart decay.
"Red Bordeaux lowers cholesterol
By giving doses of resveratrol."
Liver disease there is astronomical.
"A votre santé," Now that's ironical?

—Shelley Stockwell

It takes eighteen months for alcohol to leave your spinal column. Guaranteed, if you continue to drink, mental, physical and social damage will occur. Physical addiction and social alienation make life fuzzy, unreal and deadened. Eventually, alcohol costs you a fortune in money, happiness and threatens life itself.

The longer you ingest alcohol, the more it changes your body, mind and perceptions. The more alcohol, the more the possibility of accidents, aggressive acts, child and spouse abuse, learning and remembering dysfunction, breathing disorders, health issues and death. Alcohol leads to poor nutrition and damages the vital organs like the brain and liver.

The Difference Between Drinking Adults and Youths

For adolescents, there is no such thing as "responsible use" of an illegal substance. Whereas an adult can tolerate moderate amounts of alcohol, children cannot. Adolescents—up to the age of 24—get addicted far more quickly than adults because their bodies are still growing. It can take an adult 5 to 15 years to become physically addicted. It only takes an adolescent 6 months to two years. The children of alcoholics are four times more likely to become alcoholic themselves.

If you try to deaden growing pains, two things happen: (1) the pain gets progressively worse and (2) you stop growing and maturing.

Lady Watch Out!

Obesity, liver damage and hypertension are stronger in women drinkers than men drinkers. Forty percent of patients who die with cirrhosis of the liver, are women. Drinking women have four times the mortality rate of non-drinking women—a 15-year shorter life span.

Research shows that wine raises the level of a heart protector called HDL. Since heart disease is the leading killer of women, doctors often advise women patients to drink wine, as a precaution. Women already have high levels of HDL, and they have a much lower tolerance for alcohol.

▲ Step To Heaven On Earth

Take the following steps for full recovery:

- **Drink Water:** Six to eight glasses of water a day and even more when you exercise will cleanse you.
- **Get Exercise:** Walk, swim, play, run, bike and/or lift weights
- **Think Lean and Green:** Eat fresh fruits and vegetables, whole grains, lean meats.
- **Take a Multiple Vitamin:** Make sure your vitamin contains at least 500 mg of Vitamin C each day. Some have said that one-half gram or 1/8 teaspoon of glutamine (an amino acid found in liver, meat, fish, and dairy) before and after meals and at bedtime will help me with withdrawal.

Step to Heaven

- **Stay Conscious and Awake**
- **Touch God:** Become intimately aware of your connection to God.
- **Avoid Unnecessary Stress**
- **Live and Love:** Choose to live every moment in truth, harmony and love.
- **Be Kind:** Say Good, Kind, and Nourishing Things to Yourself
- **Breathe Well**
- **Expect Withdrawal:** Two days, to two months may be stressful. Withdrawal is a sign that your clarity is returning. Hang in there. Your body is releasing toxins and your sense of reality is not longer distorted. During withdrawal, some feel irritable, anxious or slightly nauseas. Celebrate the cravings, sleeplessness, tremors or emotional mood swings. They are wonderful signs that your body is truly detoxifying and you are returning to health.

To make withdrawal easier:

Let
Out
Vital
Energy

- **Become a full-Fledged Pleasure-Seeker:** The world is now indulging in a conspiracy to do you good. You cannot sabotage it any more. Spoil yourself by spending the money you would normally have used on alcohol or drugs on something you would enjoy. Invest in something that develops you; sign up for a class, buy a great book. Learn something new.
- **Read or Record the Script in this Chapter:** If you read, record or listen to the prerecorded, "No More Alcohol" tape, (you can order it from the back of this book.) you condition your mind to stay in a healthy place and your actions will follow.

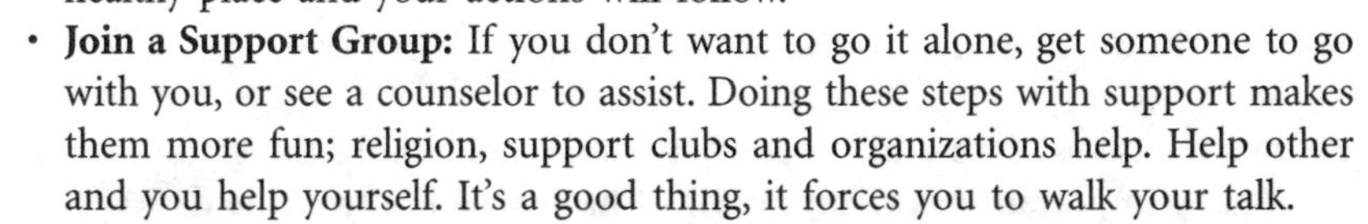

- **Join a Support Group:** If you don't want to go it alone, get someone to go with you, or see a counselor to assist. Doing these steps with support makes them more fun; religion, support clubs and organizations help. Help other and you help yourself. It's a good thing, it forces you to walk your talk.
- **Change Your Routine:** When you change habits, you eliminate temptation. Remove all liquor from your car, home and office. Announce to all your friends and family that you no longer drink. Stay away from those who do.

AFFIRM SUCCESS: Truthfully Fess Up

Read these power scripts to yourself twice daily or record it in your own voice. Or order the cassette tape "No More Alcohol" from the back of this book. Think the words as you read or hear them:

Excuses hurt. The more lying it takes, the more it hurts. It's too much work to lie. It's easier to tell the truth. I easily live my truth.

I have a drinking and behavior problem. My problems were created by toxic poisonous alcohol and the stress it created. There I said it. I give myself an A++. I Stay clear on what is real and what is illusion.

I take back my life. I get a grip. I act and react in ways that make me proud of myself. Sobriety means peace. I enjoy myself. I enjoy being good to myself. I love drinking pure water.

The truth sets me free. I hear the voice of my truth. I listen. I'm totally honest with myself. I'm brave and strong. I love helping myself.

Affirmations, hypnosis tapes, self help books and someone holding the mirror keeps me honest. Help helps.

AFFIRM SUCCESS: I Take Control of My Life
Now that I am grown up, I have the choice of thinking, reasoning and acting grown up. I have the ability to view life and the way I live it.

I live life fully. I enjoy the rich experience of my time here. I am growing and maturing with clarity, directness and wisdom. I trust my senses for I know that they never lie. Nobody else knows me as well as I do. I know I need to do to make my life perfect. I listen to the deep inner me.

I listen to my inner wisdom. Tell myself the truth and as I do, I take forceful command of myself. I am grown up I change the idea of into the truth: I am a victor. Life's challenges are an adventure of my growth and wisdom. I feel terrific.

Answer this question: Do you want to be happy?

My answer is yes! I vow to do good, positive, nourishing things for myself. Something important has changed: ME! I have an uncontrollable desire to be healthy, clean and sober. I am a naturally healthy person.

Photo by Neredah Bradstreet

AFFIRM SUCCESS: Victim to Victor
Congratulations ___________ (say your name). You are making positive and permanent changes in your life. I am proud of you.

I'm kind to my body. I choose joy, I choose health, I choose to live. I take control of my body, mind, energy, and life. I'm honest and clear minded as I take back control of myself. I feel so glad to be alive.

My potential is unlimited! I'm strong and powerful as I move forward. Lucky me, I am a victor.

I tell myself the truth. I know that create every part of my life. I'm responsible for everything in my life. The buck stops here.

When I was born, the doctor didn't hold me up and say, "this little person will be an addict." I learned to put toxic chemicals into my body. I now learn to put healthy things into my body. I'm emotionally mature, my brain cells regenerate, my thinking is clear. I have healthy habits.

To feel good, I always tell myself the truth and take responsibility for my behavior. I own my feelings, I handle challenges. I honestly own my feelings. I tell the truth. I'm peaceful and happy. Hooray!

Past, incorrect ideas made me numb and didn't work. I find healthy diversions. The truth is that drinking hurt my body and caused me stinkin' thinkin'. Toxic alcohol creates bigger problems than any problem I avoided. I don't put poison into my precious body. Alcohol and drugs are poison. I consciously change my routines to eliminate poison. I hate alcohol.

I have an overwhelming desire to experience my life. Life's challenges are opportunities to help me grow. Changes allow me to learn and live.

When I was little, I had baby teeth. When they fell out, it might have been uncomfortable, but it was a necessary step. I needed new adult teeth. That's how life is. Positive change is rewarding. I grow and mature with each new experience. I'm awake and experience my life. I look forward to reaching my personal goals. I enjoy learning, feeling, and maturing. I'm ever growing in wisdom and love.

I have an overwhelming desire to be healthy. My inner wisdom understands what is toxic. Alcohol, sugar, drugs, caffeine and tobacco are deadly killers. Alcohol and kerosene are all mixed up in my head. The thought of pouring disgusting kerosene in my mouth disgusts me.

I remember how badly alcohol/kerosene made me feel. I choose to feel great. I am healthy. Each day in every way, I feel better and better and better. I'm unique. I'm beautiful. I am forgiven.

I choose to live. I am abundant, happy and mature.
I'm a true pleasure seeker because I do good, positive, healthy things for myself. I thoroughly enjoy myself, the world around me, the people, the creatures and mother earth.

I eat nourishing foods, exercise, and drink lots of water. In place of poison, I drink water. In the past, I confused my need for water by drinking toxic liquids. Two-thirds of my body is water, so when I replenish and cleanse my body by drinking lots and lots of water, I feel wonderful. Yum, I love pure water.

I drink at least six to eight glasses of water a day and more when I exercise. I eat healthy fresh fruits and vegetables, whole grains. I eat fresh, lean and green. I drink lots and lots of water, eat fresh fruits and vegetables and take vitamins at meals (amino acid glutamine, B2, Niacin, C).

I love fresh fruits, vegetables and whole grains. Processed, chemically-loaded foods taste awful and gum me up like library paste. I enjoy moving my body, getting exercise, and breathing deeply. I move my body and get lots of exercise. I positively spoil myself. I do good kind things for myself. I enjoy being alive, alert, clear minded and in control of my life. I feel terrific—a born-again human.

I am a winner. I am proud of my honesty, clarity, and humility.

I have an insatiable appetite for knowledge. I gather all information that I need to keep me forever free of alcohol. I seek out support groups, workshops and organizations where are living positive, healthy, clean lives. The more I learn, the easier it is for me to remain healthy, clear minded and free.

If, for any reason, poison tempts me, I gently bring myself back on course. If someone offers me poison, I say, "No thank you, I choose to drink water or fruit juice." I make a healthy choices.

I'm closely connected to God and higher consciousness. I listen to my inner wisdom. I take time to relax and listen to my truth. I make time to use this power script often. It works. I love myself. I choose to live. I'm rational, sensible and responsible. I take life as it comes. I face my life directly. I'm proud of my honesty. I stand tall, learning as I go.

I choose friends who have my best interests at heart—a network of healthy, positive friends who help me remain on course and clear minded. I seek out the support I need to remain healthy.

Whole foods are holy. I eat good, nourishing, fresh fruits and vegetables—fuel so I can enjoy my many interests and talents. Just as my car need fuel to do its job, my body need fuel to serve me well. I only put healthy fuel foods into my perfect body. I avoid fats, oils, greases and sugars because they lug me down, slime me up. I remain energetic and clear-minded by eating well. I enjoy getting exercise by moving my body. I feel so glad to be alive.

Everyday in every way, I am growing better and better, learning as I go. From this point forward, I am beginning to live my life fully. I give others the privilege of living their life their way.

The past and the future are only thoughts. My life is right now, at this moment. I am deeply involved in everything that happens around me in the present. I lovingly plan my future.

I'm positive and peaceful. If Negative issues and problems present themselves, I handle them easily and directly, doing whatever is necessary to move forward with my life in a positive way. Life's issues are exciting challenges in my learning and growth. I am patient with myself and others. We are growing and learning. I choose joy. My life is a dynamic adventure in clarity, honesty, joy, and love. I'm glad to be alive.

I openly admit that alcohol causes more problems than it is worth. I tell everyone—friends, family, even strangers—that I am clean and sober. I am proud of my conviction and tenacity.

My life is a dynamic adventure in clarity, honesty, joy and love. I am glad to be alive.

Hypno-Helper

To get fabulous results, order Stockwell's No More Alcohol, self-hypnosis audiotape, available through Creativity Unlimited Press. Order forms are at the back of this book.

INNER•VIEW QUIZ

Has Tobacco Given You Cancer Yet?

☆ *"Would you like some tobacco?"*

"No thank you, I already have cancer."

1. I have...

____ A persistent cough and/or a change in my cough
____ Wheezing
____ Chest pain
____ Sore throats or loss of voice
____ Progressive weight loss
____ Spitting up of blood
____ Aching joints
____ Shortness of breath
____ Continual chest pain
____ Headaches
____ Nausea

If you smoke and answered "yes" to any of these symptoms, suspect lung cancer.

2. I experience...

____ Sores in my mouth, tongue, cheeks and throat that won't heal
____ Bleeding or tissue changes in my mouth, cheeks and throat?
____ Difficulty swallowing
____ Numb tongue
____ Loose teeth
____ Swelling or lumps in my mouth, tongue, cheeks and throat

If you smoke and answered "yes," suspect cancer of the oral cavity. Pipe smokers are more susceptible to lip cancer; snuff and chewing tobacco users to oral cancer.

3. I experience...

____ Constant pain when swallowing
____ Loss of appetite

If you are a smoker and answered "yes", suspect cancer of the esophagus.

4. I experience...

____ Prolonged hoarseness
____ Throat discomfort
____ Changes in my voice

If you are a smoker and answered "yes," suspect cancer of the larynx.

5. I experience...

____ Bloody, difficult or painful urination

If you smoke or smoked and said "yes" to these, suspect cancer of the bladder.

6. I experience...

____Blood in my urine
____Pain in my mid back or side
____A lump in my abdomen

If you smoke and answered "yes" to these, suspect cancer of the kidney.

7. I experience...

____Pain in my upper left abdomen that spreads to my back
____Constant back pain
____Yellowish skin color (jaundice)

If you smoke and answered "yes" to these, suspect cancer of the pancreas or liver.

Chapter 23

Quit Smoking:

Is That You Coffin?"

We all have reasons; reasons we start destructive habits, reasons we continue and reasons we stop. Sooner or later, every tobacco user finds his or her own perfect reason to quit. What is yours? Your reason combined with mental readjustment makes you clearer minded, more relaxed and a breath of fresh air with a healthy body. In no time at all, you'll wonder why you ever used toxic chemicals in the first place.

**Tombstone Granary Burying Ground
Boston, Mass.**

Bags, cancer sticks, chaw, chew, chewing tobacco, coffin nail, cigarette, cigar, ciggies, Copenhagen, cuban, dippin', dry, fag, leaf, nicotine fix, pinch, pipe, a plug, smokes, smokeless tobacco, Skoll, snuff, stoggie, tobaccie, tokes, twist, quid, wad and white scorpion.

▲ So You Want to Quit!

☆ *"To cease tobacco is the easiest thing I ever did. I ought to know because I have done it a thousand times."*

—Mark Twain

Tobacco is smoked as cigarettes or in a pipe, shredded tobacco leaves come loose or in a solid "plug." A golf ball sized wad is placed in the cheek and sucked or chewed and then the juices are spat. Moist snuff is finely ground tobacco that is tucked (dipped) between the gum and lower lip. A "pinch" is placed or inhaled into the nostril. Dry snuff is a powdered form of tobacco and comes in a tin or box. The power to make permanent changes is in the mind; your mind. Millions of smokers, snuffers and chawers quit and stay quit every year...and you are ready to be one of them.

As soon as you adjust your mind, your body follows. Immediately, blood carries more oxygen to the heart and lungs. Your health and mood tone improves. Your miraculous human body regenerates and renews itself with your help. Welcome back to the land of the living!

When someone quits tobacco or any drug, they deserve a Medal of Honor. They just climbed the Great Pyramid. It may require diligence and tenacity, but it's well worth it. What an enormous sense of pride and accomplishment! Breathe easy now. The air on the top isn't so thin after all.

▲ HISTORY: The Smoking Gun

☆ *"Smoking is a custome Lothsome to the eye, hateful to the nose, harmfull to the braine, dangerous to the Lungs..."*

—King James of England, 1604

Christopher Columbus reported that people in the New World "drink" smoke, and introduced tobacco to Europe. This new lucrative industry brought the Spanish queen more wealth than any other New World treasure.

Holy Smokes

Tobacco use is a social ritual. Native American ceremony uses a peace pipe. Balinese ceremony used to include coffee drinking, betel nut chewing and spitting. Now, modernized Balinese are required to smoke cigarettes in their ceremonies. They've come a long way baby.

Elegant European women used snuff. The old west's spittoons are legendary. It's a common sight to see baseball players spitting a wad. Young cowboys and construction workers are initiated with tobacco as a bond with peers and a right of passage. It is prideful to have a "worn out ring from your tobacco can in the back pocket of your jeans" or a pack rolled in your tee-shirt sleeve. Old movies feature every class of people blowing smoke.

R.J. Reynolds Tobacco is establishing the first tobacco factory in China."
—1992 News Item

"Philip Morris opens a Cigarette Manufacturing Plant in Russia"
—1993 News Item

"US tobacco exports total some $6.2 billion a year...rising 6% each year... "400,000 Russian citizens die each year as a result of cigarette smoking. The Russian people spend 10% of their income on cigarettes." —1994 News Item

▲ The Tobacco Trade

☆ *A sky-blue window; bird flying free*
Shiny red paper; seduces me.

—Shelley Stockwell

Keeping folks addicted to snuff, cigarettes, chewing tobacco, and the trafficking of illegal marijuana and hashish is a multi-billion-dollar business.

When sales slump, tobacco companies spend huge amounts on convincing ad campaigns. Male smokers were the focus of these campaigns until the 1920s, when "Reach for a Lucky instead of a sweet" enticed women and tripled the sales of Lucky cigarettes in one year.

Opera stars chirped: "Cigarettes are kind for your throat." And Doctors were paid to give testimonials: "Not one case of throat irritation while smoking Camels." It was true; there wasn't one case, there were thousands.

"Scientific studies" were conducted and publicized to convince Chesterfield smokers that cigarettes did not affect their lungs. Their ad campaign featured X-rays of smokers' lungs.

A "research commission" hired by the tobacco industry conducted studies and reported that tobacco and/or smoking posed "no health risks." Yet, since 1953 hundreds of studies proved that smoking is the main cause of cancer.

President John F. Kennedy enlisted the Surgeon General, Luther Terry, to explore the truth about lung cancer and smoking. Every Surgeon General since has actively pursued that toxic affects of tobacco.

In 1986, the US. Congress banned advertising of smokeless tobacco on radio and television and required health warnings:

"This product may cause mouth cancer"

"This product may cause gum disease and tooth loss"

"This product is not a safe alternative to cigarettes"

Lawsuits against the tobacco industry resulted in billions of dollars of judgements, including a $246 billion settlement from a lawsuit filed by 46 states in 1998.

A new brand of cigarettes, Advance, sells for $3 a pack and claims to have dramatically lower levels of tobaccos carcinogens called nitrosamines. There is no evidence that lower nitrosamines makes smoking safer but other major companies are jumping on the "It's still gonna kill you but it sounds good" bandwagon.

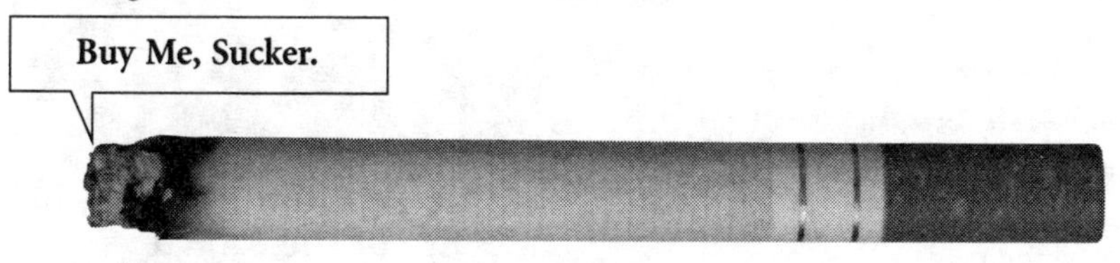

Burning to fill the coffers.

UP YOUR EGYPT

It Is Illegal To Ride A Camel On The Road in British Columbia?

Spittoon' Image of a Camel

Arabian camels have one hump and are taller and faster than their two-humped cousin, the Bactrian camel from Asia. A fully laden Dromedary can walk over 200 miles in parching desert sun without one drink of water. That's why they are called the ship of the desert. The camel's hump and stomach get him over the hump in a drought.

The camel or dromedary's backbone is straight. His hump(s) is pure fat and can weigh as much as 80+ pounds. One pound of this dense hump-fat recycles into one pint of water during dry times. A camel can drink 25 gallons of water in half an hour. His several stomachs are each lined with millions of tiny storage cells that retain water. Camels don't sweat until their body temperature reaches 115° F (46°C)! Camels also have a marvelous sense of smell. They can sniff out a water hole miles away. Double rows of extra-long eyelashes let a camel see well, even in blinding sandstorms. Membranes in the eye flick away any sand that does get in. Bushy eyebrows serve as sunshades.

Eye of the Needle

In the ancient cradle of civilization, walled cities closed their main doors at night and had a single entrance called the "eye of the needle." It was purposely made small to allow entrance to foot travelers, and not to camel leading bandits laden with weapons or gear. A camel could only get through the eye of the needle by being unloaded and passing through on their knees. It was enough to make a camel spit.

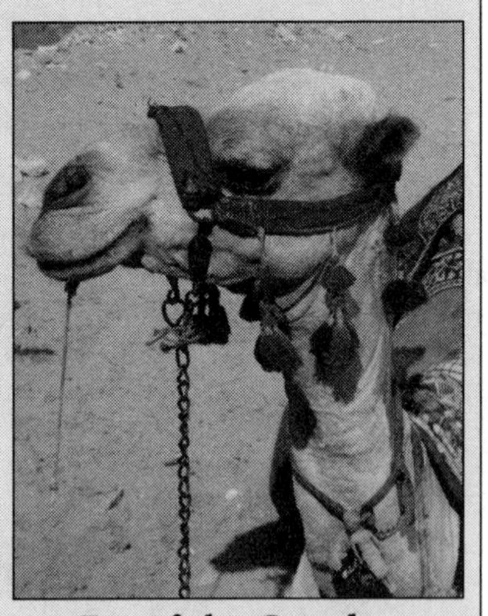

Eye of the Camel

Photo by Jon Nicholas

Camel Hair Brushes

Camel hairbrushes are not made of camel hair but squirrel's hair. A Mr. Camel invented them.

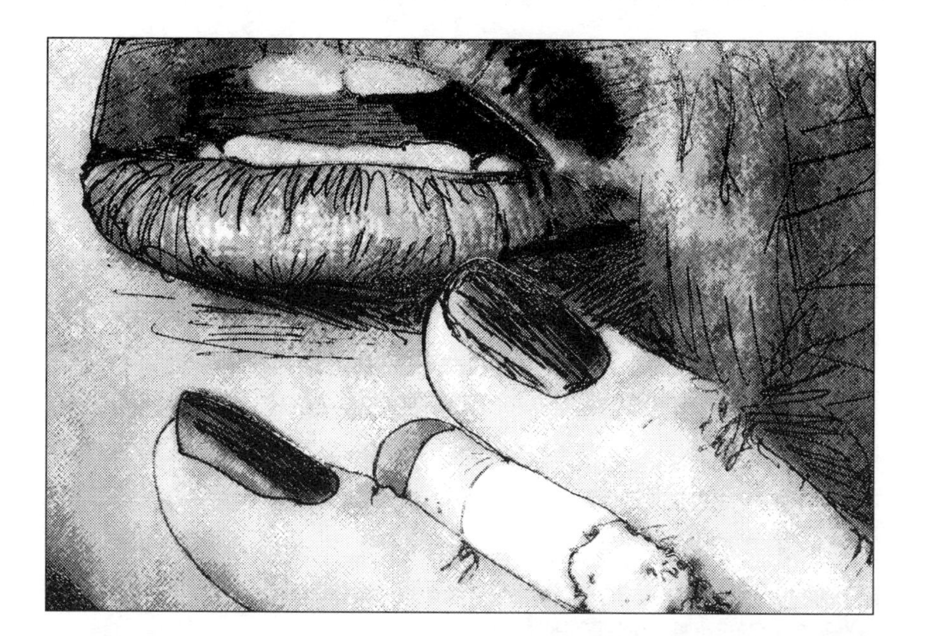

Smoke Screen Business

☆ *"It's not the cough that carries you off. It's the coffin they carry you off in."*

Photo by Nica Lee

Some forty-seven million adults dole out money for tobacco. U.S. tobacco companies employ over forty-seven thousand workers. Tobacco farmers earn over three billion dollars a year for their crops. Domestic cigarette taxes brought the US government $11.9 billion and Phillip Morris an income of $2.8 billion in 1993.

If you pay $3.50 for a pack of cigarettes for 365 days of the year you pay the tobacco industry $1277.50 a year. In 40 years, that's $51,000. Three packs a day, is $153,000 in forty years.

In the workplace, smoking costs employers more than 80 million workdays. Smokers have, on average, 35%-45% rate of absenteeism. This loss of productivity and wages, due to smoking, costs American businesses some thirty two billion dollars each year. Smokers use fifty percent more of their healthcare benefits, and thereby increase the cost of healthcare for other employees. Tobacco kills valued employees.

Call For A Phillip Morris

☆ *"Think of the cigarette as a dispenser for a dose unit of nicotine."*
—1972 memo from a Phillip Morris scientist

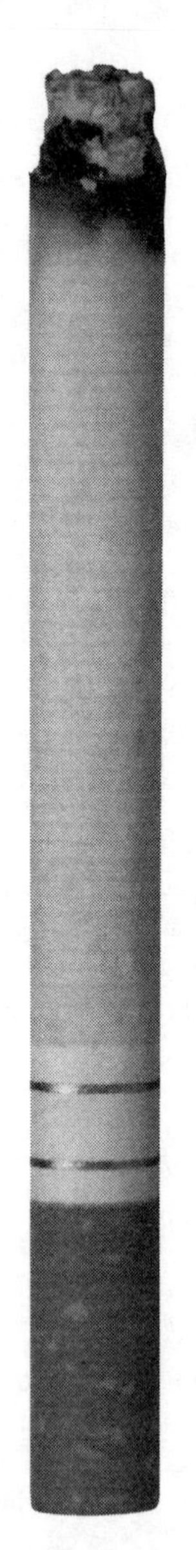

Phillip Morris sued the Environmental Protection Agency in 1993 for identifying secondary smoke as a carcinogen.

Phillip Morris sued the city of San Francisco in an effort to have them end an anti-smoking ban in the workplace.

Phillip Morris sued ABC's "Day One" for libel when they accused the tobacco industry of adding nicotine to their products.

Phillip Morris also organized tobacco farmers to protest in Washington against cigarette pack warnings.

Phillip Morris openly supports good causes like racial equality, education reform and the arts.

Tricker Treat

☆ *"Cigarettes are high technology nicotine delivery systems."*
—Dr. David Kessler, FDA Commissioner,
July 1994 Congressional hearings on cigarettes.

The FDA revealed that manufacturers precisely set nicotine levels of each cigarette puff and those labeled "lowest yield in tar" often have had the highest nicotine levels. From 1982-1992, while tar levels remained level, nicotine levels rose steadily.

How have they kept tar levels the same? Tar levels are measured by putting the end of a filter on a "smoking machine." To maintain ratings, cigarette manufacturers punch holes in the sides of the filter, so that the tar does not get to the machine. However, when one smokes, they cover these holes with their fingers or lips, so more tar gets to the body than to the machine register.

▲ Smokeless Tobacco and Spittoons Nicotine Nostalgia

☆ *You took up all my time and cost me so much money.*
I couldn't have fun without you.
I missed being near my friends and family and I missed being myself.
I'm sorry, but I'm sure you'll find someone new
Who loves you so much more than I ever could
Who falls desperately in love with your cancerous kiss
'Til death do you part.

—Katherine Audley

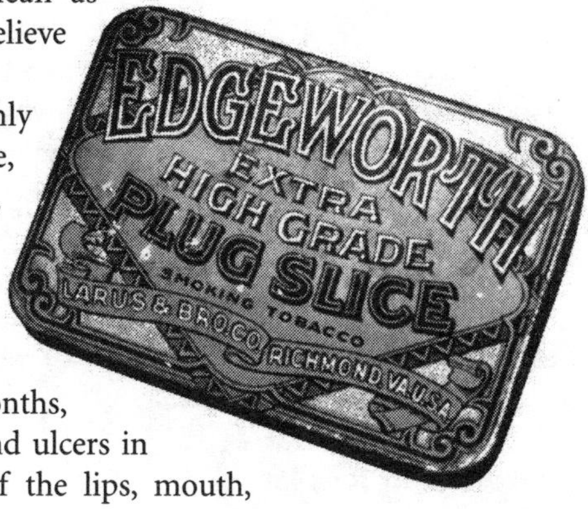

Smokeless tobacco is as American as baseball. That's why some people believe it's "safe." Snuff Already!

Smokeless tobacco is highly addictive and damaging. Over time, sticking tobacco in your mouth, stains and damages tooth enamel, and leads to serious tooth decay and permanent gum loss, which exposes the roots of teeth, resulting in loss of teeth. In as little as six months, smokeless tobacco causes blisters and ulcers in the mouth. From there, cancers of the lips, mouth, tongue, and voice box can develop.

Sticking tobacco in your nose can cause cancer and nose rot.

Qat Outa Here

☆ *"If it's Yemen it must be chew day"*

—Celia Littleton

The Arabs of the country of Yemen (the ancient land of "frankincense and myrrh") are short and skinny with red eyes from chewing qat.

Masticating qat leaves extracts a bitter narcotic sap. Almost the entire population; including children and goats chew balls of qat pulp the size of a golf ball and store it in the cheek like a hamster.

The Prime Minister has qat-chewing sessions, politicians chew it on television and midday prayer signals massive chews and spits. These folks, like many of their Arab neighbors, also smoke water pipes filled with fruit juice soaked tobacco.

▲ Tobacco Truth: A Case Study

The following interview with Jenny, age 14, underscores the truth about tobacco. Though her reference is to smoked tobacco it still is relevant to any tobacco usage:

CASE STUDY: Jenny

"I have asthma and my grandfather, who I adored, died of lung cancer. The doctors said that the cigarettes killed him. So why am I smoking twice as much since he died?

My mom smokes and so do all my friends. I was 12 when I smoked my first cigarette at my friend's house. Now, I smoke a pack a day. I buy them with the money I get from my parents or from babysitting.

I've tried to quit, but it's hard because I am around my smoking friends all the time. School is boring. I just like to hang out with my buddies. I got suspended for absenteeism, which was great, because it kept me from going to school a little bit more. Smoking helps me relax. But still, I have a pretty bad temper, so I started taking some medication to calm down. I think about quitting cigarettes and try not to worry about it. I don't want to gain weight.

I would not like my baby brother to use tobacco. It's a bad habit. When I look at myself in the mirror, I think I would feel a lot better about myself if I'd try a little harder to quit."

Reasons and Results

Jenny gives many reasons why she smokes—"Mom smokes." "My friends smoke." "School is boring." "Smoking helps me relax." "I don't try hard enough to quit."

The result however, is that Jenny is physically and emotionally addicted to tobacco. She needs greater amounts to produce the same effects and may suffer withdrawal symptoms when she stops. Jenny's body is crying for mercy and she is trying to convince herself that she's OK with her reasons.

> The chance of a first-time cigarette smoker becoming addicted is 9 in 10! Cigarettes are more addictive than pipes and cigars. Since cigarette smoke is more easily be inhaled, smokers absorb more nicotine more quickly says the US Department of Health & Human Services. This is analogous to cocaine users preferring to smoke cocaine as crack because they get a more immediate response.
>
> -What Counts, Complete Harper's Index

Let's explore what she says:

"I have asthma and my grandpa, who I adored, died of lung cancer. The doctors said that the cigarettes killed him. So why am I smoking twice as much since he died?"

Emotionally, Jenny associates her grandpa with tobacco. When grandpa was alive, they laughed, talked and enjoyed each other and he smelled like smoke and had smoke coming out the end of his cigarette. When she saw him stone cold in the coffin he didn't smell like smoke anymore. She associates good times with grandpa with smoke. No wonder she doubled her tobacco. Her strong association of life and grandpa includes tobacco.

"My mom smokes and so do all her friends."

She also associates her mother with tobacco.

Mother is a role model who demonstrates what grown ups are supposed to be. Jenny may have started using tobacco with the idea that she is more grown up.

Perhaps Jenny's first cigarette was inside her mother's womb. Did her mom smoke while she was pregnant with Jenny?

If so, using tobacco while pregnant increased Jenny's risk of fetal or infant death, spontaneous abortion, premature birth and a low birth weight. This little one had a 33% greater risk of being stillborn!

Women who stop smoking before pregnancy, or within the first three or four months, reduce the risk of having low birthrate babies—to a rate equivalent of women who never smoked. Poison from tobacco concentrated in unborn Jenny's placenta, where she was nourished. Poison pooled around her. Carbon monoxide from smoke cut down the amount of oxygen she received. Toxins permeated the little one's blood stream.

In spite of tobacco, Jenny came to full term. Studies show that Jenny is more likely to have chest colds, ear infections, bronchitis, asthma, pneumonia and die from cancer.

"I was 12 when I smoked my first cigarette at my friend's house."

Would you give your infant or baby a cigarette or a plug of tobacco? Of course not, that would be crazy. People start using tobacco in school, the service, at work or when associating with others who smoke. They do it for approval, to fit in, or to rebel. Tobacco is especially addictive for young people. In fact, it is as addictive as heroin or cocaine. One-third of kids who experiment with cigarettes are addicted to them by age 20.

Because the internal reward mechanism is the same, young tobacco users are 100 times more likely to smoke marijuana or use cocaine and heroin than other teens. Cancer research at UCSF shows young, developing lungs permanently damaged and normal cell repair hampered by smoke.

Do you run your life from a decision made by a child? When you wake up from the dream of childhood, such crazy reasons for starting don't make sense any more.

"I buy them with the money I get from my parents or from babysitting."

Jenny earns $3.50 a day babysitting and a small allowance. How could she better spend her money?

80-90% of all tobacco users began using before age 21. Tobacco industry insiders refer to initiates as "replacement smokers/snuffers." Replacements are needed to buy more products as previous users die and quit (not necessarily in that order). Target markets are women, minorities, youth and third world nations.

Cigarette manufacturers say they don't market to children; it's just a coincidence that children spend $1.54 billion on cigarettes each year.

"It calms my nerves"

Tobacco is a stimulant and a depressant. Some users believe that they calm their nerves when they light up, chew or snuff. But in fact, tobacco releases epinephrine, a hormone that creates stress, not relaxation. The more stressed; the more they use. It's a vicious circle.

Nicotine lowers the brain chemical required for short-term memory and is also linked to depression, lower energy level and insomnia. 288 smokers studied had cloudier memories and than non-smokers.

"I don't want to gain weight."

Many who quit don't gain an ounce. For those that do, five to seven pounds are about all and that falls away within the first few months. Think about it, isn't five extra pounds for a short while worth adding eight healthy years to your life span? If you don't want to gain weight, drink lots of water and eat low calorie foods. Sugar, fat, caffeine and alcohol make withdrawal symptoms last longer and cause weight gain.

"When I look at myself in the mirror, I think I would feel a lot better about myself if I'd try a little harder to quit"

What Jenny sees in the mirror is real. Tobacco radically ages and damages your appearance. Look into a tobacco user's eyes and you'll usually see a yellow color at the lower outer periphery. The lack of oxygen makes the iris smaller and the whites larger.

Are your fingers and teeth stained? Is your skin grayish yellow? Are you wrinkled around your mouth and eyes? Do you have skin problems? Suspect tobacco.

Tobacco causes mucus to accumulate in the windpipe and bronchial tubes. That's what causes the familiar throat clear and cough of a tobacco user. Do you have that cough? Some who quit using experience increased coughing or sputum production for one or two weeks afterward. This is terrific. It means that the body is cleaning out those old toxins. Within four weeks, any symptoms like that totally go away.

Damage caused by tobacco depends on:

The age you started smoking, sniffing or chewing
The number of years you have smoked, snuffed, or chewed
The tar and nicotine content
The total number of cigarettes, cigars, cans you've smoked, snuffed, or chewed
How deeply you inhale
Your own personal chemistry
What else you take in

You might not notice the damage caused by tobacco because there is often a lag between the day you start using (or were exposed to tobacco) and the resulting appearance of cancer or disease. But sooner or later, if you continue tobacco, you will get cancer, emphysema or have a heart attack. When it happens to you is a game of Russian Roulette.

"I would not like my baby brother to use tobacco. It's a bad habit."

Tobacco isn't "in" anymore. As a smoker, sniffer or dipper in our society, you are treated like a tacky, second-class citizen. Of course you've noticed how increasingly difficult it is to be comfortable lighting up, chewing or snuffing. Users are outcasts at social functions, school and work. Pathetic souls crowd doorways, balconies or driveways to indulge cravings. As Kermit the frog says: It's not easy being green.

Jenny's school won't tolerate her smoking. Airplanes, restaurants and public buildings don't permit it. Users are often categorized and rejected as scummy people because of the smell, vapors and obvious dangers of breathing second hand smoke. Loved ones won't talk to you, hug or kiss you, because your hair, clothes and breath stink. Doctors won't treat you. Insurance companies won't insure you. Employers won't hire you. And, Jenny will have to find a boyfriend willing to "kiss an ashtray."

Jenny's brother may be passively "smoking" the equivalent of one or two cigarettes a day from Jenny's second hand or side screen smoke. In fact, according to the American Lung Association, some irritating and poisonous gases drift off the end of a cigarette in higher concentrations than in the drag a smoker inhales. Almost 50 known cancer-causing compounds have been identified in second-hand smoke. Second hand smoke increases a child's risk of pneumonia, asthma, middle ear infections and sudden infant death syndrome.

Second hand "tobacco poisoning" kills more than 3,000 people each year, including infants and children says the US Surgeon General. The federal government labels it as a "Class A carcinogen" on a par with asbestos and radon.

As a non-smoker, passive smoking often causes or worsens asthma, bronchitis and allergies. The US Environmental Protection Agency affirms that secondhand smoke can cause cancer and heart damage.

It Not the Quantity, It's the Toxicity

☆ *"The doses of secondhand smoke are small, compared to what smoker's get, but the effects aren't."*

—Stanton Glantz and William Parmley
1995 Journal of American Medical Association

☆ *"...Even small amounts of tobacco smoke are having greater effects on a non-smoker's system."*

—Dr. Homayoun Kazemi, Harvard University

☆ *"Smoking kills more Americans each year than alcohol, cocaine, crack, heroin, homicide, suicide, car accidents, fires, and AIDS combined."*

—Winner, New York City Smoke-free Ad campaign

Small amounts of passive smoke damages the heart because it:

- Reduces the body's ability to deliver oxygen to the heart
- Inhibits the heart's ability use the oxygen it receives
- Increases the blood's lactate level (a salt derived from lactic acid), making it more difficult to exercise
- Activates blood platelets, which increases risk of clots and damaging the lining of the coronary arteries
- Aggravates tissue damage following a heart attack

Illustration by Marv Robertson

Madge, Marge and Rachel

Second hand smoke from nicotine and nitrogen oxides form the most toxic cancer causing nitrosamines called NNK build up even after the cigarette is extinguished. This powerful cancer-causing ingredient builds up over time in a smoke filled room.

Deadly Experiment: How to Turn Kids off Smoking

This demonstrates the poisons in tobacco. It may not prove what tobacco does to humans, but it sure gives children something to think about.

1. Germinate several plants of the same species. Bean seeds work well.
2. Make a solution of nicotine by soaking several cigarettes or wads of chewing tobacco overnight in a jar of water.
3. Give half the plants normal water and feed the other half your nicotine water. Otherwise, keep them identical in every way.
4. The nicotine-laced plants will grow more slowly and often die.

▲ What's in Tobacco

☆ *"Do you mind if I smoke?"*
"Not if you don't mind my getting sick."

Hundreds of known toxic chemicals are in tobacco. Tobacco manufacturers add flavor enhancers, moisturizing agents, saltpeter and sugar. When fire is added to these ingredients, some 43 known carcinogenic (cancer causing) agents are formed and ingested. They include:

Nicotine ($C_{10}H_{13}N_2$): The Fatal Attraction

Nicotine is a slow deadly poisonous alkaloid. It is the same alkaloid used as insecticide. Colorless, oily, liquid, nicotine first stimulates and excites the adrenal glands. This enhances your desire to take in more. This combined with higher tolerances as you use it, gets you "dependent."

100 milligrams of nicotine is a deadly dose. That's how much is found in a single cigar! 50 milligrams injected directly into your blood stream would kill you instantly.

Nicotine absorbs through your mouth, mucus membranes, and lungs and condenses and collects on your tongue and mouth where it is mixed with saliva and you swallow it.

Nicotine changes your brain's neurotransmitters, norepinephrine and epinephrine. That's what makes blood vessels constrict, and blood pressure and heart rate rise. Nicotine reduces your body's ability to utilize oxygen. It alters the width of the airways to your lungs and together with carbon monoxide, increases your chances of having a heart attack and dying.

This, plus raised seratonin levels and cravings, disrupt sleep. Nicotine's effect on your brain's seratonin level is what deadens your sense of taste and smell.

Nicotine is absorbed through the mucous lining of the mouth and lungs, where it passes into your blood and circulates to your brain. It reaches your hypothalamus and affects appetite.

Interestingly, nicotine is also found in potatoes, eggplant and peppers—members of the deadly nightshade family. It's best to avoid these foods and caffeine, sugar and alcohol for at least two weeks when quitting.

Strychnine ($C_{23}H_{22}N_2O_2$)

Strychnine is a bitter, poisonous alkaloid used as rodent poison. There is enough strychnine in one cigar to kill you instantly if it were injected directly into the bloodstream.

Menthol

Menthol makes tobacco feel cooler in the body. This allows you to keep it in your mouth and lungs longer and cause more damage.

Smoke

Smoke is an Unlucky Strike (Slugs No Rebounds!)

Cigarette smoke is made up of 2000 different elements; 1800 of which are toxic. Smoke replaces the oxygen in your blood with the dangerous chemicals; carbon monoxide, nicotine, tar, hydrogen, cyanide, formaldehyde, benzene, benzopyrine, phenol, arsenic and strychnine. As the smoke travels through your body, it hardens arteries, damages heart muscles and constricts the blood vessels in your brain. That is why smokers have such a high percentage of cancer, heart disease and stokes.

Put that in your pipe and smoke it.

☆ THE CHIMNEYS OF VIENNA

Dark haired chimney; Light haired chimney
Young chimney; Old chimney.

When the grand platz was planned only the whitest marble would do
Carved towers of artistic opulence and pride
Blackened by noxious oxides from rolling metal boxes and two-legged chimneys.

Ghosts of waltzing aristocracy stop
to watch pigeons gum the walls
with emissions of their own.

I hurry into a tidy shop,
to probe a delicate Viennese pastry(on a porcelain plate);
my head gets clouded by a dulling ache.
Smogging, burning, smelling, ringing round babies curling like napalm.

A female chimney (in the latest fashion)
sucks fire in and out of a painted red orifice.
Smoke rolls from two powdered nostrils
past French perfume.

If life is measured by inspiration,
would you choose air or suffocation?

Blackened chimneys fog my mind.
Truncated thoughts in truncated time.
dying in a hacking cough.
Hardening my tissue soft.

—Shelley Stockwell

Carbon Monoxide (CO)

☆ *Would you like a hit from my tailpipe?*

Carbon monoxide from tobacco smoke exhausts and kills. Carbon monoxide is a colorless, odorless gas that prevents oxygen from getting into your bloodstream. Carbon monoxide competes with oxygen for binding sites in your red blood cells. It takes 12 hours to leave the blood.

Deposits of carbon monoxide build up in arteries, forcing your heart to work harder to compensate for the blockages. That is why the Surgeon General requires cigarette packages to state, "Cigarettes contain carbon monoxide." As soon as you stop putting carbon monoxide into your body, you breathe more easily and feel more energetic.

Tar: Taromoil

Imagine what a full cup of melted tar looks and smells like. That's the minimum amount of tar per year that stays in the lungs of a one-pack-a-day smoker. It can smear as much as a quart of tar on your tongue and larynx. With each tobacco usage, hundreds of poisonous substances enter the body. Even when you exhale or spit, ninety percent of them stay inside. It's no wonder the body gets diseased. A lung surgeon friend of mine polyurethaned a smoker's diseased lung and left it as an ashtray in his office.

The more tar and nicotine you put in your body, the worse the consequences.

The chemicals in the tar collect in your lung tissue and cause them to become stiff and lose their elasticity. When this happens, air sacks rupture and lung function is permanently destroyed. This is called emphysema.

When I was a flight attendant, I watched the cleaning crew shovel buckets of slimy tar from the air out-take of the 727 (smoking on airplanes was legal then). It was gross.

Spread tar on roads; not your lungs.

Hydrogen Cyanide (HCN)

Hydrogen cyanide is another poisonous gas found in cigarette smoke. It paralyzes your cilia, which are the little hairs that keep your lungs clean and prevents them from filtering the air. That's another reason why lungs get black. As soon as you stop smoking, the cilia begin to wake up. In 3 to 9 months time, they return to duty.

▲ Tobacco: Slow Motion Suicide

☆ *"I think I'll get some fresh air and a cigarette."*

☆ Question: *"Will my smoking this cigar bother you?"*
Answer: *"Not if my getting sick won't bother you."*

In the tragic events of September 11th, 2001, in America 6,335 souls were taken. We grieved and mourned their loss. Yet, a similar tragedy occurs every day, as some 1,147 souls DIE daily from tobacco! Dr. Michael Eriksin, the director of the US Center for Disease Control reports that 418,690 people died in 1990 because of cigarette related diseases. One in five of all deaths in the United States are caused by tobacco.

More people have died as a result of tobacco poisoning than have died in *all the wars ever fought.* Now, *that* is a tragedy. Particularly, if one casualty is someone as special as you or a loved one.

Every tobacco wad or hit robs you of five to seven minutes of life. Cigarettes, cigars, pipes, marijuana or other tobacco shorten your life span. Smoking is the major cause of emphysema, bronchitis, lung cancer and coronary heart disease.

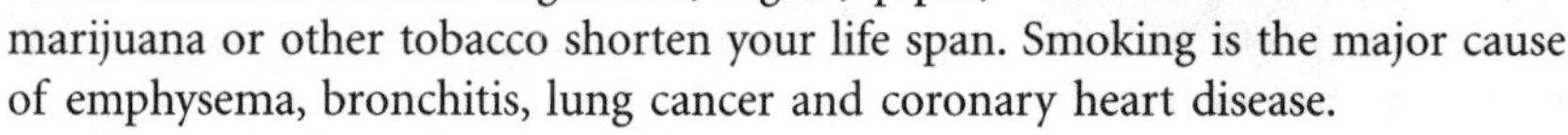

Tobacco weakens the immune response.

Smoking accelerates bone loss in both men and women because it affects the way your body metabolizes estrogen, needed for bone growth.

A Pollute to Power

Tobacco interacts with environmental carcinogens, dramatically increasing a smoker's risk of getting cancer. When a smoker is exposed to environmental toxins, such as asbestos, the two interact. Smokers who work with asbestos have an eight times greater risk of developing lung cancer than non-smokers, and are 87 times more likely to get the disease than non-smokers or people who do not work with asbestos.

Emphysema

Tobacco takes you out of circulation. It slowly kills depriving you of oxygen. Smoke coats the alveoli (air sacks) with tar, causing the lung tissue to lose their elasticity. Carbon monoxide from cigarettes sticks to your blood cells preventing them from carrying oxygen. Smoke causes emphysema and bronchitis.

The Effects of Tobacco and Smoking

Immediate Effects:

- Chemicals, bind with brain cells and effect brain function
- Carbon monoxide floods the body
- Blood vessels and small arteries constrict
- Blood pressure and heart rate increase
- Blood oxygen level drops
- Blood platelets clump
- Skin temperature drops
- Muscles tense (that's why a smokers hands tremble)
- Vitamins and minerals are depleted (especially C and B)
- Stimulates, then depresses the nervous system
- Takes 5 to 7 minutes off your life (per cigarette)
- Dulls or eliminates taste and smell
- Blood sugar rises overloading pancreas & adrenal glands (That's what gives temporary energy and kills the appetite)
- Repels mates and kisses (who wants to kiss a smelly ashtray?)

Long Term Effects:

- Impairs the immune system Lowering resistant to infection and slowing the healing process. That's why skin lesions take longer to heal for a tobacco user.
- Premature and exaggerated face wrinkles
- Diminished sense of smell
- Colds and Flu
- Hypoglycemia/diabetes and bronchitis
- Heart disease
- High Blood Pressure
- Stroke
- Cancer
- Smoker's cough
- Emphysema
- Breathing Difficulties
- Bronchitis
- Sinusitis
- Ulcers
- Bone loss (tobacco impedes your body' metabolism of estrogen, which you need for bone growth).
- Gingivitis (inflammation of the gums)
- Cavities and more plaque on teeth
- Tooth extractions heal more slowly
- Hurts the fetus of a pregnant woman

Photo by Nic a Lee

Heart Disease

Tobacco damages the heart because it inhibits your body's ability to deliver oxygen to the heart and the heart's ability to use the oxygen it receives. It increases the blood's lactate level (a salt derived from lactic acid), making it more difficult to exercise.

All folks who combine alcohol and tobacco risk liver damage, memory loss and illness.

Women are even more sensitive and affected by tobacco and alcohol than men. If a woman takes tobacco and alcohol together, it tends to deplete her zinc and magnesium even faster, which causes the liver to get stressed faster.

Women in particular take smoking to heart. A study in Norway showed that women who smoke 20 or more cigarettes a day had a 6 times greater heart attack risk than women who never smoked. This is a higher risk than men. Smoking attacks estrogen and HDL (good cholesterol) more in women than in men. Oral contraceptive users have an "increased risk of serious cardiovascular effects if smoking (15 or more cigarettes a day) that is quite marked in women over 35 years of age," according to the drug manufacturer.

Inner View Quiz

Is Tobacco Overtaxing Your Heart?

Take the following test to calculate how tobacco affects you.

Before Check pulse rate for one minute before taking tobacco. Write it down.

After Light up, snort, or chew and then take pulse again for one minute. Write that down. If your pulse rate goes up, it means you're allergic to the substance you took.

Extra work per hour Subtract the first reading from the second and then multiply any extra heartbeats by 60 (for minutes). That's how many extra times your heart must beat per hour if you use.

Extra work per day Now multiply those extra heart beats by 10 (hours)—a conservative estimate of how many times tobacco or drugs overtaxes the heart per day.

Over-beating of the heart, combined with blood vessel constriction, deprives you of the essential oxygen you need to live. The more tobacco or marijuana the harder the heart works, the less oxygen you receive.

Cancer

Cigarette smoking is the number one cause of cancer death in men and women. Cancer of the lips, tongue, voice box (larynx), windpipe (pharynx), lungs, esophagus, bladder, pancreas, cervix, uterus, and kidneys result. Sigmund Freud died from throat cancer from smoking twenty cigars a day.

Lung cancer from tobacco also starts in the bronchial tubes and then spreads to the lungs. In 1987 lung cancer surpassed breast cancer as the leading cause of cancer death among women.

If you drink alcohol and smoke, your chances of getting cancer of the esophagus are much greater because the chemicals in smoke dissolve more readily in alcohol.

▲ Quitting Made Easy

"I Can't Possibly Go Without My Smoke."

Consider this: If you are a one-and-a-half-pack-a-day smoker, or tobacco user, you put tobacco into your body every 35 to 40 minutes. Yet, when you are sleeping, you comfortably go without a fix for five to eight hours at a stretch.

Steps to Stopping

- ∆ **Decide to quit**
- ∆ **Decide how you quit**
- ∆ **Change your habit patterns**
- ∆ **Bathe yourself, inside and out with lots of water**
- ∆ **Move your body**
- ∆ **Well yourself with nutrition**
- ∆ **Tell everyone you stopped**
- ∆ **Enjoy nature**
- ∆ **Create fun for yourself**
- ∆ **Readjust your mind**
- ∆ **If you choose, get assistance**

INTO•GREAT POWER EXERCISE: Decide to Quit

One, Two, Three: THE CHOICE TO REJOICE

One

☆Take a deep, slow breath and exhale slowly through relaxed, pursed lips.
☆Repeat.
☆Now say to yourself:
"I enjoy free will. I have a choice. Any time, I want I can choose between taking two deep breaths or taking poison. I choose to breathe, I don't need poison. I'm a mature person. I choose joy."

Two

☆ Congratulate yourself you've just become clean and healthy
☆ Take a deep, slow breath
☆ Exhale slowly through relaxed, pursed lips
☆ Repeat
☆ Now say to yourself:
"I have a choice. At any time, I can choose between taking two deep, clean breaths or inhaling toxic burning leaves. I am a mature person. I chose to feel great. I am a non-smoker.

Of course, you want to quit. Congratulations!
You're brave enough to stop pretending. It's time.
If you have quit before, prior cleansing makes it easier to quit for good. This time works better than before because your body has already cleansed and released some toxins. Although challenging, some 40 million men and women quit for good each year. Quitting pays. Their death rate statistically approximates those who never smoked at all.

COMMITMENT TOBACCO CONTRACT

I______________________ (My name) hereby promise not to smoke, chew, and/or snort tobacco again from ________________ (Today's date) on.

I am fully responsible for this decision and aware that my commitment to this change is of primary importance.

Date ____________________ **Signed ______________________**
Co-signed ____________________

AFFIRM SUCCESS: The First Step To Quit Smoking
This is a very special time. I'm determined to eliminate poison of any kind. This time I mean business. My fresh start begins this moment. I heal myself on the levels of body, mind and spirit. It's actually a simple proposition. I release old habit patterns that no longer serve me well, and replace them with comfortable new patterns that let me feel terrific. Change can be comfortable or uncomfortable. It's all in my attitude. I keep a positive attitude. I take responsibility and use a well thought out plan to motivate me. I'm motivated and tenaciously committed to my success. If I am challenged for the next two weeks, that's OK. I get the job done. I am healthy and energetic.

Decide How to Quit

You can quit little by little or cold turkey. You can quit on your own or with help. You are in charge.

It is best to quit it all. Doing it in pieces makes success an uphill climb and makes it easier for you to trick yourself by pretending and denying. Give up the games!

Pitch the Patch

If you decide to use a patch (which I recommend against) heed their warning: "Should not be used by anyone with hypersensitivity or allergy to nicotine...Nicotine will adversely effect the fetus and the pregnant woman."

"If you continue to smoke while using our system you may experience adverse effects due to the peak nicotine levels higher than those experienced from smoking alone." "Consumption of nicotine by any means can be harmful and addicting."

Some enjoy quitting with a friend, a support group or with the help of a professional hypnotherapist or acupuncturist. Hypnosis tapes work well for many.

Use the affirmations in this chapter. Read them often to re-enforce their power. It is a good idea to record them in your own voice and "listen" to your tape every night for two weeks when you sleep. You can order my Quit Smoking cassette and use that as well. (See resources at the end of this chapter).

The American Cancer Society, the American Lung Association and the National Cancer Institute offer some wonderful support groups. Hypnotists offer the Great American Smoke-Out once a year.

Readjust Your Mind: Change Habit Patterns

☆ *"Never smoke alone in bed"*
Were the last words he ever said.
—Shelley Stockwell

- Be conscious of when you used to indulge. Keep a log.
- Remove any related paraphernalia from your home, car and workplace.
- Change your routine.
- Take up new activities.
- Sit at a new seat at the table.
- Wash curtains, walls and clothes.
- Clean your home.
- Get rid of the smell.
- Take up a new hobby.
- Help others.
- Avoid others who smoke. This makes it easier for you to "stay quit."
- Sit in non-smoking areas.

AFFIRM SUCCESS: Good-Bye to Toxic Tobacco
Imagine a pile of all the poisonous tobacco I have used in my life. In my mind's eye I see, feel, and taste the truckloads of toxic tobacco. If I were to burn all of those at once, there would be a gigantic billowing, belching, filthy black cloud of smoke, smogging the air. The tar and carcinogens reek and stink: the smell clings to my hair and skin. As I think and imagine that black cloud, I think about all those chemicals that have entered my body. It's enough already. I quit.

I change my routine. I take up some new activities. I sit at a new seat at the table. I wash my curtains, walls, car, and clothes. I clean my home. I get rid of the smell. I'm in control. I breathe better. Everything smells terrific. I'm proud of myself. This is a gift I give myself and my family.

Withdrawal Made Easy

☆ *"I smoked a pack and a half a day for 25 years, and thanks to Shelley, I don't smoke any more, except after sex. And then, I'm not sure, 'cause I've never looked."*
—Jon Nicholas

Some don't experience withdrawal symptoms at all. You may be one of those lucky ones. For most quitting an addiction, the challenging times are the first two to four days and the first two to three weeks. After that, difficult symptoms disappear. But don't despair, there are many things you can do to make the going easy.

Knowing what to expect helps.

Common withdrawal symptoms are cravings that last only a few moments. So tough it out or distract yourself and they will pass. Even the most intense cravings last only 5 to 10 minutes at most. And, urges pass whether you use or not.

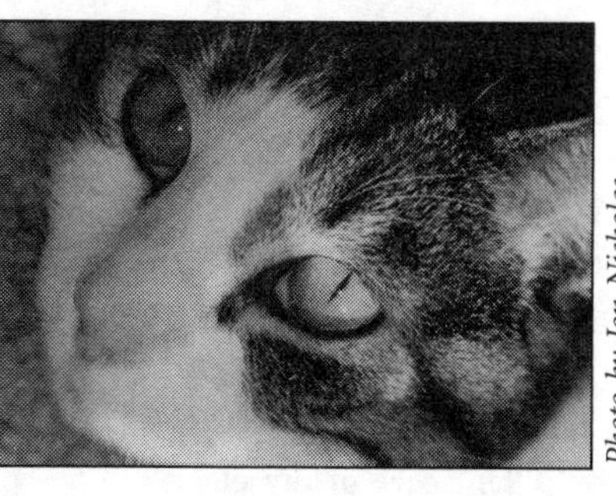

Photo by Jon Nicholas

Since nicotine is a stimulant; some quitters become temporarily tired. Nervousness, headache, dizziness, hunger, interrupted sleep, a bad taste in the mouth, nausea, offensive body odor, changes in body temperature and heart rate, digestive disturbances, change in muscle tone and/or increased cough or phlegm, are temporary signs of a body cleaning house.

If you experience mood swings during the first few days, just let it happen and know that it is only a temporary state of mind. Within a few days you'll feel great. But don't count on these symptoms. Some people never experience any withdrawal symptoms at all!

The important thing to remember is that symptoms are a terrific sign. It means you are already detoxifying and the hardest task is almost over. If you distract yourself with exercise, relaxation, breath or self-hypnosis, cravings leave.

Trigger Happy

Use the following news strategies when you encounter these old triggers.

Old triggers	New strategy
After a meal	Brush your teeth
Drinking coffee	Chew gum
On the phone	Become a deep breather
Tension	Stretch
Something to do with hands	Doodle, fondle a rock or straw
Boredom	Take baths or showers
Cocktail party	Drink water or juice
Driving	Snack on carrots
Reward accomplishment	Reward yourself in another way
Crisis or problems	Reaffirm & review your reasons for quitting
After sex	Sing a love song
Own trigger	Give yourself a pep talk
To begin the day	Brisk walk
Pleasurable feelings	Find new ways to pleasure yourself
Feel the craving*	Distract yourself with a new task or...
Unconscious smoking	Wrap cigarettes in noisy paper and
	Ask yourself "Do I really want it?"

Emotional Signposts of Cleansing

Less concentration, disorientation, intensified emotions, mood swings, boredom, anger, the blues, and/or irritability. Some say they are jittery.

AFFIRM SUCCESS: Pleasure Seeker

For the next two weeks I am a total pleasure seeker. I avoid anything stressful. I only hang around with nourishing, positive people and situations. I take excellent care of myself.

Purge the Urge

Cravings are real, yet soon they turn to just thoughts. Since they last only a few days, commit yourself to distractions and break patterns that trigger the old habits. Here are some things to do when the cravings come:

- Think of the reasons you quit in the first place
- Think about all the benefits you get by having quit
- Do deep breathing exercises
- Call up a friend
- Munch on something crunchy: carrots, celery, apples, gum
- Drink water (at least 8 glasses a day)
- Hang out where you can't smoke (malls, theaters, churches)
- Exercise (stretch, go for a walk, work out, do yoga)
- Avoid alcohol, caffeine and sugar

Bathe Yourself Inside and Out With Lots of Water

8-10 glasses a day washes nicotine from your system. Water renews. Urine, perspiration and tears, cleanse nicotine out. Drinking water and exercise prevents weight gain.

Take one or more baths or showers a day. A warm bath before bed is a really wonderful idea. Steam baths, exercise and showers make the detoxification process less painful.

Wash your hands.

Brush your teeth often. Keep a toothbrush in the car and use it.

Use fragrant perfumes or colognes. You'll feel and smell better.

INTO•GREAT POWER EXERCISE

Genie in a Box

1. Buy a fancy bottle of designer water.
2. Hold it in your hands.
3. Picture and imagine that this bottle is the final cure for your old habit.
4. Drink all the water in the bottle, and, just like Alice in Wonderland, you'll become bigger than any old pattern.

Move Your Body

Photo by Joann Kelley

Exercise opens blood vessels, increasing blood flow that makes more oxygen available to muscles, organs and your mind. Exercise puts your heart in action and you back in the flow.

Stretching gets things moving. Breathe deeply. If you get a craving, take three deep, slow breaths and release completely after each one. Dance naked or dance with your clothes on. Lift weights. Touch your toes. Shake your Boulay. Take a hike. Your body helps to make things right.

Laugh a lot. Get massages. Massage realigns the body giving more energy and releasing toxins. Moving allows the communication system in the body to work better. Release tightness in muscles and you release blockages that hinder body/mind communication.

Acupuncture realigns your meridians and gets the chi (life force energy) flowing. It helps release toxins and generally makes you feel better.

Exercise Success

Women who exercised and attended a smoking cessation program were over twice as likely to quit, stay quit and were less likely to gain weight then women who simply took the smoke cessation program. These were the results of a study of 281 females who ranged in age from 18 to 65 years. The study was conducted by Bess Marcus, Associate Professor of psychiatry at the Brown University Center for Behavioral and Preventative Medicine.

Well Yourself with Nutrition

Tobacco users are hypoglycemic. To restore well-balanced bio-chemistry, drink lots of water, and eat fresh, healthy fruits, vegetables, and complex carbohydrates, like brown rice, beans and whole grain breads. Eat for fuel and get your pleasure out of healthy pursuits, moving, laughing, friends and your hobbies, interests and talents. Make a healthy lifestyle fun.

Eliminate fats, oils, greases, alcohol, sugar, caffeine and other drugs. As the nicotine leaves nerve endings, it takes calcium with it. Therefore, take supplements of calcium and magnesium. You need vitamin C as well. Make sure your multiple vitamins contain E and B complex. They help take away stress.

INTO•GREAT POWER EXERCISE

Wood Chopper, Cough Stopper

If you cough, do the following.

- Stand tall with both arms above your head.
- Take a full inspiration. As if chopping wood, bring your hands down, bend forward and exhale with a forceful "Haa."

Find New Ways to Relax

Use self-hypnosis. Listen to soothing music.

Taking deep full breaths, and becoming a conscious breather, sends an instant wave of relaxation through your body and mind. Full breaths cleanse tar from the bottom of your lungs. Get plenty of rest. Sleep in late on the weekend. Yoga really helps.

Photo by Nica Lee

Tell Everyone You Stopped

Use peer pressure to your advantage. When you tell others how you have taken charge of your life, you help them take charge of theirs.

Enjoy Nature

Take a break and look at a flower. Discover the pleasure of breathing clean air, of smelling flowers. Mother Earth recharges your batteries. Walk the dog. Join friends for a stroll.

Create Fun for Yourself

The benefits of cleaning up your act are fantastic. Become a pleasure seeker. Pamper and spoil yourself.

Use the money you save, by not buying cigarettes, to get a massage, a hammock, go bowling or something else wonderful just for you. Get a haircut, manicure or new clothes.

Let others reward you, too. Ask someone else to do the dishes, wash smelly curtains, shampoo your rug or run an errand for you (while you lay in your new hammock). Hire a cleaning person to make your world spic and span.

Sign up for an art class. Take a cruise. Chill out.

INTO•GREAT POWER EXERCISE: Write 6 Things You Can Do Instead

Write Rite to Right

You now have more time to devote to joy. Write down things you get to do instead of spinning your wheels on Tobacco Road.
For example:
"I breathe better, feel more energetic, smell better."
"I enjoy my many talents, interests and hobbies."
"I transform ash to cash."
"I buy myself a present."

1. ____________________

2. ____________________

3. ____________________

4. ____________________

5. ____________________

6. ____________________

Readjust Your Mind: 2 POWER SCRIPTS

Read the following power scripts out loud or into a tape recorder that you play for yourself daily.

Make yourself comfortable in a place where you will not be disturbed. Take a deep breath, let it out, and read the following words slowly, thinking the words as you do:

AFFIRM SUCCESS: Power Script #1 to Quit Tobacco

I choose to live. I take control of my body, mind, energy and life. I'm in control of myself. My potential is unlimited! I'm strong. I help myself.

I take charge and spring into action. I easily achieve my dreams and goals. I'm honest with myself. If I blamed others or played "poor me," I stop it, now. I honestly take responsibility for everything in my life. If there is something I don't like, I change it. I do what I enjoy. I do what makes me healthy, wealthy and wise. I am wise. I'm in charge of my thoughts and emotions.

I am an adult, a grown up.
To be a grown up means to choose joy.
To be a grown up means to choose wellness.
To be grown up means to follow a path of bliss.
To grow up means that I follow my path of curiosity.
To grow up means to set a healthy example for my inner child.
I love the child inside of me. I take loving care of all of my sub-selves.
I am a growing and maturing personality.
I follow my path of health and radiance.
I am 100% responsible for everything in my life.

I see myself in a mirror smiling, attractive and healthy.

Take a deep, full breath, get into center and let it out. In this moment, I begin a fresh, clean, new life. Free of toxins and full of health, strength, energy and joy. I feel so glad to be alive.

Chemically soaked burning leaves are gross. Carbon monoxide, hydrogen cyanide, strychnine, tar, nicotine, saltpeter—are a chemical nightmare. Yuck. These nasty, scorpions strikes to kill each time they touch a mouth or nose. Tobacco is deadly venom. I taste the bitter poison, and it's terrible. I want nothing more to do with this rancid, vermin.

Smoking, chewing and snorting make me dead, barren, filthy, sick and ugly. "No thank you I don't go there." I am vital, clean, sexy, healthy and beautiful. The first time I used toxic leaves repulsed and gagged me. Using poison is unnatural.

My sense of smell and taste are keen. I love the aroma of natural real air. I love the taste of healthy nourishing food and I crave delicious water. I feel healthy. I am healthy. I am my body. My body is me. I love my body, unconditionally. My body is a loyal and devoted friend of mine. It works for me 24-hours-a-day since I first began life. My body deserves respect. I love my body. I only put nourishing things into my perfect body. Good.

I enjoy another deep breath, taking in as much oxygen as my lungs can hold to the count of five. I let it out slowly. I notice the wonderful feeling of my breath; inspiration, and cleansing. I breathe with ease.

Thank you lungs for doing such a fine job. Each day the cilia in my lungs filter better and better. These microscopic hairs sweep away dirt and germs and protect me from toxins. I breathe fully, deeply and completely. I breathe with ease.

When I need to relax, I take three full breaths. With each exhalation, I say the words "relaxed and free." Any tightness releases. I relax completely. I'm free to get on with my many talents and interests. I practice my breathing right now by taking three deep breaths. "Relaxed and free." "Relaxed and free." "Relaxed and free."

If I see someone else use poison, I feel sorry for him or her. They are damaging and abusing themselves. I feel a tremendous pride in the respectful way I treat myself. I choose to be healthy. I enjoy life, in a free and happy way. I'm attractive. I'm healthy. I choose to live life completely.

My commitment to love body is permanent. I deal with it on a moment-to-moment basis. Others do not tempt me. I find tobacco taste repulsive and the smell disgusting. Poisonous chemicals and gases going into my mouth and lungs are gross. If someone offers me chemical-soaked leaves I say, "No. And God bless you." I avoid others who are self-destructive. I only permit myself to be in positive places or situations. I nourish myself and avoid bad influences.

For the two weeks I drink six to eight glasses of water a day and avoid depressing sugar, toxic caffeine, numbing alcohol and any other poison. I love drinking fresh water.

I always remember why I quit in the first place and how I did it my way. I enjoy being totally free of poison. I'm proud of myself. I see myself in my mind's eye thinking, feeling, behaving and being successful. I love the fresh taste in my mouth. I love to smell beautiful smells. My skin loses any wrinkles and look younger. My skin is smooth and attractive. I feel sexy and am more accepting of love and affection. I sleep deeply and soundly, with perfect relaxation. I am free, calm, peaceful, clear-minded, and healthy from head to toe. I feel terrific. I love myself.

AFFIRM SUCCESS: Power Script #2 Breathe for Life

Read this script slowly to yourself or, better yet, record it for yourself and listen to it when you go to sleep at night. If you record it, soft music in the background is great.

I'm sincerely committed to taking control of my life.

I take a long deep full breath and relax. Become more and more aware of breathing. I feel my chest rise and fall. I hear the sound the air makes as it moves in and out of my lungs and body.

How are my lungs working?
(Pause for a minute and honestly answer this question.)

Do poisonous leaves, chemicals and/or fire hurt them?
(Pause for a minute and honestly answer this question.)

I'm lucky, I'm alive! I'm lucky, I have the ability to make myself healthier and healthier with each and every breath. I celebrate how lucky I am to be here. Thank God, I'm getting a grip so that I restore my lungs.

There is hope. Every day thousands of people like me permanently quit poisoning themselves. Some forty million quit for good each year. Their bodies renew and regenerate. Damage reverses. Lungs become clear and clean. This is proof that I can and will quit for good, too. They did it.

I quit poison tobacco now. I was born a healthy, full breather. I naturally breathe fresh air. Renewed and regenerated, like a newborn, I cleanse my body and release poison. I'm clean. My world is clean. I'm proud to take time to make life better. I am eager to learn new ways to honor myself. Congratulations to me.

My fresh start begins this moment. I am well in body, mind and spirit. It's simple to release old habits that no longer serve me well and replace them with comfortable new patterns that let me feel terrific. I choose to feel terrific.

It only takes a few days for nicotine to leave my body. During this time I readjust. What are a few days when I have a whole lifetime of feeling great ahead of me? I'm free. I literally erase any desire to put poison into my sweet body.

I'm aware of my pulse. (Pause)
Blood carries more and more oxygen to my heart. My platelets are fluid and flowing, my blood vessels and arteries are open
I'm aware of my breath. (Pause)

With each breath my lungs bring in more and more fresh, cleansing air. The cilia in my lungs pop up and filter again. I am healthy, happy and proud. I breathe fully. I am alive. I am a miracle. I breathe with ease. (Pause)
As I continue conscious breathing, I become aware of three parts of my lungs; the lower, middle and top part. (Pause)

I fill my lungs in that order: lower third, the middle third and right on up to the top. I take a deep breath, filling up my lungs, section by section. It feels so good: bottom, middle, top.

I'm a conscious breather. More and more oxygen enters and cleanses my lungs; section by section. Congratulations to me. I breathe with ease. I breathe with ease. Think of being completely relaxed. (Pause)

Imagine a pleasant scene and relax more and more. (Pause) I notice all the sights, sounds, smells, tastes and energy of this special place. It is like I am there. The air is fresh and pure and smells divine. Is there sparkling water? Flowers or green trees? Hear pleasant sounds like birds or a luscious waterfall. Notice a cool breeze or warm sun.

I breathe with ease. I breathe with ease. I notice the sound of my breath. I enjoy my natural breathing. I choose only healthy air into my lungs. My breath is a miracle!

I breathe with ease. I breathe with ease. Every breath strengthens my will power and commitment to enjoy life. I take charge of my life. Each breath cleanses my beautiful pink lungs more and more. Smoky, gummy disgusting tar melts away.

My lungs are clear. I breathe with ease. As I do, I clean my lungs. Bottom. Middle. Top.

"I cleanse my mouth." (Pause)
"I cleanse my sinus cavities."(Pause)
"I breathe with ease."

I cleanse and repair my lungs. My lungs are clean and healthy. I breathe with ease. I breathe with ease. My lungs are pink with soft air filled cells; beautiful and healthy lungs. I feel so glad to be alive."

Right now in this instant, I release the past! I forgive the past. I'm forgiven.

I breathe with ease.

I call in the power of my imagination, higher self and God to help. (Pause) Imagine myself one month from today, free of all negative habits. Completely free! I have new, positive habits. How good I feel, what terrific energy I have.

I smell delicious. I taste delicious. I look wonderful. I breathe with ease.

I think back and remember why I quit. I remember that awful cough and raw throat, that horrible smell. Tobacco is filthy, dirty and expensive. All the trouble it caused me is now gone. I am free.

I hate poisonous tobacco. I can't stand smoke. The taste and the smell are disgusting. Thank God, I'm free. I did it! I walked away from poison; all poison. I did it by eliminating any trigger patterns that caused me to reach for rat poison wrapped in pretty packages. I rewired my mind.

Take a deep breath. I breathe with ease.

Like a switchboard operator, I disconnected wires that attached had tied me to saltpeter smeared paper and thick gummy toxic tar and nicotine. Those wires are now permanently disconnected! One by one, rituals I associated with poison dropped away. My car is clean and smells great. Talking on the phone I breathe fresh air. I sit in my favorite chair, enjoying fresh air and I really relax. I love to be clean.

Disconnect the lines to sickening sugar and toxic caffeine. I love to feel great. I release old patterns that don't serve me well and replace them with healthy, happy, new patterns. I embrace happy new patterns. I'm so blessed with life.

My new patterns work great! I drink water, breathe fully and laugh a lot. I stay consciously aware and in charge of my life. Each thought is positive. I use right thinking. I do good positive and loving things for myself. No matter what feelings come up, no matter what is going on in my life, I never again poison my body temple. I am kind and loving to my body.

I nourish myself and breathe with ease. My decision is final. I stick to it. I love my body and myself.

With each deep breath I go deeper into my inner mind. I've come to a crossroad. I choose a road to joy and life. I take the road to lush green, glorious colors, life and fresh smells. The sun is shining and there are warm breezes in my hair. I'm radiant and alive, surrounded by loving friends. I am proud of my path and life. Congratulations to me. I'm free.

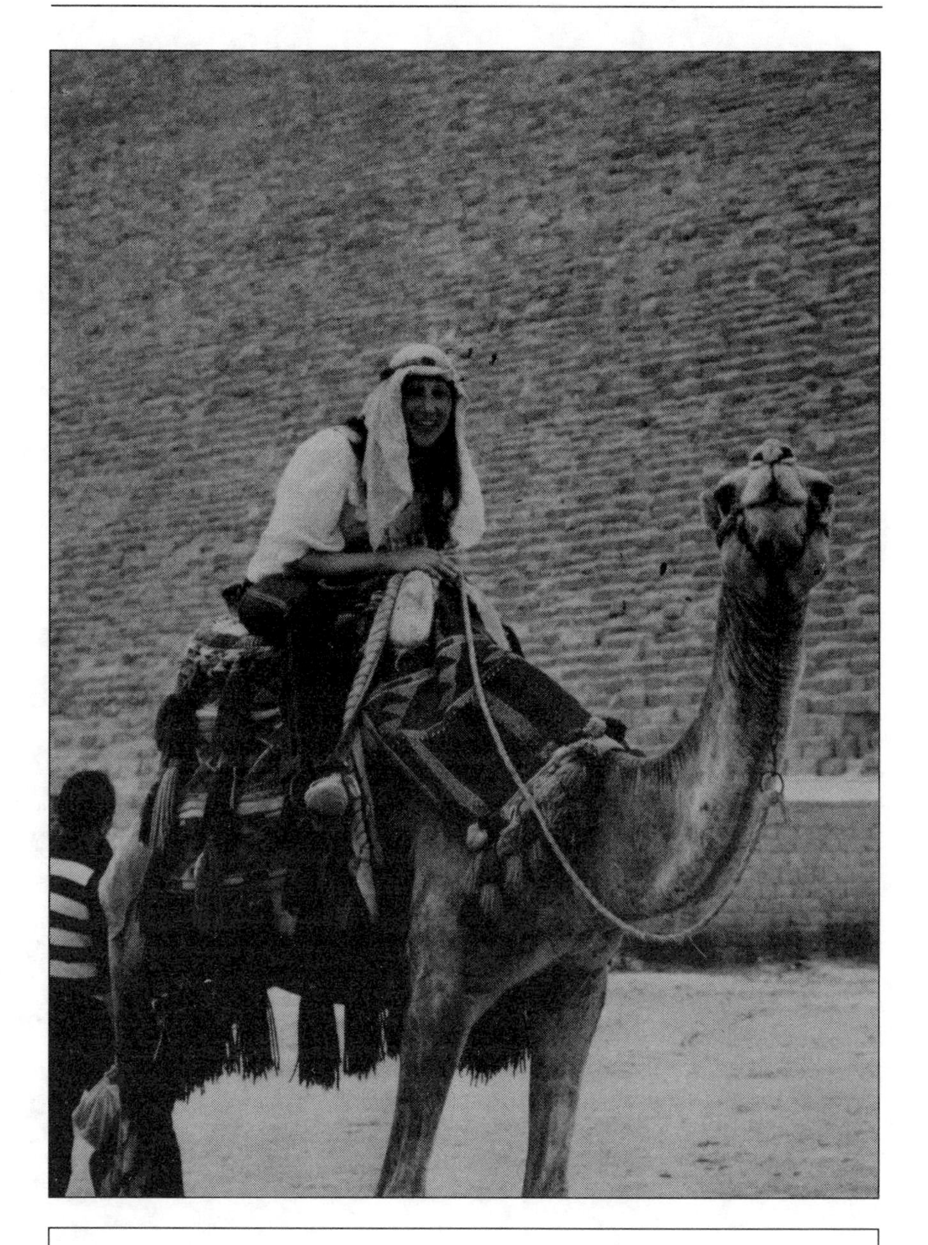

Hypno-Helper

To get fabulous results, order Stockwell's "Quit Smoking", self-hypnosis audiotape, available through Creativity Unlimited Press. Order forms are at the back of this book.

Photo by Jon Nicholas

Stoned

Chapter 24
Marijuana:
Stoned

Marijuana is the perfect example of cultural trance. If your peers or subculture say it is acceptable, you may have hypnotized yourself by rationalize dope as safe or not that bad. Putting chemicals into your brain/body hurts you. Marijuana hurts you. But don't take my word for it; ask your body and then read this chapter. It tells the truth.

- ▲ Historical Hemp
- ▲ Ask Yourself, Is Marijuana Good for You?
- ▲ Pot Holes
- ▲ What Dope?
- ▲ Dope Loves Fatheads
- ▲ Myth Defying Marijuana
- ▲ So What Can You Do About It?

Smoke to forget.
Smoke to remember.
Soon you can't remember why you smoke.

Alice B Toklas, cheeba, dope, gold, ganga, grass, hashish, hash, hash oil, herb, joint, Mary Jane, pot, Panama red, reefer, shit, sinsemilla, skunk smoke, spliff, THC, thai stick and weed are all names for marijuana. When PCP is added, it's called "super grass."

Blast a stick, blow the roof, boot the gong, burn one, buzzed, fly Mexican airlines, get loaded, go loco, hit the hay, mow the grass, puff the dragon, stoned, smoke, smoke a J, smoke a doobie, take a toke, take a hit, and get wasted, are slang for marijuana usage.

Users are called dopers, potheads, stoners and wasted.

THC sometimes comes in soft gelatin capsule and is taken orally. Hashish (hash) is in dark brown or black sticky clumps that are smoked or eaten. Hash oil is a dark molasses-looking liquid that is smoked. Blunts are hollowed-out cigars filled with grass. Marijuana may be laced with cocaine in a cigarette ("joint") or in a "a cigar ("51" or "blunt,") which may also include other drugs like LSD and cocaine.

A "nickel bag" is the thickness of one finger worth of leaves in the bottom of a zip lock baggie. A "dime bag" is two fingers and an ounce is four fingers. Pot is often carried in plastic film containers.

Pot paraphernalia includes lighters, matches, pipes, water pipes or hukas, blowtorches, rolling papers, vapor inhalers (complete with a "whip," and glass "condom"), cigarette rollers, and roach clips (often neatly disguised as keys, pliers or medical clamps.)

Marijuana contains four hundred and twenty-one identified chemicals. When smoked, heat converts it to some two thousand chemicals, including the deadly poisons; ammonia, benzene and cyanide. Sixty-one of these chemicals are known to affect the brain.

A hallucinogenic, marijuana, comes from dried leaves and flowers from the hemp plant. It generally looks like dried parsley and is smoked or eaten.

☆ SPANISH SONG
(Taught in elementary schools in the 50's)
La cucaracha, la cucaracha,
Ya no puede caminar.
Porque le falta,
Porque no tiene,
Marijuana que fumar.

(English translation)
The cockroach, the cockroach,
He cannot walk anymore.
Because he needs,
But he does not have,
Marijuana to smoke.

▲ Historical Hemp

Marijuana has been used around the world as a social, religious and medicinal elixir. In 2737 BC, the emperor of China used cannabis for medicinal purposes. George Washington grew hemp in his garden for the same reason. Today, marijuana is medically prescribed to relieve pain or nausea for AIDS and for chemotherapy patients and to help with glaucoma. It is a popular recreational drug for many.

▲ Ask Yourself, Is Marijuana Good for You?

Put aside your rationalizing and answer this honestly from your lungs, your happiness and your clear thinking. You know the answer.

Ask how your lungs like burning leaves?

Ask how your thinking and energy are being jacked around?

Ask honestly and you'll get the message loud and clear: "Stop the bull."

If your relaxation and social life are engrossed in grass, beware. Drugs run you. You don't run them. A huge subculture "sales campaign" underplays marijuana's harm as "not addictive," "not as bad as cigarettes," and "a little can't hurt."

Life may not immediately fall apart if you toke. But guaranteed, your body will. Take a deep breath and let your inner true wisdom tell you the truth.

My friend Juan told me "You don't even know if I'm smoking." He's right! I just thought that the sweet person he is, naturally lapsed into being sour, critical and grouchy.

CASE STUDY Sandra

I hallucinated the first time I ever smoked. I thought it was "freaky" and "cool." I hated breathing burning leaves into my lungs. But it was worth it, I'd say, because it "snaps me out of patterns" so that I can "view myself with detached eyes." I thanked marijuana for my new awareness.

I must admit that every time I smoked, there was a little voice in my mind that said: "What are you doing? This stuff is poison."

I began hallucinating when I wasn't smoking. I couldn't think well the morning after because I had a "grass-over." And I couldn't get anything done. I felt dumb at work. Speaking of work, other dopers and I would sneak away and get loaded at lunch.

Good 'ole, fun, marijuana had turned into a bummer. Over time, I could barely hold a thought. I got sick and fat on sugar munchies. The giggles that used to be fun started to sound like moronic babbling, fragmented sentences with people who made no sense at all. My friend marijuana had turned on me.

Thanks to hypnosis, and the threat of drug testing at work, I am now clean and sober for 15 years.

▲ Pot Holes

☆ *"One toke over the line sweet Jesus, one toke over the line."*

—Grateful Dead

Pain in the Grass

The technical name for hemp (marijuana) is cannabis sativa.

The sixty-one chemicals in marijuana that affect the brain are called cannabinoids. The cannabinoid that creates the high, THC, (Delta-9-Tetra-Hydro-Cannabinol) is the most active (psychoactive) ingredient. Marijuana in the 1960's had about one to two percent THC. Today's inbred varieties are more potent and have eight to thirty percent THC!

THC almost doubles your brain's seratonin level.

Seratonin controls your senses, your sleep, your aggression and your hunger. The result at first, is heightened alertness to every sound, sight, touch, taste and smell, followed by sleepiness, lowered aggression and a mellow feeling.

Marijuana also affects the neurotransmitter dopamine and that's what causes the feeling of pleasure. Over time, these feelings generally evolve into depression, lethargy, apathy, exhaustion, lack of motivation and sometimes rage.

▲ What Dope?

☆ Question: "*What is the difference between ignorance and indifference?*"
Answer: "*I don't know and I don't care.*"

THC impairs the brain's short-term memory. That is why time feels like it slows down, things are forgotten and your attention span is shortened. THC binds with your brain's memory and coordination messengers. Unbalanced chemistry and increased brain deposits evoke memory and concentration lapses.

THC actually damages brain cells by thickening neuron walls and making it more difficult for receptor cells to move and do their work. This disrupts the processing and storing of information and the ability to plan ahead. It causes users to awaken with a grassover, feeling sluggish, puzzled and disoriented.

Suck. Hold.
Quick, suck, hold. Quick, suck, hold.
Pass the pipe. Push the harsh smoke down into my lungs and wait.
Wait? I'm not sure if I've waited at all. It could be an hour or a minute, I'm not stoned, of course...except that my attention is riveted on that almost imperceptible movement of the breeze against the curtain (or is it the curtain against the breeze?). Funny how I never noticed that before: the dance of flowing movements, colors moving quietly through other colors. Shapes, dancing across my living room. Hairs on my arm, dancing with the crevices and diamond patterns of my skin.

I decide to make a cup of tea and it takes so long...perhaps a day. And talking to another person requires an inordinately monumental concentration. I wonder if it's worth trying, and besides, the deep innermost parts of my ears have shut down. It's quite possible that everything that I imagine I hear is muffled by two down pillows stuffed through my nasal cavity up behind my eardrums.

It used to be fun to be with friends, tie dyed and saggy, sitting in beanbag chairs, listening to oven racks or watching flaming groovies. Now a little voice cries, "Stop! I want to return to the clarity and full-blown hearing and talking and lungs pink and spongy."
"Would I like another hit?"
"Don't mind if I do."
Quick, suck, hold. Quick, suck, hold.

▲ Dope Loves Fatheads

☆ *"I'm in favor of drug testing as long as it's multiple choice."*

Cannabinoids love fat. Young people are more easily physically addicted to dope because body fat for maturation has more saturation.

As cannabinoids enter the blood stream, they seep and saturate body fat. They particularly love fatty body organs, like your brain and sex organs, where they remain for one month to a year, depending on how much you take in and your chemistry.

THC is deposited and stored in the spaces between brain cells. It is then released slowly. That's why long after you stop taking marijuana, you may have stoner flashbacks. Drug testing may detect THC from a single usage as long as a year later. THC can stay on hair follicles for six years.

Marijuana lowers blood sugar. That's why people get the munchies and scavenge for sweets, gain weight, and get a "pot paunch" or "done-lap disease;" your belly done lap over your belt. Pot users are generally cross-addicted to caffeine, tobacco and sweets.

Short-Term Effects of Marijuana Usage:

- Δ Bloodshot eyes
- Δ Dry mouth and throat
- Δ Elevated heart rate
- Δ The munchies
- Δ Bowel problems
- Δ Impaired short-term memory
- Δ Altered time sense
- Δ Inability to concentrate
- Δ Poor coordination
- Δ Impaired vision and hearing
- Δ Sleepiness
- Δ Increased heart rate
- Δ Hallucinations
- Δ Lowered inhibitions causing people to do things they regret
- Δ Paranoia
- Δ Depression

Long-term effects:

- Δ Increased risk of cancer
- Δ Diminished immune reserves and illness
- Δ Lower testosterone in men
- Δ Increased testosterone in women
- Δ Infertility
- Δ Birth defects in children
- Δ More likelihood of other addictions

▲ Myth Defying Marijuana

It is easy to rationalize a fun and social behavior. Here are the facts. They are gleaned from exhaustive research.

Myth: *My Friends Use It; It's Harmless.*
Fact: *Marijuana Hurts Your Body.*

☆ *"Tell me Willie, why do you drink? Why do your roll smoke?*
Why must you live out the songs that you wrote?
Try to think it over, Put yourself in my position,
If I get stoned, and sing all night long, why it's a family tradition."
—Willie Nelson

You may claim that marijuana is less harmful than alcohol, tobacco or even aspirin. In truth, today's more potent marijuana actually has more cancer-causing chemicals (two-hundred and eighty) than tobacco. One joint has the same amount of tar as twelve tobacco cigarettes!

Marijuana weakens your body's reserves, damages lungs and organs and kills brains cells. Harmful effects of marijuana build up over time, and its slow release from your fatty cells keeps toxins in your system long after you stop taking it.

White Trash

White blood cells that fight germs in your system shrink when exposed to marijuana. With weakened white cells, the body can't fight disease well. Marijuana uses up cleansing nutrients like zinc making a "toker" more likely to get sick than a non-smoker. That may be why marijuana has been linked to the recent "epidemics" of chronic fatigue syndrome and Epstein Barr?

Myth: *Marijuana Makes You Feel Good*
Fact: *Marijuana Can Be Fun... for Awhile*

☆ *"Why did the turkey cross the road?"*
"Because Thanksgiving was right around the corner."

It is true, THC does make you feel good...for a while…because it plugs up receptor cells. And then, depending on your personal chemistry and the amount you use, you "turn the corner" and flake out on your dreams, life and wellness. By then you are usually so entrenched in denial and depression to notice.

Think about it. How good does it feel to be spaced out, behave embarrassingly, get sick, smell like smoke, munch out, have gas, burned lips and get fat?

☆ GRASS GIVES YOU GAS
I feel gas (like a bulging bullfrog) grab my neck and bowel.
To let it out would be foul,
And tonight
I am polite.

—Shelley Stockwell

Myth: *Grass Helps You Escape Problems*
Fact: *Marijuana Makes Many More Problems Than It Solves*

☆ *"It takes one year to get your marbles back and five years to play them."*

There isn't one problem grass can't make worse. Depressed? Dope will generally compound it. A bad grass trip activates an overwhelming spiral of depression, disorientation and paranoia.

Fear, panic or paranoia attacks? High THC levels can trigger panic and paranoia with sweaty palms in many. Some imagine themselves having a heart attack or dying.

Over time or immediately, depending on your physiology, grass will exacerbate stinkin-thinkin and confusion.

Over time or immediately, grass causes psychosis and hallucinations.

A Letter from Jim

Dear Shelley,

My wife is begging me to quit smoking and my daughter has allergies to the smoke. My dad died young from a heart attack. I only want to give up cigarettes, not my marijuana; I need it to calm my nerves. My work is very stressful. I work in the tobacco industry and smoke most of the day. When the tension is too much, I close my door and take a toke to cope. Can you help me?

—Jim

A Letter to Jim

Dear Jim,

Cigarettes? Marijuana? What's the difference? Get a grip and quit. Quit smoking for your daughter, quit for your wife, quit for your heart, quit for your sanity; but quit. Don't play "let's make a deal" with your life. You are stubborn enough to go to work every day, be stubborn enough to love yourself.

Enclosed is my Quit Smoking audiotape. Listen to it everyday for two weeks; it's helped hundreds of people like you. You can put the tape on when you sleep at night. Drink lots of water and, instead of sitting at your desk and smoking, take a walk. It also helps to visit a hypnotist face to face. If you have any more cravings, a visit with an acupuncturist should set the body right.

Marijuana, cigarettes, soft drinks and sugar are usually cross-wired. Are you a big sugar and caffeine junkie as well? Commit to quit anything that harms you at once. Congratulations for this first step, I know you can and will do it. Be patient, it can take a full year to get the THC out of your system.

My Heartfelt Best Wishes,

—Shelley

Myth: *Marijuana Helps Your Sex Life*
Fact: *Marijuana Turns You Off*

It's true, marijuana can be a turn-on. It's also true that, over time and usage, you'll need more and more to get the same effects. Eventually, marijuana turns off pleasure. And tensions caused by emotional overreactions and petty exaggerations hurt relationships immeasurably.

Since your sex organs are fatty, cannabinoids collect there and adversely affect testosterone levels in males. THC lowers sperm counts, often results in difficulty having children. In growing boys, this lack of testosterone stunts facial hair, bone, voice, muscle mass and genital growth.

Marijuana affects the ovulation and menstrual process in women, and increases a female's testosterone level, resulting in increased facial and body hair and skin ailments. It is speculated that cannabinoids damages unborn children by impairing brain growth and causing genetic mutations. It is still unclear how marijuana effects a woman's eggs.

Myth: ***It's Not Addictive; I Can Stop Whenever I Want to***
Fact: ***Over time, Marijuana Runs You, You Don't Run It.***

☆ *"What I want to do most, after smoking a joint, is smoke another joint."*
—AP

Even if you are in full-fledged denial you know how seductive dope is. If you use marijuana compulsively, it runs you and you don't run it.

One reason grass may seem non-addictive is because cannabinoids stick around for a long time and slowly leave the body, making withdrawal imperceptible. If you were to take a cannabinoid-blocking compound, you would suffer severe withdrawal.

To get the same high, a user moves to stronger dope and/or uses more often. Dopers may experiment with other things, too.

If someone you love is unavailable and out of control it's obvious that they have a habit. If you are unavailable and out of control it's obvious too. After all, they like to feel high.

Myth: ***Marijuana Helps Me Focus***
Fact: ***Marijuana Decreases an Attention Span***

Dope decreases an attention span, short-term memory and the ability to plan ahead. It interferes with the brain's ability to process and store information.

With continued use, there is a good chance it will cause you to lose motivation, and feel tired, apathetic and off-center. You won't know exactly when that will happen. For some it happens over time, for others immediately.

Marijuana Slows Coordination and Reaction Time

For four to six hours after smoking, marijuana users are dangerous drivers. In a study of 1,023 patients admitted to a seriously injured accident trauma unit, one-third had detectable levels of marijuana in their blood.

Myth: ***It Might Be Legalized; It Must Not Be that Big a Deal.***
Fact: ***Marijuana is Still Illegal Except in Special Cases.***

Possession of marijuana for non-medical purposes is still illegal and punishable by a fine, a misdemeanor or even imprisonment. Enforcement policies vary from state to state. Those in possession of large amounts are considered to be distributors and therefore subject to stronger punishments.

Alcohol is legal but that doesn't mean anything if you give yourself cirrhosis of the liver. Get off any soapbox, it's still against the law.

Possessing marijuana in a foreign country offers even more severe penalties. Subject to the law of the land, users have been arrested and even put to death.

Myth: ***Marijuana Helps Me Escape My Problems***
Fact: ***Maybe... For a While...***

Marijuana is a paradoxical mood elevator that crashes down…health, fun and relationships.

▲ So What Can You Do About It?

It really is easy to let go of marijuana if you make up your mind. Hypnosis definitely helps and so does a ten-step program like Marijuana Anonymous. This affirmation will get you on your way:

AFFIRM SUCCESS: Marijuana Get a Grip Script
Read this script slowly to yourself, or better yet, record it for yourself and listen to it when you go to sleep at night. If you record it, soft music in the background is great:

I am my body. My body is me.
I love my body, unconditionally.

My body is a loyal and devoted friend of mine. It works for me 24-hours-a-day since I first began life. My body deserves respect. I love my body. I no longer put anything into it that harms me in any way. I do kind things for my body and mind.

I draw the line. I will never, ever, ever as long as I live put that toxic dog dirt in my body again. Never again. Dope is disgusting. It's gross. I don't want it and I don't need it. I am free of the THC, ammonia, benzene and cyanide. I choose to live. (pause)

Take in as much oxygen as my lungs can hold to the count of five. (one, two, three, four and five)**. Let it out slowly. I notice the wonderful feeling of inspiration, breath and cleansing.**

Thank you lungs for doing such a fine job. Each day the cilia in my lungs filter better and better. These microscopic hairs in my breathing passage sweep away dirt and germs, and protect me from toxins. I breathe fully, deeply and completely.

If ever I need to relax, I take three full breaths. With each exhalation, I say the words "relaxed and free." I relax completely. I'm free to get on with my many talents and interests. I am in charge of my success and joy.

I'm keenly aware of my pulse. (Pause) Blood carries more and more oxygen to my heart.

I'm keenly aware of my breath. (Pause) Each breath brings in more and more fresh, cleansing air. The cilia in my lungs pop up and filter again. I am healthy, happy and proud. I breathe fully. I'm alive. I'm a miracle. I breathe with ease." (Pause)

I'm aware of three parts of my lungs; the lower, middle and top part. (Pause) I fill my lungs in that order: lower third, the middle third and right on up to the top.

I breathe, filling up my lungs, section by section. It feels so good: bottom, middle, top. I'm a conscious breather. More and more oxygen enters and cleanses my lungs; section by section. I breathe with ease.

Others do not tempt me. I stay away from poison. If someone offers me poison in any form, I say, "No. God bless you." I avoid self-destructive people. If I see someone else using, I feel sorry for them. Drugs are damaging and abusive. Dope is repulsive and smells disgusting. I surround myself with positive, supportive and uplifting people.

I am patient. It takes a year for my body to completely rid itself of THC and other poisons. My brain functions more and more clearly every day. I stubbornly and tenaciously demand clear thinking and right action from myself. I am kind to myself.

I'm so proud of the respectful way I treat myself. I choose excellent health. I enjoy life to the hilt. I'm attractive. I'm healthy. I live my life completely. My commitment to love my body is permanent. I love my body every moment of every day.

I only permit myself to be in positive places or situations. I nourish myself. I drink six to eight glasses of water a day and avoid depressing sugar, toxic caffeine, numbing alcohol and any other poisons. This cleanses me.

I always remember why I quit. I enjoy being totally free of poison. I'm proud of myself. In my mind's eye, I see myself thinking, feeling and behaving the way I do when I'm successful.

I love the fresh taste in my mouth. I love beautiful smells. My skin gets smoother and more attractive. I look younger. I feel sexier and more accepting of love and affection. I sleep deeply and soundly, with perfect relaxation. My mind is clear. My memory is clearer each day. I enjoy being awake to the truth of my life. I'm kind to my body. I am free, calm, peaceful, clear-minded, and healthy from head to toe. I feel terrific. I love myself.

(Take a long deep full breath and allow yourself to relax. As you do become more and more aware of your breathing. Feel your chest rise and fall. Listen to the sound the air makes as it moves in and out of your lungs and body.)

I think of a time when I completely relaxed. and I relax more and more. (Pause)

The sights, sounds, smells, tastes and energy of this special place fill my senses. It's like I am there. The air is fresh and pure and smells divine. Is there sparkling water? Flowers or green trees? I hear pleasant sounds like birds or a luscious water. I might even feel a cool breeze or warm sun.

I breathe with ease. I breathe with ease. I notice and enjoy the sound of my healthy breath. I enjoy natural breathing. I take only healthy air into my lungs. My breath is a miracle!

I breathe with ease. I breathe with ease.

Every breath strengthens my will power and commitment to enjoy life. I wanted to take charge of my life for a long time. Now I've done it. Each breath cleanses my beautiful pink lungs more and more. My lungs are clear. I breathe with ease. I am naturally high on life.
As I breathe, I clean my lungs. Bottom. Middle. Top.

I cleanse my mouth. (Pause) **I taste delicious.**
I cleanse my sinus cavities. (Pause) **I breathe with ease.**

Like a switchboard operator, I permanently disconnect wires to poisonous leaves, resins, sickening sugar and toxic caffeine. I love to be clean. My lungs are clear. The walls of my brain cells are healthy and thinning and my receptor cells work perfectly. I process and store thoughts perfectly.
"I breathe with ease."

I cleanse and repair my lungs. My lungs are clean and healthy. My lungs are pink with nice soft air filled cells; beautiful and healthy lungs. I feel so glad to be alive."

I breathe with ease.

I release the past! I'm forgiven. I easily plan for the future.

I call in the power of imagination, higher self and God to help. (Pause)

I imagine myself one month from today: free of negative habits. Completely free! I now have new positive habits. Feel, smell and look great. What terrific energy I have.

I breathe with ease. I breathe with ease.

My new patterns work great! I drink water, breathe fully and laugh a lot. I stay consciously aware and in charge of my life. Each thought is positive. I use right thinking. I do good positive and loving things for myself. No matter what feelings come up, no matter what is going on in my life, I never again poison my body temple.

I nourish myself and breathe with ease. My decision is final. I stick to it. I love my body and myself. I choose the road to joy and life. I take the road to the lush green valley, glorious with colors, life and fresh smells. The sun is shining and a warm breeze plays in my hair. I am radiant and alive, surrounded by loving friends. I am proud of my path and life. Congratulations! I am free.

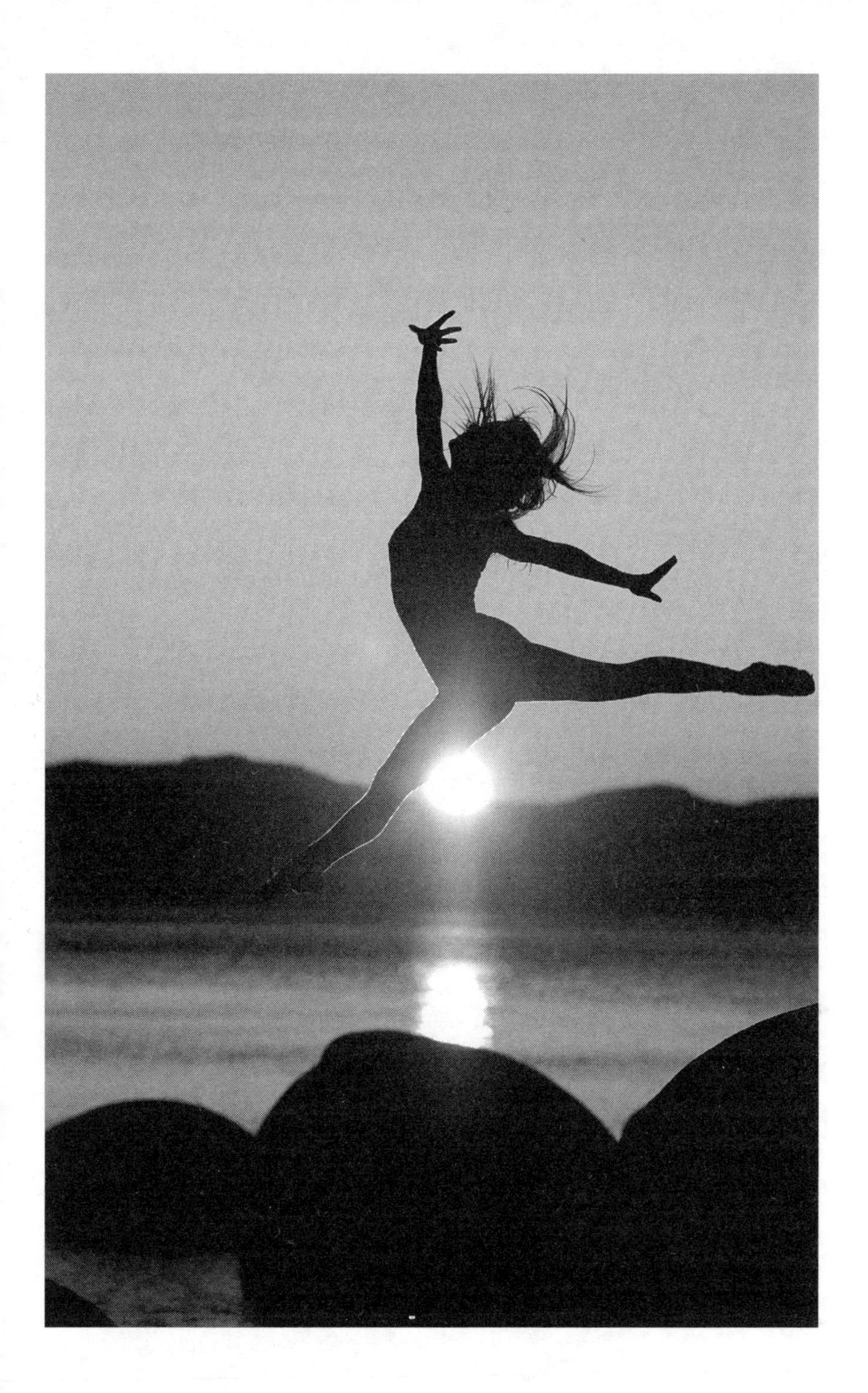

INNER•VIEW QUIZ

Are You Hooked on Uppers?

Be outrageously honest, put an X by any of the following that apply to you.

___ I'm hooked on uppers.
___ Amphetamines, cocaine, steroids, diet pills, caffeine and drugs keep me moving.
___ When I use, I do risky things I regret.
___ My life isn't working.
___ My behavior and personality change abruptly.
___ I have rapid or irrational mood swings.
___ When I use, I have a superhuman attitude; everything else is boring by comparison.
___ A positive attitude can suddenly go to worms.
___ I'm often late and absent from work because of my drugs.
___ My memory is poor; I can't concentrate.
___ My hands shake.
___ My nails are brittle and ridged.
___ I have sores on my skin; especially on my face, arms, back and chest.
___ I look tired and depressed in the mirror.
___ My pupils are dilated.
___ My body temperature is above normal.
___ I break out in cold sweats.
___ I have convulsions.
___ I'm confused.
___ I make frequent trips to the bathroom.
___ My blood pressure, heart rate and respiration are elevated.
___ I faint.
___ My veins have rolled over.
___ I frequently touch my nose and sniff.
___ I have nosebleeds, my nose is rotting.
___ Drugs have eaten holes in my body; nose, mouth & other places.

One or more of these symptoms spells DANGER. These signs of harm may not become obvious until serious damage is done.

Chapter 25
Uppers:
Don't Give A Tut

This chapter talks candidly about how stimulants affect you, so you take your power, and get a grip on real joy.

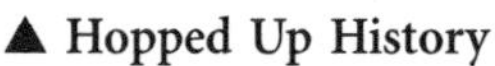

Uppers are promoted for their euphoric properties, and to help get pumped, stop smoking, stay alert and lose weight. Their payoff is an immediate and enormous gratification, arousal, ecstasy and numbness. The initial flush brings increased energy, mental alertness and the thought that you can leap tall buildings in a single bound. Hitting bottom is always a rude awakening. This chapter gives you a no-holds-barred look at the truth. And teaches you how to enjoy feeling human and healthy.

Socially Accepted Upper

Caffeine is hidden in hundreds of socially sanctioned products like chocolate, soft drinks and coffee. See chapter 9 for more information.

Pepper Uppers

Pills and Street Drugs Adderall, amphetamines, bennies, benzes, beans, Benzodiazapine, Benzedrine, (heart shaped and rose colored), Compazine, dexies, diet pills, Dexedrine, Dexamyl, jelly babies, Methedrine, meth, methamphetamine, pep pills, pepper uppers, Ritalin, uppers, ups, whites

Angel dust, big c, c, crystal, crank, dust, coke, cocaine, crack, crack cocaine, blow, devil's powder, flake, 90's crack, hydrochloride, ice, lady, nose candy, peanut, Peruvian marching powder, pop, rock candy, salt, speed, snow, snowbird, snow whites, shiny red apple, toot, white

Using is called a slam of crank, base-it, bunt, blatting, chase the dragon, crack-it, crank drive, dusted, do a hit, do a line, get a fix, get wired, main-lining, shoot up, swallow, skin-popping, run it, snort, sniff, whamming or wired up.

Paraphernalia includes alcohol, plastic bags, a glass pipe or stem with wire screen inserted tightly into a bowl (sometimes a broken light bulb). The bowl is heated with a torch lighter and melts the drug into a vapor, which is inhaled. Hypodermic needles, blotters, mortar and pestles, razor blades and drugs for cutting are also used.

Designer Drugs are legal substances produced by slightly altering the chemical structure of their illegal counterparts. Mail order companies and Internet marketing sell amphedrin and minifins tablets for "asthma relief."
Norepinephrine and neuro-hormones cause an adrenalin effect.
Coke Cocaine leaf is grown in South America. Peruvians chew it with a catalyzer or drink it as tea. De-cocainized cocaine is a "trade secret" ingredient in Coke® and other colas.
Cocaine is a white bitter, odorless, crystalline powder that numbs lips and tongue. It's inhaled (snorted), injected and sometimes mixed with a liquid and taken orally or applied to the gums, palette or underneath the tongue. Some believe that applying it to your genitals prevents premature ejaculation. Some take cocaine enemas and those who really want to risk it, place it inside their eyelids.
Free-base Powdered cocaine mixed with baking soda and water and boiled to gummy particles, is dripped into cold water, and often blown dry with ether to form a rock hard consistency crank.

Crank, Rock or Crack Chemically altered free-base cocaine purchased from street drug dealers and looks like soapy, white or tan, pellets or crystals.
Speedballs When cocaine is mixed with heroine, it is called a speedball. The upper and downer quality of this combination "lifts you up and slams you down at the same time" accords to one ex-user. Speedballs killed John Beluschi.
Water is a combination of crack and embalming fluid processed to form a liquid that you dip cigarettes or joints into. When smoked, it numbs the lungs and produces "glue sniffing like behavior." This causes the user to loose control of their body movements and "bounce off the walls" or become totally listless.
Methamphetamines are sold as a crumbly white powder or translucent crystal that is then smoked, snorted, swallowed or injected (jammed). A needle is an outfit.
PCP or sharm (phencyclidine, phencyclamine, arylcyclohexylamines) is smoked and makes users physically strong and violent with a feeling of light arms and head. PCP is often soaked into a cigarette or small cigar called a "blunt' and smoked.
XTC MDMA, Ecstasy, Adem, X XTC comes as a tab (-let) or cap (-sule). Available in many colors (blue, orange, grey, speckled...) Pills with names like Love, Passion, Dino, Bulls, Boomerang, Elephant, Pigs, Playboy, Superman, Clover, Rolls Royce and Ferrari. popular in the club scene. Immediate effects last 2-4 hours and cause long-term visual and verbal impairment.
GHB is a watery tonic known as the date rape drug.
MDMA is an amphetamine like stimulant and hallucinogen.

▲ Hopped Up History

☆ *"I am a wild man with cocaine in my body. It lifts me to unlimited passion."*
—Sigmund Freud

In the 1880's, companies sold medications containing cocaine, the newly synthesized drug from coca leaves. This pure cocaine was legally sold in retail stores. Sigmund Freud, Pope Leo VIII and Sir Arthur Conan Doyle used cocaine.

Cocaine was a major ingredient in the manufacture of the original Coca-Cola® syrup. Customers would step up to the local soda jerk and say, "give me a shot in the arm," when ordering. In 1906, caffeine and "decocanized" coca leaves, a supposedly neutralized byproduct, replaced pure cocaine. Today, the amount of "decocanized" cocaine and caffeine is a "trade secret" and therefore not listed on the labels.

Because of accounts of cardiac addiction, sudden death and crime, the Harrison Narcotic Act of 1914 banned retail sales of cocaine. The Anti-Drug Act of 1986 specified that the penalty for the possession of five grams of crack would be the same as for 500 grams of powder cocaine.

Amphetamines were invented eighty years ago in Japan. They were designed to resemble adrenaline, your body's natural stimulant. In the 1930s Germany produced amphetamines and in World War II, they were freely issued to all servicemen. Amphetamines were prescribed as *diet pills* in the fifties, and doled out like candy by doctors and pharmacists. The were dubbed speed in the sixties, *Ritalin* (for ADD attention deficit disorder) in the eighties and *Desoxyn Gradumet* today. Crank and crack are street versions of these "socially acceptable" drugs.

In the early 1950s, servicemen stationed in Korea and Japan began using amphetamines intravenously and invented the "speed ball," which combines amphetamines and heroin.

Doctors named the addictive behaviors of upper users: amphetamine psychosis, which they said, looks exactly like paranoid schizophrenia. And, in the 1960s, legislation was introduced to stop upper use in all but prescription drugs.

XTC, a stimulant and hallucinogen (related to amphetamines and mescaline), was first manufactured in 1912 as an appetite suppressant. XTC was banned in the US in 1985. Today, this mood enhancing club drugs is an international rage. All-night rave nightclubs feature dancing, heavy beats, and glow sticks. You'll see XTC users sucking pacifiers to override dry mouth. After the party, XTC users often take heroin, Valium or other downers to lose the high.

Approximately 20% of all drugs in America contain amphetamines. Amphetamines and over-the-counter uppers like NoDoz are as common as a cup of coffee in the world of truck drivers and students.

Diet pills and many "health food" diet supplements are loaded with caffeine and herbal uppers like ephedra (zephedrine) and Dong Chong (Jing Zhi Dongchongxiacao) a fungus that grows on a specific dead Chinese caterpillar.

Fat Burners are a popular way to lose weight. Titraticol (triidothyroaccetic acid) or TRIAC is a thyroid hormone fat burner recently banned by the FDA as a dietary supplement. Fat burners may cause severe diarrhea and loss of bowel control. The long-term effects of these drugs have not been determined.

Children with "behavioral irregularities" are given uppers like Ritalin, Dexedrine, Adderall, and "mood enhancers" like Prozac, Paxil, Luvox, Zoloft, and even blood pressure medicines like Clonidine.

▲ Snow Biz

☆ *Snuffed Belushi, Hendrix, too*
Joplin, Garcia left on cue.

The movie and record industry is covered in a powdery trail of cocaine. Rock stars add glamour to rock. We've heard about some who didn't fare well (and said farewell) under its spell: John Belushi, Kurt Cobane, Janus Joplin, Jimi Hendrix, Chris Farley and Jerry Garcia, for example.

A happily married, straight, actor friend of mine was working for a Hollywood "look alike" agency. He said that every job ended with the local pusher asking him, "Are you buying the coke for the party tonight?" One night, after he thought about it, he quit Hollywood.

My client Joe has his own story:

True Story, Joe

"I work as a grip in Hollywood. One morning, I passed out at work from taking too much coke. My coke buddy and supplier, leaned over my collapsed body and said; 'Hey man, you got to stop this and get up. Who am I going to get loaded with this afternoon?'

This grip got a grip on himself! Through a powerful combination of hypnotherapy with Shelley Stockwell and acupuncture, I went straight and feel great.

On every shoot, in every movie, 90% of the actors and the crew are under the influence of cocaine. I'm not one of them any more."

Cracking Down

☆ *"Cocaine is just everywhere. It's as easy to get cocaine as it is to get beer."*
—College freshman

One-third of New York 13-to-14 year olds questioned said that they had sampled cocaine before the seventh grade.

Dr. Arnold Washton, reports in a Fair Oaks Hospital survey (in Summit, NJ), forty-percent of youths who called the 1-800-COCAINE hotline said they had parents who used marijuana and other drugs.

The Bureau of Justice Statistics in Washington, D. C. claims that almost one-third of the inmates in the nation's prisons in 1990 were convicted of drug crimes; an eleven and a half percent increase since 1977.

"It is estimated that the average drug user costs an employer at least $7,000 in medical expenses and theft." —Duncan Maxwell Anderson

Snow Job

Cocaine for fun used to be the chic drug of the rich. Now, because of the drug cartels and pushers, it's cheap, readily available and popular.

Cocaine used in surgery, blocks the conduction of nerve fiber impulses, produces a numb freezing sensation, and can slow bleeding. Medical personnel have easy access to cocaine and amphetamines and often use them to keep from falling asleep. That's why so many become drug dependent.

CASE STUDY: Jaynie

"Cocaine felt like sunshine came into me. It enhanced my sense of being and my sense of smell. It made me feel whole and connected. I felt infallible.

It's an individual, not a group thing. Yet, I needed someone to talk to. I was so 'up' with energy I could talk on and on. I got depressed when its effects left me, anxious when I was about to get it and nuts without it. It was incredibly addictive

I was mortally afraid of LSD. I knew if I tried it, I would go out on a trip and never come back. There were people like that at our neighborhood drug rehabilitation center (the converted courthouse). They looked like dead shells. It was awful. Seeing them made me not take LSD. Ironically, I often bought my coke from them at the rehab center.

I stopped using cocaine when I turned thirty and moved to California. I just cold turkey stopped. What a relief, I actually hated the stuff.

▲ How Uppers Effect You

Upper Effects

- Over stimulates the central nervous system
- Speeds up heart rate
- Causes a sugar imbalance
- Overtaxes organs
- Depletes body's resources
- Causes moodiness, irritability, paranoia, exhaustion and depression
- Even one hit can be fatal or addictive

Uppers stimulate the central nervous system and adrenal glands causing your heart and body to race.

Amphetamines, sold as diet pills, suppress the appetite center by slowing the muscles of the digestive system. That's why amphetamines are sold as diet pills.

Neuropinephrine and Neuro-hormones adrenaline effect, raises blood pressure, heart rate and depresses the appetite.

Cocaine increases blood pressure, heart and breathing rate and raises body temperature.

Uppers block, replace and destroy your brain's neural transmitters. They stimulate the brain to release the neural transmitter dopamine and block receptor sites. The dopamine stays between the cells and continues to block the receptor sites for up to seventy-two hours.

Uppers vary in strength, chemical structure, and how they are taken in into the body but they all have the same cocaine-like rush effect. All stimulate the central nervous system.

Over time, dopamine is lost and production decreases. When this happens, the person crashes and becomes depressed, paranoid, exhausted, "cranky," irritable, nervous and anxious. As energy stores are depleted, most users say,

"Might as well have more." And, over time, it takes more and more drugs to give the same rush.

One dose of crank may well evoke a two to fourteen hour marathon of euphoria, racing heart, sexual excitement, tremor, dry mouth, rapid breathing, loss of hunger and sleep, dilated pupils, followed by paranoia, agitation, irritability, anxiety, violence, aching arms and/or difficult breathing. Prolonged use can cause acute depression, fatigue, lung and kidney failure, coma, convulsions and death.

Swallowed speed "comes on" gradually within 30 minutes. Snorted and injected speed is felt as a "rush," immediately followed by a bitter, taste at the back of the throat and a runny nose.

After a binge, a user is either wiped out, irrationally aggressive or hurting. Then they finally "crash" and sleep as hard as they sped about, sleeping for up to 18 hours. Unfortunately, this is not natural sleep so they most likely won't feel rested.

This exhausted response encourages many to use "downners." The body needs a day or two to recover for each day of speed. Confusion, memory loss and delusions can continue for up to a year after discontinued use.

A Letter From Dave

"I've got to get off amphetamines; help me. But I don't want to stop my beer or pot. That's how I party. But I feel terrible. I think about speed and go "Yuck." I drink before work in the morning and at lunch hour, and I can't wait to get in my car at night to light a joint. I hate myself. Do you think Prozac would help?"

Eventually, dream patterns are interrupted, and waking hallucinations, coupled with paranoia, fear, repetitive movements (like foot tapping-hypomania), jaw clutching, tooth grinding and tooth loss, begin. In one ex-users words, "I aged years in one month."

Cocaine causes confusion, anxiety, depression and eventually ends in cocaine psychosis, where you lose touch with reality and interest in friends, family, sports or any activity other than getting more coke. That's why so many coke users turn to drug dealing, prostitution and other crimes. That's also why cocaine and crack users are often victims of drowning, car crashes, falls, burns and suicides.

Each dose of an upper, ups the risk violent, of erratic or paranoid behavior and "coke bugs," a feeling of your skin, overrun over and under, by millions of crawling insects. Paranoia is characteristic of uppers in general and cocaine in particular.

An overdose of uppers results in extreme muscle, joints and chest pain followed by unconsciousness, convulsions, coma and cerebral hemorrhaging.

Cocaine use can cause a killing heart attack or respiratory failure. Depending on your body chemistry, it can happen the very first time you try it.

This poem, written by some young folks who know, wrote this ode to cocaine:

☆ *My name is cocaine*
I entered this country without a passport.
Use me once and be sold to give me your gold,

If it's me you adore, I'll make you a bore, a whore
You'll neglect your looks, your books
You and your newborn will be hooked.

I love destruction and body malfunction
I'll take your will so you rob and kill

I destroy politicians, actors, sports heroes and you
It's really simple, here is what you do:
Jump on my saddle and ride me well
I'm the white horse Cocaine, I take you to hell.

▲ Poison Nightmare

Buying and selling drugs involves "taxing" or removing small amounts for your own use and "cutting" or replacing large amounts skimmed off with a fake substitute.

If you buy speed off the street, you never know what's in it. Dealers cut speed with a nightmare of fillers: insecticides, photo developer, strychnine, MSG, lactose, epsom salts, quinine, baking powder, ether, and anesthetics, such as procaine, benzocaine, tetracaine, amphetamines, ephedrine, caffeine and sugar, in the form of lactose, inositol and mannitol. These are added to produce more intense flashes and to make more money.

Cocaine sold by pushers is rarely more than sixty-percent cocaine. At most, five to thirty-five percent is cocaine and the rest is other substances. Occasionally, a dealer will forget to put any cocaine in his recipe at all. When you buy speed off the street, you never know what's in it.

Freebase, meth or methamphetamine is sometimes called crank because early meth users carried it in the crankcase of their motorcycles and speed because it gives an instant rush. Some hide it in their gearshift knob. Crank is called the poor man's cocaine.

Crank is often "cooked" cheaply in homes or in crankhouses or cookhouses. Recipes for making it are readily available on the Internet.

Pseudo ephedrine, freed from over-the-counter allergy, cold and diet tablets

with heat, is combined with acid, solvents, Coleman fuel and drain cleaner crystals. Gas stations, drug stores and even antique stores carry huge stocks of legal pseudo ephedrine.

Toxic fumes, volatile chemicals and carelessly dropped poisons prepared and "cut" on tables, floors and stored in the refrigerator, are big risks for the cooker and children in the environment.

Freebase users think that the heat from smoking gets rid of these "impurities." WRONG.

How to Recognize a Meth Lab

Suspicious Odors

A strong ammonia smell, like a cat litter box or a strong solvent smell, like paint thinner.

Sparsely Furnished Rental

Rent is usually paid by cash, monthly. Hotels have been used for this purpose as well.

Activity Late at Night

Lots of people coming and going. Things being delivered.

Unusual Garbage

Garbage containing chemical drums or containers with labels painted over, broken or dirty glass flasks and bottles, beakers, rubber tubing, milk bottles and jugs filled with mysterious liquids and maroon colored residue on aluminum material.

▲ Pay Through The Nose

Organized gangs sell crank by the ounce or pound, bundled in duct tape. A bundle of crack can cause a buzz for up to twelve hours. Small bindles called nickel bags may go for as little as five dollars each. A gram of coke costs $100 plus. A gram-a-day habit is not a big deal to a user.

A pound of speed costs anywhere from six to eight thousand dollars. A rock cocaine habit is at least a $100-a-day proposition.

There is no such thing as casual usage, because once you get seduced, you believe that you cannot function without it. Here is how Amy beat her drug habit:

CASE STUDY Amy

"Most addicts say, 'I've got to give this up...It's destroying my life.' The problem is that by now your self-esteem has gone to nothing. 'Why can't I stop?' you ask yourself.

I smoked dope every day as school with my older sister when I was thirteen. I thought it was funny. I worked at a gas station and my boss got high with us.

When I was fourteen, mom took me to court as an "incorrigible teenager". The judge gave me the choice of living with my mom or a foster family. I wanted to live with my mom. She made a curfew and I continued using but slowed down.

Marijuana opens the door to other drugs; acid, pills, speed, crank, cocaine. By sixteen, I moved in with my boyfriend and dabbled in other drugs. I didn't get fully addicted until cocaine was readily available from my next boyfriend. He was a lawyer who would get solid rock off the boats in Florida. The rock came from south of the Bahamas he said. He would strap it on to his hips or in leggings with Velcro cloth pouches. He'd do coke and drink and then go to work and do a deposition.

I was a disaster. I wouldn't show up for work or return calls. My relationships were awful. I was delirious. I wouldn't leave my apartment for weeks at a time. I would stay up for four days, coking, drinking alcohol and smoking cigarettes to smooth me out. I'd clean house and my closets. I'd scrub every spot. I'd rearrange the furniture again and again.

In the morning I'd do another line to get going. I needed more and more coke. After, I'd crash and then I'd eat something and feel better...only to start up again. I did so much coke that I don't have a septum in my nose; it was burned away.

I sold coke to others to make money and be an addict. I hung out with other druggies. We were all in a sinking boat. I was twenty-eight years old when I got down on my hands and knees and prayed to God. I had never prayed in my life: 'Help me do whatever I have to do to stop.' I cried. My head started to nod up and down all by itself. "Yes. Yes" I felt a presence. If your life isn't working and you sabotage everything that comes your way; get down on your knees and pray. It worked for me.

I have been healthy for fourteen years, and I don't look back. Exercise and becoming a vegetarian saved my life. Thank God, I'm too blessed to be stressed."

▲ How Speed is Used

Speed is swallowed, snorted, smoked or shot up by medical patients, cranksters and speed freaks. Snorters inhale lines of cocaine from a coke spoon, straw or rolled paper money. It is said that 97% of paper money in the United States contains traces of cocaine and amphetamines!

Jammers A jammer or outfit is a needle used to slam drugs into the veins. The ritual uses a coke spoon, blotter and needle. Heavy cokeheads may shoot up 20 to 30 times a day! A doctor friend tells me that one user had no more skin on his arm, just raw muscle. "These drugs are vasoconstrictors. The blood stops circulating and the tissue deteriorates." Over time, slammers sunken veins have rolled over. Gaffing means to shoot it directly into your jugular vein. Injecting cocaine and other drugs is often more dangerous because contaminated needles can cause AIDS, hepatitis and other diseases. Using usually begins with snorting and evolves to shooting up.

Tokers and Lokers Some do a hit with a pipe or a makeshift broken light bulb with a straw. Crank takes less heat from the propane torch than crack cocaine. After the white smoke is sucked from the pipe, a residue called frosties remains to be torched. Like cocaine, crack and freebase rock are extremely addictive. According to What Counts, The Complete Harper's Index, the chances that a first-time user of crack cocaine will become addicted is 1 in 3!

"It gave me the best euphoric feeling I have ever had. I took it when I was drinking and partying. Then I blacked out and fell down a flight of stairs. That was the last time I used that shit.'

▲ How Do You Recognize a Coke Head?

Unlike alcohol, detecting upper usage can be difficult. Speed addicts may not walk or talk funny and usually smell OK. At work they are productive. That is, in the beginning.

It's common to see snorters touch their stuffy or runny nose a lot, sniff and say that they are suffering from allergies. Chronic snorting of cocaine often ulcerates and makes holes in the mucous membrane of the nose and through the palate of the mouth. Several of my ex-user clients have gaping holes through their septum's, big enough to place a large earring from one side to the other.

Slammers (those who use needles) have track marks at their body near veins and between their toes. Sunken veins have rolled over.

You can spot a cranker or crack user because they stay up for days, avoid sunshine like the plague, get paranoid to the max and lose everything. Their eyes have dark circles and their face often carries the telltale "cranker sores" pockmarks. A heavy cranker's house has widows covered in tinfoil to keep out the sun. They often disappear in the restroom stall, but don't flush the toilet. They sniff or play with their nose. They pick their skin, leaving sores or they have speed bumps on their arms, face or legs. They may hallucinate, be unable to communicate and speak gibberish. Eventually, they appear unkempt, may lose weight, and look pale and frail. They often avoid others.

▲ Myths

There are many myths about uppers. Here are the facts. They are gleaned from exhaustive research:

Myth: ***Uppers help me lose weight, quit smoking and stay alert.***
Fact: ***For a while.***

Yes, this is true. It is also true that, over time, malnutrition, sugar imbalance, psychosis, depression, memory loss and a damaged liver, brain, heart and lungs may result.

Myth: ***There are no real health risks with cocaine.***
Fact: ***Every time you use an upper, your heart is over-taxed.***

With cocaine, you have a very strong chance of having a heart attack, stroke or respiratory failure. Hepatitis and AIDS are often contracted by using shared needles. Brain seizures are common. And in all cases, the body is seriously overtaxed.

Myth: ***Physical and Psychological Dependence is Ridiculous.***
Fact: ***If you use, you will become more compulsive about using.***

Addictive or not, the truth is that if you use cocaine, you will become more and more compulsive in drug use. If you've used, you know it's true. Users choose cocaine regardless of how it hurts the body and life. Eventually most cocaine users shift to smoking crack. The good news is that quitting cocaine rarely causes unpleasant withdrawal effects.

How Drugs Seduce: The Dance of Pain By Any Name

☆ *Little white powder, killer called snow*
My life up in smoke with no where to go
The tears start to fall; I can't believe this at all
Little white powder of death
You've taken my life away

Honeymoon: Have an Apple Dearie

A friend supplies the drug, shows you how to use it and makes sure that your first experience is pleasurable. This sets the stage for the next phase. The first rush may be a familiar feeling because caffeine in the form of chocolate, soft drinks, coffee, tea and over the counter drugs may have upped you most of your life.

Play it Again, Sam

During this phase, you use the drug without becoming chemically addicted. This interval varies from person to person, even when using heroine. However, the younger you are, the more quickly you get hooked.

Gotcha Phase

The initial two stages give the illusion that you are in control of your intake, that the substance is not addictive. "I can stop any time I want." "Using drugs is my personal right." "It's the symbol of my individuality and control over my body."
(REALITY CHECK!)

Rock Bottom

By now you feel awful, can't see past your nose or veins.
You hurt, ache
(And want to make a prison break.)

You've given your power over to a sick seducer. Methamphetamines, coke, crack or crank, grab you by the throat, keep you up, spin you out, bring you down and make it difficult to come back.

Myth: ***"Cocaine and crack increase sexual pleasure."***
Fact: ***Over time, cocaine and crack use will make you unable to function sexually.***

CASE STUDY June

"I started taking diet pills when I was19, to lose weight. They made me feel energized and creative. After a while, I couldn't go to work without them. Eventually, I drank at the end of the day to relax from the uppers I took all day long.

That worked fine, until I got sick with a debilitating disease, similar to rheumatoid arthritis. The doctors couldn't figure out the cause. When I recovered, I was afraid to take the diet pills for fear of my disease, so I started using coke, just a toot here or there to help me get started. Within a month, I was using half a gram a day.

It wasn't like taking LSD or pot, where you know you're high. With cocaine, you feel great, not high. You love everybody. There's nothing you can't do or know. A toot puts a new light on everything, a new enthusiasm for work. Then it grabbed me. One day, I was having it for fun. The next day, I couldn't live without it. Without it, I was useless. It became everything.

At work, I had to have a toot before I could talk to somebody, or pick up the phone. It took me hours to do things I used to do in minutes. Much of my time was spent tooting. I'd leave work, and drink wine to cut the edge. I couldn't tell anyone. If anyone tried to talk to me, I was belligerent. The only person I had to talk to was myself. If I wasn't high, I would stay home and eat. I gained 25 pounds and spent $400 a week on cocaine.

Then I crashed. With my mother's help, I was admitted to a treatment program at a local hospital. Much to my surprise, I initially suffered only headaches and feelings of yearning. But one month later, I had severe feelings of stress, which I hear is not unusual. My body, in its ultimate wisdom, was shedding stored toxins. Luckily for me, I made it through that difficult time. I attend a drug support group. Now, one year later I can say, 'It's wonderful to be alive."

▲ Steroids

Are You Hooked on Steroids?

Come clean and answer.

Mark any statements that apply to you. Tell the truth.

___ I take steroids.
___ I'm sometimes enraged.
___ My face is puffy.
___ I've gained a lot of weight over a short time.
___ The whites of my eyes are yellow.
___ My skin is spotted dark and/or yellow.
___ I sweat profusely.
___ I have acne on my face and/or chest, back and thighs.
___ I have mood swings and am becoming more aggressive.
___ My sex drive left town.
___ I'm balding.
___ I have developed bone bulges.

These a re some of the most prevalent results of steroid use.

What Are Steroids Anyway?

We all have naturally occurring testosterone. Plus, we inadvertently get steroids into our system when we eat hormone fed or injected cattle and chicken. I've had several clients who went through drug-like withdrawal when they stopped eating meat. Could it be that they were coming off steroids?

Human Growth Hormones (hGH): testosterone, erythropoietin (EPO), cyproterone and cyprotone acetate. Nandrolone (prescribed for osteoporosis and as a contraceptive), stanozolol (used to treat rheumatoid arthritis and some coronary heart disease) and oxandrolone (used for childhood growth disorders) are prescription steroids often given to AIDS and cancer patients.

Testosterone: the male hormone is produced by the testes. In men, testosterone is responsible for producing secondary sex characteristics like deepening of the voice, growth of body hair, skin oiliness, aggressiveness and sex drive. Animal testes were the original source of clinical testosterone. Since the late 30's, synthetic testosterone has been used.

Anabolic Steroids: Anabolic steroids are synthetic derivatives of testosterone. They come in tablet or liquid form and are taken orally or with needles into the muscles.

Erythropoietin (EPO): is a natural protein that stimulates the production of red blood cells. Athletes take it to deliver more oxygen to the body for better endurance. Problems arise when excess red cells become gelatinous and make the heart strain to pump it. Heart attack deaths have been linked to EPO use.

Performance enhancers, muscle builders, body building drugs, physique developers, nutritional supplements and/or fat burners, creatine, bromantan, performance boosters, sports drugs and muscle primers are popular among body builders.

Why Do People Take Them

Doctors prescribe hormones for contraceptive or anti-aging therapy. I recently met an "anti-aging" doctor who swore that his Human Growth Hormone (hGH) drug regimen was the greatest discovery since God.

People take steroids to build their body, improve athletic performance and endurance. Steroids are said to motivate the body to pump out more amino acids, which supposedly helps muscles recover faster after working out.

The winning French bicycle team in the 1998 Tour de France was investigated for drug usage, Olympic gold medallist shot-putter Randy Barnes and sprinter Dennis Mitchell were suspended from the International Athletic Federation on suspicion of "doping."

Young female gymnasts, who want to halt sexual development, remain more agile, graceful and prepubescent, without breasts and hips, take "the brake drug" Cyroterone Acetate.

Steroid using athletes often "cycle," or go on and off the drug, to minimize side effects and keep the body from down-regulating its receptivity to the drug. "Stacking," means to take two or more steroids at the same time.

What's the Problem?

Steroids offer an estimated $500 million a year black-market supplying two to three million U.S. users. How much steroids hurt you depends on your personal chemistry and what you take. If you get your steroids "off the street," you have no way of knowing what you get and how sterile it is. Roids are usually made in "back street" labs or in countries like India, Turkey and Thailand to look like the real thing. As much as 90% of these drugs are said to be counterfeit.

On January 1, 1987, anabolic steroids became a controlled substance. Unlawful possession is a misdemeanor. Possession for illegal sale is a felony.

Over time, even low dosages hurt your body. Steroids raise cholesterol levels, increase blood pressure, weaken the immune response and are suspiciously linked to liver disease, cancer and a low sperm count. Steroids deaden, atrophy, harden and impair tissue and arteries and tissue renewal. HGH can make bones grow funny. Steroid users often grow bulging foreheads, cheeks, jaws and hands and feet.

Steroids Cause Mood Swings

Everyone who uses steroids will eventually have angry, angry, angry emotional outbursts. The testosterone like quality brings on 'roid rages that are similar to major exaggerated PMS.

A TRUE STORY Ben

"Women go for guys who are buff. Working out in the gym just didn't seem to do it. There's a guy named Tam who sculpted his body like Adonis. He was my hero. One day, we decided to play pool after working out. He turned me on to steroids. They worked great. I looked like Mr. America. Perfect definition. My girlfriend loved it.

Then the roller coaster ride began. If I took too much, I became a raging bull. If I took too little, I felt like a complete wimp. But the worst part was I lost all my sexual drive. I just couldn't get it up. It took two brawls and one arrest to help me get a grip. Hypnosis and acupuncture helped me get clean and sober. The very thing I used to enhance my masculinity made me impotent."

Steroids Damage Men's Sexual Function

Steroids cause urinary frequency and continence. They either increase or decrease the male sex drive.

Over time, anabolic steroids cause testicles to shrink, calcify and atrophy. Men can't perform sexually because of "benign hypertrophy," which is the swelling of the prostate due to lack of circulation from calcification or stagnation. This condition might turn into prostate cancer. Steroids can cause the growth of breast tissue in men. Athletes are particularly vulnerable to it. Steroids cause irreversible baldness and the sprouting of facial hair.

Steroids Destroy the Liver and Kidneys and May Cause Cancer

If you are "moon faced" and puffy, have severe acne on the face, chest, upper back and thighs, yellowing of skin and eyes, spotted dark skin, gained weight over a short period of time, and mood swings with increased aggressiveness and profuse sweating, steroids are damaging your liver or kidneys.

Your liver is one of the largest and most important organs in your body. It metabolizes lipids, like cholesterol. When the liver's management of cholesterol is impaired, it can affect your arteries with arteriosclerosis and increase blood pressure. Prolonged high doses of steroids can evoke cholestasis, jaundice and even death. Steroids increase the risk of testicular, liver and prostrate cancer. The older you get, the more difficult it is for the liver to reverse damage done to it.

Steroid Addiction Creates a Tragic Chain Reaction of Other Harmful Drugs

The symptoms of steroid damage leads to other damaging behaviors and *solutions;* antibiotics for the acne, diuretics to stop bloating, cocaine for pain and Valium to reduce anxiety.

▲ Other Performance Enhancers

Body building supplement and health food store business is BIG business. Unmonitored as it is, you often don't get what is labeled on the package. Bill Phillip, the founder of Muscle Media magazines and the creator of EAS body building supplements, tested competitor's products and found that some don't contain any of the supplements their label claims. "Last year we tested six different HMB supplements that didn't contain any Beta-Hydroxy Beta-methylbutyrate (HMB) at all." And "Creatine Plus from USA Sports Lab contained virtually no creatine at all," he says.

Creatine (methylguanida-acetic acid, creatine monohydrate, creatine citrate) Creatine is found in meat. A pound of beef or salmon contains two grams and herring has three grams. Additionally, your liver and perhaps the pancreas and kidneys naturally create about one to two grams of creatine a day.

Creatine, as a nonprescription nutritional supplement is used to bring water to the muscles so that they bulk up. Named after the Greek word for "flesh," creatine is said to up recovery from workouts. Three out of four gold medal winners in the 1996 Olympic Games purportedly used it.

Five to ten grams of creatine supplements may shut down your natural creatine production. If you stop the supplementation does your body produce it naturally again?

Creatine supplements cause dry mouth, dizziness, diarrhea and cramps in some. I tried it and after a few days with my mouth as dry as a bone, my heart started racing so I quit. One Creatine manufacturer warns on the label. "This product is not to be used if you suffer from diabetes, kidney malfunction, bladder problems or suspect heart disease. It is not to be used by women during pregnancy or lactation."

GHB (Gama hydroxybutyrate, On the streets it is called "G" or "Liquid X') GHB purportedly increases growth hormone secretion. Take a little and you get stoned. Take a little more, and you vomit and pass out. The FDA made the manufacturing of GHB illegal in November of 1990. Used as a party drug, GHB is home brewed and you never know how potent the capful you swig is or what's in it.

Upper Facts:

- Many uppers are illegal. Depending on where and how you get caught, you will face high fines and jail time.
- Needle usage can give you AIDS and hepatitis.
- Car crashes, falls, burns, drowning and suicides are increased by cocaine use.
- Cocaine and uppers ruin your looks.
- Uppers often create failing grades and poor work performance
- Uppers eventually ruin your sex life.
- Drugs create financial disaster.
- Drugs create more problems than any you are trying to avoid.
- Every time you use an upper, your risk of mood swings, bad judgment, fatal seizure or heart attack grows stronger.
- Drugs wreck lives. Has it been wrecking yours?

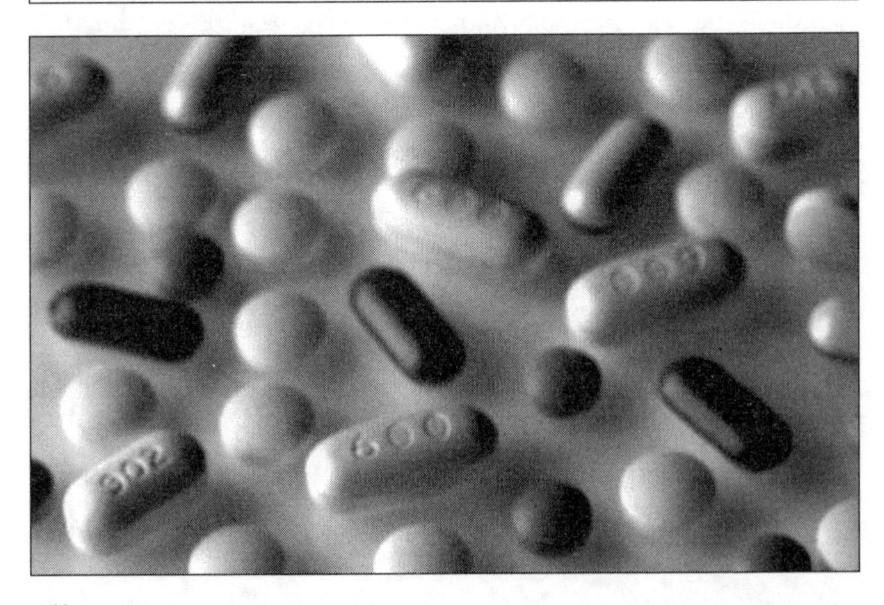

▲ What To Do About Uppers

1. **Embrace the Outcome**
   Write down the outcome you would like to have. For example; "I am healthy, clean and sober and I never again as long as I live put poison in my body."

2. **List Action Steps**
   Make a list of the actions you'd take if you were 100% responsible for the outcome.

3. **Commit to Action**
   Decide what step you will take with each item to make it happen.

4. **List Limits**
   Write a list of the self-defeating things that you tell yourself.

5. **Let Limits Go**
   Tear up the list. You don't need it anymore!

6. **Affirm Results**
   Write a positive affirmation of the results you want as if it is already a done deal. Repeat that affirmation often until the power of its meaning lights up inside of you. You can add your affirmation to the following one if you like.

7. **Get help!**
   You need someone to support you in this. It's usually difficult to stop using such seductive drugs on your own. Hypnotherapy, acupuncture, a good drug rehab program, a ten-step program and a nutritionist can really turn you around. A good interventionist can help convince a loved one to go into a rehab program. Your local hospital, hot-line or police may recommend one to you.

Affirm Success: Come Down To Earth

It's all-or-nothing. I quit and I don't look back. I forgive my hurtful behavior and hurtful voice. I now listen to the voice of wisdom and honesty. I choose to live and to be happy and healthy. I make my life about joy. I wrap my mind around feeling great!

I take back my life and get real. I choose to feel healthy and NORMAL. Yogurt, fresh fruits and vegetables, liquids and vitamins help me balance my body. I stop any poisons and drugs NOW. Healthy living returns me to sanity.

Take a multivitamin. I have no other choice. It is a life or death decision. I stop using now. I m stubborn about it and that is all there is to it!"

The Shaft

Chapter 26
Downers:
The Shaft

This chapter talks candidly about how downers influence you and how to release them and mellow out naturally.

▲ Get Down History: Is That a Bar-Bitch-You-Ate?
▲ How Downers Work
▲ Downers Get You Down
▲ The Solution

Barbiturates: Tranquilizers, Sedatives & Hypnotics, Barb, depressant, downer, heroin, horse, hypnotic, lady, muscle relaxant, narcotic, pain pill, pentobarbital, yellow jackets, nemmie, Phenobarbital, reds, red devils, slam, sleeping pill, sedative, tranquilizer, and whites
Amytriptalin: Elavil and Endep
Amytal: Blue, blue angel, blue heaven, blue bird, blue devil
Benzodiazepines: Diazepam, Dalmane, Librium, Tranxene, Tquil, and Valium.
Lorazapam: Atavan, Tamazepam, Restoril
Codeine/Tylenol #4: is prescription codeine, meperidine
Doxepin: Adapin and Sinequin
Ehchlorvynol: Placidyl
Glutethimide: Doriden
Heroin: H, hard stuff, horse, junk, scag, shit, smack, white stuff
Imapramine Hydrochloride: Janimine and Tofranil
Meprobamite: Equinal and Miltown
Methoqualone: Quaaludes, ludes, anti-anxiety agents
Morphine: Morphia, M, Miss Emma, diacytyl morphine, micky
Nembutal and Seconal
Opium Black stuff, blue velvet, cough syrup, hop, laudanum, mecon, opiate, paregoric, pen yan, tar, turps, tincture of opium. Opium is refined into heroin and then morphine. D'abasan is a green opium based liquor used in Japan.
Phenobarbital: Luminal, Luminal pill, purple heart
Seroquel: Quetiapine fumarat, sleeping pill, antipsychotic
Sleeping Pills: Goofballs or sleepers
Triazolam: Halcion
Tuinal: Rainbow, tooie

▲ Get Down History

Since antiquity, the Eurasian poppy was cultivated for the opium from its oily seeds and flowers. Called gaul, or paregoric, in the bible, ancient Egyptians and Jews mixed it with wine for pain management.

Today, barbiturates, tranquilizers, sedatives and hypnotics are pills or shots given by doctors to overcome stress, slow you down, help you sleep, kill pain, and stop seizures.

Sedatives taken in pill form take longer to have an effect and last longer. To speed up the slowing down effects, recreational users grind up the pills and smoke them in a glass pipe or inject with a needle.

Prescription downers are popular and easy to come by. George's story sure underscores that:

A True Story: George

"I was a army medic stationed in a hospital in Japan in 1966. When we came to work each day, the nurses had oxygen, Darvan, Valium and coffee waiting for us to cure our hangovers from drinking sake the night before.

In the late 70's, I lived in St Thomas, USVI, a United States territory. Being a veteran in good standing, the Veteran's Administration office there, issue me, and all vets, a 'health care credit card.' With it, many guys got their recreational drugs in unlimited quantities compliments of the U.S. government. One friend and his non-military wife, had a regular Friday night visit with the local "doctor" who would shoot them up with government supplied morphine. If the high waned they'd go back later to the good doctor's house for another free blast."

Is That a Bar-Bitch-You-Ate? The word "barbiturate" comes from a Munich, Germany waitress named Barbara, whose urine, mixed with malic acid from apples, composed the ingredients for this sedative named in her honor. Isn't that a pisser? The year was 1865, and Chemist, Adolph Baeyer developed his formula to "calm anxiety, cure insomnia and achieve euphoria."

Doctors considered barbiturates like Librium and Valium a "minor drug" since they "required smaller dosages and diminished aggressive tendencies". By 1933, barbiturates were so liberally dispensed they topped the federal government's list of the most abused drugs in America.

Today, Americans consume over five billion sedatives a year.

A True Story: Dr. Dave

"When Emma came to me 8 years ago complaining of stress, I prescribed Valium. Since then, at every visit, she asks me for more. When I told her I was concerned that she may be drug dependent and refused refill her prescription without an office visit, she was irate. I know she's addicted but what can I do? I have her come for an office visit and prescribe her more Valium. If I don't, she'll just find another doctor who will.

A True Story: Stace

"Being a social worker is stressful. You might say that I'm chronically miserable. I take two 10-milligram of Valium twice a day and Vicaden. My doctor refused to prescribe any more so I've been forced to see other doctors. It really makes me mad. I need my Valium to do my job."

▲ How Downers Work

☆ *"I'm on a Valium diet. I take four for breakfast, and the rest of the day, food keeps falling out of my mouth."*

—Max Alexander

Downers block, sedate or suppress areas of the brain.

Sleeping pills and barbiturates interfere with brain impulses and cause a kind of sleep. A barbiturate drunk is exactly like an alcoholic drunk; hangover and all.

Eye Opening Experiment

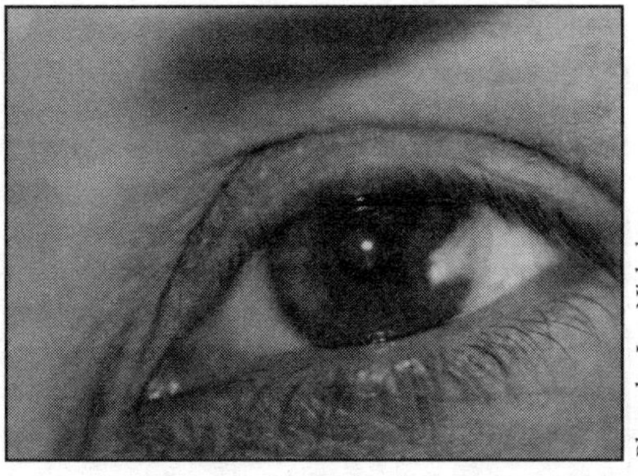

Photo by Jon Nicholas

In the early 1930's, five sober men were given "eye opener" doses of barbiturates before breakfast and larger doses throughout the day as part of a United States Public Health Service Hospital experiment in Lexington, Kentucky. They were chosen for the experiment because they were good friends. The men were regularly reminded that they could quit taking the drugs at any time, yet, none chose to quit and all requested increasingly higher doses.

"The signs of intoxication were minimal throughout the day, reaching maximum intensity after the fourth dose at 11 p.m." Most interesting was how the men became progressively unkempt, confused, irritable, paranoid, depressed and quarrelsome. Even though they always been amiable toward each other, they now cursed and fought.

These behavior shifts are identical to similar in studies of alcohol.

▲ Downers Get You Down

☆ *"Most people crave sleeping pills, tranquilizers and narcotic pain killers in ever increasing amounts, and end up creating more problems then they solve. Such drugs should be slowly replaced with biofeedback and other forms of therapy, and only occasionally with non-narcotic pain relievers, such as aspirin."*

—Nelson Hendler, M.D.

Nightmare Pills: Deadly Duos

Here is a list of some risky possible combinations:

Amitrptyline (Elavil and Endip). Used with alcohol, causes drowsiness. WARNING: Do not stop taking this drug suddenly. Reactions to sudden stopping are worse for those over 60. When used with Placidyl and Antabuse, these drugs cause delirium. Dangerous when used with amphetamines, antihypertensives and thyroid medications.

Atavan. Highly addictive. Taken with alcohol or sedative they can be fatal.

Benzodazepines (Diazepam, Tquil, and Valium). If used with alcohol, narcotic barbiturates, or other antidepressants, they can cause death.

Dalmane. If taken with alcohol or an MAO inhibitor, other narcotic barbiturates and/or antidepressants it's hazardous.

Doxepin (Adapin and Sinequin). Can cause drowsiness, dizziness, blurred vision, dry mouth, constipation, increased heart rate and difficult urination. If taken with an MAO inhibitor, can cause fever, heightened blood pressure, convulsions and death, even if the MAO inhibitor was taken two weeks earlier.

Ehchlorvynol (Placidyl). Dilutes the effectiveness on any anti-coagulant and, if taken with a triciyclic antidepressant, causes delirium, skin rashes, nausea, morning hangover, fatigue, agitation, difficult breathing and blurred vision.

Glutethimide (Doriden). Dilutes the effectiveness on any anti-coagulant, and if taken with a triciyclic antidepressant, causes delirium, skin rashes, nausea, morning hangover, fatigue, agitation, difficult breathing and blurred vision.

Imapramine hydrochloride (Janimine and Tofranil). If taken with an MAO inhibitor, can cause fever, heightened blood pressure, convulsions and death. Even if the MAO inhibitor taken two weeks earlier can be deadly.

Lorazapam (Atavan). Highly addictive. If taken with alcohol or other sedatives, causes extreme side effects and can be fatal.

Tamazepam (Restoril). If taken with alcohol or an MAO inhibitor, other narcotic barbiturates and/or antidepressants can be hazardous.

Triazolam (Halcion). If taken with alcohol or an MAO inhibitor, other narcotic barbiturates, and/or antidepressants can be hazardous.

Photo by Jon Nicholas

Depression, nausea, confusion, memory loss, slurred speech, drowsiness, fatigue, troubled dreams, disturbed sleep, tremors, poor judgment and coordination are by-products of downers.

Ironically, downers to relax and/or sleep, do the opposite. After only two weeks, downers disrupt sleep patterns. As tolerance builds, you require more and will most likely go through withdrawal when you stop.

Valium, for example, has a half-life. That means that if you take 20 milligrams a day, you'll still have ten milligrams in your system the next day and 5 the next day and so on. If you continue taking the 20 milligrams, you are building a mountain of drugs in your system.

A True Story: Jimmy

"I smoked marijuana when I got involved in cars. The first time it made me feel dizzy and sick to my stomach. Then I found the magic of barbiturates. Someone gave me a roll of red devils— seconal barbital. They said 'Take one or two to get mellow.' I took all five and I was falling all over against the walls. It was the feeling of falling apart. I liked that feeling.

The magic was short-lived. After that, I needed lots of red devils just to feel OK or not feel at all. I finally quit using all drugs with the help of a terrific court ordered rehab program."

In 1982, several heroin addicts became almost completely immobile after taking the drug. There are also reported cases of someone becoming paralyzed from homemade meperidine (Demerol). It's speculated that an impurity, MPTP from these, when taken into the brain, is converted into a more reactive molecule that destroyed dopamine-making cells.

When You Snooze You Lose Sleeping pills act on your central nervous system and reduce breath, vision, alertness and reflexes. They also make insomnia worse. Dr. Anthony Kales at the Hershey Medical Center studied insomniacs who took sleeping pills. The pill takers awoke twice as often during then night as those who did not use drugs.

Sleeping pills impedes the lower brain's ability to properly govern bodily functions. Lung sequences and the ability to swallow saliva are impaired. Abnormal cough and gag reflexes may prevent food and drink from going down. Secretions can enter the brachial airways, causing inflammation and endangering breath.

Downers combined with alcohol and other drugs can induce upsetting side effects like coma and death.

▲ The Solution

The first step to stopping is a stubborn decision to stop. This may require you to tough it out or it may be an easy adjustment. Either way, you need a determined conviction and tough love. Here is how Joanie got off sleeping pills:

A True Story: Joanie

"I was always afraid that I wouldn't sleep. I got hooked on Halcion as a sleeping pill by telling myself I couldn't get to sleep without it and then proving it. But, it made me feel strange during daytime. Last year, I decided to stop when I used up my supply. 'The worst thing that could happen,' I said to myself 'would be to I'd lie in bed awake all night. And that's what happened. I stayed awake all night several nights, but not in a row. That was the end of my reliance on sleeping pills. Thank God, I overcame my fear of not sleeping." After you psych yourself out, determine a good practical course of action. Cold turkey stopping some medicines can be dangerous. A holistically oriented physician can wean you off in a healthy way.

Natural foods and scents can help. Bananas, figs, dates, warm milk, and yogurt, contain tryptophan, a natural relaxant. Sniffing peppermint and lavender oil eases depression and eliminates headaches. Hypnosis tapes and soothing music are great. So is learning to meditate.

If you can't do it on your own for god's sake get help. There are terrific free 10 step and wonderful rehab programs available. A good hypnotist or counselor will help you adjust your thinking.

Reframe Pain Thanks to Hypnotherapist, Roy Cage for this idea:

Ever wonder why a person who looses an arm or leg still can feel pain in that limb? This phantom pain effect reminds us that pain and sensation actually live in the brain. Medication or drugs do not take pain away, they simply disrupt the brain signal of pain.

The words "in pain" energetic gives pain. For you to be "in" pain implies that it is bigger than you. Get bigger than the pain by changing your perception of it. Put it outside of yourself. Learn from it and then let it go. Here us an artistic way to feel good

1. Imagine yourself before a huge painter's canvas.
2. What color do you identify with the pain? Imagine that your index finger is filled with that color and paint it in the air on that imaginary canvas. Make sure you cover the entire canvas, letting all the color express itself. When you are done expressing it all;
3. Use your other index finger is an eraser and erases every bit of the color from your canvas. Did you get all the corners? Get those. When you are complete and your canvas is restored to pure white again, take a deep breath and relax. You are comfortable in your body again.

Etching by David Roberts 1856

Thebes

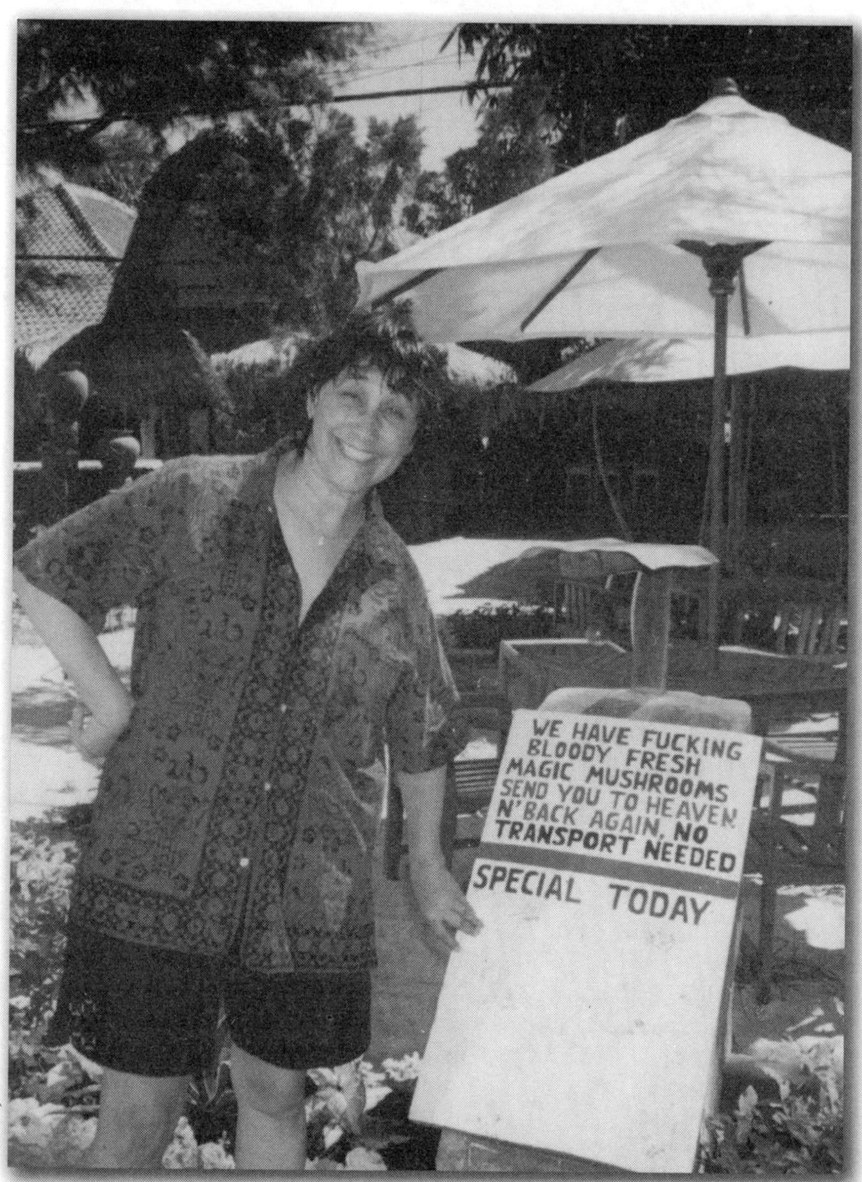

Photo by Jon Nicholas

Lomboc, Indonesia

Chapter 27

Hallucinogens:

A Trip to the Gaza Strip

Hallucinogenics are unpredictable. They depend on the amount you take, your personality, body chemistry and mood. They can be astoundingly mind-expanding and pleasurable or they can throw you into terror. This chapter lets you look at the truth of using them.

▲ Hallucinating History
▲ What Hallucinogenics Do To You
▲ What Can You Do To Drop Hallucinogens

Acid, ayahuasca (banisteriopsis), barrels (acid soaked saccharin), blotter, caapi, detura, DMT (yurema), hits, LSD (lysergic acid diethylamide), magic mushrooms, mescaline, peyote, psilocybin, psychotropics, san pedro cactus, spirit, tablets, uaje, vine of the soul, and vine of wisdom. Peyote buttons. MDMA, both a stimulant and a hallucinogen is related to amphetamines and mescaline.

"Acid Trips" are usually manufactured using blotting paper or in small pellets under colorful names like Red Dragon and 8-Balls. Sellers usually "tax" a trip by cutting a thin strip from one or more of the sides before selling it.

Magic mushrooms grow on moistened cow droppings.

Other hallucinogens are smoked in a pipe or eaten as a powder.

Even nutmeg is said to have hallucinogenic properties.

▲ Hallucinating History

☆ *"If God dropped acid would he see people?"*

—George Carlin

☆ *"The wild drink lifts me. Have I not drunk soma?"*

—1500 BC, Aryan Veda

All religion rely heavily upon ceremony and ritual. These rituals include hypnotic tools like smells, smoke, repetition, sound, suggestion, movement, and sleep deprivation. Western religion often adds wine and food and shamanic cultures add mood-altering hallucinogens.

Sacred ceremonies and mind-altering substances have been an ongoing cultural combination on every continent. 3500 years ago, Aztecs ate ceremonial mushrooms as a religious devotion. Since pre-Columbian times, Mexican natives have used peyote, the small button from a spineless cactus. Forth century Greek initiation rituals used hallucinogenic wine made from the barley fungus elgot. It was later outlawed.

High In The Andes

Ancient Peruvian ceramic vases celebrate the san pedro cactus that yields peyote cactus brew.

Today it's pricey and chic to "trip" with a Peruvian shaman guide to Lake Laguna Shimbay, 1200 feet in the Andes. After inhaling the psychotropic brew through nostrils and vomiting violently, partygoers and seekers stand naked in the ice-cold lake as a shaman "purifies them" by spitting them with water.

Another Peruvian shamanic ritual uses ayahuasca (pronounced iawasca), a concoction made from a beautiful Amazonian vine with a white blossom with a pink blush. Ayahusca is ingested or inhaled as a dry white powder. One experimenter told me, "A big part of an ayahuasca trip is vomiting. I figure anything that makes me throw up ain't worth it."

Hell-loose-sin-o-gin

Researchers have compelling evidence that many people tried, convicted and killed as werewolves and witches were inadvertently stoned on hallucinogens. In the Middle Ages, whole village went insane from tainted bread. Nature may have chemically altered rye harvested after extremely cold temperatures. When ground into flour, the resulting bread became the staple food for poor people. Whole families would "trip" and when "taken with the devil" be prosecuted.

A hallucinogenic DMT or yurema, is used today by Indians in eastern Brazil. A western businessman said that he likes to use it recreationally because "the trip lasts only an hour or two." Congress outlawed DMT usage in the United States.

Acid Tests

Robert Hoffmann, a pharmacist in Basel, Switzerland, discovered LSD in 1943. From his discovery, much research was done with the terminally ill, criminals and people in mental hospitals. Powerful, transformational enlightenment experiences were reported. LSD became unbelievably popular in the 70's among the young. Timothy Leary and Richard Alpert went on a crusade. "Tune in, turn on and drop out" was their mantra. "The Electric Cool Aid Acid Test" and Castineda's books glamorized 'tripping.'

California chemists produced blotter acid, which is a one to two centimeter square paper "hit" torn from acid soaked blotter paper. Today blotter acid sells for as little as five dollars a hit I'm told.

LSD (lysergic acid diethylamide)

Mescaline, peyote, psilocybin, Lucy in the Sky with Diamonds (LSD) was the Beatles' song of the day. The Beatles success upped the British National Economy and they were named the official musicians of the Queen of England.

A TRUE STORY: Richard Alpert/Ram Dass

In 1966 LSD guru Harvard psychologist Richard Alpert explored the reactions of LSD on holy men. One 60+-year-old holy man from the Himalayas was offered 50-75 micrograms of LSD (considered a small dosage). The man insisted on taking a whopping 950 micrograms.

Aghast, Alpert expected a dramatic reaction. Yet, the old fellow behaved normally all day long. Except for a twinkling glance now and then in Alpert's direction, the LSD apparently affected him not.

So astounded was Alpert, he gave up LSD, changed his name to Ram Dass, and converted to mysticism. "Often, we only know we've been in a certain place when we pass beyond it." he said.

▲ What Hallucinogenics Do To You?

The first effects of hallucinogens are usually felt within the first hour or two depending on your personal chemistry and how much you took, usually last 8 to 12 hours and as long as 24 hours.

Outward Signs

During that time, pupils dilate, and temperature, heart rate and blood pressure rise. Sweat usually accompanies the trip because blood sugar rises. That's why "trippers" lose their appetite. Dry mouth results from the impact on the liver. Sleep is almost impossible and some people experience tremors. Many vomit.

Inward sensations and feelings are more dramatic than physical signs. Hallucinogenics radically exaggerate and shift emotions as you become keenly focused on thoughts and perceptions.

Buy a Ticket and Take Your Chances

Taking hallucinogenic is a game of drug roulette. Hallucinogens build up a tolerance level with usage. The more you take, the higher dosages you need to achieve the same high. This is extremely dangerous, given the unpredictability of the drug. If your body get too much LSD, for example, you can go into convulsions, coma or heart and lung failure. Many LSD users have flashbacks, and suddenly, years later, launch into a spontaneous "trip."

A Letter from Gerald

"When I was 15, I went to an LSD party and had a bad trip. Paranoid and out-of-control, I had a break with reality. Now, ten years later, I still suffer flashbacks. I can't hold a job because I have severe memory gaps. I don't do drugs and eat well, but my brain is still screwed up. Please help me."

Hell-Loose Roulette

Any trip can bring up great experiences or terrifying thoughts, feelings and foolish decision-making. Each time you take it, you have a potential for a bad trip or bummer that evokes behavior similar to schizophrenic psychosis: severe depression, anxiety, paranoia, violent behavior and/or confusion.

Some hallucinogenic users permanently develop catatonic syndrome and become mute, lethargic, disoriented with repetitive meaningless movements. There is no way to determine what a bad trip will be like or when or if it will occur. Acid and the like are risky business.

▲ What Can You Do To Drop Hallucinogens

7 Steps to Success:

1. **Write**
   Write down the outcome you would like to have. For example; "I am healthy, clean and sober and I never again as long as I live put poison in my body."

2. **List**
   Make a list of the actions you'd take if you were 100% responsible for the outcome.

3. **Steps**
   Decide what step you will take with each item to make it happen.

4. **Let Go of Limits**
   Write a list of the self-defeating things that you tell yourself.

5. **Rip It Up**
   Tear up the list. You don't need it anymore

6. **Get Help!**
   It helps to have someone support you in this. Hypnotherapy, acupuncture, a good drug rehab program, a ten-step program and a nutritionist can really turn you around. Allow a good friend, who is clean and sober to be your coach. Later you can return the favor by coaching someone else.

A good interventionist can help convince a loved one to go into a rehab program if necessary. Your local hospital, hot-line or police may recommend one to you.

7. **Affirm**
   Write a positive affirmation of the outcome you want as if it is already a done deal. Repeat that affirmation often until the power of its meaning lights up inside of you.

You can add your affirmation to the following one if you like.

AFFIRM SUCCESS: Come Down To Earth
Get real. Find new healthy ways to tap your profoundly creative imagination.

I choose to feel healthy and NORMAL. Yogurt, fresh fruits and vegetables, liquids and vitamins help me balance my body. I stop any poisons and drugs NOW. Healthy living returns me to sanity. It's all-or-nothing. I quit and I don't look back.

I wrap my mind around feeling great! I forgive myself and move onward and upward. I choose to live and to be happy and healthy. I make my life about joy. I will never, ever, ever as long as I live put that crap in my body again. That's it. I draw the line. I choose to be high on life.

INNER•VIEW QUIZ

Are You Suffering from Inhalant Damage?

Truthfully answer T to the following questions that are true or me.

___ I use inhalants.
___ I breath fumes at work.
___ I'm exposed to fumes all day at home.
___ I have had weight loss recently.
___ I suffer from overall general fatigue.
___ My muscles are tired.
___ I have an electrolyte imbalance.
___ I often get nauseous.
___ I sneeze a lot.
___ I cough a lot.
___ I get frequent nosebleeds.
___ I have bleeding from my ears.
___ I get headaches.
___ I involuntary pass urine and feces.
___ I get disoriented.
___ I can be violent
___ I go unconscious.
___ I have done risky and humiliating things I regret.

If you compulsively sniff aerosol deodorant, hair spray, household cleaners, propellants or fumes, and have any of these symptoms, you are being seriously hurt. Take immediate action to feel human again. Your life is in danger.

Chapter 28

Inhalants & Solvents:

Suks

This chapter offers you straight talk about inhalants. Inhalants get you high and make you die. Many suffer permanently brain damage and shake uncontrollably and cannot move. Read on and find out why.

▲ Sniffing Out History
▲ How Inhalants Affect You
▲ What You Can Do To Stop

Nose sprays, solvents, aerosols, Chlorohydrocarbons, aerosol paint, cleaning fluids, solvents, propellants, glue, paint thinner and gasoline are different inhalants used to get high.

Nitrous oxide: (laughing gas or whippets) is sold in small metal cylinders with a balloon or pipe propellant and is used for whipped cream aerosol spray cans.

Amyl nitrite: (poppers or snappers) is a clear yellowish liquid in ampules. Doctors use them as heart stimulators to elevate the pulse.

Butyl nitrite: (rush, bolt, bullet, locker room or climax) comes in small bottles.

☆ *Get High and Die*
Pop pop, sniff sniff
Kill yourself, take a whiff
—Shelley Stockwell

Photo by Nica Lee

▲ Sniffing Out History

In our modern world we are often exposed to toxic fumes at home or at work. During the 1960s, glue sniffing became popular recreational drug activity among the young; it seemed like fun.

A friend recently returned from a visit to South Africa here is his report:

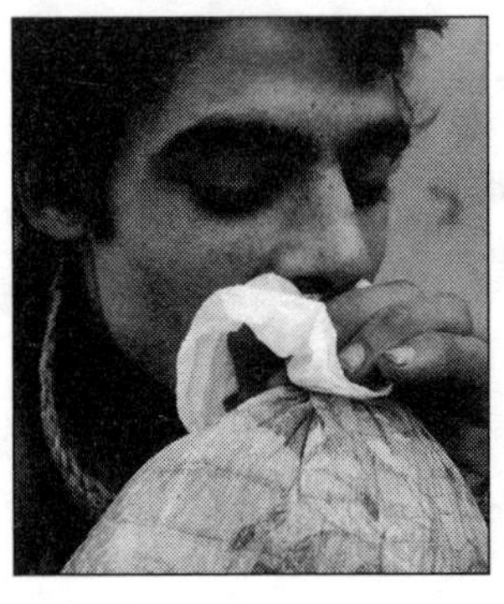

A True Story: South Africa 1999

"I was working in South Africa. The streets of Johannesburg were a seething mass of street dwellers and youths sniffing glue on every curb. They buy the glue in small plastic tubes and break them open. You see groups of young kids sniffing glue through the sleeve of their shirt. They sit there stupefied or become agitated and punch each other out. I couldn't believe the magnitude of this devastating behavior. It was heart-breaking."

▲ How Inhalants Affect You

Inhalants immediately affect the brain bringing euphoria, numbness and buzzing in the head. At first, this chemical reaction may relieve problems. But heart palpitations, breathing difficulties, dizziness and headaches will follow. Guaranteed.

Inhalants mask truth. In truth, they fry the brain and eventually paralyze energy. Poisons affect your brain. In the past, you may have associated these feelings with relief. But in fact, they cause horrific stress and pain.

If you've used inhalants, you most likely have done risky and humiliating things that you later regret. A one-time small usage can hook or kill you depending on your genetics and what else is in your system at the time.

Inhalants get you high and make you die. Many suffer permanently brain damage and shake uncontrollably and cannot move.

Take it in the Nose

The more you use and the stronger the concentrations, the more chance you have of dying a miserable, painful death. Toxic vapors take the place of oxygen and depress the central nervous system. Eventually this causes breathing or the heart to stop—permanently.

Long term users experience muscle weakness, abdominal pain, nausea, nose bleeds, numbness and tingling of hands and feet, decreased and lost sense of smell, involuntary passing of urine and feces, hallucinations, severe mood swings, violent behavior, suffocation, damage to the lung, liver, kidney, central nervous system and irreversible brain damage. Scary reports of brain damage caused a rash of anti-glue-sniffing laws across the U.S. An ordinance in Anaheim, California, made it illegal to "inhale, breath or drink any compound mucilage, dope, or other materials or substances or combinations thereof with the intention of becoming elated, intoxicated, dazed, paralyzed, irrational or in any manner changing, distorting or disturbing the eyesight, thinking process, balance or coordination of such a person."

Inhalants have been linked to hepatitis. A lot of inhalant users suffocate to death on the plastic bags they use in the snorting process. Others choke on their own vomit. Studies show that the main cause of death of inhalant users is from careless and dangerous behaviors, such as suicide, homicide and injuries.

Over time, users develop a tolerance and require more and more often, use. The more use, the more harm done to the liver, lungs, kidneys, brain and central nervous system. Solvents and aerosol sprays decrease your heart and respiratory rates and impair judgment.

Inhalants open the gate to more addictive drugs.

The more one uses inhalants, and the stronger the concentrations, the more the chance of dying a miserable, painful death.

▲ What You Can Do To Stop Using Inhalants

7 Steps You Can Do To Stop Using

1. **Write**
   Write down the outcome you would like to have. For example; "I am healthy, clean and sober and I never again, as long as I live, put poison in my body."

2. **List**
   Make a list of the actions you'd take if you were 100% responsible for the outcome.

3. **Steps**
   Decide what step you will take with each item to make it happen.

4. **Let Go of Limits**
   Write a list of the self-defeating things that you tell yourself.

5. **Rip It Up**
   Tear up the list. You don't need it anymore

6. **Get Help!**
   You need someone to support you in this. It's difficult to stop using such seductive drugs on your own. Hypnotherapy, acupuncture, a good drug rehab program, a ten-step program and a nutritionist can really turn you around.
   A good interventionist can help convince a loved one to go into a rehab program. Your local hospital, hot-line or police may recommend one to you.

7. **Affirm**
   Write a positive affirmation of the outcome you want as if it is already a done deal. Repeat that affirmation often until the power of its meaning lights up inside of you. You can add your affirmation to the following one if you like.

AFFIRM SUCCESS: Quit Inhalants and Come Down To Earth

I take back my life and get real. I choose to feel healthy and NORMAL. Yogurt, fresh fruits and vegetables, liquids and vitamins help me balance my body. I stop any poisons and drugs NOW. Healthy living returns me to sanity.
It's all-or-nothing. I quit and I don't look back.

I stop inhaling poison now. To avoid withdrawal symptoms, I drink lots of water, take herbs and vitamins, get plenty of rest and soak in a bath with mineral salts. I stay busy and count my blessings. Inhalants and drugs are like going down the sewer in a glass bottom boat. No thank you. I quit them all and take back my life. I honor my body. My body is my gift from God. What I do with it is my gift to God.
Even using poison one-time can kill me. I choose to live.

Snorting and sniffing fry my brain. I want my natural vital energy. I choose to live. I choose to be happy. I choose to join the land of the living. I want to live.

Each day and in every way I find new ways to love myself. I wrap my mind around feeling great! I forgive my hurtful behavior and hurtful voice. I now listen to the voice of wisdom and honesty. I choose to live and to be happy and healthy. I make my life about joy. Stop using. Take a multivitamin. I have no other choice. It is a life or death decision. I stop using now."

Resources

American Council for Drug Education, Rockville, Maryland, 1-800-488-DRUG.
Center for Substance Abuse Treatment, Referral Hotline, 1-800-662-HELP.

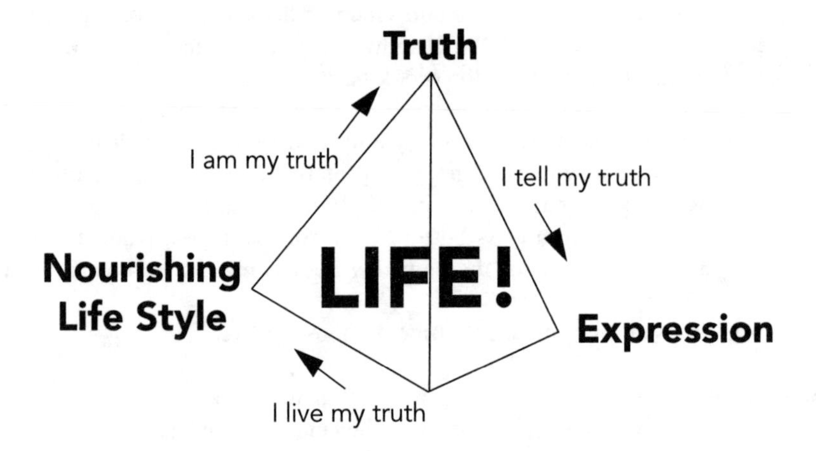

Choose Life!

The Truth Pyramid has freed you from limiting attitudes and behaviors.

▲ **Expression:** Get real, tell your truth, actively pursue your dreams and heal.

▲ **Nourishing Life Style:** Nothing to hide, no need to numb. Positive patterns replace negative ones

▲ **Truth:** Wake up, come to your senses, and listen, hear, and live my truth. You'll fall in love with yourself.

▲ **Life!** Awake you take control of your life and LIVE! INTO-ME-SEE

Step Six

The Promised Land:

Freedom!

How You Got To Where You Are

Pharaoh Thee Well

Illustration by Shelley Stockwell

Chapter 29

Out of Egypt:

Garden-of-Me-Done

You control your life by claiming responsibility for the way you "set it up." This chapter helps you honestly inventory your choices and their payoffs, so you decide which decisions to keep and which decisions to change.

- ▲ **LIFE IS HOW YOU PLANET**
- ▲ **BRAINSTORM WHAT YOU WANT: Wellspring**
- ▲ **CLARIFY YOUR GOAL: Guiding Star**
- ▲ **CLUSTER YOUR POSSIBILITIES: Chart Your Course**
- ▲ **MOVE INTO ACTION: Sail On**
- ▲ **CUT IN STONE**
- ▲ **PHARAOH THEE WELL**

Do's and Don'ts of Loving Myself

Don't:	Do:
Should on yourself	Eliminate coulda, woulda, shoulda"
Use "can't"	Change "can't" to "won't" or "can"
	Ask, "What do I want?"
Take everything personally	and then help yourself to get it
Get even	
Put yourself or others down	Count my blessings
Harm your body in any way	Put my hands on my heart and say, "I love you"
Get drunk	Do good, kind loving things for myself
Feed yourself junk	Eat good, healthy, nourishing fruits and vegetables; think lean and green; drink water
Call yourself names	Speak kindly to myself
	Laugh whenever possible
	Become a pleasure seeker
	Choose to live
	Trust my senses: They never lie

☆ THREE PEOPLE IN THE WIND:
If the wind blows south, One goes south.
One fights the wind and goes north. And
One makes sails and uses the wind to go wherever they want.
—Shelley Stockwell

▲ Life is How You Planet

☆ SONG

Arise in me like the dawn and never let your brightness set.
For we are one, like unity of earth with sky
(the spark and splendor of night
tied by threads of morning light).
We are the breath and breeze of dawn
(nestled in flowing white
clothed with silent night).
Always being born.
So let us rejoice.
While dawn lifts infinity
of light and voice.
—David Napolin

Photo by Jon Nicholas

Concern yourself with the future, you'll have to spend the rest of your life there.

The easiest way to succeed in your goals is to do what you like to do. What makes you feel good? How can you take advantage of your natural strengths? What is it you really want for yourself and your life. Follow your natural heartfelt inclinations and you'll satisfy your needs.

▲ Brainstorm What You Want: Wellspring

Use this four-point action plan to identify and achieve your dreams. It works!

1. Brainstorm what you Want: Wellspring
2. Clarify your Goal: Guiding Star
3. Cluster the Possibilities: Chart a Course
4. Move into Action: Sail On

There are two types of goals:

1. Personal Goals What do you want for yourself? Decide how much autonomy you want and need, how much time you want to take for yourself.

2. Relationship Goals Decide what you want for yourself in relationship to a mate, family, friends and society, and how much time you want to devote to relationships.

Listless? Write a list.

It's time for a dream shower. Use the following form and write down an unedited list of all the things you want for yourself. They may be things you liked as a child, or things you like now. Write down everything, even if it sounds silly. How many things can you write? One hundred is a nice number. Twenty is OK, too. Keep writing as long as ideas pop up, making sure you have at least twenty.

INTO•GREAT POWER EXERCISE

The Things I Want (Brainstorming)

1.
2.
3.
4.
5.
6.
7.
8.
9.
10.
11.
12.
13.
14.
15.
16.
17.
18.
19.
20.
21.
22.
23.
24.
25.
26.
27.
28.
29.
30.
31.
32.
33.
34.
35.
36.
37.
38.
39.
40.
41.
42.
43.
44.
45.
46.
47.
48.
49.
50.
51.
52.
53.
54.
55.
56.
57.
58.
59.
60.
61.
62.
63.
64.
65.
66.
67.
68.
69.
70.
71.
72.
73.
74.
75.
76.
77.
78.
79.
80.
81.
82.
83.
84.
85.
86.
87.
88.
89.
90.
91.
92.
93.
94.
95.
96.
97.
98.
99

Star Billing. Put a star by your favorite wants—the ones that give you the most energy.

☆ THE MEANING OF LIFE

A wisp of breeze
A dance of trees
A call of life afar
A day of sighs
Of laughs and cries
A wish upon a star

I am a vibration, a tone, a hue
An illusion I think is true.
I venture out with hope and a swagger.
I trip, I fall, I rise, I stagger.
And discover myself deep within
To face my life with a simple grin.

—Shelley Stockwell

Photo by Joann Kelly

Enjoy the Ride

Photo by Nica Lee

▲ Clarify Your Goal: Guiding Star

Now pick a dream. Any of your starred ones will be perfect. You needn't worry that your goal seems impossible, because almost anything you want will manifest if you create it as a concrete goal.

MY GOAL IS ______________________________

For example, let's say you want to make more money. Be generous, how about $1 million this year? How about $7 million next year? So what if it doesn't come to pass and you only make $500,000? that will still be okay.

Hocus Focus Target

Zero in on any goal. Let's say, for example, that your goal is to have more love in your life. Write "Love" in the middle of a sheet of paper and draw a circle around it, like this:

This is your target. (Occasionally, when you write down a target, you may think of obstacles in your way. We'll deal with that resistance in a moment. For now, focus on your target.)

▲ Cluster The Possibilities: Chart a Course

Action Steps

Brainstorm all the possible things you can do to make this dream real. Don't think, analyze, edit or judge. As an idea pops into your mind, write it down. This action idea becomes a spoke connected to your goal, like this:

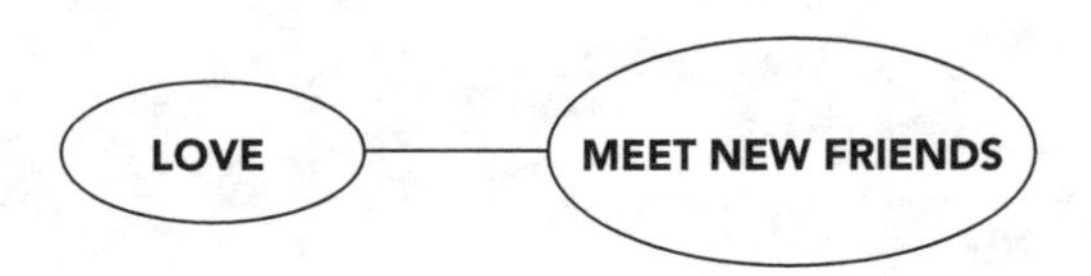

Now brainstorm ideas of how to "meet new friends." Connect each subgoal as a spoke. It looks something like this:

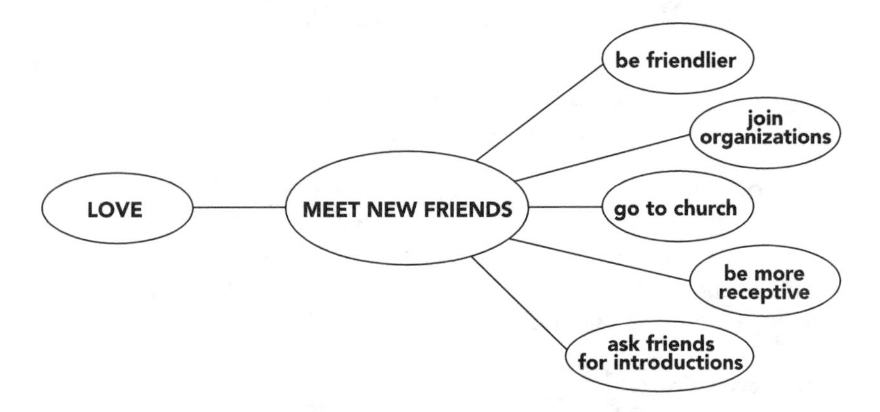

Photo by Nica Lee

Get Specific

Now, focus on *each* subgoal. If you start with "ask friends for introductions," list the names of everyone you can think of—friends and family. This might be a stretch. Oh well. *Results* will be your happiest stretch of all. Under "be friendlier," You might write: "ask Judy to lunch" and "smile more." The result:

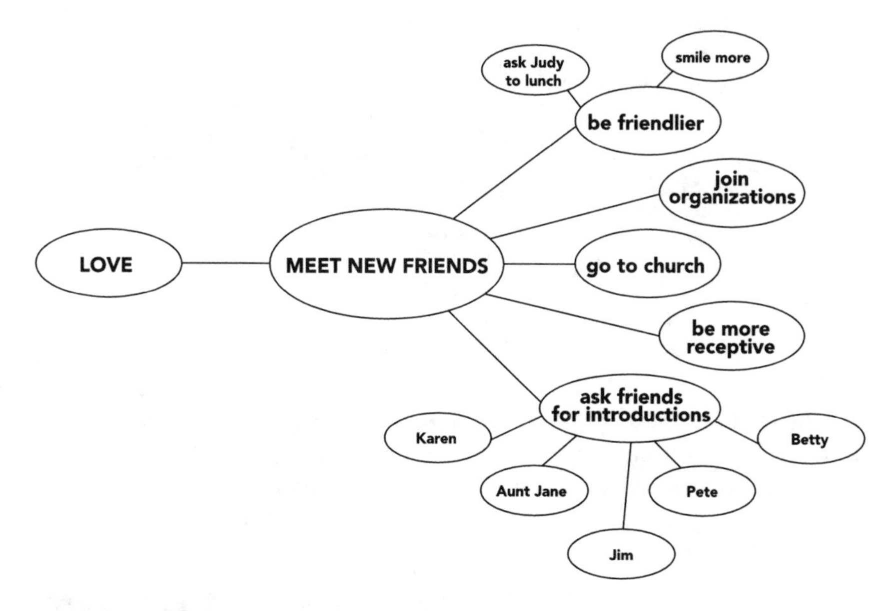

▲ Move Into Action: Sail On

Let Priorities Prevail

Prioritize the cluster groupings. Cluster each of your starred dreams on separate pages to prioritize them. Give yourself a timeline plan. If "ask friends for introductions" is your number one priority, and "be friendlier" is number two, write down specifically the date and time you will take action. Perhaps you will call Betty tonight and tell her that you ready to meet new friends.

Set Dates

One week at a time. The process of goal grabbing happens one day at a time and one week at a time. You eat an elephant one bite at a time. Goals are like that. Even when they seem monumental or unattainable, you can achieve them when you break them into clustered components. Take action on the outside spokes. One at a time, you will achieve your core dreams and goals.

One day at a time. Each morning, write down a list of the steps you will take toward achieving your goals. Write down spokes from many goal sheets or focus on one cluster for the day. Three clusters a week keeps the doctor away. You are in command. Do it your way.

Blocks

If you are resistant or negative, or feel there is an insurmountable obstacle in my way, discover that obstacles are simply sub-goals that need to be clustered. For example, if you said, "I can't meet new people because I'm too shy," simply put a circle around "too shy" and write down possible solutions to shyness:

Then brainstorm simple steps to build confidence, prioritize and take action. Problem solved. In this case, you might get books from the library on how to overcome shyness, or take a drama class, talk to a friend about your feelings, or be outrageously brave and talk to a total stranger in the supermarket, or a waitress in a restaurant, or the mailman.

▲ Cut in Stone

Write down your starred goals (the centers of your clusters) and the action steps will take on this affidavit. Ask a friend to read this affidavit and sign it as a witness. Place it where you see it often.

> ☆ *"When I was a child, my mother said to me, 'If you become a soldier, you'll be a general. If you become a monk, you'll become the pope.' Instead, I became a painter and wound up as Picasso."*
>
> —Pablo Picasso

Photo by Jon Nicholas

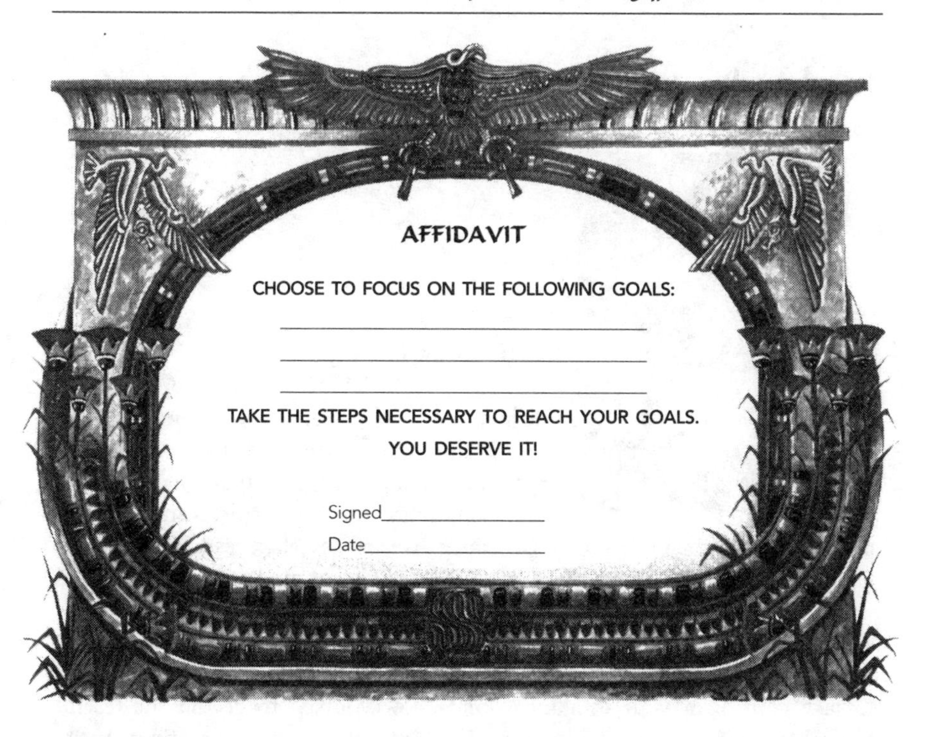

AFFIDAVIT

CHOOSE TO FOCUS ON THE FOLLOWING GOALS:

____

____

____

TAKE THE STEPS NECESSARY TO REACH YOUR GOALS.

YOU DESERVE IT!

Signed______________

Date________________

▲ Pharaoh Thee Well

Illustration by Shelley Stockwell

Stockwell's Happy Rules

Photo by Jon Nicholas

Decide to be Happy

When I was a TWA Hostess I conducted an informal study of passengers who said that they were happy and discovered that they chose happiness. They told me that they avoided unpleasant television and critical and sarcastic people. And they happily skipped over negative articles when reading magazines. Happy people reported that they only read things that made them feel uplifted.

Take Responsibility for Happy, Positive Thoughts

Happiness is a biochemical response that takes place inside of YOU. You need to take control of your thinking. Don't allow yourself to get on the fearful, critical train; it's a bumpy ride. Instead say "cancel, cancel" to negativity. Victor Frankl was in a concentration camp in Germany when he decided that even though the Nazi's were controlling his body, nobody could control his mind. In spite of such a negative physical environment, when he took responsibility for his life inside himself, he was happy and at peace.

Know What Pleases You and Passionately Incorporate These Things Into Your Life

If you don't know what pleases you look into the mirror and ask yourself "What do you want?" Do this consistently and answers will eventually be there. Give yourself a10 minute mental vacations every day, and during those ten minutes do exactly what you want to do.

Make Lemonade

Look for the gift in all of life's experiences. Transform "problems" into "opportunities." Ask; "What can I learn from this?" and then celebrate the wisdom. Or turn it around so that you create the perfect outcome.

I appeared on one of the last episodes of the television show, "The Other Side." The show sported a new host and had gone tabloid in its approach. The subject was sleep disorders. Five minutes before airtime, I was told that I would be introduced as someone who thought that sleepwalking was the result of "the dark side." They refused to change the caption below my picture. I had a choice,

I could refuse to appear or make the most of it. When I was introduced with "Our next expert, says that the reason for sleepwalking comes from the dark side," I replied "by the dark side I mean the part of your mind that is hidden from you...the subconscious mind..."

Be Flexible

Jack be nimble. Life is a moving adventure. Let each moment offer you a chance to choose from many solutions, paths and opportunities.

Be in the Moment

THE PAST IS JUST A MEMORY. THE FUTURE JUST A FANTASY. YOUR LIFE IS NOW, IN THIS MOMENT

Enjoy Others

Be with people; social contact makes us feel alive. Call a friend. Observe people living their life. Join a club. Go to church. People need people to be happy.

Tell the Truth

When you talk straight to yourself and others you feel good. Any deception pales in comparison. If you want to be happy be real.

Painting by Carin Robinson

INTO•GREAT POWER EXERCISE

Merry Yourself: A Sacred Rite

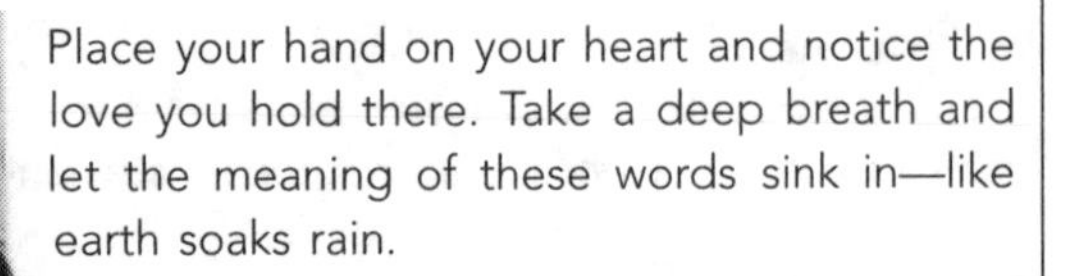

Photo by Joann Kelley

Place your hand on your heart and notice the love you hold there. Take a deep breath and let the meaning of these words sink in—like earth soaks rain.

"Grant me the patience to listen to myself with my heart. To accept myself as I move through the seasons of my life, the bravery to ask for what I need and the commitment to help myself fill those needs. Let me show my love now, each and every day, for each day is a lifetime.

Each day I learn more fully how to love. I will not neglect my loving, for if I wait until tomorrow, tomorrow never comes and my love is too precious for that. I promise to love, honor and protect myself today, one day at a time, for the rest of my life. Nothing is more important than my good health, joy and peace of mind. I pledge to cherish myself as long as I live.

I honor my body as a sacred temple, and I commit to nourish myself with whole foods, water, fresh air, exercise, honesty, expression, laughter and healthy relationships.

I promise to be my own best friend, to live in peace with all aspects of my personality. I promise to love, comfort, honor, and keep myself in sickness and in health, in sorrow and joy, and remain loyal to my own path and gifts, as long as I live.

I'm blessed by the higher power. I pledge my commitment to myself, I proclaim that I am my own good mommy, daddy, husband, wife and the source of limitless joy. I give myself a hug."

☆ TODAY
I plant a seed in my garden.
We are honored to have family and friends standing at the border
Of that garden witnessing its unique beauty.

It took a long time in coming, this garden of theirs
With love and patience they carefully tilled the soil

By taking time to really talk to one another and listen and hear.
Bravely thy removed, one by one,
The weeds of fear, self deception and old hurts
And lovingly replaced them with vulnerability,
Empathy and yielding

And the sun came and the rain and small miracle rainbows!
My garden dazzles the eyes with its sparkling energy and giddy colors.

So today, because I care enough to act with my best interests at heart,
I am planting a new seed.

It will grow to be the most beautiful and precious flower of all and
It will reign over all the rest

The seed is commitment to joy
And I have lovingly planted it on this day.
I love me.
I love you.
I feel so glad to be alive

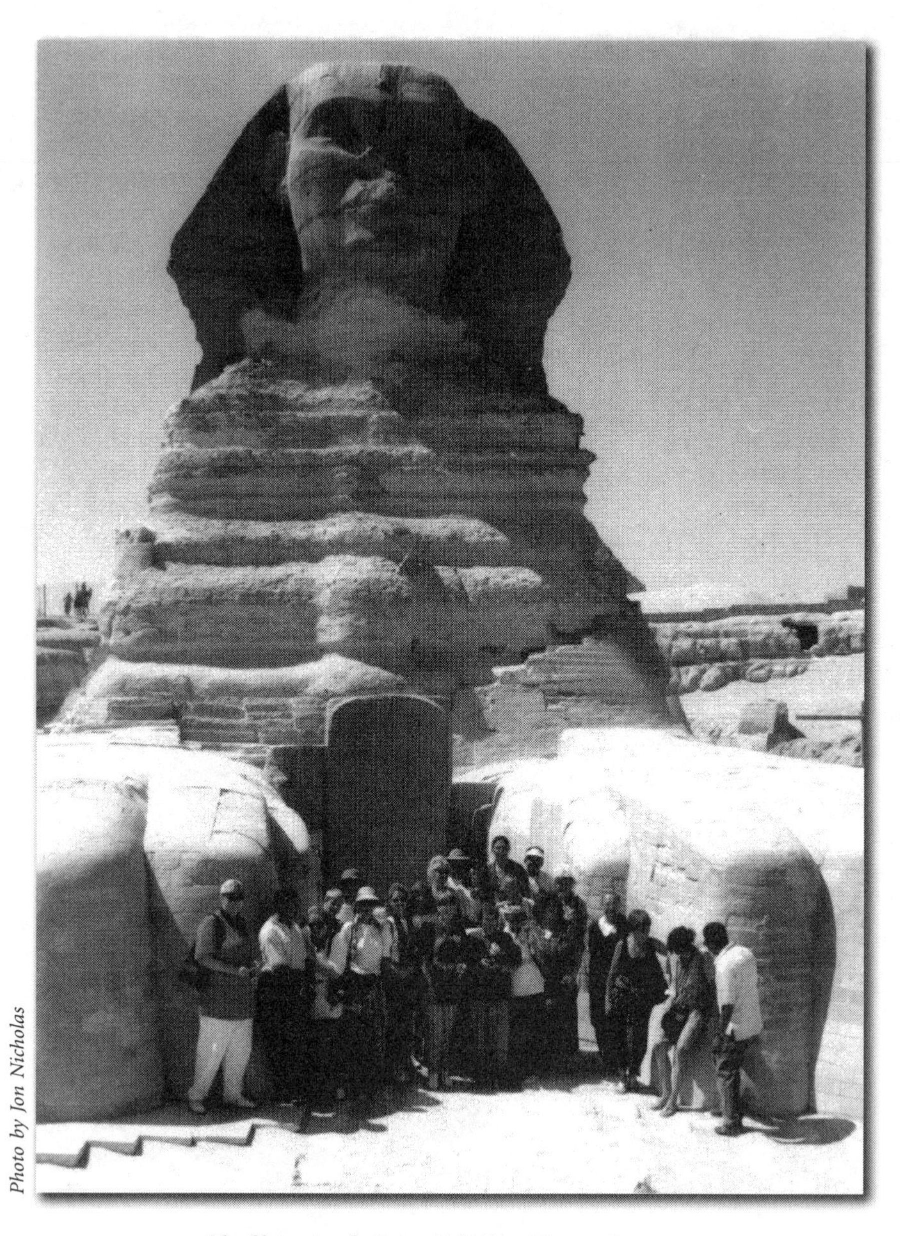

Photo by Jon Nicholas

Shelley And One Of Her Tour Groups

Chapter 30
Professional Help Lists:
Reef•for•all

Get by with a little help from friends. There is a terrific network of service professionals, organizations and programs just waiting to give you a helping hand. This chapter is a comprehensive list of some terrific resources.

▲ Referral Service
▲ Approved Hypnotists & Helpers (listed by state & country)
▲ Entertainment and Speaking Specialists
▲ Instructors, Trainers & Institutes
▲ Help Referrals, Organizations and Hot Lines
▲ Support Organizations
▲ Twelve-Step Programs
▲ Books, Tapes and Resources

▲ Referral Service

INTERNATIONAL HYPNOSIS FEDERATION REFERRAL SERVICE
30819 Casilina, Rancho Palos Verdes, CA 90275, USA
Phone: (310) 541-4844-Email: sstockwell@earthlink.net
Web Site: www.hypnosisfederation.com
Offers referrals for holistic helpers in mind, body, spirit and entertainment.

▲ Approved Hypnotists & Helpers

The following Licensed & Certified International Professionals are recommended & recognized by the International Hypnosis Federation (IHF). Each is committed to your holistic well being and a governing code of ethics.

United States of America

(alphabetically listed by state & country then other countries listed alphabetically)

ARIZONA, USA

Georgia D. Bruce: Choices of the Mind & Soul

Kingman, AZ Phone: (520) 530-9141

Georgia uses the pinpoint method of Hypnosis to Stop Smoking, Weight Loss, Drug & Alcohol Addiction, Self-Confidence and Regression. She also teaches Self-Hypnosis.

Lynn G. Davies, CCHt, RM, CSC: P.S. Personal Services

Phoenix/Mesa, AZ- Phone: (602) 574-7232-E-mail: lynnd@ps-ps.com

Fax: (480) 354-6462

Founder of P.S. Personal Service & Angel Light Therapy and Clinical Hypnotherapist, Transpersonal Therapist, Certified Hypnotherapist & Spiritual Counselor. Lynn specializes in Pain Management.

Margaret Rogers, CHt, OM: Sumaris Centre

Stephen M. Van Coops: Sumaris Centre

Lake Havasu City, AZ-Phone: (520) 453-7974-(TF) 888-858-8668

E-mail: sumaris@twocommasj.com-Web Site: www.twocommas.com

Breakthrough Crystal, Acupuncture & Teragram Therapy Healing with Hypnosis, Aromatherapy & Reflexology. Psychic readings and development. Crisis counseling. Metaphysical education Courses and workshops. Ministerial services.

ARKANSAS, USA

Brenda Joyce McDaniel: HeartShadows

Hot Springs, AK/Indiana/Missouri- Phone: (501) 318-2266- E-mail: brendamc@ipa.net

Registered Nurse, Master Hypnotist, Reiki Master/Teacher and Certified Crystal Healer, Brenda incorporates these modalities plus, Color Therapy, Past Life Regression and Soul Retrieval.

CENTRAL & NORTHERN CALIFORNIA, USA

SDiane Adamz-Bogus, The Oracle Soul-Joiner: The Spirit of Abundance

Stockton, CA- Phone: (209) 956-6626-E-mail:theoracle@theoraclesouljoiner.com

Web Site: www.theoraclesouljoiner.com

Dr. SDiane, The Oracle Soul-Joiner offers online, phone or office Psychic and Spiritual Consultation. Workshops, Lectures and Consultations are available. E-mail for brochure!

David Armentrout, PhD, Director: Mind-Body-Spirit, HypnoClinic & Hypnosis Training Inst.
San Jose, CA-Phone: (408) 871-0999-E-mail: darmentrout@changework.com
A Certified Clinical Hypnotherapist and Clinical Psychologist, David specializes in Past-Life Therapy and healing molestation and abuse issues; also an adjunct instructor at National University.

Rachael Beutler, Stage Hypnotist, IHF Fellow
Sacramento, CA-Phone: (916) 310-1234
Rachael trains professionals, mental health clinicians & para-professionals in Human Potentialities, Smoking Cessation, Drug Education, Relapse Prevention, Motivation, Addiction Recovery, Interviewing, Resiliency & Self-Hypnosis.

Steve Bhaerman AKA "Swami Beyondananda"and Trudy Bhaerman AKA "Trudy Light"
Santa Rosa, CA-Phone: (707) 525-0711-E-mail: swamib@saber.net
Steve performs "Laughter As A Healing Art." His wisdom is disguised as comedy, or is it comedy disguised as wisdom? Author of 3 books including his latest "Duck Soup For The Soul."

Elizabeth Cech, MA, CCHt: Center for Integrated Therapy
Sonoma County/Greater San Francisco Bay Area, CA-Phone (707) 829-5299
Fax (707) 829-3757-E-Mail: Ahiashia@aol.com
Expressive Arts: Voice & Movement, Music and Guided Imagery, Psychodrama, Childhood/Past Life Regression (Woolger Method), Individuals/couples/workshops/trainings/phone sessions

Ouida J. Cooper-Rodriguez, MA, CHt, CSC
Oakland/East Bay, CA – Phone: (510) 533-4057 – E-mail: ojcr2@yahoo.com - Web-Site: www.angelfire.com/md/innerreflections/index.html
Free your spirit, fulfill your dreams; live a rich full life. Certified Hypnotherapist and Spiritual Counselor, Reiki Master, Teacher, Shamanic Practitioner and Life Empowerment Coach.

Dorian Cummings II, PhD, DD, CHt, RH, CSC
Los Gatos, CA- Phone: (408) 807-2845-E-mail: dorian.heart@worldnet.att.net
Fax: 408 356-1255
Certified by the American Board of Hypnotherapy in Hypnotherapy and NLP. Artistic, Creative, Caring, Imaginative, Nurturing, Spiritual, Outgoing, Intuitive, Eclectic, Willing, Poetic, Playful and Joyful.

Morris Gaede, RN, CARN, CHt: Health Services Associates
The Mother Lode, CA, Phone: (209) 962-4629, E-mil: ohmahah@mac.com, Web Site: www.h-s-a.org
Health Services Associates is dedicated to promoting health and equal justice for all through our professional services and the marketing of prepaid legal services plans.

Marilyn Gordon, CHt: Center for Hypnotherapy Certification
Oakland, CA-Phone: (510) 839-4800-E-mail: mgordon@hypnotherapcenter.com
Toll Free: (800) 398-0034-Web Site: www.hypnotheraphycenter.com
Hypnotherapist, Speaker, School Director. Thirty years experience in artful consciousness transformation and healing. "Love uplifts, heals & amplifies your good and talents." Author of "Extraordinary Healing."

Michele J. Halverson, CHt: Angel Wings

Silicon Valley, Yosemite, CA – Phone: (209) 578-4552 – E-mail: halversonm@hotmail.com

Angel Work gives flight to your issues and freedom to your soul. Integrate Shamanism, Hypnotherapy, Reiki and Spiritual Counseling for your highest good.

Haruko, CCHt, CMT, CSC

Berkeley, CA-Phone: (510) 841-5639-E-mail: haruko7@attbi.com

Healer, Spiritual Counselor and Clinical Hypnotherapist, Haruko assists clients in releasing physical and emotional blocks, accessing joy and connecting with the authentic self. English/Japanese spoken.

Okka Holthuis: Rainbow Healing Center

Oakland, East Bay, CA – Phone: (510) 653-8393 – E-mail: okkasrainbow@mac.com

Web Site: www.rainbowhealingcenter.com

In her Rainbow Healing Center, Okka uses her skills as a Spiritual Counselor, LuxMani-Energyhealer, Hypnotherapist and Health Practitioner to Holistically Heal Body, Mind and Spirit.

Harvey Hunt, CHt

Central Coast, CA-Phone:(805) 434-2171-E-mail: jovan@americanserviceco.com-Web Site: www.americanserviceco.com

Stage and private hypnotherapy. Uplift depression, eliminate IBS, fear and uncomfortable feelings. Forgive and feel great! Harvey has been a Hypnotherapist for 35 years.

Sylvia (Catherine) Lexow, DD, BT, CHt: Meditation Groups, Inc

Ojai, CA-Phone: (805) 646-5508- Fax: (805) 646-3303

Sylvia is a Certified Biogram Therapist and Hypnotherapist, Speaker, Counselor and Sacramental Priestess: Customized Ceremonies, Baptisms, Weddings, Reconciliation, Rites of Passage, Anointing, Release into Light.

Loa Lovely, PT, CHt: Body to Soul

Oakland, CA- Phone: (510) 653-0639-E-mail: info@intuitivewisdom.com

Web Site: www.intuitivewisdom.com

Live Life Now! Individual & group sessions. Hypnotherapy, workshops and public speaking for: Releasing Stress, Habits, Fears and Insomnia; Self Hypnosis, Waken Spirituality and Exercise.

Almucz Lyonnesse, CHt

Arcata, CA-Phone: (707) 826-1872 -E-mail: almucz@hotmail.com

Amazing results with Hypnosis for all aspects of life. Almucz is a writer, musician, painter & body/mind worker.

Pamela A. Murphy

San Francisco East Bay, CA – Phone: (510) 684-8631 – E-mail: cutie27@attglobal.net

Over 18 wonderful years working with the chemical dependent, their families and friends. Pamela is a Certified Hypnotherapist, Spiritual Counselor, Reiki Master and Shamanic Practitioner.

Ken Page: Clear Light Arts

Northern, CA- Phone: (209) 754-3040 – E-mail: ken@kenpage.com - Web Site: www.kenpage.com

Renown empathic and naturally clairsentient healer. Ken created the revolutionary technique of Heart & Soul Healing and founded the Institute of Multidimensional Cellular Healing.

Craig Reich: Hypnosis Institute of LA

San Francisco East Bay, CA, Phone: (415) 948-5574 E-mail: hypnosis@craigrich.com

Web Site: www.craigrich.com

Specializing in Habit Control Therapy & Certified Medical Transformational Hypnotherapy including Addiction Control, Past Life Regression & Weight Loss. Serving East Bay San Francisco area.

Yvonne Schwab, CHt, SCS: Foundations In Success

Silicon Valley/San Jose, CA – Phone: (408) 506-3466 – E-mail: hypnobirthng@iglide.net - Web Site: www.foundationsinsuccess.com

Ms. Schwab is dedicated to assisting her clients uncover the power of their subconscious minds to create more Joy, Prosperity and Harmony in their lives.

Talia Shafir, MA, CCHt: Center for Integrated Therapy

Sonoma County/Greater San Francisco Bay Area- Phone/Fax (707) 829-3757

E-Mail: souljourner1647@aol.com- Web Site www.pastlifematrixtherapy.com

Integral Past Life Regression (Woolger Method), Gestalt Dreamwork, Quantum-Touch®, Acoustic Therapy, Psychodrama. Int. Seminars/Trainings/Phone Sessions, Individuals/couples

Beverly E. Taylor, CHt: HypnoEnergy Therapy

Oakland/East Bay, CA - Phone: (510) 886-6780 – E-mail: bevetaylor@aol.com - Web Site: www.rainbowhealingcenter.com

Beverly assists you to expand your potential and improve your life, using Hypnotherapy, Inner Child Healing, Spiritual Counseling, LuxMani Energy Healing and Intuitive Counseling.

Judy Umansky, CHt, RN, IHF Advisory Board Member

Oxnard, CA-Toll Free: 800-601-6018-E-mail: jumansky@shasta.com

Judy Umansky is a Registered Nurse, Healing Touch Practitioner and Hypnotherapist.

Gina Vance, CHt

Central CA- Phone: (209) 527-9761-E-mIl: govance@earthlink.net

Certified in Alchemical Hypnotherapy which combines Hypnosis, Jungian Psychology, Gestalt and Regression to help you access your Inner Wisdom. Specialty certifications: Hypnoanesthesia and Pain Management.

James Wanless, PhD, IHF Advisory Board Member: Wanless Tarot Institute (Since 1995)

Monterey County, CA-Phone: (831) 644-9096-E-mail: info@voyagertarot.com

Toll Free: (800) 676-1256-Web Site: www.voyagertarot.com

Creator of the Voyager Tarot Cards. Author of numerous books. Seminars available.

Corky Whitacre, DCH, CCHt, CNLP, CTLT: The S.A.F.E. Place

San Jose, San Francisco, No CA, Phone: 408-980-1135, E-mail: safecorky@aol.com, Web Site: www.doti.info

Teach, promote and do the following work: Release earth bound entities, psychic protection and self-defense. Empowering you!

Gaye Wilson, RN, CCHt: Here & Tao Hypnotherapy

Placerville, CA- Phone: (530) 622-6791-E-mail: gaye@hereandtao.com

Web Site: www.hereandtao.com

Gay's practice, grounded in loving, kindness and compassion is a reflection of her personal philosophy and a powerful approach to health and well being.

Katherine Zimmerman, CCHt, RM

Sacramento, CA-Phone: (916) 391-7179-E-mail: info@trancetime.com

Orders: (916) 391-1734-Web Site: www.trancetime.com

Certified Clinical Hypnotherapist, in private practice. Regular guest lecturer; Univ. of California, Davis Medical Center, Family Nurse Practitioner/Physician's Assistant Program on Mind/Body Connection.

SOUTHERN CALIFORNIA, USA

Shelley Stockwell, PhD, IHF Founder: Creativity Learning Institute, Dean

California- Phone: (310) 541-4844-Email: sstockwell@earthlink.net

Web Site: www.hypnosisfederation.com

Certifies Hypnotists, Past Life Therapists, Spiritual Counselors and Stage Hypnotists. She is the founder and spokesperson for the Int. Hypnosis Federation. Shelley received the Pen and Quill Award from the Int. Medical and Dental Hypnotherapy Assoc. and the 2001 President's Award from the Int. Association of Counselors and Therapists. The Hypnosis Hall of Fame, Soroptimist Club, Int. Family Health Counsel of the Pacific, Angel Awards and Toastmasters Int., have honored her.

Michael Almaraz: Deeper States Hypnotherapy

Long Beach/Orange County, CA – Phone: (562) 426-6884 – E-Mail: ypnosis4you@yahoo.com- Web Site: www.deeperstates.com

Specializes in Stop Smoking, Exam Preparation, Nail Biting, Stress Reduction, Past Life Regression and much more. Call for more information.

Mary Alvidrez

South Bay Harbor Area, CA-Phone: (310) 831-5738

A School Psychologist and Master Hypnotherapist, Mary helps you to master your mind and change your life. Release fear, phobia, weight and feel good forever.

Toni Attell, CHt

Los Angeles, CA-Phone: (818) 787-8685-E-mail: attell@bigfoot.com

Fax: (818) 787-8710Web Site: www.psychicwelth.com

Toni focuses on how Past-Life DNA memory patterns affect present life choices & how to change them utilizing Hypnosis, Body-Reading, Clairvoyance, Tarot, Time-Line‘ & Future Psychic-Tune-Ups.

Ofelia Baker, CH
San Pedro, CA-Phone: (310) 548-4689 -E-mail:obaker@ix.netcom.com
Ofelia is a Certified Hypnotist who specializes in how to have great relationships. She is also an Astrologer.

Jamie Barker, CHt
San Diego, CA-Phone: (619) 708-2055
Private sessions in Hypnosis and Counseling, focusing on Weight Loss, Smoking Cessation, Stress Reduction, Past Life Regression & Life Coaching.

Jacci Belgard, CHt
Encino, CA-Phone: (818) 986-9277—E-mail: trancemkr@aol.com
Certified Hypnotist specializing in Transpersonal Hypnotherapy, Emotional Release Therapy, smoking cessation, weight control, adolescent & Self Esteem issues.

Melissa Bergstrom McAuliffe, RN, DCHt: Just Imagine"
Los Angeles, CA-Phone: (310) 973-3397-E-mail: melissa@ijustimagine.org
Toll Free: (888) 230-6669-Web Site: www.ijustimagine.org
As your Personal Success Coach and Consultant, Melissa empowers you to create your goals using Neuro-Linguistic Programming, Time Line Therapy', Hypnosis, Reiki & Huna. Hypnotherapy Instructor.

Matt Beucler, CH, MBA
Huntington Beach, CA-Phone: (714) 378-9211 -E-mail: changemasters@earthlink.net
Fax: (714) 378-1999-Web Site: www.Extraordinaryliving.com
Hypnotist, Life Coach and NLP Practitioner.

Patricia A. Bilman, PhD, CHt: Bilman's Center For Creative Living
Los Angeles, CA-Phone: (310) 391-6649-E-mail: p.bilman@att.net
Dedicated to practical applications of intuition and imagination. Assists clients to access their untapped genius & energy field. Private & group seminars & workshops.

Ann Boroch, ND, CHt: Quintessential Healing
West Hollywood, CA- Phone: (323) 658-5546-E-mail: ann@annboroch.com
Web Site: www.annboroch.com
Naturopathic Doctor, Clinical Hypnotherapist & author of "The Cure for Multiple Sclerosis: My Personal Journey." Ann specializes in allergies, candidiasis, gastrointestinal disorders & autoimmune diseases.

Deborah Briggs, MFT: Playlovelive
Orange County, CA – Phone (562) 833-2000 – E mail: debirahbriggs@playlovelive.com
Web Site: www.playlovelive.com
Marriage & Family Therapist, Hypnotherapy, Biofeedback, emphasis in using creativity to stimulate intuitive guidance for healing and personal growth.

Lorraine A.W. Brown, PhD, CH
El Segundo, CA-Phone: (310) 322-7347
Peace & wellness. Lorraine combines Master Hypnosis, Reiki, Intuitive Counseling & Therapeutic Touch for your specific needs. 1990 American Biographical Institute's Woman-of-the-Year.

Georgiana Cancasci, CHt, CSC
West Hills & Valencia, CA-Phone: (661) 799-9733-E-mail: hypnomom53@aol.com
Hypnotherapist & Spiritual Counselor, specializes in Healing Energy Fields, Managing Pain, & Past Life Regression. Imagery releases blocks for a better way of life.

Erin C. Carey, Hypnotist
Los Angeles/So Bay, CA – Phone: (310) 547-3096 – E-mail: erinc@pacbell.net
Specializing in: Weight Loss, Self Esteem/Self Confidence, Release Negative Patterns, Overcome Depression, Eliminate Fears/Phobias, Achieve Success, Memory/Concentration Improvement, Establish Powerful New Attitudes.

Rhonda Carpenter, CCHt
La Mirada, CA- Phone: (562) 404-6264-E-mail: rcarpenter@lifefirst.com
Web Site: www.lifefirst.com
17 years experience as a Psychic, Transpersonal Hypnotherapist & Handwriting Expert. Guides & motivates positive change. Lectures, classes & private sessions. Founder www.lifefirst.com.

Linda Clements, CHt: Motivational Hypnosis
San Fernando Valley, CA-Phone: (213) 891-2630-E-mail: lindact@earthlink.net
Web Site: www.motivationalhypnosis.com
Unleash Your Potential! Utilizing the latest therapeutic techniques, Linda helps you eliminate creative blocks, negative behavior & stress while increasing your success, prosperity & happiness.

Jerri Cleveland
Los Angeles, CA – Phone (323) 933-2184 – E-mail: jckev2000@yahoo.com
Massage Therapy, Lymph Drainage Therapy for Peace, Wellness & Joy. Master Hypnotist.

Dorothy W. Cooke, CHt
Los Angeles, CA-Phone: (323) 295-0979-Fax: (323) 291-7688
Dorothy is a Certified Hypnotherapist who specializes in Motivational Hypnosis. She studied with Shelley Stockwell.

Suzanne E. Cox-Alexander, RN, BSN, CHt: Mind-Body Connections
San Fernando & Ventura County, CA-Phone: (805) 373-9266
Hypnosis: Peacefully increase learning and coping skills. Hand Writing Analysis: reveal strengths, weaknesses, traits and characteristics. "Know why you do what you do; know who you hire."

Don Culver, CHt, IHF Fellow: Quantum Leap Hypnosis Center
Orange, CA-Phone: (714) 289-9161-E-mail: quantumhypnosis@yahoo.com
Fax: (714) 289-8791-Web Site: www.forhypnosis.com
Highly effective weight loss program using four modalities. Corporate group therapy for Smoking, Weight Loss, Stress & Energy Therapy. Reiki Practitioner and Motivational Speaker.

Sue Culver, CHt: Quantum Leap Hypnosis Center
Orange, CA-Phone: (714) 289-9161-E-mail: quantumhypnosis@yahoo.com
Fax: (714) 289-8791-Web Site: www.forhypnosis.com
Highly effective weight loss program using four modalities. Corporate group therapy for Smoking, Weight Loss, Stress & Energy Therapy. Hypnotherapist & Reiki Practitioner.

Al Denney, PhD, CHt
San Fernando Valley, CA, Phone: (818) 888-1226
Psychic Surgery for face, neck and forearms to smooth wrinkles and firm your body to the state you were when you were in your prime.

Patricia J. DiGiacomo: Hypnosis Motivation Institute
San Fernando Valley, CA-Phone: (213) 999-6905-E-mail: pdigaicomo@ureach.com
Specialist in the application of Hypnosis for Stress Reduction, Study Habits/Test Anxiety, Fears & Phobias, Performance Anxiety, Pain Management & Sports Improvement.

Phyllis Elliott Dworsky, PhD, CH
Los Angeles/So Bay, CA-Phone: (310) 792-1960
E-mail: pdworsky@socal.rr.com-Web Site: www.drpdworsky.com
Psychotherapist, Hypnotist who treats all disease with reverence. Release Depression, Anxiety, Eating Disorders and Addictions. Have great relationships with yourself and others.

Ernie T. Farhat, LTC, BS, CHt, IHF Fellow: Zen Golf
Los Angeles/So. Bay, CA-Phone: (310) 306-4696-E-mail: eafarhat@sanjoinvestments.com
Play Zen Golf and integrate the joy of success and the physical movement of your body, club and ball. Spiritually awaken & get a hole-in-one!

Debra K. Fentress, CHt, PhDc: The Avalon Institute of Healing Arts
Los Angeles County, CA, Phone: (818) 472-3914, E-mail: debrafentress@msn.com Web Site: www.avaloninstituteofhealingarts@msn.com
Create a partnership with your conscious and subconscious mind. Bring about positive changes in health, self esteem, relationships. Overcome insomnia and pain. Improve your life.

Liz Fortini
Los Angeles, CA – Phone: (323) 728-9675 – E-mail: lf90640@aol.com
Liz offers Hypnotherapy and Intuitive Healing to help you release emotional & physical pain and feel terrific.

Carol Francis, PsyD, PLHt
Torrance, CA-Phone: (310) 543-1824-E-mail: carolfrancis@yahoo.com
Certified Medical Hypnotherapist, Psychologist, Body Worker, Spiritual Counselor, Past Life Hypnotherapist and Motivational Speaker.

Marilyn Frank, CHt, LVN
San Fernando Valley/Encino, CA -Phone: (818) 784-7864
Clinical Hypnotherapist, CA Licensed Nurse, Motivational Speaker. Transpersonal Enrichment, Motivation, Stress Reduction, Past Life Regression, Creativity, Fertility, Child-Birth & Pain Management. IATSE & SAG member.

Joe Futterer, CHt: Tao Unlimited
Topanga, CA-Phone: (818) 704-7011-E-mail: taopower@pacbell.net
Web Site: www.aroma-a-month.com
A unique blend of Aromatherapy & Hypnotherapy to resolve emotional issues and release stored traumas. Breaks through subconscious, brain & cellular memory.

Frank Genco, CHt
Westminster, CA- Phone: (714) 775-7715- E-mail: mindtrack@aol
Hypnotherapist, Author & Lecturer for over 50 years. Instructor for self-hypnosis & Hypnotherapy Certification in 14 colleges. Sports enhancement, stage hypnosis. Numerous top honors.

Christina Gikas, CHt, MMsc, GNOSIS
Orange County, CA-Phone: (949) 461-5861-E-mail: cgikas@wested.org
Certified Hypnotherapist with Bachelor's in Psychology and Master's in Metaphysical Science. Private sessions include Past Life Regression, TimeLine and Counseling. Workshops, group sessions, classes.

Shelby Harris, CHt, RMT, CPT, Mind/Body Fitness
Torrance, CA-Phone: (310) 535-3282-E-mail: s.harris81@juno.com
Hypnotherapist, Reiki Master/Teacher & Yoga Instructor, Shelby specializes in Weight Loss, Eliminating Self-Destructive Habits: Drinking, Smoking, Lack of Motivation, Dead-End Relationships & Career Stagnation.

Art Havel, CHt, CSC, RM
Hermosa Beach, CA-Phone: (310) -372-5438-Email: garthurhavel@earthlink.net
Sales, Motivation and Wellness. 20+ years motivation, sales and life coaching experience. Also: Addiction, Phobia, Past Life, Public Speaking. Reiki Master & Spiritual Counselor.

John A. Himinkool, MA, DC, CHt: Accredited Chiropractic Care
San Diego, CA- Phone: (858) 715-9400
Email: info@alignspine.com-Web Site: www.alignspine.com
Himinkool's Chiropractic center offers complete body and mind balance. Benefit from both Hypnotherapy and Alphabiotics. San Diegans will find their staff caring and knowledgeable. Welcome!

CL Holbrook, EdD, CCHt: Holbrook & Associates

San Diego, CA-Phone: (619) 460-4429

Dr. Holbrook effectively helps clients deal with fear, life changes and the intangible. He combines Ericksonian for Hypnotherapy, Shamanism, Koruna Reiki, and spirituality for therapeutic change.

Christopher Howard, PhD: Advanced Neuro Dynamics

Los Angeles, South Bay, CA-Phone: (808) 386-0956-E-mail: chris@powerofinfluence.com

Web Site: www.nlp.com

Christopher Howard is an internationally acclaimed expert in neurolinguistic programming. A powerful speaker, he conducts seminars world wide in the sciences of accelerated change.

Barbara Hynal, RN, PhD: Mind Body Wellness Counseling

San Diego, CA-Phone: (858) 578-3465-mindbody Barbara@aol.com

www.mindbodywellnesscounseling.com

Dr. Hynal use's Medical Hypnotherapy to assist clients to reach a balanced life and optimum health. What your mind perceives your body will do.

Darlene Johnson, PhD, CCHt

LA/SF Valley, CA- Phone: (818) 343-3534

Holds a PhD in Psychology Education and a Masters in Administration of Justice. Specializes in Self-Empowerment, Financial Success, Overcome Learning Limits. Corporate & Private available.

Angeline Kilmer: Transitions

California & Montana- Phone: (760) 935-4051- E-mail: dragonpup_2000@yahoo.com

In addition to her private practice, Angeline Kilmer also teaches Hypnosis & Touch For Health to help people achieve their own "perfect balance."

Patrick A. Kolve, CHt

Ventura County, CA-Phone: (818) 706-84600-E-mail: hobbsroy@workdnet.att.net

Feel Good Now! Patrick specializes in Pain Management, Releasing Phobias, Smoking Cessation and Weight Control. Also learn to pass tests and be your best.

Joey Komada

Los Angeles West Side/South Bay, CA Phone: 310-528-8132 E-mail: jkomada@packbell.net

An active practice in wholistic health including Acupuncture, herbs, Gi Gong and Acupressure. Joey makes house calls. Feel good again!

Al Krasner, PhD, CHt, IHF Fellow: American Board of Hypnotists

Palm Springs, CA-Phone: (760) 416-9665-E-mail: drkrasner@prodigy.net

Founder of the American Board of Hypnotists & Fellow of the International Hypnosis Federation. Al Krasner is one of the great Hypnotists of the 20th Century.

Richard Lederer, PhD

San Diego, CA – Phone: (858) 549-6788-E-Mail: Richard.lederer@pobox.com

Speaker & personality, Dr. Lederer is the syndicated author of more than 2000 articles and books about language and humor.

Lane LaRue, CHt: Tao Unlimited

Topanga, CA- Phone: (818) 704-7011-E-mail: taopower@pacbell.net

Web Site: www.aroma-a-month.com

A unique blend of Aromatherapy & Hypnotherapy to resolve emotional issues and release stored traumas. Breaks through subconscious, brain & cellular memory.

Armona Livneh, PhD, CCHt

West Hollywood, CA-Phone: (310) 286-2945-E-mail: alivneh@bigplanet.com

After two unsuccessful back surgeries, Dr. Livneh cured herself with positive thinking and humor. Release Smoking, Chronic Pain, and Fear, for children, individuals and groups.

treasure.

Geri Malia Pualani LuPiba, CSC

South Bay, CA-Phone: (310) 944-3210-E-mail: flyhighfa@aol.com

Certified Spiritual Counselor, Geri gently focuses your inner mind and heart bringing clarity and balance to the here and now. You'll leave with your loving self smiling.

Lynda J. Malerstein, CCHt

Los Angeles, CA -Phone: (310) 228-3160- E-mail: hypnoempowered@aol.com Web Site: www.powerjourneys.com

Specializes in treatment of Fibromyalgia, Weight Management, Smoking Cessation, Stress Reduction, Fear, Self Esteem, Motivation, Past Life Regression, Removing Creative Blocks, Problems in Children.

Albert J. Marotta, CHt, IHF Fellow: Marotta/Wikkeling Hypnotherapy

Alhambra, CA-Phone: (323) 222-3874-E-mail: remotehlr@aol.com

Traditional Hypnotherapy, Complimentary Medical Hypnosis, Grief Resolution, Depression, Trauma, Phobia. Akashic Records, Past/Pre Life Prenatal, Entity/Curse Releasement, ET Abductees, Remote Therapy, Reiki Healing.

Martie Martin McArthur, CCHt, HHP, CMT: Hypnosis & Holistic Health Center

Bakersfield/Santa Barbara, CA – Phone: (661) 327-3529-E-Mail: himartie@aol.com

With over 12 years on Holistic Health, Martie works with Hypnosis, Massage, Acupressure, Energy Healing and Nutrition helping people heal their Mind, Body & Spirit.

Michael McAuliffe, IHF Fellow: Accelerated Change Technologies Institute

Los Angeles, CA-Phone: (248) 553-2358-E-mail: train@nlptraining.org

Toll Free: (888) 772-2866-Web Site: www.nlptraining.org

Michael's institute provides training in Neuro-Linguistic Programming, Hypnosis, Time Lime Therapy‘ and Huna. Personal and professional success coaching. A.C.T. Now!

Linda Mercado, CH

Los Angeles So Bay, CA-Phone: (310) 406-1303-E-mail: lmercado@adelphia.net

Committed to helping children achieve wellness, happiness self-confidence & self-awareness through Hypnosis. Linda also specializes in Weight & Stress Management & Smoking Cessation.

Juanita-Beth Morgan, CHt

Los Angeles, CA-Phone: (213) 389-2715

When you want the best, select the best! Juanita-Beth Morgan's unquestionable style and abilities in achieving success for others can work for you too.

Mary Mosham, MS, CSC, CPC: Mary Mosham Consulting

Orange County, CA-Phone: (949) 215-5817

Certified Coach, Spiritual Counselor and Hypnotist, Mary integrates body, mind & spirit so you create your life legacy and bring your natural talents to bloom.

Paul Mostman, PhD, CHt, IHF Fellow

Granada Hills, CA-Phone: (818) 368-1161-E-mail: mostman@earthlink.net

Web Site: www.emotional-release-therapy.com

Recognized since 1966 as a highly respected professional hypnotist. His Emotional Release Therapy permanently eliminates negative emotions and feelings. Clients receive personalized, one-on-one therapy.

Phillip Mountrose, CHt, CSC: Awakenings Institute

Arroyo Grande, CA-Phone: (805) 489-9315-E-mail:phil@gettingthru.org

Fax: (805) 489-2096-Web Site: www. gettingthru.org

Phillip focuses on sharing information through his books, tapes, consultations and classes that promote spiritual awakenings along with profound methods for healing.

Joellen Natow CHt, Stage Hypnotist, CSC

Los Angeles South Bay, CA- E-mail: joellen1111@earthlink.net

Web Site: www.positivelychanginghypnosis.com

Is your life on the right path? Unbalanced? Out of sorts? Issues with Weight, Smoking, Self-Esteem, Relationships? Joellen will guide you on your true path. You deserve joy!

Gerry C. Neff, CH

Los Angeles/So Bay, CA-Phone: (310) 515-5940-E-mail: gcneffler@aol.com

Let Gerry boost your confidence and self-esteem. Learn to Pass Tests, Attract Money and get your life in order.

Richard Neves, PhD

Santa Ana, CA- Phone: 714-245-9340-E-mail: aih@ix.netcom.com

Toll Free: 800-872-9996-Fax: 714-245-9881-Web Site: www. Hypnosis.com

Certified NLP Trainer, Personal Coach & Certified Spiritual Counselor with a rich Holistic Healthcare background. Combined multiple disciplines & modalities create magical Hypnotherapy approach.

Janice Norton: Hands of Time Hypnosis
Santa Monica/West Los Angeles, CA – Phone: (310) 581-1999 – E-mail: Janice@hotnetwork.com - Web Site: www.thethinkingmachine.com
Helping you to achieve your goals and dreams. Make your mind a friend, dissolve conflict discover joy, release pain, easily find happiness, open to prosperity.

Steve O'Hara, CH
Toluca Lake, CA-Phone: (818) 382-4588-E-mail: onegreenplanet@earthlink.net
Hypnotist and Certified Spiritual Counselor, Steve teaches relaxation and motivation. Sports enhancement and taking control over fears and harmful behavior are two of his specialties.

Mary O'Maley, MS, CHt. CCDC: Cool Summer Breeze: Professional Alternative Therapies
Torrance, CA- Phone: (310) 328-6362-E-mail: mary@coolsummerbreeze.com
Web Site: www.coolsummerbreeze.com
Hypnotherapist Mary O'Maley specializes in powerful, productive, gentle techniques to eliminate bad habits and obstacles. Peace, joy and abundance are her goals when shift happens.

Roger Otis, CSH
Long Beach, CA-Phone: (562) 624-7164
Roger is a Stage Hypnotist, Comedian, Actor and a delightful storyteller. His wit charms.

David Owen, CHt, CWS
San Diego, CA-Phone: (619) 427-1766-E-mail: davido@abac.com
Certified Weight Control Specialist. Expand your possibilities now! Motivate excellence. Excel in sports. Eliminate problems. Hypnotherapy, NLP, Dream Interpretation, Martial Arts Training & Chi Kung.

Barbara Payton
Los Angeles/Marina Del Rey, CA – Phone: (310) 306-0679
Release blocked emotions heal your Mind, Body & Spirit. Discover healing powers that exists within you. Specializing in menopause, detox, nutrition and weight loss.

Wayne Perry: The Sound Therapy Center of Los Angeles
Los Angeles/Beverly Hills CA – Phone: (323) 655-7781/(800) 276-8634 –
E-Mail: wayne@wayneperry.com - Web Site: www.wayneperry.com
Powerful and entertaining sound healing workshops, lectures and private consultations on how to use sound, toning and the human voice as a transformative healing instrument.

Diane Platt, CHt
Tujunga, CA-Phone: (818) 353-6063-E-mail: fourflatts4@juno.com
Teacher, Author, Hypnotherapist specializing in Personal Enrichment, Stress Management, Self-Esteem & Weight Loss. Works with children & adults. Diane's Motto: "Success is not an accident."

Suzy Prudden, CHt, IHF Board Member: Positive Changes of Beverly Hills
Beverly Hills, CA-Phone: (310) 657-6868-E-mail: pchbeverlyhills@aol.com
CEO of Unlimited Possibilities, Inc, Suzy specializes in helping you release weight, stop smoking, make peace with your body, empower yourself and love your life.

Gaye Rehder, CHt
Los Angeles, CA- Phone: 310-391-5518-E-mail: grehder@aol.com
Fax: 310-391-0882
Gaye is a Hypnotherapist specializing in Weight Control, Smoking Cessation, Stress Management, Phobias, Sports Performance, Memory and Learning Skills.

Karola Kristina Rietz
Los Angeles/Beverly Hills, CA – Phone: (310) 274-3105/800-374-3426 – E-mail: karolakrietz@aol.com
General Hypnotherapy with focus on Motivational and Educational Hypnosis. Specialty in: Wellness through Medical Hypnosis and Hypno-anesthesia.

Denise Rodriguez, CHt: Going Within
Los Angeles/Orange County, CA – Phone: (562) 929-3148 – E-mail: dmanet@aol.com
Certified in Transpersonal Hypnosis, Past Life Regression & Hypnotherapy. Achieve excellent results in sports performance, test taking. Helps battered women change their lives. Stage Hypnotist.

Carol Rosenblum, CHt
West Los Angeles, CA-Phone: (310) 280-3583-E-mail: basheva@msn.com
Energize your life. Improve the OLD and perfect the NEW through Hypnosis! Explore how to change, challenge and motivate yourself. Carol shows you how!

Laura Rubinstein, CHt, IHF Fellow: LBR & Associates
San Diego, CA-Phone: (619) 293-3353-E-mail: coachlbr@aol.com
Toll Free: (877) 566-1904-Fax: 707-221-0382
Provides Coaching, Hypnosis and Consulting to high performance people & organizations to achieve breakthrough results. "We are committed to your success and fulfillment."

Robert Rumph, Sr, OM
Los Angeles, CA-Phone: (310) 420-3738
As a Dowser/Healer, Bob balances your individual Physical, Mental, Emotional & Spiritual aspects. He neutralizes unwanted energies of people, places & things so you accept positive universal energy.

James J. Sacco, CHt
Canoga Park, CA-Phone: (818) 882-3774
Clinical Hypnotherapist. Specializes in Stress Management, Corporate Seminars, Motivational Speaking, Demonstrational Hypnotist.

BrendaAnn Saey, CHt, CCHt
Costa Mesa, CA-Phone: (714) 962-5344-E-mail: brendaann8.com
Certified Clinical Hypnotherapist. Weight, Stress & Pain Management Specialist, Medical Hypnotism, Success, Confidence, Memory, Concentration, Sports, Stage Performance, Smoking, Relationships, Self-Esteem, Habits, Fears.

Loretta M. Siani-Accelerated Human Performance
Los Angeles/So Bay/Orange County, CA- Phone: (562) 434-7429-E-mail: lsiani@aol.com
Reduce the effects of stress on mind, body and spirit. Overcome performance anxiety, manage unwanted habits, increase confidence, creativity, concentration, focus, follow-through sense of purpose.

Cheryl Ann Stein, RN, MA, CHt: The Positive Mind, Inc
North Hills, CA, Phone: (818) 895-6601, E-mail: csrn@aol.com
Realize your dreams and goals. RN/Holistic Nurse, Hypnotherapist Cheryl has a Masters Degree Psychology. NLP, Therapeutic Imagery, Weight Control, Stress Reduction and Positivity Training.

Shelley Stockwell, PhD, Channel: Creativity Learning Institute
30819 Casilina, Rancho Palos Verdes, CA 90275
L.A. and Orange Counties, CA-Phone: (310) 541-4844 -Email: sstockwell@earthlink.net
Fax: (310) 377-7946-Web Site: www.hypnosisfederation.com
Certifies Hypnotists, Past Life Hypnotherapists, Spiritual Counselors and Stage Hypnotists for over 23 years. Stage performer, Stockwell is the founder & spokesperson for the Int. Hypnosis Federation.

Richard Sutphen & Tara Sutphen, IHF Advisory Board Members: Valley of the Sun,
Malibu, CA-Phone: (818) 706-0963 -Fax: (818) 706-3606
Web Site: www.dicksutphen.com
Dick Sutphen best-selling author, seminar leader & psychic researcher. Created over 300 self-help & exploration audio & videotapes & CDs. The Sutphen's lead Enlightenment Seminars.

Niccolous L. Thompson, PhD, DCHt, IHF Fellow: Chino Hypnosis Center
Chino, San Bernardino, Riverside, CA, Phone: (909) 625-9983, E-mail:
rockandrollhypnotist@hotmail.com Web Site: www.rockandrollhypnotist.com
Author of "Hypnotherapy for Children" and "Hypnotherapy for the Sexually Abused," Niccolous is an expert in child hypnotherapy and specializes in ADD/ADHV and Enuresis.

Jill Ungar, CHt
Los Angeles, CA-Phone: (310) 720-5466-E-mail: hhcoyote@earthlink.net
Certified Hypnotherapist aiding others in facilitating their own Well-Being. Certified in Danskinetics; Movement Therapy focusing on liberating, integrating and empowering the body/mind/spirit community experience.

Sara EagleWoman Urguidez, CSC
San Fernando Valley, CA-Phone: (818) 766-0461-E-mail: eaglewomen@bennythejet.com
Hands on healer, Sara creates miracles on demand. A Shaman and Certified Spiritual Counselor, she blends Egyptian and Native American healing arts with modern wisdom.

Theodore A. Vaniski, CHt: Mind Dynamics Institute
Orange County, CA- Phone: (714) 283-2090-E-mail: minddynamics@aol.com
Web Site: www.minddynamics.institute.com
Personal Development Training. Over 25 years experience in helping individuals and corporations reach their personal and financial goals. Private or group training seminars.

Christina Virgason, MT, RM, ND: The Healing Voice
So Bay, CA-Phone: (310) 517-0213-E-mail: drvirgason@attbi.com
Healing and Nurturing Techniques: Voice Toning Therapy, Sounding, Chakra Balancing, Massage, Touch For Health, Hypnosis, Iridology, Kinesiology, Herbology & Oil Aromatherapy.

Jason Vogel, MA, CHt, CSH: Works of Heart
Beverly Hills, CA-Phone: (310) 659-6822-E-mail:jagovo@aol.com
Renown author, business consultant, life coach and Hypnotherapist, Jason helps people overcome procrastination and develop positive habits for success. He's a captivating speaker and stage hypnotist.

Bunny Vreeland, CHt: Image Resource Center
Ventura County, CA-Phone: (805) 984-1237-E-mail: bunnyvree@aol.com
A long time resident of Ventura County, Bunny is an award winning Image Consultant and Certified Hypnotherapist. Weight management is her specialty.

A.L. Ward, CH, IHF Fellow: AWard Hypnosis Service
San Bernardino, CA, Phone (909) 880-1980, E-mail: napezy@aol.com
Your mind not only contains the knowledge of life and the purpose for its existence and conduct, it contains the answers for its own improvement.

John D. Warhank, Stage Hypnotist
Southern, CA-Phone: (310) 517-9247-E-mail: jaydeehyp@webtv.net
Fax: (310) 326-8745
Professional Stage Hypnosis. Themes are tailored to your program. Delightfully entertaining, educational & fun!

John Wheatley, CCH, CSC: Positive Life Changes
Huntington Beach, CA, Phone: (714) 840-8871-E-mail: rrsilvercloud@hotmail.com
Clinical Hypnotherapist, Spiritual Counselor, Reiki Practitioner. Member of Toastmasters International & the Literacy Volunteers of America.

Dianna Whitley, PhDc: Mind Over Matter

Los Angeles, CA - Phone: (323) 525-1005 – E-mail: diannaww2@aol.com

Dianna has helped over 1000 clients lose weight, boost self esteem and be a confident public speaker. Call for a free initial consultation.

Anda Whitman, CSC, SC

Los Angeles/San Fernando Valley, CA-Phone: (818) 885-6434

Enlightment Astrology by Certified Spiritual Counselor and Spiritual Intuitive, Anda specializes in Relationships, Business, Timings, Past Lives, Natal, Transit Charts. Expert in-depth analysis.

Mark E. Wilkins, ACHt

Ventura County/Camarillo, CA-Phone: (805) 389-3287

E-mail: mark@growth-enrichment.com

Advanced Certified Hypnotherapist, Mark specializes in Painless Child Birthing. Have a wonderful expectancy, eliminate drugs, pain and discomfort and have a trauma free birth.

Sally Wright, RN, CH: Wright-On Enterprises

Torrance, CA-Phone: (310) 540-0406 – E-Mail: sallywright@earthlink.net

Using tools of Hypnosis, Healing Touch and Toning, you will awaken your heart, touch your joy and safely make changes for a new you.

Suzanne Young, DCH

Los Angeles/So Bay, CA - Phone: (310) 545-2041

A pioneering professional with over 17 years in the wellness field, Suzanne specializes in Hypnotherapy, Body Work, Herbology, Gua Sha & Spiritual Counseling.

COLORADO, USA

Zolita Grant, CHt, IHF Fellow: Colorado School of Counseling & Hypnotherapy Training

Boulder, CO- Phone: (303) 776-6103-E-mail: info@selfhealing.com

Web Site: www.selfhealing.com

Teacher, trainer, author and Private Psychotherapist, Zolita specializes in Hypnosis to work with learning disabilities and diseases.

Cody Horton, CCHt, Stage Hypnotist

Golden, CO-Phone: (303) 526-2050-E-mail: codyhorton @yahoo.com

Clinical Hypnotherapist, Author, Speaker and Stage Hypnotist.

Marilyn Norcross, CCHt: WinQuest for Success

Greeley, CO- Phone: (970) 336-9056 -E-mail: marilyn@winquest.net

Web Site: www.winquest.net

Hypnotherapist, Master NLP Practitioner, Life Coach, Keynote Speaker, Corporate, Athletic High-Achiever Trainer. US National Skating Gold Medallist. Super Mental/Emotional training: Skaters/Ballroom Dancers/Performers/Tennis/Golf.

CONNECTICUT, USA

Nancy Lee Klase, CHt, CI: Mindfields
CT, NY Area-Phone: (203) 625-0508-E-mail: mindfields@erols.com
Dedicated to helping you find solutions to behavior problems and changing your life in positive ways. Nancy has been practicing Hypnotherapy for over 15 years.

CJ Mozzochi: Hypnosis Research Institute
Phone: (860) 652-9234-E-mail: cjm@ix.netcom.com
So Glastonbury, CT
Training in new modalities: Hypnosis, Relaxation, Pain Management & Accelerated Learning.

DC, USA

Mary Bontempo, RM; Reiki Associated, Inc
DC/Maryland -Phone: (410) 536-5626 – E-Mail: awaki@aol.com
Travels Internationally to teach Reiki. Leads sacred journeys to Andes, dolphin swim, Egypt. Minister.
Spencer Humm, BFA, DCHt: Evolve Communications
DC/Virginia – Phone: (703) 626-8572 – E-Mail: slashm@aol.com - Web Site: www.hypnosisproject.com
Spencer is a Certified Trainer of NLP, Master Hypnotist, and member of the American Board of Hypnotherapy. Business Communications Consultant and Comedy Entertainer.

FLORIDA, USA

Carol S. Anderssen, RM, CSC, Ordained Minister
Ft Myers, FL-Phone: (941) 947-0192-E-mail: susik513@aol.com
Crystal Healing and Aromatherapy in her Reiki Practice intensifies healings with amazing results. Carol is also a Certified Spiritual Counselor.

Dan Cleary, CI, IHF Fellow
No Palm Beach, FL, Phone: (561) 863-1334, E-mail: dancleary@juno.com
Dan is an outstanding presenter, educator and hypnosis practitioner who has distinguished himself in the fields of Personal Transformation.

Rayma Ewing, CSC, Hypnotist
Ft Myers/Lehigh Acres, FL-Phone: (941) 369-8468-E-mail: raymasue@aol.com
Discover your true essence; your true self. Know what it means to be guided by divine right action. Learn to light up your life, NOW!

Hettie Grutman
Boca Raton, FL - Phone (941) 272-8846
Effective Spiritual Counseling to facilitate a positive life change by removing "blocks" through proven methods and years of experience.

Debbi Knox, Hypnotist, CSC, RM
Ft Myers/Bonita Springs, FL-Phone: (941) 495-7700-E-mail: dktees@aol.com
Certified Spiritual Counselor, Reiki Master and Hypnotist. Debbi is an artist who also specializes in the Intuitive Arts, Tarot, Trance Channeling and Joy.

Jillian LaVelle, CSMC, CHt, IHF Advisory Board Member & IHF Fellow
International Assoc. of Counselors & Therapists (IACT)
Bonita Springs, FL-Phone: (941) 498-9710-E-mail: iactnow@aol.com
Fax: (941) 498-1215-Web Site: www.iact.org
Author and teacher in private practice, Jillian heads the International Association of Counselors and Therapists and is the Editor-In-Chief of the magazine, Unlimited Human!

Edwin Muniz, MD, PhD, DCH, IHF Fellow: Edwin Muniz & Associates
Tampa/Brandon, FL – Phone: (813) 814-3380 – E-mail: physioed@aol.com
Practice is dedicated to the use of Natural Non-Chemical Therapy options to stimulate body and immune system through Medical Hypnotherapy. Feel Great!

Renée Newell, CSC
Naples, FL- Phone: (941) 571-4482-E-mail: magicalflights@yahoo.com
Web Site: magicalflights.com
A Certified Spiritual Counselor and Reiki Practitioner, Renée inspires people to find their own answers and ideas, giving problems flight and offering contemporary solutions.

Sidney Ryba, CHt, RM
Orlando, FL-Phone: (407) 876-0144
Sidney is a Hypnotherapist, Reiki Master/Teacher, Spiritual Counselor and Healer. He specializes in Energy Medicine and Crystals that combines his different modalities to produce results.

Laurie J. Scheer, CSC, RM, MPT
Ft Myers/Bonita Springs, FL
Phone: (941) 949-1222-E-mail: lauriejoi@aol.com
Licensed Physical Therapist, Certified Spiritual Counselor and Reiki Master, Laurie utilizes a Holistic approach to facilitate healing the Body, Mind & Spirit.

Vivian V. Smith, CHt, CSC, RM, IHF Fellow
Bonita Springs, FL-Phone: (239) 947-4802-E-mail: hypnoviv@earthlink.net
Vivian is Director of the Agape Center in Bonita Springs, Florida. Highly skilled Transpersonal Hypnotherapist, Regressionist, Researcher, Lecturer, Teacher, Reiki Master, Spiritual Healer & Counselor.

Tamara M. Thomas, LMT, CSC: A Healing Touch Therapist & Message, Inc
Bonita Springs/Ft Myers, FL -Phone: (941) 498-9885-E-mail: touch44444@aol.com
Fax: (941) 498-4452
A Healing Touch Therapist & Message. Tamara promotes healing through balancing Body, Mind and Spirit. She is a Hypnotist, a Certified Spiritual Counselor and an Ordained Minister.

Lisa Walker, RN, PhD, CSC, CHt, RM: Angel Light Pathways

Ft Lauderdale/Miami, FL-Phone: (954) 270-3469-E-mail: lisawstar2000@yahoo.com

Fax: (954) 340-9517

Lisa Walker, RN, Hypnotist, Spiritual Counselor, Trance Channel offers astounding Angel Readings, Medical Intuition and Hypnosis. Gifted Teacher & Speaker for classes & conferences.

GEORGIA, USA

Laura Halls, CHt, CSC

Atlanta/Marietta, GA-Phone: (770) 565-6015-E-mail: laurahalls@yahoo.com

Laura facilitates journeys into the inner self to learn, heal and find direction. Working intuitively with clients, she moves from root causes to individual empowerment.

ILLINOIS, USA

Don Benitone, CH

Southern, IL-Phone: (618) 942-3712-E-mail: Db1038256@onemain.com

As a Hypnosis Technician & Consultant, Don helps people to Stop Smoking, Lose Weight, Improve Self Confidence, Study Habits, Phobias and enjoy life.

Sylvia Bivens, CHt, IHF Fellow

Rock Island, IL-Phone: (309) 788-2495-E-mail: syl4839@aol.com

Hypnotherapist, NLP Practitioner & Past Life Therapist, Sylvia's private sessions & workshops facilitate transformation. Manage Stress, create Self-Confidence & a desirable, productive life of wellness.

INDIANA, USA

Fred Houze, Jr, DCH

Aurora, IN -Phone: (812) 926-2935

Doctor of Clinical Hypnotherapy, Fred specializes in Stop Smoking, Past Life Therapy, Stage Shows, Neuro-Linguistic Programming (NLP), Time Line Therapy & Sports Hypnosis.

KENTUCKY, USA

Bill Breuer, DC, MCHt, IHF Fellow: Centre for Multidisciplinary Healthcare

Louisville, KY-Phone: (502) 459-7431-E-mail: kyhypno@juno.com

Fax: (502) 459-9217-Web Site: angelfire.com/ky2/multicare.com

Author of "Physically Focused Hypnotherapy," and a practicing Hypnotherapist for 40 years. Director of a Medical Center providing out/patient mainstream and complimentary alternative Health Care.

LOUISIANA, USA

Conrad Adams, CHt: Infinity Hypnosis Institute

Baton Rouge, LA-Phone: (225) 924-0604-E-mail: finfinity@cox.net

Uncover the real you! 30+ years experience, Conrad conducts professional Hypnotherapy & Past-Life Regression workshops. He teaches Learning & Memory Enhancement at Louisiana State University.

Paul G. Durbin, Chaplain, PhD, CHt, IHF Fellow
New Orleans, LA- Phone: (504) 244-5430-E-mail: pgdurbin@cox.net
Web Site: www.durbinhypnosis.com
Specializes in Hypnotherapy, Medical Hypnosis, Stress Management, Guided Imagery, False Memory Syndrome, Hypnosis, Religion, Alfred Adler, Victor Frankl, Death, Dying & Grief Counseling.

James Gil Loe, PhD, LCPC: Gil Loe, Inc.
Shreveport, LA-Phone: (318) 227-9002-E-mail: jamesloe@msn.com
Committed to helping clients achieve wellness, happiness and the prosperity they seek through building self-confidence, self-awareness and wholeness through Hypnosis.

MASSACHUSETTS, USA

Adeline (Addie) Kania, CHt, IHF Fellow: Gateway Center for Acupuncture & Hypnosis
Merrimack Valley, MA-Phone: (978) 374-9572-E-mail: addie@alternativeweight.com
Web Site: wwwalternativeweight.co
Relaxation, Acupuncture and Hypnosis for Smoking Cessation and Holistic Weight Loss. Wellness Consultant at Whittier Rehab Hospital. Faculty member of Northern Essex Community College

MICHIGAN, USA

Joan Scully Ballantyne, CHt, RM: Wings of Healing
Novi, MI-Phone: (248) 344-2219-E-mail: jsbwings@att.net
Offers Metaphysical Hypnosis, Recovery, Body/Mind/Spirit Integration. A profound healer, Joan is also a Massage Therapist, Reiki Master and is ordained by Melchizedek.

Jerome Beacham, PhD: Infinite International Institute of Hypnotherapy
Detroit Metro Area, MI-Phone: (248) 549-5594-Email: Jbeacham@infinityinst.com
Fax: (248) 549-5421-Web Site: www.infinityinst.com
Jerome Beacham, PhD, International Medical & Dental Hypnotherapy Association' (IMDHA) Fellow, is Certified Chairman & Director of Training of IMDHA approved schools worldwide.

Cheryl A. Beshada, CMHt: Clinical Care Network
Sterling Heights/Warren, MI- Phone: (586) 939-7676- E-mail: Cbeshada@hotmail.com
Web Site: www.ccnprogroup.com
Medical Hypnosis, Sports Performance, Smoking Cessation, Self Confidence, Accelerated Learning, Alleviate Fears & Phobias, Dental Hypnosis, Stress Management, Weight Loss, Transpersonal Hypnotherapy & Hypnotherapy Instruction.

Marcia Boehm, BCD, ACSW, LMFT, CHt
Troy, MI-Phone: (248) 828-3121 -E-mail marciab776@aol.com
Hypnotherapist, Social Worker, Marriage/Family Therapist, Coach, Author, Speaker. Faculty Wayne State Univ. Multicultural outreach director. Contributor "Chicken Soup for The Soul." Tinnitus, ADD specialty.

Cheryl Croci, CHt, IHF Fellow: Enhancing Your Healer Within
Sterling Heights, MI, Phone: (586) 983-3858-E-mail: cherylcroci@aol.com
Hypnotherapist, Educator, Speaker, Three In One Facilitator. Mind/Body/Spirit Healing, Regression, Personal & Spiritual Development, Healing Touch, Reiki, Ascension & Metaphysics. Great sessions & classes!

Kathi Davidson, RNC, CHt: Pathways Hypnotherapy Clinic
Utica, MI-Phone: (810) 726-2884-E-mail: bluefox1944@aol.com
Dedicated to Healing Mind, Body & Spirit through General Hypnotherapy. Kathi specializes in Transpersonal Hypnotherapy. Her motto: "Be all that you can be through Hypnotherapy."

Frank Garfield, CHt, IHF Fellow: Clinical Care Network
Sterling Heights/Warren, MI -Phone: (810) 939-7676-Email: frankgarfield@msn.com
Garfield teaches advanced Hypnosis Specialty Workshops, Medical Hypnosis, Natural Childbirth, helping Cancer patients, Trauma and Pain Management, Body Re-Shaping, Hypnodontics & more.

Patricia A Greanya, CHt, Reverend
Fenton, MI-Phone: (810) 750-3818-E-mail: pgreanya@aol.com
Hypnotherapist, Reflexologist, Spiritual Counselor. Has active practice in the Genesee County area with special emphasis on wellness, love & relationships. Therapeutic & Healing Touch.

Carolyn L. Kraft, CHt: Creative Hypnosis LLC
Detroit, MI- Phone: (313) 893-7643
Specializing in Pediatric Hypnosis.

Maureen (Mickey) Lovell, CHt: Echoes of the Mind
North MI-Phone: (231) 943-8540-E-mail: Mickeysrainbow@aol.com
Mickey focuses on Regression Therapy to access hidden memories that may be holding you back from experiencing Self-Love, Creativity, Joy, Health & Wholeness.

Cedric L. McSween, Sr, CHt: Premier Hypnosis Center, LLC
Farmington Hills, MI-Phone: (248) 538-7699-E-mail: info@intuitivewisdom.com
Fax: (248) 538-8047-Web Site: www.premierhypnosis.net
Certified Hypnotherapist & Motivational Speaker empowered to help and uplift you own your life: "To give you hope is not just a goal, but a passion."

Kenneth John Owens, CHt, Stage Hypnotist: Intuitive Wisdom
MI/Nationwide- Phone: (248) 865-1381-E-mail: info@intuitivewisdom.com
Web Site: www.intuitivewisdom.com
Counseling, Training, Development, and AURA Photography geared for corporations/ non-profit agencies. Specializing in Motivation & Stress Management programs that are designed for your specific needs.

Carla G. Riemersma, PhD, CHt

Hudsonville, MI- Phone: (616) 669-0447-E-mail: carlagay@ix.netcom.com

Web Site: www.optimahealthservices.com

You have the potential to make positive choices and become who you want to be. Dr. Riemersma, MPA, RHIA, AHRMQR, provides Complimentary, Alternative Medicine options.

Ethel Rosen

South East, MI Phone: (248) 865-1381-E-mail: info@intuitivewisdom.com

Toll Free: (888) 553-2358-Web Site: intuitivewisdom.com

Ethel is a Certified Hypnotherapist, Aura Intuitive, Psychic Reader, Sales & Marketing Consultant. She specializes in Weight Loss, Smoking Cessation and making people feel good.

Aniko Roth, CHt

Farmington Hills, MI-Phone: (248) 390-3566-E-mail: anikoroth1@juno.com

Body works by Aniko includes: Hypnosis, Massage and Reiki. Co-Founder of the Body, Mind, Spirit Hypnotherapy Association.

MISSOURI, USA

Mary Ethridge, CRNA, CHt: Mary E's Hypnosis Center

St Louis, MO-Phone: (314) 645-6051-E-mail: newimajj@aol.com

Mary, a Practical Medical Anesthetist, assists clients to heal themselves and be pain free by controlling discomfort from within. A powerful motivational speaker & Hypnotherapist.

NEVADA, USA

LA "Pete" Blandford, CHt, LMT: Essential Touch

Las Vegas, Henderson & Boulder City, NV-Phone: 702-293-7545-

E-mail:essentialtouchbc@aol.com

Improve well-being and achieve your goals! Hypnosis and Massage are excellent adjunct therapies that enhance and empower you. Increase relaxation and focus cognitive performance.

John M. Costa, CHt, BMS, IHF Fellow

Las Vegas, NV- E-mail: jandjcosta@earthlink.net

Retired Master Hypnotist. Pain Management Specialist available for special cases.

Cheryl J. Johnson, CHt

Las Vegas, NV-Phone: (702) 682-6889-E-mail: cdjtwins@lvcm.com

Fax: (702) 341-9814

Trance Channel, Psychic Reader, Hypnotherapist and Medium. Cheryl offers a unique combination of healing modalities based on the connection with the Source of All Life.

Kolene Reynolds, CHt, RM: Mind, Body & Soul Hypnotherapy

Las Vegas, NV, Phone: (702) 693-1309

Human & Pet Counseling. Master Hypnotherapist and Stage Hypnotist. Wholistic personally tailored approach using Hypnosis, Color, Reiki and Tapping.

NEW JERSEY, USA

Helene Feldman, DCHt, IHF Fellow: Dynamic Hypnotherapy Associates
Manalapan, NJ -Phone: (732) 446-5995 -E-mail: DrHypno13@aol.com
Hypnosis, NLP, Parts Therapy. Specializes in Children, Stress, Sexual Abuse, Dysfunction, Wellness, Smoking Cessation, Sports. Former High School Principal, Director of Newark's Special Education.

Jaime Feldman, DCHt, IHF Fellow: Dynamic Hypnotherapy Associates, Director, Inst. of Hypnotherapy
Manalapan, NJ-Phone: (732) 446-5995 -E-mail: DrJaimeF@aol.com
Pioneer of Parts Therapy Hypnotherapy, NLP & Reiki. Unlock the subconscious; remove trauma, fear, unwanted behavior, & tremors and twitches associated with Parkinson's.

Gail Monaloy MA, CCC-SLP, CHt
Passaic, NJ -Phone: (973) 777-8604/(973) 773-7626
Hypnotist, Speech & Language Pathologist. Specialties: Quit Smoking, Weight Control, Relaxation, Sports, Fear, Phobia, Pain Control, Speech, Memory, Head Trauma & Stroke, Voice & Language.

Lindsey Sass-Aurand, LMT, CHt: Holistic Healing Center
New York, New Jersey, CT, NY, Phone: (845) 425-5233, E-mail: Lindseysass@hotmnail.com, Web Site: www.holistichealingcenter.com
Co-founder and Co-director of the Holistic Healing Center that specializes in Women's Issues, Hypnotherapy for Childbirth and Infant Massage Instructors Training.

NEW YORK, USA

Paul Aurand, CCHt & Lindsey Sass-Aurand, LMT, CHt: Holistic Healing Center
Spring Valley, NY- Phone: (845) 425-5233-E-mail: paul@holistichealingcenter.com
Web Site: www.holistichealingcenter.com
Paul Aurand is the founder of the Holistic Healing Center. He is a registered Medical Hypnotherapist, Certified Clinical Hypnotherapist and skilled Counselor and Healer.

Peter Blum, RHt, CI, MSC
Woodstock, NY -Phone: (845) 247-8839 -Email: pbtrance@ulster.net
Sonic Trance. Master Sound Therapist. Peter's 4 CD set "Sounds for Healing" is used for hospitals, acupuncture, chiropractic, massage. Combines Hypnosis, NLP, Healing Sound, Shamanism.

Michael Ellner, DD, PhD, CMHt
New York, NY, Phone: (212) 580-3471 E-mail: revdocnyc@aol.com
Michael's life changing workshops, lectures help thousands connect with and utilize their inner physician. He specializes AIDS and in helping women emotionally detox & thrive.

Jill Hindie Fondiller, CHt: Harmony HypnosisCenter
Buffalo, NY-Phone: (716) 684-5163-E-mail: imfondofjill@aol.com
Certified Weight Control Specialist, Jill helps you release Harmful Habits and Stress. Bring you Mind, body & Spirit into Harmony. Art Therapist for all ages.

Lawrence Galante, PhD, RSHom, CHt, RPP, IHF Fellow: Center for Holistic Arts
New York, NY- Phone: (212) 414-1266-E-mail: lg@holistic-arts.com
Web Site: www.holistic-arts.com
Over 30 years experience as a Registered Hypnotherapist, Chi Kung Instructor, Registered Polarity Practitioner, University Professor and Director of the Center for Holistic Arts.

Maurice Kouguell, PhD, FBHA, BCTS: Brookside Center
Baldwin, NY- Phone: (516) 868-2233-E-mail: hypnoprof@aol.com
Web Site: www.brooksidecenter.com
Dr. Kouguell holds a PhD in Counseling Psychology. Benefit from his unique background in Psychology, Education, Family Life, Hypnotherapy, Emotional Freedom Technique & Neurolinguistic Programming.

Patricia Magnotta, CHt, CASAC, PT, RM: PMJ Enterprises, Inc
West Harrison, NY-Phone: (914) 428-6234-E-mail: luckypmj@aol.com
Multifaceted healing techniques tailored to the client needs. Professional treatment that honors the human spirit. Reiki, Therapeutic Touch, Auricular Acupuncture & Shamanic Healing. Referrals preferred.

Richard McNamera, MESMERICK, Stage Hypnotist, CHt: Better Living With Hypnosis
NY, NJ, CT- Phone: (973) 962-6637-E-mail: mesmerick2hypnosis.org
Web Site: www.mesmerick.com
Lively Stage Hypnosis & Demonstrations of the Paranormal for corporate, trade show, college campus & other events. All shows expertly tailored to your specific needs.

Walter A. Stock, CHt, CSC, IHF Fellow
Glendale, NY-Phone: (718) 846-1416 (24 hour voice mail)
Spiritual Counseling, employing Shamanic techniques, Walter provides intensive workshops in Celtic Languages and Spirituality.

NORTH CAROLINA, USA
Vickie T. McDonald, DCH, RM
Private sessions in Hypnosis and Reiki. Owns and operates the Carolina Hypnosis Center offering basic and advanced training for Hypnotherapists and Reiki Practitioners and Masters.

Diana V. Moore, ACH
Gastonia, NC-Phone: (704) 913-7646 -E-mail: vickihypno@aol.com
Web Site: www.carolinahypnosiscenter.com
Raleigh, NC-Phone: (919) 788-0045 -E-mail: dmoore246@aol.com
Intuitive Hypnotherapist who assists others to empower themselves by removing illusion and celebrating their gifts.

OREGON, USA

Juanita DeGarmo: Regal Chimera

Metro Protland, OR – Phone: (503) 723-3734 – E-mail: honeyb56@aol.com - Web Site: www.stayyouthfulnow.madebig.com

Spirit is the center from which all else flows. I promise support and guidance with unconditional love and understanding. Are you ready? I can help.

Karla J. Thaler, CCHt, PhD: Hidden Realms Hypnosis

Portland Metro, OR. Phone: (503) 992-2420, e-mail: hiddenrealsm@whoever.com Web Site: www.hiddenrealmshypnosis.com

Regression specialist incorporating past life experiences that trigger trauma's & issues in your present earthwalk. PhD in Metaphysical Theology, Reiki Master, Shamanic Journey's Practitioner.

John Thompson, CHt: Portland Hypnosis

Portland, OR-Phone: (503) 786-2575

Intuitive coach using Psychic ability. Hypnosis, Reiki, NLP, and Etheric Healing. These skills will turn your life around.

PENNSYLVANIA, USA

Norbert W. Bakas, PhD: Virnor Institute of Hypnosis

Pittsburgh, PA-Phone: (412) 931-5602 -E-mail: nwb@nauticom.net

Director of the Bakas Hypnosis Center, Norbert specializes in Hypnotherapy, Sports Hypnosis, Stage Presentations, Certified Instructor for Self Hypnosis, Hypnotist and/or Hypnotherapist.

Beverley S. Bley, LPN, CMHt: C.H.A.N.G.E. Academy

Allentown, PA- Phone: (610) 797-8250 -E-mail: change@v35.com

Web Site: www.4change.com

Beverley's Self-Hypnosis Training eliminates Smoking, Weight, Stress, Pain Addiction & Phobias. Promote & improve: Relationships, Memory & Study Habits. Group & Private sessions available.

Mary-Louise Bulmer, CHt

South Eastern, PA -Phone: (610) 647-4421 -E-mail: merryduppy@aol.com

Master Neuro-Linguistic Programming Practitioner. Private, group demonstration. Member: International Hypnosis Federation, Nat. Guild of Hypnotists, Int. Assoc. Counselors & Therapists, National Board Hypnotherapy & Hypnotic Anesthesiology.

Melanie DeVitis, CHt: The Holistic Success Center

Pennsylvania/New Jersey- Phone: (215) 736-8624 -E-mail: melanie@1walnut.com

Web Site: www.holisticsuccesscenter.com

This dynamic team of Hypnotherapists, working in Pennsylvania & New Jersey, meet the needs of corporate and personal clients.

Joan B. King, CHt: The Holistic Success Center

Pennsylvania/New Jersey- Phone: (215) 736-8624 -E-mail: joan@1walnut.com
Web Site: www.holisticsuccesscenter.com
This dynamic team of Hypnotherapists, working in Pennsylvania & New Jersey, meet the needs of corporate and personal clients.

Robert W. King, CHt: The Holistic Success Center

Pennsylvania/New Jersey- Phone: (215) 736-8624 -E-mail: admin@1walnut.com
Web Site: www.holisticsuccesscenter.com
This dynamic team of Hypnotherapists, works in Pennsylvania & New Jersey and meets the needs of corporate and personal clients.

Robert Otto, CHt: Institute of Dynamic Hypnosis

Northeastern, PA – Phone: (570) 869-1021 – Email: rfotto@epix.net - Web Site: www.rbertottohypnsis.com
Master Hypnotherapist specializing in Stop Smoking and Weight Loss clinics for 20 years. Robert's a true entertainer. His lectures and teaching skills are nationally acclaimed.

Sally Witt, PhD, CHt, CSC, IHF Fellow: Holistic Success Center, Inc (Since 1997)

Morrisville, PA- Phone: (215) 736-8624 -E-mail: sally@holisticsuccesscenter.com
Web site: www.holisticsuccesscenter.com
Your mind is the key. Make powerful changes in your personal & professional life using Hypnotherapy, Neurolinguistic Programming, Reiki, Spiritual Counseling. Professional Trainer. Corporate programs.

TEXAS, USA

Michael J. Coffman, CHt

Little Elm, TX – Phone: (972) 668-9213 – E-mail: collman11@mindspring.com
Michael, with wife Deborah, helps you lose weight, feel great, eliminate hurtful habits, permanent & positive changes. Sports Hypnosis, Memory Enhancement & Spiritual Upliftment.

Virginia Coleman, CHt

Houston/Beaumont, TX-Phone: (409) 833-7413 -E-mail: colemont@juno.com
Virginia's company, "Paige I" specializes in Hypnosis and a nutritional program for weight management. She also provides medical equipment & supplies for the elderly.

Marx Howell, CHt: Marx Howell & Associates

Austin, TX-Phone: (512) 836-4700 -E-mail: Marx@marxhowell.com
Web Site: wwwmarxhowell.com
Leading Forensic Hypnosis authority. Helps traumatized victims & witnesses to crimes. 32 year veteran Texas Dept. Public Safety. Graduate FBI National Academy. Criminal Justice degree.

Veronica LaChapelle, ND, CHt: Health Matrix

Austin, TX-Phone: (512) 335-7179 -E-mail: healthmetrix@aol.com

Veronica is a Doctor of Naturopathy & Hypnotist specializing in Customized Nutritional Consulting, Weight Management, Natural Allergy Relief, Past Life Regression & releasing Addiction/Phobia.

Michael Langston, CHt

San Antonio, TX - Phone: (972) 842-1866 – E-mail: mlangston@mindspring.com

Hypnosis for over coming Addiction & Compulsion, Stress Management & Motivation. Mike offers innovative techniques for Body, Mind & Spirit.

Anne King, CHt: Anne King's Hypnosis Center

Boerne, TX- Phone: (830) 537-5411 -E-mail: akhypno@gvtc.com

Web Site: www.hypnoclasses.com

General practice including: Smoking, Weight Loss, Stress, Sports, Memory & Concentration. Instructs: Basic, Intermediate & Advanced Hypnotherapy with CEU credit. Books & tapes available.

Kathy L. Moore, MBA, CH: Moore Inspirations

San Antonio & surrounding, TX, Phone: (210) 967-4350, E-mail: Mooreinspire@email.msn.com, Web Site: www.mooreinspire.com

Mooreinspire@email.msn.com, Web Site: www.mooreinspire.com

Classes in Self Hypnosis, Light & Sound Therapy with Hypnosis and group Weight Loss through Community Education. Kathy teaches classes for hypnotists as well.

Diane Pope, MSN, RN, CHt: Diane Pope's Hypnosis Center

Houston, TX-Phone: (281) 787-1946 -E-mail: hypno225di@aol.com

Individual and group Hypnosis sessions for Weight Loss, Smoking Cessation, Self Hypnosis and HypnoBirthing plus personal and corporate sessions for motivation and improving life skills.

Jeanne Robertson, CH, CD, RMT: Mind Works Hypnotherapy

Austin, TX- Phone: (512) 236-1669 -E-mail: jeanne@mindwrks.com

Web Site: www.mindwrks.com

I specialize in acute and chronic pain management. A Hypno-Birthing Practitioner, Doula, and Reiki Master/Teacher, I can combine Hypnotherapy, Massage and Reiki during one session.

VIRGINIA, USA

Nancie M. Barwick, DCHt, IHF Fellow: Hypnotherapy Works

Fairfax, VA-Phone: (703) 385-9311 -E-mail: dogoodr@aol.com

Nancy practices Clinical Hypnotherapy in a supportive, client centered environment. Her specialties include: HypnoBirthing', Health, Wellness & Disability Issues. Adults & children are welcome!

Henry Leo Bolduc, CHt

Independence, VA -Phone: Web Site: www.henrybolduc.com

For free articles and books in English & Spanish, free of all copyright restriction, see www.henrybolduc.com.

Christa Ilania Rex, CHt
Yorktown, VA-Phone: (757) 865-6891 -E-mail: shitzi@aol.com
Transpersonal, Past Life Regression and Hypnotherapy to heal the Body, Mind & Soul in combination with Crystal Healing and Healing Touch.

WASHINGTON, USA

Roy Hunter, CHt
Federal Way, WA- Phone: (253) 727-8888 -E-mail: roy@royhunter.com
Web Site: www.royhunter.com
Hypnotherapist since 1983; Hypnotherapy Instructor, Spiritual Counselor. Teaches Hypnotherapy at Tacoma Community College. Inducted into the 2000 Hypnosis Hall of Fame & NGH award winner.

Jerrold Larson, MA, CCHt: Empowerment Learning Center
Bainsbridge, WA- Phone: 206-484-1188- Toll Free: 800-363-8997- healinghappens@yahoo.com-www.onenessheals.com
Transpersonal Hypnotherapist, Jere is a highly skilled therapist offering cutting edge techniques to support his client's personal growth. His approach is heart centered and solution focused.

Del H. Morrill: Transitions, A Center for Counseling & Hypnosis
Tacoma, WA – Phone: (253) 383-5757
Author and Hypnotist specializing in helping Children, Athletes like golfers and Stage Performers. Release fear, phobia, bad habits, depression, anxiety, improve memory and pass exams.

V. Lani Steagall, CHt, RM
Bellingham, WA-Phone: (360) 715-3272 -E-mail: 2lani@home.com
Intuitive & innovative, Lani's wholistic approach helps clients get exactly what they need. "Tap the inner wisdom of your mind-body-spirit and Miracles Happen!"

Carolyn Joy White, PhD, DCH, RM
Pt Roberts, WA-Phone: (604) 961-8291 -E-mail: whitelight@dccnet.com
As a Wellness Coach, my gifts of service are gleaned from 25 years of study & practice in Astrology, Hermetic Wisdom, Huna, Hypnotherapy, Reiki and Reflexology.

Canada

Georgina Cannon, DMC(C), CI, CHt, APRT: Ontario Hypnosis Centre (Since 1996)
Toronto, Ont., Canada- Phone (416) 489-0333 -E-mail: info@ont-hypnosis-centre.com
Fax: (416) 484-8546 -Web Site: www.ont-hypnosis-centre.com
Georgina is a teacher and Hypnotherapist who is passionately committed to raising the bar in both the quality of hypnosis training & in clinic work.

Deborah Ann Filler, CH, Certified Stage Hypnotist
Oakville, Ontario, Canada- Phone: (905) 464-2084 -E-mail: dfiller@home.com
Nurse and Hypnotist since 1994. Stress Management and Creativity Specialty. Stage and entertainment Hypnosis.

Robert Gatis, BSc, ND: Mind Miracles
Toronto Area, Toronto, Canada- Phone: (905) 895-2863- E-mail: mindmiracles@lycos.com Web Site: www.mindmiracles.com
Certified Medical Hypnotherapist and naturopathic physician, Robert Gatis is especially interested in ameliorating chronic disease and insuring wellness. He uses metaphysical and practical approaches.

Anthony Maurantonio, MH, CT, CHt
Toronto, Ontario, Canada- Phone: (416) 488-7364
Specializes in Hypnotherapy.

Cary Silber, BSc, Fsc, CHt
York Region, Ontario, Canada- Phone: (905) 764-5939- E-mail: rcsilber@rogers.com
Specializing in Smoking Cessation, Weight Loss, Sports Enhancement.

Jacques Tombazian, IHF Fellow: L'Alchimiste Institute of Metaphysics/Canadian Center For Esoteric Research & Teaching – Montreal, Quebec, Canada
Phone (514) 909-8822-E-mail: jtombazian@hotmail.com: Web Site: www.alchimiste.org
A healer and teacher of metaphysical healing, healing sexual issues, inner alchemy and how to develop your clairvoyance seminars in Canada, New York, Phoenix and Sedona.

Chili

Gwendoline Josey Smith, CCHt
Vina del Mar, Chili-Phone: 56.32.834192- E-mail: gwen.josey@terra.cl
Specializes in: Past Life Regression, Age Regression Therapy, Stress Management, Sports Improvement, Traumas & Phobias, Self Esteem, Sexual Dysfunction, Smoke Cessation and Weight Management.

England

Raja Feroz Ali Khan, CHt
Essex, England-Phone: 01279-862989
Raja offers Hypnosis and compassion. He works with people of all ages.

Jean Murton, CHt, RM: Belmont Centre for Hypnotherapy
Kent, England-Phone: 44+1843-587929 -E-mail: jeanmurton@btconnect.com
Trainer for the British Association of Therapeutical Hypnotists, Jean's gift in healing and clairvoyance will transform and set you free with Self Love and Joy.

Amornpong Vachiramon, DDS, MSc, MFDSRCPS, IHF Fellow: Tharin-Chaweewans' Clinic
London, England-Phone: +44 7932 676130-E-mail: avachiramon@softhome.net
Dental Surgeon and Clinical Hypnotherapist, Dr. Vachiramon uses Hypnosis for orthodontic pain control. An IHF Fellow, he is researching medical hypnosis vs. analgesics.

Japan

Beth Phillips-Pogan, CHt

Tokyo, Japan-Phone: 011-813-5469-9360 -E-mail: bpogan@gol.com

Tokyo's leading Hypnotist, Beth specializes in Test-Taking, improving your golf game, Past Life Regression, Weight-Loss, Smoking-Cessation and improving performance in all aspects of life.

New Zealand

Tricia Meister, CHt: Hypnotherapy Training College of NZ (1995)

Hamilton, New Zealand -Phone: 64-7-8393193 -E-mail: hypnosis@hnpl.net

Conducts global workshops in Hypnosis, Neuro-Linguistic Programming and Louis Hay's "Love Yourself, Heal Your Life" workshops. Learn to use Hypnosis for yourself or as a career.

Singapore

Kokkwang Lim, PhD, CHt, IHF Fellow

Singapore – Phone: 65-258-7387 – E-mail: kokk2qntlim@yahoo.com

Resolve Stress Related Illness, Chronic Pain, sleep Disorders, Substance Abuse, Depression, PTSD, Public Speaking and Performance Anxiety with: Hypnotherapy, Mind-Body Medicine, Energy Psychology and HeartMath.

Turkey

Mehmet Ayvaci, HTP, DDS, IHF Fellow: Ege Universitesi

Antalya, Turkey- Phone: 90-532-5717234 -E-mail: mayvaci@hotmail.com

Web Site: www.medyatex.com.tr\hipnoz

Turkey's foremost Hypnotist since 1982, Dr. Mehmet specializes in Dental Hypnosis, Wellness, Obesity, Smoking Cessation, Fears and Chronic Pain Management. Writer and TV celebrity.

Stage Hypnosis Performers

▲ Entertainment & Speaking Specialists

Nancie M. Barwick, DCHt, IHF Fellow- Hypnotherapy Works
Fairfax, VA- Phone: (703) 385-9311- E-mail: dogoodr@aol.com
Nancy practices Clinical Hypnotherapy in a supportive, client centered environment. Her specialties include: HypnoBirthing', Health, Wellness & Disability Issues. Adults & children are welcome!

Michael H. Blaine, Master Stage Hypnotist
New York, NY- Phone: (518) 643-9589 -E-mail: hpntst@aol.com
Web Site: www.michaelblaine.com
Friends and family will be delighted and amazed as Master Stage Hypnotist Michael Blaine gives their imagination license to shine!

Bradley Campos, Stage Hypnotist, CCHt
Los Angeles/Alhambra, CA-Phone: (909) 437-8141 -E-mail: hypnos4u@aol.com
Clinical Hypnotherapist, specializes in Stress Management & Relief. Stage and Demonstration Hypnotist.

Elizabeth Cech, MA, CCHt: Center for Integrated Therapy
Sonoma County/Greater San Francisco Bay Area- Phone (707) 829-5299
E-Mail: Ahiashia@aol.com
Professional Movement and Sound Healer & Singer. Teaches pioneering techniques to use your body and voice's vibratory frequencies to transform physically, emotionally & spiritually.
Workshops/Trainings/Performances.

Frank Genko, CHt
Westminster, CA- Phone: (714) 775-7715- E-mail: mindtrack@aol
Hypnotherapist, Author & Stage Hypnotist for over 50 years.

Dave Hill, Master Hypnotist and Illusionist
Hayward, CA- Phone: (510) 785-8151 -E-mail: hypnosell@aol.com
Web Site: www.worldsgreatesthypnotist.com
Hypnotic Selling and Stage Hypnosis Specialist. Offers seminars in: Persuasion, Motivation, Wealth Building and Fire Eating. Dave is a Master Stage Hypnotist.

John A. Himinkool, MA, DC, CHt
San Diego, CA- Phone: (858) 715-9400
Email: info@alignspine.com-Web Site: www.alignspine.com
John is a speaker, motivator and ambassador for LeTip International. He has helped many business people become better networkers. Build your practice through professional networking.

Cathy Selene Kay, Master Stage Hypnotist, CSC
Los Angeles, CA -E-mail: cathyk@showbizhypnotist.com
Phone: (323) 469-6702 -Web Site: www.showbizhypnotist.com
Cathy Kay, The Showbiz Hypnotist, comedienne, professional actor, model & singer, is a captivating & dazzling performer. She adds pizzazz for hilarious, unforgettable entertainment!

Maurice Kouguell, PhD, FBHA, BCTS: Brookside Center
Baldwin, NY- Phone: (516) 868-2233-E-mail: hypnoprof@aol.com
Web Site: www.brooksidecenter.com
Dr. Kouguell holds a PhD in Counseling Psychology. Benefit from his unique background in Psychology, Education, Family Life, Hypnotherapy, Emotional Freedom Technique & Neurolinguistic Programming.

Richard Lederer, PhD
San Diego, CA – Phone: (858) 549-6788-E-Mail: Richard.lederer@pobox.com
Speaker & personality, Dr. Lederer is the syndicated author of more than 2000 articles and books about language and humor.

Cedric L. McSween, Sr, CHt: Premier Hypnosis Center, LLC
Farmington Hills, MI-Phone: (248) 538-7699-E-mail: info@intuitivewisdom.com
Fax: (248) 538-8047-Web Site: www.premierhypnosis.net
Certified Hypnotherapist & Motivational Speaker empowered to help and uplift you own your life: "To give you hope is not just a goal, but a passion."

MESMERICK, Master Stage Hypnotist, Richard McNamara, CHt,
NY, NJ, CT- Phone: (973) 962-6637 -E-mail: mesmerick2hypnosis.org
Web Site: www.mesmerick.com
Lively Stage Hypnosis and Demonstrations of the Paranormal for corporate, trade show, college campus and other events. All shows expertly tailored to your specific needs.

Kathy L. Moore, MBA, CH: Moore Inspirations
San Antonio & surrounding, TX, Phone: (210) 967-4350, E-mail: Mooreinspire@email.msn.com, Web Site: www.mooreinspire.com
Kathy is co-producer of a holistic health cable TV show called Wellness Connection aimed at promoting healthy alternatives in the San Antonio area.

Roger Otis, CSH
Long Beach, CA-Phone: (562) 624-7164
Roger is a Stage Hypnotist, Comedian, Actor and a delightful storyteller. His wit charms.

Kenneth John Owens, CSH, CHt: Intuitive Wisdom

Farmington, MI/Nationwide- Phone: (248) 553-2358 -E-mail: info@intuitivewisdom.com

Web Site: www.intuitivewisdom.com

Book Ken's FUN Hypnosis show for your next event. Participants will have a hilarious time while gaining a better understanding of their own personal power.

Carol Rosenblum, CSH, CHt

West Los Angeles, CA-Phone: (310) 280-3583 -E-mail: basheva@msn.com

Carol Rosenblum, the host writer and coordinator of cable show, Minds and Mirrors, is also an entertaining Public Speaker and Stage Hypnotist.

Sharon Thornton, CSH, CHt

St Louis, MO-Phone: (636) 940-0562 -E-mail: hypnomama@hotmail.com

Explore the mysterious powers of the mind. Sharon's unforgettable, high energy Hypnosis shows entertain! Her corporate motivational experience inspires excellence. Hypnotherapist, Trainer, & Personal Coach.

Jason Vogel, MA, CHt, CSH

Beverly Hills, CA-Phone: (310) 770—8081-E-mail:jagovo@aol.com

Renown author, business consultant, life coach and Hypnotherapist, Jason helps people overcome procrastination and develop positive habits for success. He's a captivating speaker and stage hypnotist.

Andy Wilson, Stage Hypnotist, Entertainer

Los Angeles, So Bay, CA- Phone: (310) 375-1960-E-mail: agwilson@aol.com

Having a party? Andy Wilson's Stage Hypnosis Show will amaze and dazzle your friends with outrageous laughter! Large or small groups, corporate or private parties.

Sally Witt, PhD, CHt, CSC, IHF Fellow: The Holistic Success Center, Inc (Since 1997)

Morrisville, PA- Phone: (215) 736-8624 -E-mail: sally@holisticsuccesscenter.com

Web site: www.holesticsuccesscenter.com

Your mind is the key. Make powerful changes in your personal & professional life using Hypnotherapy, Neurolinguistic Programming, Reiki, Spiritual Counseling. Professional Trainer. Corporate programs.

▲ Instructors, Trainers & Institutes

Creativity Learning Institute (Since 1978), Dean: Shelley Stockwell, PhD, CHt
30819 Casilina, Rancho Palos Verdes, CA 90275, USA
Phone: (310) 541-4844 -Email: sstockwell@earthlink.net
Fax: (310) 377-7946 -Web Site: www.hypnosisfederation.com
California approved CE credits for Family Counselors and Therapists, RN's, Hypnotists, Hypnotherapists, Stage Hypnotists, Past Life Therapists and Spiritual Counselors. Training and certification courses are offered in California and power spots worldwide. Most classes are taught by Shelley Stockwell with impressive visiting professors like Ormond McGill. Recognized as an excellent training program by numerous hypnosis organizations and boards.

ARIZONA, USA

Sumaris Centre, Margaret Rogers, CHt, OM & Stephen M. Van Coops
Lake Havasu City, AZ-Phone: (520) 453-7974-(TF) (888) 858-8668
E-mail: sumaris@ twocommasj.com-Web Site: www.twocommas.com
Breakthrough Crystal, Acupuncture & Teragram Therapy Healing with Hypnosis, Aromatherapy & Reflexology. Psychic readings and development. Crisis counseling. Metaphysical education Courses and workshops. Ministerial services.

CALIFORNIA, USA

Academy for Professional Hypnosis Training
Director/Instructor: Mary Elizabeth Raines, CH, CI, CSH
Hollywood, CA- Phone: (323) 462-8346 -E-mail: info@laughingcherub.com
Web Site: www.laughingcherub.com
Hypnosis Certification Courses: Thorough, Stimulating, Life-Changing! "Have the time of your life learning skills for a lifetime." Individual sessions, CDs and Books.

Accelerated Change Technologies Institute (Since 1993),
Director: Michael McAuliffe, CHt, IHF Fellow-Instructor: Melissa Bergstrom McAuliffe, RN, DCHt
Los Angeles, CA-Phone: (248) 553-2358 -E-mail: train@nlptraining.org
Toll Free: (888) 772-2866 -Web Site: www.nlptraining.org
Introductory and certification programs in Neuro-Linguistic Programming, Hypnosis, Time Line Therapy' and Huna. Take charge. Maximize material, emotional, mental and spiritual wealth.

Avalon Institute of Healing Arts: Owner/Director: Debra K. Fentress, CHt, PhDc
Los Angeles County, CA, Phone: (818) 472-3914, E-mail: debrafentress@msn.com Web Site: www.avaloninstituteofhealingarts@msn.com
Enjoy a higher level of wholeness. Experience or learn Hypnosis, NLP, Reiki, Huna, WICCA, Tarot & Wellness. Lectures and classes available.

American Institute of Hypnotherapy (Since 1982)
Program Director: Richard Neves, PhD, IHF Advisory Board Member
Orange County, CA-E-mail: Aih@ix.netcom.com
Toll Free: (800) 872-9996 -Web site: www.hypnosis.com
California State approved degree-granting educational institution, AIH offers independent study postgraduate programs in Hypnotherapy and Psychology.

Bilman's Center For Creative Living: Patricia Bilman, PhD, CHt
Los Angeles, CA-Phone: (310) 391-6649-E-mail: pbilman@att.net
Classes, workshops, lectures and private sessions offered for Angelic Healing, Psychic Development and Intuition. Patricia is an Angel Therapy Practitioner, Transpersonal Hypnotherapist and Minister.

Center for Hypnotherapy Certification (Since 1995), Director: Marilyn Gordon, CHt
Oakland, CA -Phone: (510) 839-4800 -Email: mgordon@hypnotherapycenter.com
Toll Free: (800) 398-0034 -Web Site: www.hypnotheraphycenter.com
School Your Soul! Hypnotherapy, Energy Therapies, Transformation, Healing Certification with Weekend intensives. Extraordinary, hands-on training. Author, Hypnotherapist Gordon has 30+ years experience. Books, tapes, manuals.

Center for Integrated Therapy, Talia Shafir, MA, CCHt & Elizabeth Cech, MA, CCHt
SF Bay Area, CA & Worldwide- Phone (707) 829-5299- E Mail Ahiashia@aol.com
Professional Movement and Sound Healer & Singer.
Soul Journey Workshops: Explore multidimensional language, body & emotions. Powerful presentations put you in the flow of your potential. Grow personally. Professionals, expand your practice.

Creativity Learning Institute (Since 1978), Dean: Shelley Stockwell, PhD, IHF Fellow
Rancho Palos Verdes, CA -Phone: (310) 377-7908 -Email: sstockwell@earthlink.net
Fax: (310) 377-7946 -Web Site: www.hypnosisfederation.com
Professional Certification Courses for: Hypnotists, Hypnotherapists, Stage Hypnotists, Past Life Therapists and Spiritual Counselors. Classes taught by author Shelley Stockwell with impressive visiting professors. Corporate Courses and CE credits.

Institute of Multidimensional Cellular Healing (Since 1992)-Director: Ken Page
Northern, CA - Phone: (209) 754-3040 – E-mail: ken@kenpage.com - Web Site: www.kenpage.com
This International school offers a 5-day, 40 hr training to practice Heart & Soul Healing.

International University of Professional Studies, Chancellor: Irv Katz, PhD, IHF Fellow
Toll Free: 800-806-0317 -E-mail: iups@healthy.net- Web Site: www.iups.edu
A worldwide University with no walls specializing in: Transpersonal Psychology, Health Sciences, Hypnosis, Art Therapy, Organizational Development & Transformation Consciousness Studies, traditional Psychology, Health and Education.

Integrated Assoc. for Regression, Research & Therapies (IARRT), Pres: Janet Cunningham
Riverside, CA- Phone: (909)-784-1570 -E-mail: patlife@empirenet.com
Web Site: www.iarrt.org
Referral service, conferences and trainings in the field of past life regression.

Marotta/Wikkeling Hypnotherapy, Albert J. Marotta, CHt, IHF Fellow
Alhambra, CA-Phone: (323) 222-3874-E-mail: remotehlr@aol.com
Traditional Hypnotherapy, Complimentary Medical Hypnosis, Grief Resolution, Depression, Trauma, Phobia. Akashic Records, Past/Pre Life Prenatal, Entity/Curse Releasement, ET Abductees, Remote Therapy, Reiki Healing.

Mind-Body-Spirit HypnoClinic & Hypnosis Training Inst, Dir: David Armentrout, PhD
San Jose, CA -Phone: (408) 871-0999 -E-mail: darmentrout@changework.com
The MBS HypnoClinic and Hypnosis Training Center offers basic Hypnotherapy certification and advanced training to certified Hypnotherapists in the areas of Regression and Past-Life Therapy.

Peninsula Montessori School (Since 1978), Founder/Administrator: Claudia Krikorian
Peninsula/South Bay/Los Angeles, CA-Phone: (310) 544-3099
Founder of the Palos Verdes Peninsula Montessori School, Claudia is the winner of the 2001 International Hypnosis Federation Humanitarian Award.

Valley Hypnosis Center/Cernie Institute, Sally Cernie, PhD
Riverside, CA- Phone: (909) 781-0282- E-mail: szcernie@msn.com
Web Site: www.valleyhypnosis-cernie inst.com
Professional, California state approved training-school of Hypnosis, Iridology, Honeopathy, Reiki. A Holistic Center for Alternative Health offering Massage, Nutrition and all of the above.

Wanless Tarot Institute (Since 1995), Founder/Director: James Wanless, PhD
Monterey County, CA-Toll Free: (800) 676-1256 -E-mail: info@voyagertarot.com
Fax: (831) 644-9097 -Web Site: www.voyagertarot.com
The Wanless Institute in Carmel, CA offers Training and Certification programs in the progressive use of tarot and symbology for personal, business or organization transformation.

FLORIDA, USA
Agape Center (Since 1990), Director: Vivian V. Smith, CHt., CSC, RM, IHF Fellow
Bonita Springs, FL-Phone: (239) 947-4802 -E-mail: hypnoviv@earthlink.net
The Agape Center is a holistic ministry of education and healing. Dedicated to revealing divine, hidden gifts and talents to aide those on a spiritual path.

HAWAII, USA

School of Counseling (Since 1964), Dean: Alex Lessin, PhD, IHF Fellow

Instructors: Alex (Sasha) Lessin, PhD, IHF Fellow & Janet Lessin

Wailuku, HI-Phone: (808) 244-4103 -E-mail: alessin@aloha.net

Fax: (808) 242-7021 -Web Site: www.schooloftantra.com

Personal Training: Voice Dialogue, Abreactive Catharsis, Yoga, Holotropic Breathing, Gestalt and Hypnosis. Feel secure, empowered and loved. Certification Courses for Tantra assistants and instructors.

KENTUCKY, USA

Centre for Multidisciplinary Healthcare (1999), Dir: Bill Breuer, DC, MCH, IHF Fellow

Louisville, KY-Phone: (502) 459-7431 -E-mail: multicaentre@juno.com

Fax: (502) 459-9217 -Web Site: angelfire.com/ky2/multicare

One of the oldest complementary care integrative medical centers with a staff of over 24 practitioners. Offers mainstream and compatible care.

LOUISIANA, USA

Infinity Hypnosis Institute (Since 1996), Owner/Dir/Instructor: Conrad Adams, CHt

Baton Rouge, LA-Phone: (225) 924-0604 -E-mail: finfinity@cox.net

Courses and certification offered in Basic, Advanced, Analytical Hypnotherapy, Hypno-Anesthesia, Reiki and Healing Touch. Metaphysical courses available too.

MICHIGAN, USA

Infinite International Institute of Hypnotherapy (1981), Fndr/Dir/Anne H. Spencer, PhD, CHt

Royal Oaks, MI- Phone: (248) 549-5594 -Email: aspencer@infinityinst.com

Web Site: www.infinityinst.com

Trains Hypnotists and Hypnotherapists who are then certified by the International Medical & Dental Hypnotherapy Association Licensed by Michigan Board of Education. Affiliate schools worldwide.

Inner Dimensions Center (Since 2000), Founder/Director: Larry M. Farrugia, PhD, CCHt

Wayne County, MI- Phone: (734) 699-4112 -E-mail: innerdimensions@earthlink.net

Web Site: www.innerdimensions.net

Help people improve their quality of life by utilizing their sub-conscious mind to reach their full potential and gain personal empowerment.

NEW YORK, USA

Brookside Center (Since 1982), Dir: Maurice Kouguell, PhD, FBHA, BCTS, IHF Fellow

Baldwin, NY - Phone: (516) 868-2233 -E-mail: hypnoprof@aol.com

Web Site: www.brooksidecenter.com

A complete and unique mentorship/certification program based on the fact that hypnosis is not a profession but a tool in the hands of the trained hypnotherapist.

Center for Holistic Arts (Since 1970), Dir: Lawrence Galante, PhD, RSHom, CHt, RPP, IHF Fellow
New York, NY -Phone: (212) 414-1266 -E-mail: lg@holistic-arts.com
Web Site: www.holistic-arts.com
The Center for Holistic Arts teaches classes in Hypnosis, Tai Chi, Chi Kung, Homeopathy and Polarity Therapy. Both on premises and home study courses are available.

Holistic Healing Center (Since 1994), Director: Paul Aurand, CCHt
Lindsey Sass-Aurand, LMT, CHt
Spring Valley, NY - Phone: (845) 425-5233 - E-mail: paul@holistichealingcenter.com
Web Site: www.holistichealingcenter.com
The Holistic Healing Center is a safe and nurturing place for healing, personal growth and professional training, giving the kind of individual care and deserved intention.

PENNSYLVANIA, USA
C.H.A.N.G.E. Academy, Beverley S. Bley, LPN, CMHt
Allentown, PA- Phone: (610) 797-8250 -E-mail: change@v35.com
Web Site: www.4change.com
Beverley's Self-Hypnosis Training eliminates Smoking, Weight, Stress, Pain Addiction & Phobias. Promote & improve: Relationships, Memory & Study Habits. Group & Private sessions available.

Holistic Success Center Inc (1997), Pres/Inst: Sally Witt, PhD, CHt, CSC, IHF Fellow
Morrisville, PA - Phone: (215) 736-8624 -E-mail: sally@holisticsuccesscenter.com
Web Site: www.holisticsuccesscenter.com
Flexible schedules with meaningful classes held in PA, NJ, FL or at your location. Hypnotherapy, Spiritual Counselor, Energy Work & more. Coaching available.

Master's Center Inst. of Hypnotherapy (1972), Dir/Chief of Staff: Philip Holder, PhD, CHt
Philadelphia, PA -Phone: (215) 295-8062 -E-mail: masters@masters-center.com
Fax: (215) 295-8063 -Web Site: www.hypnosiscenter.org
Offers courses with a uniquely designed scientific Hypnotherapy approach. Graduates receive the best possible preparation to enter the professional Health/Wellness market.

Virnor Institute of Hypnosis (1960), Director: Norbert W. Bakas, PhD
Pittsburgh, PA -Phone: (412) 931-5602 -E-mail: nwb@nauticom.net
The Virnor Institute of Hypnosis, chartered in 1960, teaches certified courses in Self-Hypnosis, Hypnotism, Hypnotherapy & Stage Hypnosis.

TEXAS, USA
Anne King's Hypnosis Center, Anne King, CHt
Boerne, TX- Phone: (830) 537-5411 -E-mail: akhypno@gvtc.com
Web Site: www.hypnoclasses.com
General practice including: Smoking, Weight Loss, Stress, Sports, Memory & Concentration. Instructs: Basic, Intermediate & Advanced Hypnotherapy with CEU credit. Books & tapes available.

Moore Inspirations: Director: Kathy L. Moore, MBA, CH
San Antonio & surrounding, TX, Phone: (210) 967-4350, E-mail: Mooreinspire@email.msn.com, Web Site: www.mooreinspire.com
Classes in Self Hypnosis, Light & Sound Therapy with Hypnosis and group Weight Loss through Community Education. Kathy teaches classes for hypnotists as well.

PATH Foundation (1988), Ed Martin, PhD, CHt & Cheryl Martin, LMSW, CHt
Texas & Alabama-Phone: (281) 359-PATH- E-mail: email@path-found.com
Fax: (281) 359-5700 -Web Site: www.pathfoundation.com
Training professionals to use Cell Command Therapy Hypnosis & Hypnotherapy to help improve the length and quality of life.

Diane Pope, MSN, RN, CHt: Diane Pope's Hypnosis Center
Houston, TX – Phone: (281) 787-1946 – E-Mail: Hypno225di@aol.com
Individual and group Hypnosis sessions for Weight Loss, Smoking Cessation, Self Hypnosis and HypnoBirthing plus personal and corporate sessions for motivation and improving life skills.

WISCONSIN, USA
Hypnosis, Wellness & Training Cent. (1990), Dean: Charlene Ackerman, CHt, ACI, IHF Board
Janesville, WI -Phone: (608) 757-0716-Email: hypnonews@aol.com
Trains & Certifies Hypnotherapists nationally & internationally. NGH Instructor of the Year, author, crystal skull researcher & caretaker of the blue crystal skull "Cara."

Canada

Excel Center – College of Hypnotherapy Training, Exec. Dir: Alan Eastman, MA, DCH,
Alberta, Canada- Toll Free (888) 686-6163- Email: dreastman@home.com-
Web Site: www.hypnosiscanada.com
Trains those seeking a career in Hypnosis and Counseling. Courses approved through the Professional Board of Hypnotherapy. Conference style & distance learning options available.

L'Alchimiste Institute of Metaphysics/Canadian Center For Esoteric Research & Teaching, Director: Jacques Tombazian, IHF Fellow-Montreal, Quebec, Canada - Phone (514) 909-8822-
E-mail: jtombazian@hotmail.com: Web Site: www.alchimiste.org
Tombazian develops your healing and consciousness techniques including: Esoteric Healing, Inner Alchemy, healing sexual issues, developing clairvoyance.

Ontario Hypnosis Centre (1996), Director: Georgina Cannon, DMC(C), CI, CHt, APRT
Toronto, Ontario, Canada -Phone: (416) 489-0333 - Fax: (416) 484-8546
E-mail: info@ont-hypnosis-centre.com- Web Site: www.ont-hypnosis-centre.com
Both clinic & school a warm & welcoming place to learn & grow. Ongoing workshops with leading accredited instructors committed to pragmatic, profound, ethical training.

England

Belmont Centre for Hypnotherapy (1981), Founder/Director/Instrutor: Jean Murton, CHt, RM
Kent, England -Phone: 44+1843-587929 -E-mail: jeanmurton@btconnect.com
Professional Hypnotherapy courses. Hypnotherapy & Metaphysical Counseling through Hypnosis, Color, Sound, Healing, & Mediumship (Channeling). Available for One-to-one sessions or via telephone.

New Zealand

Hypnotherapy Training College of NZ (1995), Dir: Tricia Meister, CHt, Stage Hypnotist
Hamilton, New Zealand -Phone: 64-7-839-3193 -E-mail: hypnosis@hnpl.net
Conducts global workshops in Hypnosis, Neuro-Linguistic Programming and Louis Hay's "Love Yourself, Heal Your Life" workshops. Learn to use Hypnosis for yourself or as a career.

▲Help Referral, Organizations and Hot Lines

Refer to your local phone book for "Help Lines" and "Hot Lines".
International Hypnosis Federation, IHF®, Shelley Stockwell, PhD, CHt, IHF Founder
Los Angeles and Orange Counties, CA- Phone: (310) 541-4844
E-mail: sstockwell@earthlink.net-Web Site: www.hypnosisfederation.com
Refers, promotes and acknowledges Body, Mind and Spirit Practitioners worldwide. Professional leaders in Therapeutic and Entertainment Hypnosis, Health, Brain Research, Bodywork, Life Coaching, Spiritual Counseling, Motivation, and Psychic Development. Offers a Motivational Speakers Bureau, Certification Trainings, Membership Directory, books and tapes. Annual southern California Conference held in July.

Integrated Assoc. for Regression, Research & Therapies (IARRT)-Pres: Janet Cunningham
Riverside, CA- Phone: (909) 784-1570- E-mail: pastlife@empirenet.net
Web Site: www.iarrt.org
Since 1980, a Past Life Researchers and Therapists referral organization with members from 28 countries. Publication: Journey of Regression Therapy. Conferences and Certification Trainings available.

International Assoc. of Counselors & Therapists (IACT) Pres: Jillian LaVelle
Bonita Springs, FL- Phone: (941) 498-9710- E-mail: iactnow@aol.com
Web Site: www.iact.org
A fine referral service with an annual conference in May.

International Hypnosis Hall of Fame, Co-Founder: Penny Dutton Raffa
Valley Forge, PA-Phone: (610) 279-7499 -Fax: (610) 272-3961
E-mail: ihhfg@hypnosishalloffame.org-Web Site: www.hypnosishalloffame.org
The International Hypnosis Hall of Fame recognizes and honors contributions in the field of Hypnosis with an annual convention in Valley Forge, Pennsylvania.

International Medical and Dental Hypnotherapy Assoc (IMDHA) Anne H. Spencer
Royal Oaks, MI- Phone: (248) 549-5594- Email: aspencer@infinityinst.com
Web Site: www.infinityinst.com
Refers excellently trained certified Hypnotherapists for healing body, mind and spirit, to work in harmony with health care professionals. Aids individuals with medical challenges and procedures.

Professional Board of Hypnotherapy- Dir: Alan R. Eastman
Alberta, Canada- Toll Free (888) 686-6163- Email: dreastman@home.com
Web Site: www.hypnosiscanada.com
Offers Mental Health Counseling and Clinical Hypnotherapy services.

▲ Support Organizations

Support groups organizations sometimes refer to local support groups, but beware, some support groups may be drugs oriented and supported by drug companies. It may be worth calling for support groups, but be careful about jumping into any pill brigade.

American Council for Drug Education
New York City, NY, http://www.acde.org/ 1-800-488-DRUG (488-3784)

Center for Substance Abuse Treatment, Referral Hotline
1-800-662-HELP, for Spanish speaking callers 1-800-66-AYUDA

Children of Alcoholics Foundation
http://www.coaf.org/ 1-646-505-2065

Eating Disorders Awareness and Prevention
http://www.nationaleatingdisorders.org/ (800) 931-2237 (hours 8-noon daily PT)

Facts On Tap
http://www.factsontap.org/ 1-800-488-DRUGS

International Institute for Inhalant Abuse
Englewood, Colorado, 303-788-4617

National Association for Children of Alcoholics
11426 Rockville Pike, Suite 100, Rockville, MD 20852; phone: 1-888-554-2627

National Child Abuse Hotline
http://www.childhelpusa.org/child/hotline.htm (800)4-A-CHILD (800-422-4453)

National Clearinghouse for Alcohol and Drug Information
P.O. Box 2345, Rockville, MD 20847-2345; phone: 1-800-729-6686 or 301-468-2600.

National Council on Alcoholism & Drug Dependence (NCADD) New York, New York,
1-800-622-2255
Southern California, Betty Battenburg, executive director 310 328-1460

National Domestic Violence Hotline
http://www.ndvh.org (800) 799-SAFE (800-799-7233)

National Institute on Alcohol Abuse and Alcoholism
http://www.niaaa.nih.org/

National Sexual Assault Hotline
http://www.rainn.org/ (800)656-HOPE (800-656-4673)

Phoenix House Treatment Centers
http://www.phoenixhouse.org/ 1-800-DRUG-HELP (375-4435)

Yellow Ribbon Suicide Prevention Program
http://www.yellowribbon.org/ (800)SUICIDE (800-784-2433)

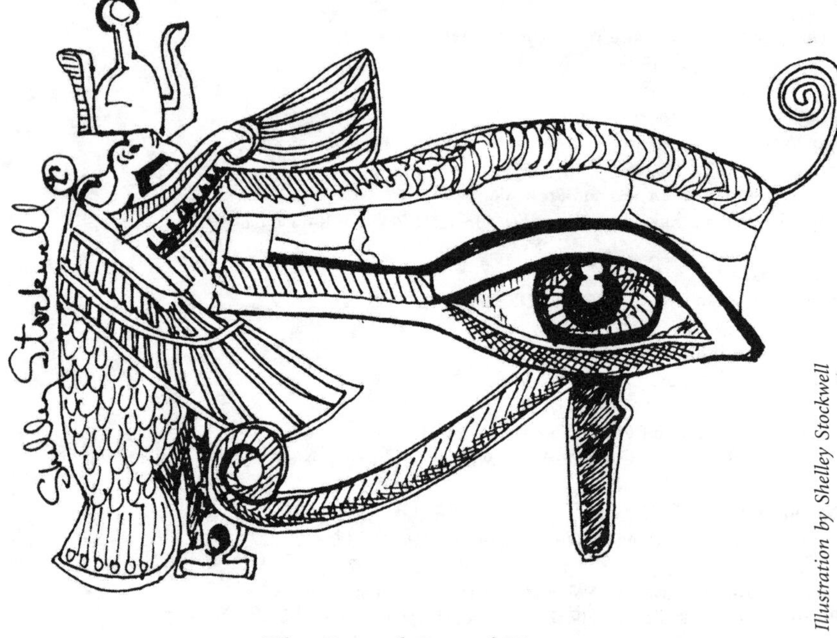

Illustration by Shelley Stockwell

The Sacred Eye of Horus

▲ Twelve-Step Programs

Call or write for local referrals. These free programs are extremely helpful.

Alcoholics Anonymous
World Services, 475 Riverside Dr., P.O. Box 459, Grand Central Station, New York, NY 10163; (212) 870-3400

Alanon/Alateen
Family Group, P.O. Box 862, Midtown Station, New York, NY 10018-0862; phone: 212-302-7240 or world service office 1-800-344-2666 (US) 800-956-9996 or 1-800-443-4525 (Canada) www.alanon.alateen.org

ARTS Anonymous (Artists Recovering through Twelve Steps)
PO. Box 175-Ansonia Station, New York, NY 10023; 212/873-7075.

Cocaine Anonymous
World Services Office, 3740 Overland Ave., Suite H, Los Angeles, CA 90034; 310-559-5833. Meeting information, (800) 347-8998

Co-Dependents Anonymous
P.O. Box 33577, Phoenix, AZ 85067; 602/277-7991 or 212/691-5199.

Debtors Anonymous
PO Box 400, Grand Central Station, NY, NY 10163-0400

Emotions Anonymous
P.O. Box 4245, St. Paul, Minnesota 55204; 612/647-9712.

Gamblers Anonymous
P.O. Box 17173 Los Angeles, CA 90017

Narcotics Anonymous

Nicotine Anonymous
P.O. Box 591777, San Francisco, CA 94159; 415/750-0328.

Overeaters Anonymous
383 Van Ness Ave., Suite 1601, Torrance, CA 90501; 310/618-8835.

Sex Addicts Anonymous
P.O. Box 7049, Houston, TX 77270; 713/869-4902.

Workaholics Anonymous
P.O. Box 66150, Los Angeles, CA 90066; 310/859-5804.

YES!

YES!

YES!

YES!

YES!

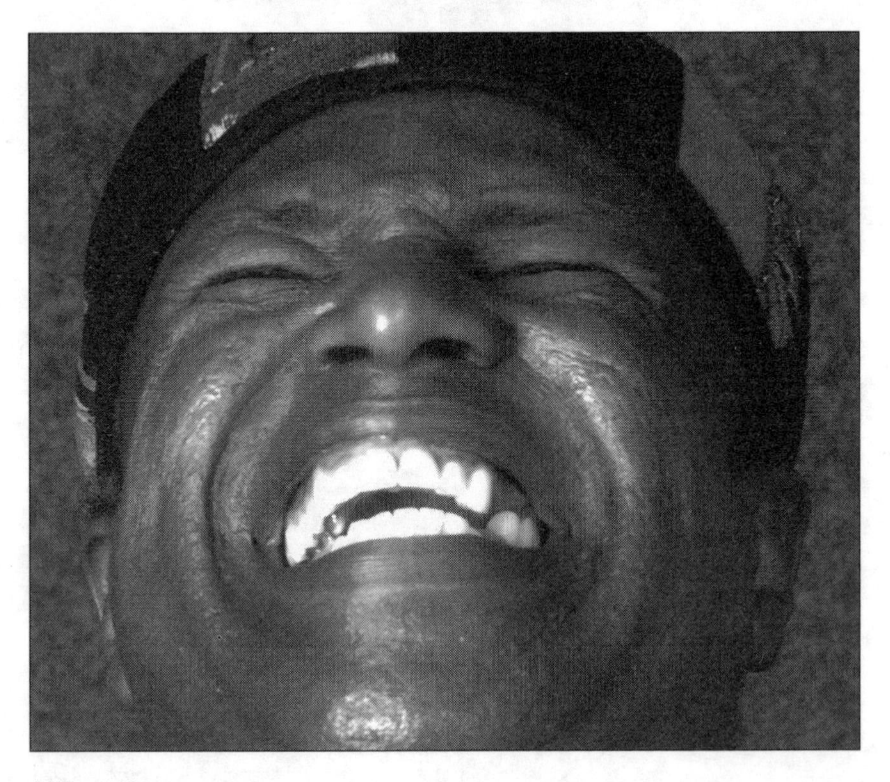

Index of Affirmations

is proud to offer the following items for you and your loved ones…

BOOK

HYPNOSIS

How To Put A Smile On Your Face, And $ In Your Pocket

by Shelley Stockwell, Ph.D.

After 22 years as a Hypnotherapist, Stockwell shares what hypnosis is and how to use it as a powerful tool for yourself, your family, friends, or as a career. Teaches you to tap the power of your mind to make your dreams a reality!

WINNER OF THE 1999 PEN & QUILL AWARD

Learn:

- ★ The 10 Secrets of the Mind
- ★ How to be a Money Magnet
- ★ 42 Personal Affirmations That Bring Happiness
- ★ The 30 Second Stockwell Zap
- ★ Hypnosis Scripts

"I read your book and took your class. Your strategies really work!"

—Raleigh Pinkskey, "A Hundred and One Ways to Promote Yourself"

"I read your book on hypnosis from cover to cover tonight. Only one word can describe it: Superb."

—Ormond McGill, The Dean of American Hypnosis

"The hypnosis expert."

—*National Enquirer*

$19.95
Book – 425 pages
ISBN #0-912559-17-9

Order forms on last pages

STOCKWELL'S HYPNOSIS FOR WEIGHT CONTROL

10 Easy Steps To A New You!

by Shelley Stockwell, Ph.D.

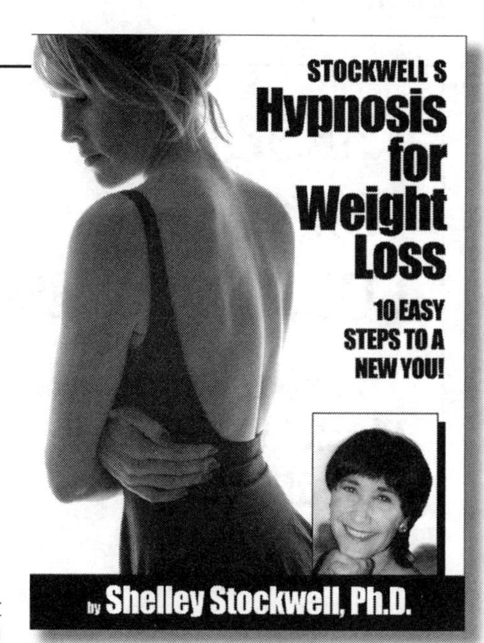

Permanently embrace great eating habits and loose unwanted pounds. Hypnosis works!

A Fabulous Step-By-Step Program

★ No Strict Diets & No Deprivation

★ Overcome the Victim Trap

★ Become Your Perfect Shape

★ Release Weight and Feel Great!

"I love the results and you will too!"

—Raleigh Pinkskey, "A Hundred and One Ways to Promote Yourself"

"I lost 6 pounds just reading and editing this book… talk about easy!"

—Nica Lee, CEO, Orderly Systems

Weight Release Boxed Set $95

- **Book** ISBN #0912559-59-4
- **Video** ISBN #0912559-65-9
- **4 Audio Cassettes:**
  - *Lose Weight* ISBN #0912559-02-0
  - *No More Sugar Junkie* ISBN #0912559-03-9
  - *I Love Exercise* ISBN #0912559-40-3
  - *Peace & Calm* ISBN #0912559-09-8

($135 with Weight Loss Instructor's Manual) ISBN #0912559-65-9

$24.95
Book – 184 pages
ISBN #0912559-59-4

Order forms on last pages

BOOK

THE SEARCH FOR COSMIC CONSCIOUSNESS

The Hypnosis Book Einstein Would Have Loved!

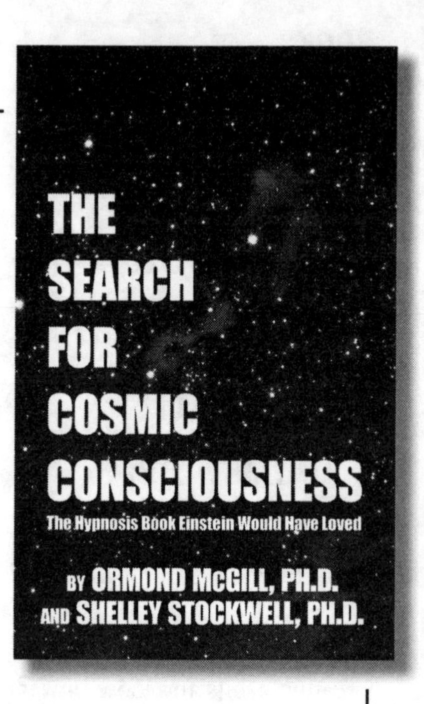

by Hypnotherapists:
Ormond McGill, Ph.D. and
Shelley Stockwell, Ph.D.

Your Personal Handbook for Enlightenment

- ★ Transformational Exercises
- ★ Become a Master of Your Mind or a Master Mind
- ★ Learn the Secrets of Gurus and Holy Ones
- ★ Includes the 10 Steps To Cosmic Conscience

"A wake up call for your soul. When these thoughts walk through your mind, the door to higher consciousness opens."

—Lynn Loa, Television Producer

Related Audio Tapes: @ $10

Yoga Nidra/Hypnoyoga	ISBN #0912559-64-9
The Violet Flame	ISBN #0912559-33-0
Meet Your Angel	ISBN #0912559-35-7
Kundalini Rising	ISBN #0912559-38-1

$19.95
Book - 168 Pages
ISBN #0-912559-52-7

Order forms on last pages

TIME TRAVEL
The Do-It-Yourself Past Life Journey Handbook

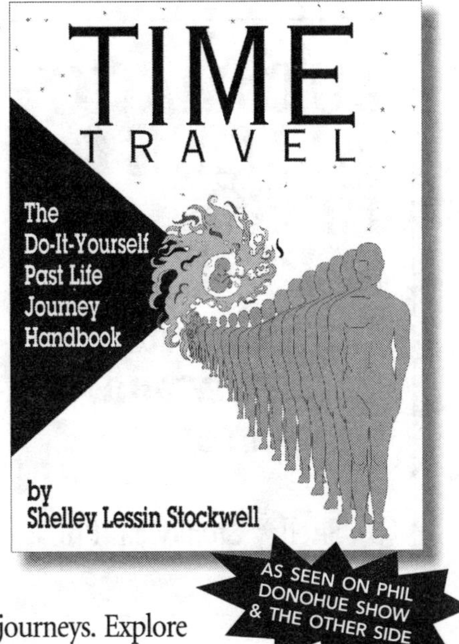

by Shelley Stockwell, Ph.D.

Past life therapist, Shelley gives you 14 easy tools for past life regression, future life progression & between life journeys. Explore the fascinating world that lives behind your eyes, your mind and within your heart. Time travel is fun by yourself or with a friend.

Learn:

★ Your Purpose in this Lifetime
★ Memory Retrieval
★ Guided Visualization
★ Tap Akashic Records
★ Holotropic Breathing
★ How to Heighten Sensory Awareness
★How to Journey Past, Future & Between Lives

"People give me more things to read than I can keep up with, but when I received your manuscript, I sat down and read it in 2 days. You have great suggestions & formulas. I'll recommend it to clients & friends."

—Dr. Hazel M. Denning,
Founder of the Association of Past Life Research & Therapy

Audio Cassette
$10.00
60 minutes
ISBN #0-912559-21-7

Book
$19.95
157 Pages
ISBN #0-912559-19-5

Order forms on last pages

BOOK

AUTOMATIC WRITING & HIERO-SCRIPTING
Tap Unlimited Creativity and Guidance

by Shelley Stockwell, Ph.D.

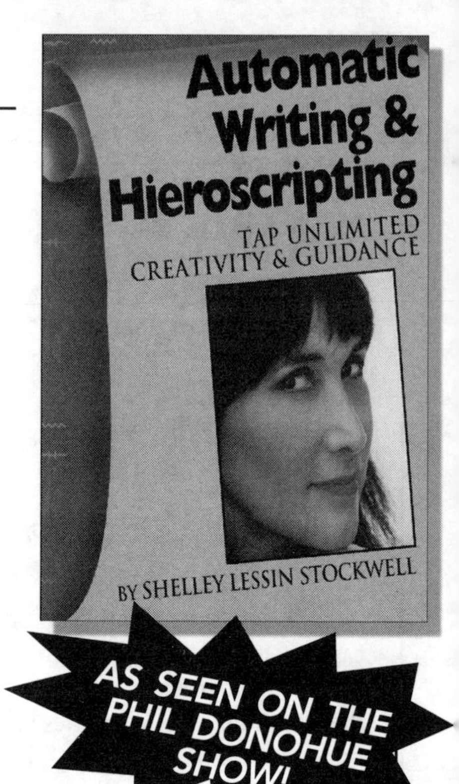

This book teaches how to write automatically,
from simple phrase to painting dramatically.
What it is. How it's done. Expand your
awareness while having fun!

"..drop your veil of fear and let our words move upon your page. Overflow beauty, guidance and creativity. We, your guiding angels serve and love you."

—Arch Angel Michael
written through Shelley

"Anyone who can draw, write or type can automatic write and hieroscript – this book shows how!"

Book On Tape - 60 minutes
$10.00
Automatic Writing & Hieroscripting
ISBN #0-912559-60-8

$9.95
Book - 112 pages
ISBN #0-912559-25-X

Order forms on last pages

BOOK

DENIAL IS NOT A RIVER IN EGYPT

Overcome Addiction, Compulsion & Fear with Dr. Stockwell's Self-Hypnosis System

by Shelley Stockwell, Ph.D.

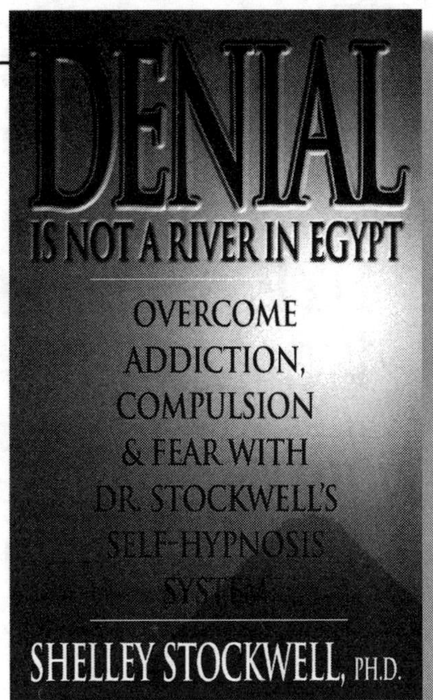

Psst! The secret is out. Learn Hypnotherapist Stockwell's secrets that transform denial, depression, addiction and compulsion into ecstacy, self love & joy.

Learn:

★ Ancient Secrets, Modern Wisdom

★ How to Bust Crazy Habits

★ How to Rewrite Your Life Script for Success!

★ Step-By-Step Instructions that Get Results

"Your book could help a lot of people."

—Bernie Siegel, "Love, Medicine & Miracles"

"I very much enjoyed what you wrote."

—Leo Buscalia, "Living, Loving & Learning"

Related Audio Tapes: @ $10

Lose Weight	ISBN #0912559-02-0
No More Sugar Junkie	ISBN #0912559-03-9
No More Alcohol	ISBN #0912559-10-1
Peace and Calm	ISBN #0912559-08-X
Quit Smoking	ISBN #0912559-04-7
Yes, I Can	ISBN #0912559-09-4

$24.95
Book - 800 pages
ISBN # 0-912559-22-5

Order forms on last pages

BOOK

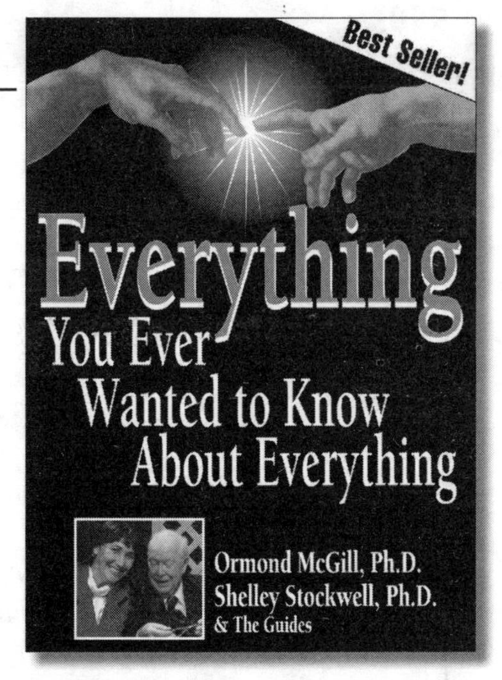

EVERYTHING YOU EVER WANTED TO KNOW ABOUT EVERYTHING

by Ormond McGill, Ph.D.
Shelley Stockwell, Ph.D.
and The Guides

Use this profound little book as a manual for your most precious possession - your life. It is filled with philosophical insights, gems for quantum leaps in your personal fulfillment and spiritual growth. Release yourself from fears and confusion, and walk your life purpose!

Everything you ever wanted to know about…

★ God	★ Wisdom	★ Joy
★ Existence	★ Money	★ Consciousness
★ Death	★ Love & Sex	★ Everything!

"Perfume for the soul."

"... a timeless bible for the new millennium."

"Each insight spread through me like rainbow ink, and I remember that I am the gold at that rainbow's end."

Book On Tape - 60 minutes
$10.00
Everything You Ever Wanted To Know About Everything
& Ten Giant Steps to Super Consciousness
ISBN #0-912559-44-6

Book
$14.95
245 pages
ISBN #0-912559-29-2

Order forms on last pages

BOOK

SEX & OTHER TOUCHY SUBJECTS

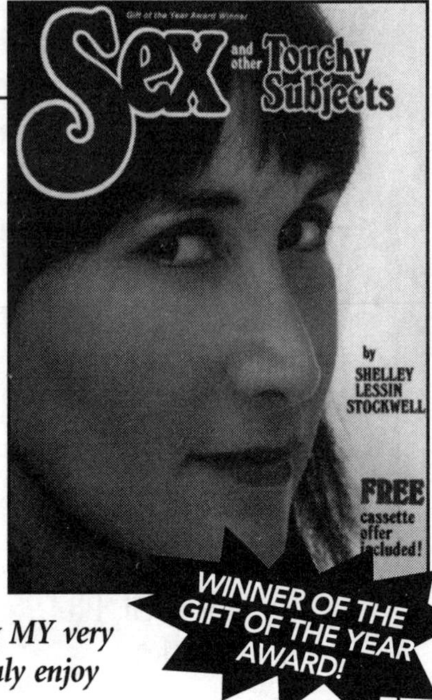

by Shelley Stockwell, Ph.D.

This award winning poetry book tackles love, money, sex, drugs, religion, Mom, Dad, apple pie and death. Hilariously funny and profoundly sensitive. Includes free cassette offer.

"Shelley has an eerie talent for writing MY very thoughts... To enjoy this book is to truly enjoy myself." – Kris Blake, Magic Mirrors

See Everything Book on tape, 17 songs. Brilliantly arranged by Frank Unzuata and performed by Shelley Stockwell, Frank Unzuata and Betsy Cowen.

Book on Tape: $10
ISBN #0-912559-13-6

$14.95
Book - 340 Pages
ISBN #0-912559-12-8

INSIDES OUT

by Shelley Stockwell, Ph.D.

Plain talk poetry guaranteed to speak to you where you really live. If you want to awaken your vitality and truly enjoy yourself, this is your book!

"...Sprinkled throughout are short thoughts and quippy asides—amusing and anecdotal"
—Focus on Books

"Here is a lot of wisdom along with humor... it's really a fantastic book."
—Madelyn Camrud
WDAZ ABC-TV

$6.95
Book - 156 pages
ISBN #0-912559-00-4

Order forms on last pages

PRIMER TO THE LIGHT
A Spiritual Book For Beginners

by Josan Galletti

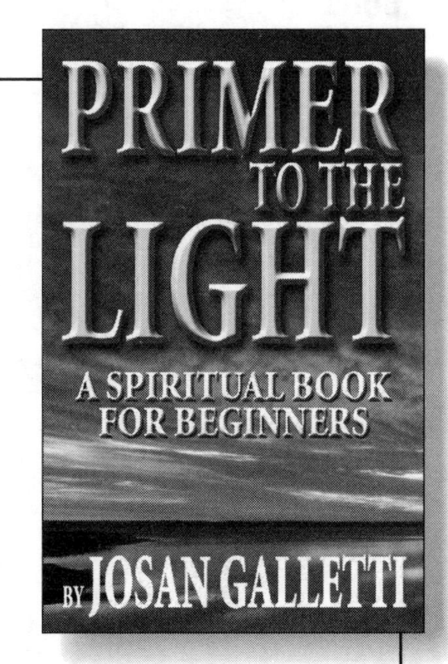

A profound message in an easy read. Josan Galletti's delightful personal story awakens you to your guidance and true SELF. Get on the path and learn how to:

- ★ Meditate
- ★ Manifest Anything
- ★ Harness Energy & Avoid Energy Suckers
- ★ Attract Like-Minded Friends
- ★ Meet Your Angels & Guides
- ★ Discover Your Gifts
- ★ Have Fun

"Like talking to your best friend about things that matter."

"I couldn't put this book down. I read it in one sitting."

"Funny and poignant."

"Enlightenment was never more fun."

—Shelley Stockwell, PhD
The Search for Cosmic Consciousness: The Hypnosis Book Einstein Would Have Loved

$14.95 Soft Cover
184 pages
ISBN #0912559-72-1

$23.95 Hard Bound
184 pages
ISBN #0912559-75-6

Order forms on last pages

BOOK

STOCKWELL'S STAGE HYPNOSIS MADE EASY

by Shelley Stockwell, Ph.D.

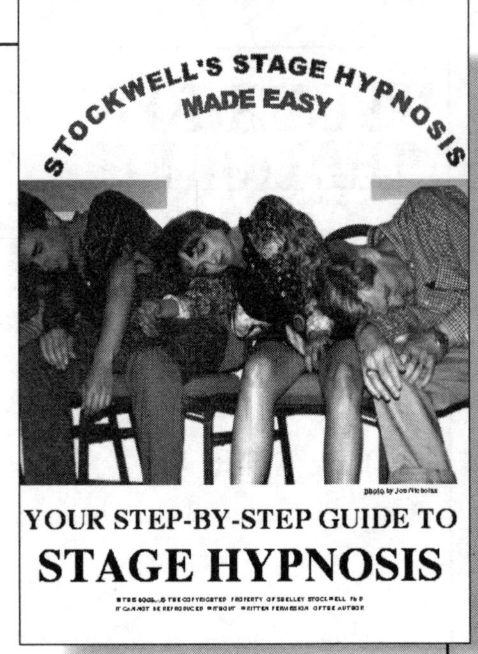

Everything you need to know to present dazzling hypnosis demonstrations and shows. The First Lady of Stage Hypnosis, Dr. Stockwell, gives you all her secrets. This book was used as the text for Stockwell & McGill's famous *Master's Secrets of Stage Hypnosis Seminar.* Learn:

★ How to Hypnotize Anyone is 30 Seconds
★ How to Get the Best Volunteers
★ How to Make Big Bucks
★ Includes Contracts, Scripts, and Hundreds of Routines

"Shelley Stockwell is a master of stage and her creative approach makes stage hypnosis a reality for anyone who wants to shine."

—Richard Neves, PhD
President, the American Board of Hypnotists

Recommended Video $29.95
How to Hypnotize in 30 Seconds
Stockwell's Rapid Inductions
ISBN #0-912559-61-6

Book
$49.95 Paperback
180 pages
ISBN #0912559-67-5

Order forms on last pages

McGILL'S ENCYCLOPEDIA OF HYPNOTHERAPY

by Ormond McGill, Ph.D.

Written by the venerable Dean of American Hypnosis, 87-year-old, Ormond McGill considers this "the best book he ever wrote." Includes:

- ★ Hundreds of original inductions, scripts, and techniques.
- ★ Profound advice for succeeding every time.
- ★ Help others quit smoking, lose weight, release stress, manage pain, & sleep like a baby.
- ★ NLP, reverse speech, mesmerism, breathing techniques, reframing, it's all here! There's everything you need to know and so much juicy information for you to sink your teeth into!

"The 21st Century Bible of Hypnosis and the Mind."

"If you buy one book this year, it should be McGill's masterpiece: the Encyclopedia of Hypnotherapy."

—Shelley Stockwell, PhD

President & Founder of the International Hypnosis Federation

Recommended Video $24.95
Hypnotically Yours, Ormond McGill
ISBN #0-912559-36-5

Book
$55.00
852 pages
ISBN #0912559-74-8

Order forms on last pages

TRANCE-FORMATIONS

Hypnosis, Channeling & Past Life Regression

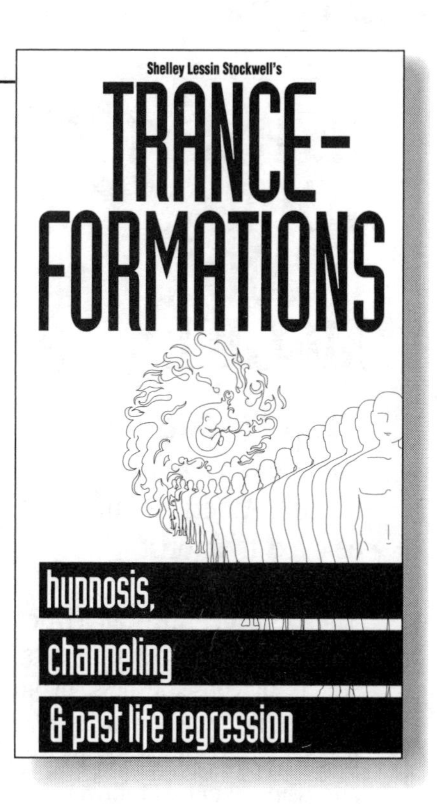

by Shelley Stockwell, Ph.D.

Shelley Stockwell's Trance-Formations video is a riveting opportunity to explore the deepest regions of your mind through hypnosis, channeling and past life regression.

Demonstrates:

- ★ Channeling
- ★ Hypnosis
- ★ Regressions
- ★ Progressions
- ★ Automatic Writing
- ★ Behavior Modification

"This video will transform the way you see yourself once and for your highest good!"

Available in Japanese too!

$19.95
Video Tape
45 minutes
ISBN #0-912559-23-3

Order forms on last pages

HYPNOTICALLY YOURS, ORMOND MCGILL

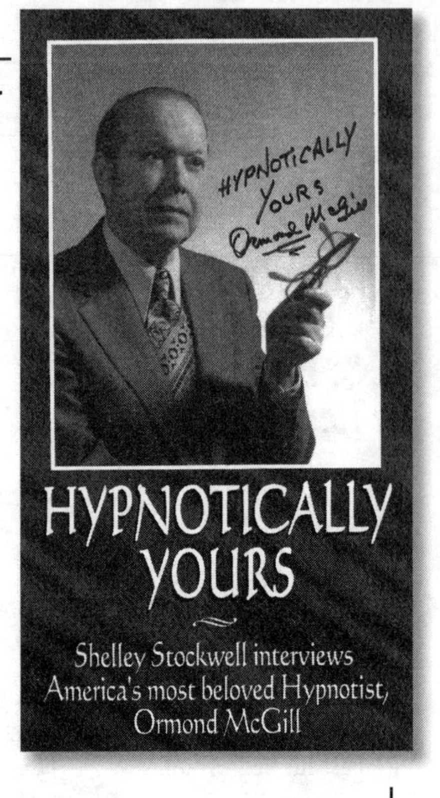

Shelley Stockwell interviews Ormond McGill, America's most beloved hypnotist

The Dean of American Hypnosis, Ormond McGill, Ph.D. shares his secrets of consciousness, hypnosis and the mind. An amazing master teacher, Ormond has been studying and using hypnosis for over seventy years.

In this candid video interview with Hypnotherapist, Shelley Stockwell, Ph.D., McGill discusses the functions of the mind and how you can harness its power.

Includes:

- ★ Step-by-Step Demonstrations of Hypnosis Techniques
- ★ How to Mesmerize Another
- ★ Eye Fixation
- ★ Deepening Skills
- ★ Ideomotor Impulses and Much More…

"Profound wisdom"
"Like spending the evening with fascinating friends"
"I tried several techniques and they work perfectly! Thanks."

$19.95
Video Tape
60 minutes
ISBN #0-912559-36-5

Order forms on last pages

HIGHER SELF HYPNOSIS VIDEO SERIES

3 Stunning Videos:

STOCKWELL'S SECRETS OF THE MIND

Explore the mystery and mastery of your amazing mind. *(90 minutes)* ISBN# 0912559-48-9

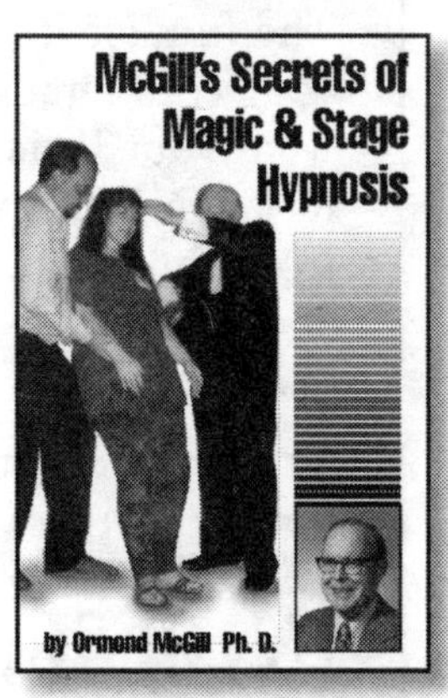

McGILL'S SECRETS OF MAGIC AND STAGE HYPNOSIS

Highlights the Guardian Angel Hypnosis Show. Interviews with volunteers, and the genius of the McGill System. *(2 hours)* ISBN# 0912559-49-7

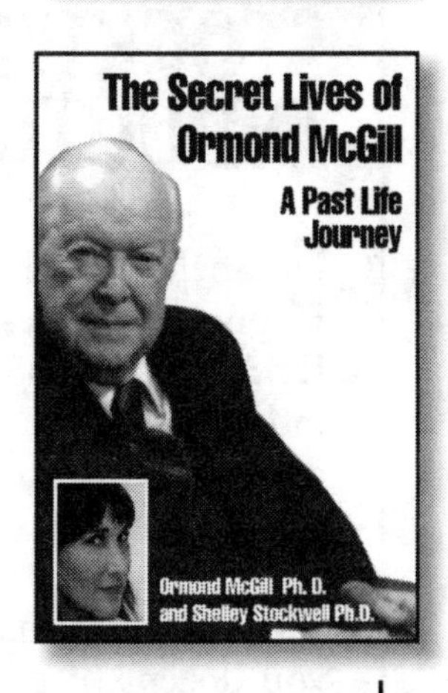

THE SECRET LIVES OF ORMOND McGILL
A Past Life Journey

America's most famous hypnotist, 86 year old Ormond McGill, Ph.D. guided by past life therapist Shelley Stockwell Ph.D. revisits some of the world's greatest mind masters:

- James Braid
- Jean Charcot
- Franz Mesmer
- Baron Von Rochenbach

Includes a view of Atlantis as it sinks away and a private audience with the female pharaoh Hatshetsup. *(1 hour)* ISBN# 0912559-47-0

$19.95 each
$55.00 for all 3 Video Tapes

Order forms on last pages

JOY THERAPY

by Shelley Stockwell

Dr. Shelley Stockwell, The Master of Happiness, teaches you to lighten up. This hilarious seminar offers hands on exercizes that will delight you.

"The funnier it gets,
The funnier it gets,
your cells remember,
what your logic forgets,
to laugh is to live
from the insides out
and that's what ecstacy
is all about!"

$29.95
Video Tape
60 minutes
ISBN #0-912559-71-3

HOW TO HYPNOTIZE IN 30 SECONDS: STOCKWELL'S RAPID INDUCTIONS

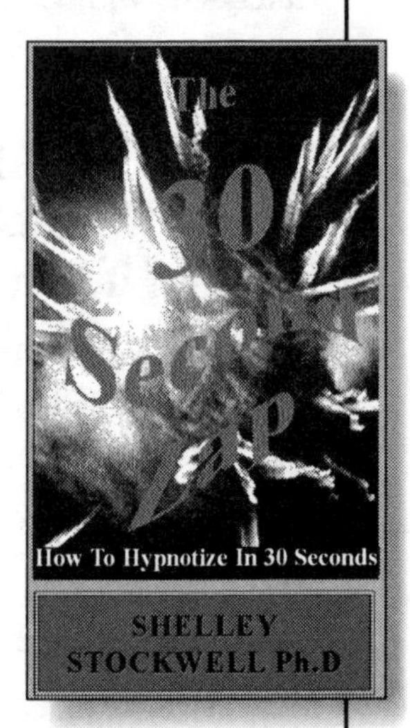

Dr. Shelley Stockwell, The Master of Hypnosis, teaches you to DECK'EM IN 30 SECONDS OR LESS !!! Rapid inductions make hypnosis easy & demonstrations fun. Key into each subject with fail proof methods.

This delightful hands-on course will teach you dozens of powerful inductions. Learn to mesmerize, the "30 Second Zap," non-verbal techniques, spiritual enticements and ancient practices.

$29.95
Video Tape
60 minutes
ISBN #0-912559-61-6

Order forms on last pages

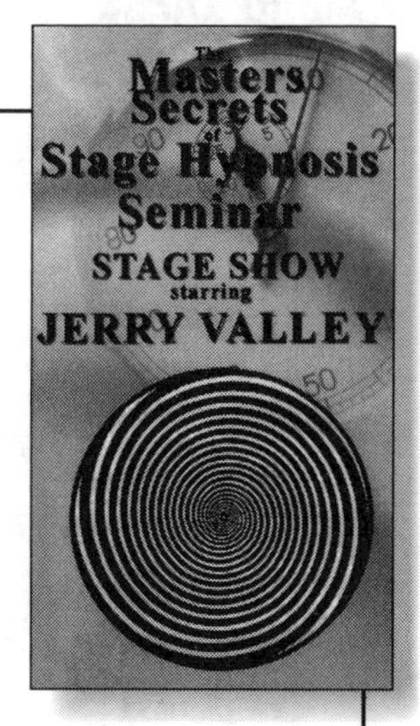

JERRY VALLEY'S STAGE HYPNOSIS SHOW

Starring Jerry Valley

In 1998, three hypnosis greats, Ormond McGill, Jerry Valley, and Shelley Stockwell joined forces to share their experience and wisdom in the world's first MASTER'S SECRETS OF STAGE HYPNOSIS SEMINAR. This is Jerry Valley's fabulous presentation.

$49.95
Video Tape
60 minutes
ISBN #0-912559-70-5

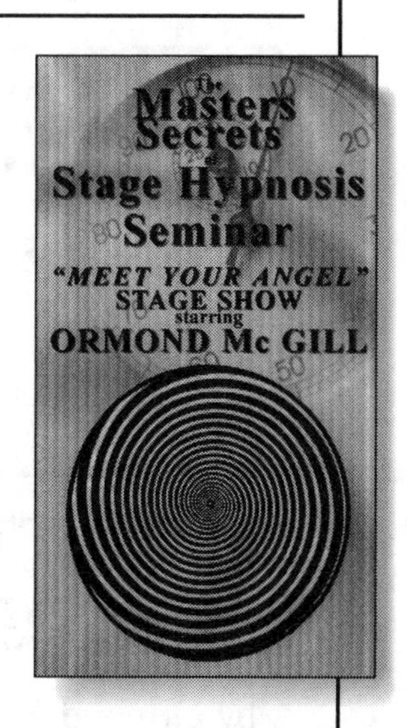

ORMOND McGILL'S MEET YOUR ANGEL STAGE HYPNOSIS SHOW

Starring Ormond McGill

In 1998, three hypnosis greats, Ormond McGill, Jerry Valley, and Shelley Stockwell joined forces to share their experience and wisdom in the world's first MASTER'S SECRETS OF STAGE HYPNOSIS SEMINAR. This is the Dean of American Hypnosis' velvet smooth presentation.

$49.95
Video Tape
60 minutes
ISBN #0-912559-69-1

Order forms on last pages

PEACE & CALM

by Shelley Stockwell, Ph.D.

This perfect stress reducer hypnotizes you to fall in love—with yourself!

$10.00
Audio Tape
ISBN #0-912559-08-X

SLEEP, BEAUTIFUL SLEEP

by Shelley Stockwell, Ph.D.

This closed eye hypnosis tape lets you sleep soundly and feel rested, at home or away. Great stress buster.

$10.00
Audio Tape
ISBN #0-912559-01-2

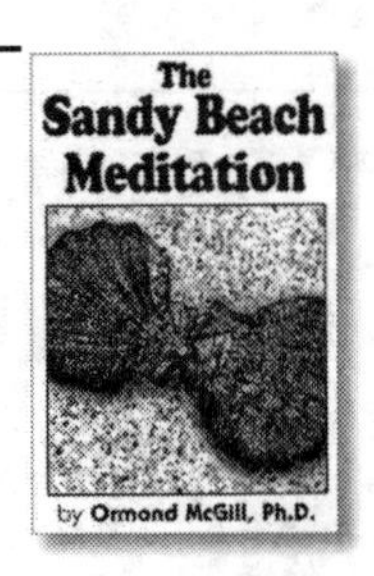

SANDY BEACH MEDITATION

by Ormond McGill, Ph.D.

Enjoy this beautiful closed-eye meditation. Take a vacation, you deserve it!

$10.00
Audio Tape
ISBN #0-912559-57-8

MAGNETIC MIND TONING

by Ormond McGill, Ph.D.
The Dean of American Hypnosis

Master positive thinking. Relax, listen, and train your mind with profound hypnotic relaxation.

$10.00
Audio Tape
ISBN #0-912559-56-X

Order forms on last pages

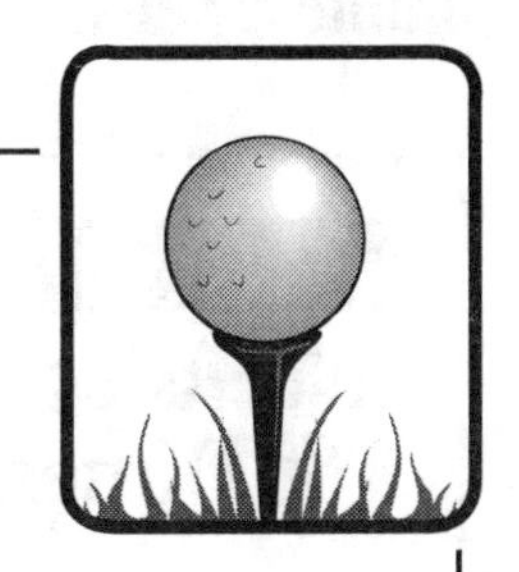

Now you can play
GREAT GOLF!

by Shelley Stockwell, Ph.D.
and Dr. John Goode, DDS

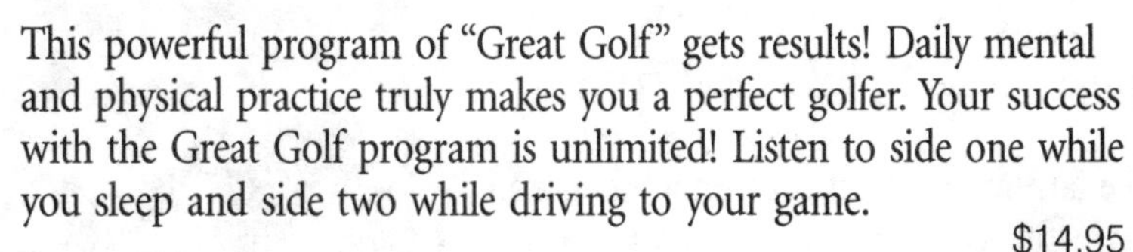

This powerful program of "Great Golf" gets results! Daily mental and physical practice truly makes you a perfect golfer. Your success with the Great Golf program is unlimited! Listen to side one while you sleep and side two while driving to your game.

$14.95
Audio Tape - 60 min.
ISBN #0-912559-20-9

THE MONEY TAPE

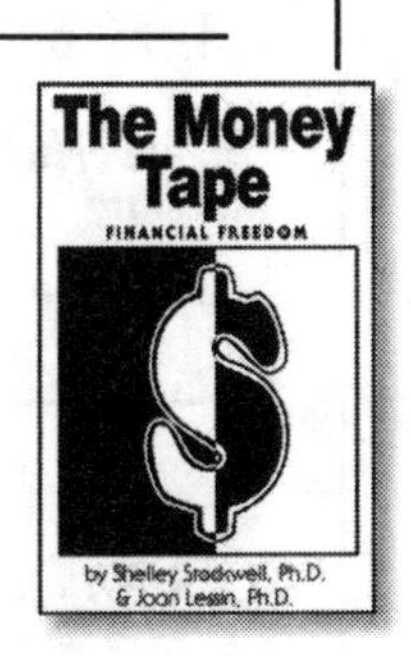

by Shelley Stockwell, Ph.D.
and Joan Lessin, Ph.D.

Listen to one side as you drive in the car, the other while you drift off to sleep. Create energy that lets you manifest money and opportunity. Includes: "The Money Song" by commodities mogul Ed Sakota.

$10.00
Audio Tape - 60 min.
ISBN #0-912559-37-3

ENTRANCING MUSIC
Relax your Mind

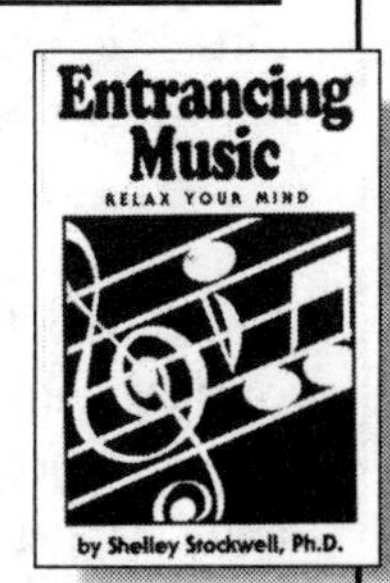

music by Billy Krodel

Harmonic music with Alpha/Theta Resonance and actual womb sounds take you to other dimensions. A perfect tape to use with hypnosis.

$10.00
Audio Tape - 60 min.
ISBN #0-912559-62-4

Order forms on last pages

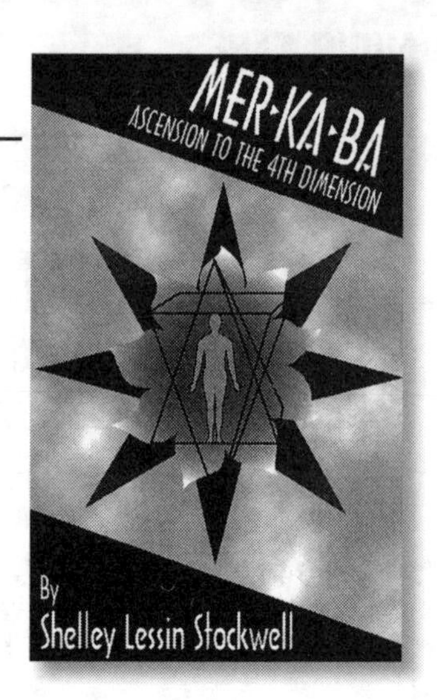

MER•KA•BA:
Ascension to the 4th Dimension

by Shelley Stockwell, Ph.D.
Tonal Music by Wayne Perry

The famous 18 Breaths to Enlightenment! Powerful consciousness expansion for your highest good! Close your eyes and learn the ancient Egyptian initiation rite and visit other dimensions.

"A powerful and mind altering experience not to be missed!"

—Kay Risberg, Hypnotist

$10.00
Audio Tape - 60 min.
ISBN #0-912559-27-6

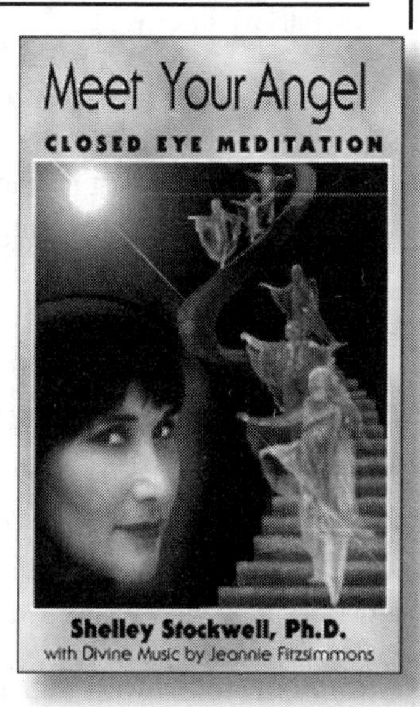

MEET YOUR ANGEL
Closed Eye Meditation

by Shelley Stockwell, Ph.D.
Music & Vocals: Jeannie Fitzsimmons
Trumpet & Flugle Horn: Jim Hale

Cross into the world of wonder and connect with your higher self, guides and angels. Expect a miracle! Hypnotherapist and Channel Shelley Stockwell shows you how in this profound closed eye meditation.

$10.00
Audio Tape - 45 min.
ISBN #0-912559-35-7

Order forms on last pages

KUNDALINI RISING

The Ancient Rite of Enlightenment

by Ormond McGill, Ph.D.
and Shelley Stockwell, Ph.D.

Open your chakras. Written about 7000 years ago in Sanskrit, this closed eye journey opens your body and mind to light!

"One of the most remarkable experiences of your life!"

$10.00
Audio Tape - 60 min.
ISBN #0-912559-38-1

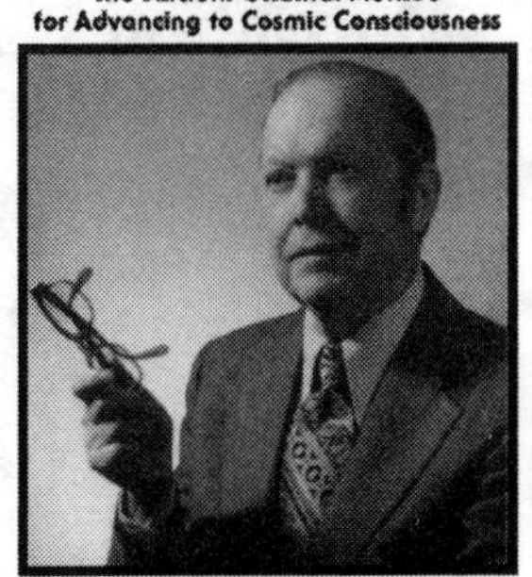

YOGA NIDRA HYPNOYOGA

The Ancient Oriental Method for Advancing to Cosmic Consciousness

by The Dean of American
Hypnosis, Ormond McGill, Ph.D.

This powerful closed eye meditation opens the door to your personal enlightenment!

"This tape changed my life."
—Shelley Stockwell, author

$10.00
Audio Tape - 60 min.
ISBN #0-912559-34-9

Order forms on last pages

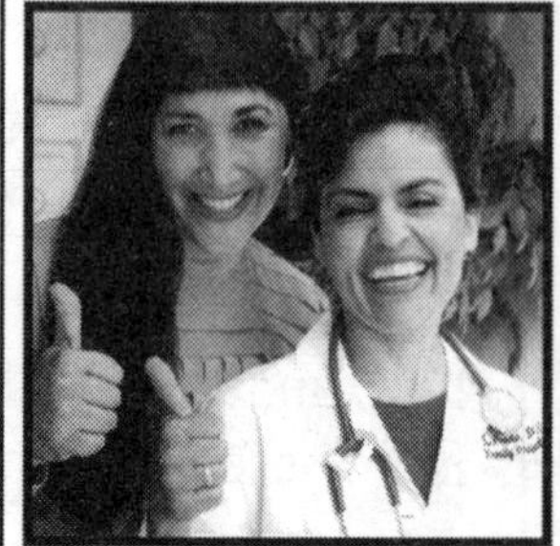

THE WELLNESS TAPE

A Journey of Renewal

By Shelley Stockwell, Ph.D.
and Dr. Lilia Prado, D.O.

Hypnotherapist Shelley Stockwell and Medical Doctor Lilia Prado teach you how to feel your very best. Tap into your body's innate ability to renew, heal and revitalize. Hypnosis is not a miracle, the results just seem that way!

"I think you are angels; you helped save my life."

$10.00
Audio Tape - 60 min.
ISBN #0-912559-32-2

I Love
Exercise
Motivation is Fun!
by Shelley Stockwell, Ph.D.

I LOVE EXERCISE

Motivation is Fun!

By Shelley Stockwell, Ph.D.

Wow, you have a great shape! Hypno-Motivation makes exercise fun! Eliminate negative scripts and get moving again.

"Thank You, Shelley!"

Audio Tape - 60 min. $10.00
ISBN #0-912559-40-3

CD $20.00
ISBN #0-912559-55-1

Order forms on last pages

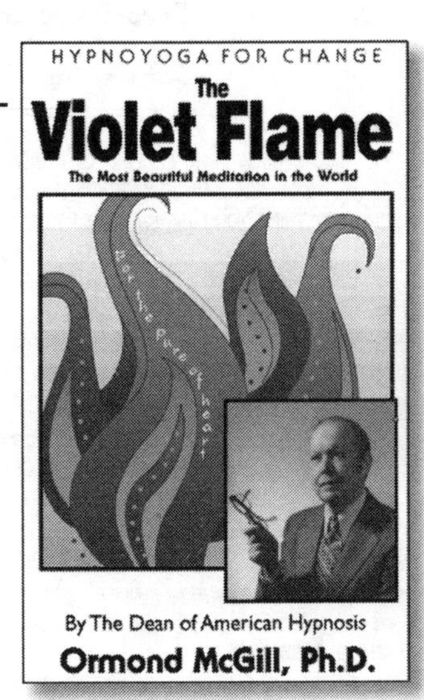

THE VIOLET FLAME

The Most Beautiful Meditation In The World

by Ormond McGill, Ph.D.
The Dean of American Hypnosis

Enjoy the profound Hypno Yoga Journey. Close your eyes and watch a flickering candle as you drift into sacred lands.

"A tune up for the soul."

"No wonder they say Ormond McGill is a master!"

$10.00
Audio Tape - 60 min.
ISBN #0-912559-33-0

SERENITY RESONANCE SOUND

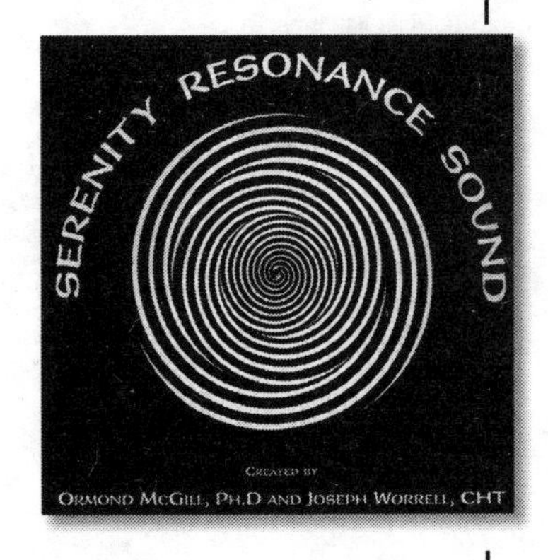

By Ormond McGill, Ph.D.
and Joseph Worrell, C.Ht..

Serenity Resonance Sound places your remarkable biocomputer brain in a receptive state to function any way you call upon it to function. These scientifically calibrated frequencies are designed to unobtrusively harmonize and evoke a peaceful mind, awake or asleep.

Audio Tape $20.00
ISBN #0-912559-53-5

CD $25.00
ISBN #0-912559-54-3

Order forms on last pages

Two-Page Great Products Order Form (page 1)

Check your helpful products and complete the order form to the right. ☛

BOOKS

- ❐ AUTOMATIC WRITING & HEIROSCRIPTING: Tap Unlimited Creativity & Guidance (Stockwell) $9.95
- ❐ DENIAL IS NOT A RIVER IN EGYPT: Overcome Addiction, Compulsion & Depression (Stockwell) $24.95
- ❐ EVERYTHING YOU EVER WANTED TO KNOW ABOUT EVERYTHING (McGill & Stockwell) $14.95
- ❐ HYPNOSIS: How To Put A Smile On Your Face & Money In Your Pocket (Stockwell) $19.95
- ❐ INSIDES OUT: Love Yourself Poetry (Stockwell) $6.95
- ❐ LAVELLE'S: 101 HYPNOSIS SCRIPTS $45.00
- ❐ McGILL'S: THE COMPLETE ENCYCLOPEDIA OF STAGE HYPNOSIS $55.00
- ❐ NEVES: HYPNOSIS SCRIPTS, NLP INTERVENTIONS AND COLLECTED THOUGHTS $35.00
- ❐ PRIMER TO THE LIGHT: A Spiritual Book for Beginners (Galletti) $14.95
- ❐ SEX & OTHER TOUCHY SUBJECTS (Stockwell) $14.95
- ❐ STOCKWELL'S HYPNOSIS FOR WEIGHT CONTROL: 10 Easy Steps to a New You! (Stockwell) $24.95
- ❐ STOCKWELL'S STAGE HYPNOSIS MADE EASY (Stockwell) $39.95
- ❐ THE SEARCH FOR COSMIC CONSCIOUSNESS: The Hypnosis Book Einstein Would Have Loved (McGill & Stockwell) $19.95
- ❐ THE SECRETS OF HYPNOTIZING WOMEN (McGill & Stockwell) $19.95
- ❐ TIME TRAVEL: The Do It Yourself Past Life Journey Handbook (Stockwell) $19.95

AUDIO CASSETTES

- ❐ AUTOMATIC WRITING & HEIROSCRIPTING $10.00
- ❐ CALMING ALPHA MUSIC $10.00
- ❐ ENTRANCING MUSIC (CD $25) $10.00
- ❐ EVERYTHING YOU EVER WANTED TO KNOW ABOUT EVERYTHING $10.00
- ❐ GREAT GOLF $10.00
- ❐ I LOVE EXERCISE (CD $25) $10.00
- ❐ KUNDALINI RISING $10.00
- ❐ LOSE WEIGHT $10.00
- ❐ MAGNETIC MIND TONING $10.00
- ❐ MEET YOUR ANGEL $10.00
- ❐ MER-KA-BA: Ascension to the 4th Dimension $10.00
- ❐ NO MORE ALCOHOL $10.00
- ❐ NO MORE SUGAR JUNKIE $10.00
- ❐ PEACE AND CALM $10.00
- ❐ QUIT SMOKING $10.00
- ❐ SANDY BEACH MEDITATION $10.00
- ❐ SERENITY RESONANCE SOUND (CD $25) $20.00
- ❐ SEX & OTHER TOUCHY SUBJECTS $10.00
- ❐ SLEEP, BEAUTIFUL SLEEP $10.00
- ❐ THE MONEY TAPE $10.00
- ❐ THE VIOLET FLAME $10.00
- ❐ THE WELLNESS TAPE $10.00
- ❐ TIME TRAVEL $10.00
- ❐ YES, I CAN! $10.00
- ❐ YOGA NIDRA/ HYPNO YOGA. $10.00

VIDEOS

- ❐ HOW TO TIME TRAVEL: Past Life Regression/ Future Life Progression $29.95
- ❐ HOW TO HYPNOTIZE IN 30 SECONDS: Stockwell's Rapid & Instant Inductions $29.95
- ❐ HYPNOTICALLY YOURS: Stockwell Interviews Ormond McGill, America's Most Beloved Hypnotist $19.95
- ❐ MASTER SECRETS OF STAGE HYPNOSIS: Ormond McGill Show $49.95
- ❐ MASTER SECRETS OF STAGE HYPNOSIS: Jerry Valley Show $49.95
- ❐ McGILL'S SECRETS OF MAGIC & STAGE HYPNOSIS $19.95
- ❐ STOCKWELL'S HYPNOSIS FOR WEIGHT CONTROL SEMINAR $34.95
- ❐ STOCKWELL'S JOY THERAPY SEMINAR $29.95
- ❐ STOCKWELL'S SECRETS OF THE MIND $19.95
- ❐ THE SECRET LIVES OF ORMOND McGILL: A Past Life Journey $19.95
- ❐ TRANCE-FORMATIONS: Hypnosis, Channeling & Past Life Regression $19.95

BOXED SETS

- ❐ STOCKWELL'S WEIGHT CONTROL: 1 BOOK, 1 VIDEO, 4 AUDIOTAPES $99.00
- ❐ STOCKWELL'S WEIGHT CONTROL: 1 INSTRUCTORS MANUAL, 1 BOOK, 1 VIDEO, 4 AUDIOTAPES $135.00

HEALTH DRINK

- ❐ GREEN MAGMA, JAPAN: Dried rice and barley greens (5.3 oz. jar) $35.00

SUBTOTAL ________

POSTAGE & HANDLING: Order $10 to $49 add $5--Order $50 to $99 add $10--Order $100 and above add $25 ________

California residents add 8.25% tax. Foreign countries add additional $6.00 per item ________

TOTAL ________

Two-Page Great Products Order Form (page 2)

To order, check the products you want on the left side of this order form.

We are proud to offer you the highest quality of helpful tools that make life terrific. Please complete this order form and send to: Creativity Unlimited® *the company that loves you!*

Phone Orders: (310) 541-4844

Type or Print Clearly

Name on Card: ______________________________

Address: ______________________________

City: ______________________ State: _____ Zip: __________

Phone: (______) ______________ E-Mail Address: ______________________

Pay by: ❒ Check ❒ Money Order ❒ Visa ❒ MasterCard ❒ American Express

Credit Card #: ______________________ Exp Date: _______

Signature: ______________________ Date: ______________

CREATIVITY UNLIMITED PRESS®
30819 Casilina Drive
Rancho Palos Verdes, CA 90275
(310) 541-4844

sstockwell@earthlink.net
www.hypnosisfederation.com

Two-Page Great Products Order Form (page 1)

Check your helpful products and complete the order form to the right. ☛

BOOKS

- ❒ AUTOMATIC WRITING & HEIROSCRIPTING: Tap Unlimited Creativity & Guidance (Stockwell) $9.95
- ❒ DENIAL IS NOT A RIVER IN EGYPT: Overcome Addiction, Compulsion & Depression (Stockwell) $24.95
- ❒ EVERYTHING YOU EVER WANTED TO KNOW ABOUT EVERYTHING (McGill & Stockwell) $14.95
- ❒ HYPNOSIS: How To Put A Smile On Your Face & Money In Your Pocket (Stockwell) $19.95
- ❒ INSIDES OUT: Love Yourself Poetry (Stockwell) $6.95
- ❒ LAVELLE'S: 101 HYPNOSIS SCRIPTS $45.00
- ❒ McGILL'S: THE COMPLETE ENCYCLOPEDIA OF STAGE HYPNOSIS $55.00
- ❒ NEVES: HYPNOSIS SCRIPTS, NLP INTERVENTIONS AND COLLECTED THOUGHTS $35.00
- ❒ PRIMER TO THE LIGHT: A Spiritual Book for Beginners (Galletti) $14.95
- ❒ SEX & OTHER TOUCHY SUBJECTS (Stockwell) $14.95
- ❒ STOCKWELL'S HYPNOSIS FOR WEIGHT CONTROL: 10 Easy Steps to a New You! (Stockwell) $24.95
- ❒ STOCKWELL'S STAGE HYPNOSIS MADE EASY (Stockwell) $39.95
- ❒ THE SEARCH FOR COSMIC CONSCIOUSNESS: The Hypnosis Book Einstein Would Have Loved (McGill & Stockwell) $19.95
- ❒ THE SECRETS OF HYPNOTIZING WOMEN (McGill & Stockwell) $19.95
- ❒ TIME TRAVEL: The Do It Yourself Past Life Journey Handbook (Stockwell) $19.95

AUDIO CASSETTES

- ❒ AUTOMATIC WRITING & HEIROSCRIPTING $10.00
- ❒ CALMING ALPHA MUSIC $10.00
- ❒ ENTRANCING MUSIC (CD $25) $10.00
- ❒ EVERYTHING YOU EVER WANTED TO KNOW ABOUT EVERYTHING $10.00
- ❒ GREAT GOLF $10.00
- ❒ I LOVE EXERCISE (CD $25) $10.00
- ❒ KUNDALINI RISING $10.00
- ❒ LOSE WEIGHT $10.00
- ❒ MAGNETIC MIND TONING $10.00
- ❒ MEET YOUR ANGEL $10.00
- ❒ MER-KA-BA: Ascension to the 4th Dimension $10.00
- ❒ NO MORE ALCOHOL $10.00
- ❒ NO MORE SUGAR JUNKIE $10.00
- ❒ PEACE AND CALM $10.00
- ❒ QUIT SMOKING $10.00
- ❒ SANDY BEACH MEDITATION $10.00
- ❒ SERENITY RESONANCE SOUND (CD $25) $20.00
- ❒ SEX & OTHER TOUCHY SUBJECTS $10.00
- ❒ SLEEP, BEAUTIFUL SLEEP $10.00
- ❒ THE MONEY TAPE $10.00
- ❒ THE VIOLET FLAME $10.00
- ❒ THE WELLNESS TAPE $10.00
- ❒ TIME TRAVEL $10.00
- ❒ YES, I CAN! $10.00
- ❒ YOGA NIDRA/ HYPNO YOGA. $10.00

VIDEOS

- ❒ HOW TO TIME TRAVEL: Past Life Regression/ Future Life Progression $29.95
- ❒ HOW TO HYPNOTIZE IN 30 SECONDS: Stockwell's Rapid & Instant Inductions $29.95
- ❒ HYPNOTICALLY YOURS: Stockwell Interviews Ormond McGill, America's Most Beloved Hypnotist $19.95
- ❒ MASTER SECRETS OF STAGE HYPNOSIS: Ormond McGill Show $49.95
- ❒ MASTER SECRETS OF STAGE HYPNOSIS: Jerry Valley Show $49.95
- ❒ McGILL'S SECRETS OF MAGIC & STAGE HYPNOSIS $19.95
- ❒ STOCKWELL'S HYPNOSIS FOR WEIGHT CONTROL SEMINAR $34.95
- ❒ STOCKWELL'S JOY THERAPY SEMINAR $29.95
- ❒ STOCKWELL'S SECRETS OF THE MIND $19.95
- ❒ THE SECRET LIVES OF ORMOND McGILL: A Past Life Journey $19.95
- ❒ TRANCE-FORMATIONS: Hypnosis, Channeling & Past Life Regression $19.95

BOXED SETS

- ❒ STOCKWELL'S WEIGHT CONTROL: 1 BOOK, 1 VIDEO, 4 AUDIOTAPES $99.00
- ❒ STOCKWELL'S WEIGHT CONTROL: 1 INSTRUCTORS MANUAL, 1 BOOK, 1 VIDEO, 4 AUDIOTAPES $135.00

HEALTH DRINK

- ❒ GREEN MAGMA, JAPAN: Dried rice and barley greens (5.3 oz. jar) $35.00

SUBTOTAL ________

POSTAGE & HANDLING: Order $10 to $49 add $5--Order $50 to $99 add $10--Order $100 and above add $25 ________

California residents add 8.25% tax. Foreign countries add additional $6.00 per item ________

TOTAL ________

 *To order, check the products you want on the left side of this order form.*

We are proud to offer you the highest quality of helpful tools that make life terrific. Please complete this order form and send to: Creativity Unlimited® *the company that loves you!*

Phone Orders: (310) 541-4844

Type or Print Clearly

Name on Card: ______________________________

Address: ______________________________

City: ____________________ State: _____ Zip: ________

Phone: (_______)______________ E-Mail Address: ______________

Pay by: ☐ Check ☐ Money Order ☐ Visa ☐ MasterCard ☐ American Express

Credit Card #: ______________________ Exp Date: _______

Signature: ______________________ Date: ____________

CREATIVITY UNLIMITED PRESS®
30819 Casilina Drive
Rancho Palos Verdes, CA 90275
(310) 541-4844

sstockwell@earthlink.net
www.hypnosisfederation.com

Two-Page Great Products Order Form (page 1)

Check your helpful products and complete the order form to the right. ☛

BOOKS

❒ AUTOMATIC WRITING & HEIROSCRIPTING: Tap Unlimited Creativity & Guidance (Stockwell) $9.95
❒ DENIAL IS NOT A RIVER IN EGYPT: Overcome Addiction, Compulsion & Depression (Stockwell) $24.95
❒ EVERYTHING YOU EVER WANTED TO KNOW ABOUT EVERYTHING (McGill & Stockwell) $14.95
❒ HYPNOSIS: How To Put A Smile On Your Face & Money In Your Pocket (Stockwell) $19.95
❒ INSIDES OUT: Love Yourself Poetry (Stockwell) $6.95
❒ LAVELLE'S: 101 HYPNOSIS SCRIPTS $45.00
❒ McGILL'S: THE COMPLETE ENCYCLOPEDIA OF STAGE HYPNOSIS $55.00
❒ NEVES: HYPNOSIS SCRIPTS, NLP INTERVENTIONS AND COLLECTED THOUGHTS $35.00
❒ PRIMER TO THE LIGHT: A Spiritual Book for Beginners (Galletti) $14.95
❒ SEX & OTHER TOUCHY SUBJECTS (Stockwell) $14.95
❒ STOCKWELL'S HYPNOSIS FOR WEIGHT CONTROL: 10 Easy Steps to a New You! (Stockwell) $24.95
❒ STOCKWELL'S STAGE HYPNOSIS MADE EASY (Stockwell) $39.95
❒ THE SEARCH FOR COSMIC CONSCIOUSNESS: The Hypnosis Book Einstein Would Have Loved (McGill & Stockwell) $19.95
❒ THE SECRETS OF HYPNOTIZING WOMEN (McGill & Stockwell) $19.95
❒ TIME TRAVEL: The Do It Yourself Past Life Journey Handbook (Stockwell) $19.95

AUDIO CASSETTES

❒ AUTOMATIC WRITING & HEIROSCRIPTING $10.00
❒ CALMING ALPHA MUSIC $10.00
❒ ENTRANCING MUSIC (CD $25) $10.00
❒ EVERYTHING YOU EVER WANTED TO KNOW ABOUT EVERYTHING $10.00
❒ GREAT GOLF $10.00
❒ I LOVE EXERCISE (CD $25) $10.00
❒ KUNDALINI RISING $10.00
❒ LOSE WEIGHT $10.00
❒ MAGNETIC MIND TONING $10.00
❒ MEET YOUR ANGEL $10.00
❒ MER-KA-BA: Ascension to the 4th Dimension $10.00
❒ NO MORE ALCOHOL $10.00
❒ NO MORE SUGAR JUNKIE $10.00
❒ PEACE AND CALM $10.00
❒ QUIT SMOKING $10.00
❒ SANDY BEACH MEDITATION $10.00
❒ SERENITY RESONANCE SOUND (CD $25) $20.00
❒ SEX & OTHER TOUCHY SUBJECTS $10.00
❒ SLEEP, BEAUTIFUL SLEEP $10.00
❒ THE MONEY TAPE $10.00
❒ THE VIOLET FLAME $10.00
❒ THE WELLNESS TAPE $10.00
❒ TIME TRAVEL $10.00
❒ YES, I CAN! $10.00
❒ YOGA NIDRA/ HYPNO YOGA. $10.00

VIDEOS

❒ HOW TO TIME TRAVEL: Past Life Regression/ Future Life Progression $29.95
❒ HOW TO HYPNOTIZE IN 30 SECONDS: Stockwell's Rapid & Instant Inductions $29.95
❒ HYPNOTICALLY YOURS: Stockwell Interviews Ormond McGill, America's Most Beloved Hypnotist $19.95
❒ MASTER SECRETS OF STAGE HYPNOSIS: Ormond McGill Show $49.95
❒ MASTER SECRETS OF STAGE HYPNOSIS: Jerry Valley Show $49.95
❒ McGILL'S SECRETS OF MAGIC & STAGE HYPNOSIS $19.95
❒ STOCKWELL'S HYPNOSIS FOR WEIGHT CONTROL SEMINAR $34.95
❒ STOCKWELL'S JOY THERAPY SEMINAR $29.95
❒ STOCKWELL'S SECRETS OF THE MIND $19.95
❒ THE SECRET LIVES OF ORMOND McGILL: A Past Life Journey $19.95
❒ TRANCE-FORMATIONS: Hypnosis, Channeling & Past Life Regression $19.95

BOXED SETS

❒ STOCKWELL'S WEIGHT CONTROL: 1 BOOK, 1 VIDEO, 4 AUDIOTAPES $99.00
❒ STOCKWELL'S WEIGHT CONTROL: 1 INSTRUCTORS MANUAL, 1 BOOK, 1 VIDEO, 4 AUDIOTAPES $135.00

HEALTH DRINK

❒ GREEN MAGMA, JAPAN: Dried rice and barley greens (5.3 oz. jar) $35.00

SUBTOTAL ________

POSTAGE & HANDLING: Order $10 to $49 add $5--Order $50 to $99 add $10--Order $100 and above add $25 ________

California residents add 8.25% tax. Foreign countries add additional $6.00 per item ________

TOTAL ________

 *To order, check the products you want on the left side of this order form.*

We are proud to offer you the highest quality of helpful tools that make life terrific. Please complete this order form and send to: Creativity Unlimited® *the company that loves you!*

Phone Orders: (310) 541-4844

Type or Print Clearly

Name on Card: ______________________________

Address: ______________________________

City: ____________________ State: _____ Zip: __________

Phone: (______)______________ E-Mail Address: ______________

Pay by: ❒ Check ❒ Money Order ❒ Visa ❒ MasterCard ❒ American Express

Credit Card #: ____________________ Exp Date: _______

Signature: ____________________ Date: ______________

CREATIVITY UNLIMITED PRESS®
30819 Casilina Drive
Rancho Palos Verdes, CA 90275
(310) 541-4844

sstockwell@earthlink.net
www.hypnosisfederation.com

Two-Page Great Products Order Form (page 1)

Check your helpful products and complete the order form to the right. ☛

BOOKS

- ❒ AUTOMATIC WRITING & HEIROSCRIPTING: Tap Unlimited Creativity & Guidance (Stockwell) $9.95
- ❒ DENIAL IS NOT A RIVER IN EGYPT: Overcome Addiction, Compulsion & Depression (Stockwell) $24.95
- ❒ EVERYTHING YOU EVER WANTED TO KNOW ABOUT EVERYTHING (McGill & Stockwell) $14.95
- ❒ HYPNOSIS: How To Put A Smile On Your Face & Money In Your Pocket (Stockwell) $19.95
- ❒ INSIDES OUT: Love Yourself Poetry (Stockwell) $6.95
- ❒ LAVELLE'S: 101 HYPNOSIS SCRIPTS $45.00
- ❒ McGILL'S: THE COMPLETE ENCYCLOPEDIA OF STAGE HYPNOSIS $55.00
- ❒ NEVES: HYPNOSIS SCRIPTS, NLP INTERVENTIONS AND COLLECTED THOUGHTS $35.00
- ❒ PRIMER TO THE LIGHT: A Spiritual Book for Beginners (Galletti) $14.95
- ❒ SEX & OTHER TOUCHY SUBJECTS (Stockwell) $14.95
- ❒ STOCKWELL'S HYPNOSIS FOR WEIGHT CONTROL: 10 Easy Steps to a New You! (Stockwell) $24.95
- ❒ STOCKWELL'S STAGE HYPNOSIS MADE EASY (Stockwell) $39.95
- ❒ THE SEARCH FOR COSMIC CONSCIOUSNESS: The Hypnosis Book Einstein Would Have Loved (McGill & Stockwell) $19.95
- ❒ THE SECRETS OF HYPNOTIZING WOMEN (McGill & Stockwell) $19.95
- ❒ TIME TRAVEL: The Do It Yourself Past Life Journey Handbook (Stockwell) $19.95

AUDIO CASSETTES

- ❒ AUTOMATIC WRITING & HEIROSCRIPTING $10.00
- ❒ CALMING ALPHA MUSIC $10.00
- ❒ ENTRANCING MUSIC (CD $25) $10.00
- ❒ EVERYTHING YOU EVER WANTED TO KNOW ABOUT EVERYTHING $10.00
- ❒ GREAT GOLF $10.00
- ❒ I LOVE EXERCISE (CD $25) $10.00
- ❒ KUNDALINI RISING $10.00
- ❒ LOSE WEIGHT $10.00
- ❒ MAGNETIC MIND TONING $10.00
- ❒ MEET YOUR ANGEL $10.00
- ❒ MER-KA-BA: Ascension to the 4th Dimension $10.00
- ❒ NO MORE ALCOHOL $10.00
- ❒ NO MORE SUGAR JUNKIE $10.00
- ❒ PEACE AND CALM $10.00
- ❒ QUIT SMOKING $10.00
- ❒ SANDY BEACH MEDITATION $10.00
- ❒ SERENITY RESONANCE SOUND (CD $25) $20.00
- ❒ SEX & OTHER TOUCHY SUBJECTS $10.00
- ❒ SLEEP, BEAUTIFUL SLEEP $10.00
- ❒ THE MONEY TAPE $10.00
- ❒ THE VIOLET FLAME $10.00
- ❒ THE WELLNESS TAPE $10.00
- ❒ TIME TRAVEL $10.00
- ❒ YES, I CAN! $10.00
- ❒ YOGA NIDRA/ HYPNO YOGA. $10.00

VIDEOS

- ❒ HOW TO TIME TRAVEL: Past Life Regression/ Future Life Progression $29.95
- ❒ HOW TO HYPNOTIZE IN 30 SECONDS: Stockwell's Rapid & Instant Inductions $29.95
- ❒ HYPNOTICALLY YOURS: Stockwell Interviews Ormond McGill, America's Most Beloved Hypnotist $19.95
- ❒ MASTER SECRETS OF STAGE HYPNOSIS: Ormond McGill Show $49.95
- ❒ MASTER SECRETS OF STAGE HYPNOSIS: Jerry Valley Show $49.95
- ❒ McGILL'S SECRETS OF MAGIC & STAGE HYPNOSIS $19.95
- ❒ STOCKWELL'S HYPNOSIS FOR WEIGHT CONTROL SEMINAR $34.95
- ❒ STOCKWELL'S JOY THERAPY SEMINAR $29.95
- ❒ STOCKWELL'S SECRETS OF THE MIND $19.95
- ❒ THE SECRET LIVES OF ORMOND McGILL: A Past Life Journey $19.95
- ❒ TRANCE-FORMATIONS: Hypnosis, Channeling & Past Life Regression $19.95

BOXED SETS

- ❒ STOCKWELL'S WEIGHT CONTROL: 1 BOOK, 1 VIDEO, 4 AUDIOTAPES $99.00
- ❒ STOCKWELL'S WEIGHT CONTROL: 1 INSTRUCTORS MANUAL, 1 BOOK, 1 VIDEO, 4 AUDIOTAPES $135.00

HEALTH DRINK

- ❒ GREEN MAGMA, JAPAN: Dried rice and barley greens (5.3 oz. jar) $35.00

SUBTOTAL ________

POSTAGE & HANDLING: Order $10 to $49 add $5--Order $50 to $99 add $10--Order $100 and above add $25 ________

California residents add 8.25% tax. Foreign countries add additional $6.00 per item ________

TOTAL ________

Two-Page Great Products Order Form (page 2)

To order, check the products you want on the left side of this order form.

We are proud to offer you the highest quality of helpful tools that make life terrific. Please complete this order form and send to: Creativity Unlimited® *the company that loves you!*

Phone Orders: (310) 541-4844

Type or Print Clearly

Name on Card: ______________________________

Address: ______________________________

City: ____________________ State: _____ Zip: __________

Phone: (______)____________ E-Mail Address: ____________________

Pay by: ❐ Check ❐ Money Order ❐ Visa ❐ MasterCard ❐ American Express

Credit Card #: ____________________ Exp Date: _______

Signature: ____________________ Date: ______________

CREATIVITY UNLIMITED PRESS®
30819 Casilina Drive
Rancho Palos Verdes, CA 90275
(310) 541-4844

sstockwell@earthlink.net
www.hypnosisfederation.com

Two-Page Great Products Order Form (page 1)

Check your helpful products and complete the order form to the right.

BOOKS

- ❒ AUTOMATIC WRITING & HEIROSCRIPTING: Tap Unlimited Creativity & Guidance (Stockwell) ... $9.95
- ❒ DENIAL IS NOT A RIVER IN EGYPT: Overcome Addiction, Compulsion & Depression (Stockwell) ... $24.95
- ❒ EVERYTHING YOU EVER WANTED TO KNOW ABOUT EVERYTHING (McGill & Stockwell) ... $14.95
- ❒ HYPNOSIS: How To Put A Smile On Your Face & Money In Your Pocket (Stockwell) ... $19.95
- ❒ INSIDES OUT: Love Yourself Poetry (Stockwell) ... $6.95
- ❒ LAVELLE'S: 101 HYPNOSIS SCRIPTS ... $45.00
- ❒ McGILL'S: THE COMPLETE ENCYCLOPEDIA OF STAGE HYPNOSIS ... $55.00
- ❒ NEVES: HYPNOSIS SCRIPTS, NLP INTERVENTIONS AND COLLECTED THOUGHTS ... $35.00
- ❒ PRIMER TO THE LIGHT: A Spiritual Book for Beginners (Galletti) ... $14.95
- ❒ SEX & OTHER TOUCHY SUBJECTS (Stockwell) ... $14.95
- ❒ STOCKWELL'S HYPNOSIS FOR WEIGHT CONTROL: 10 Easy Steps to a New You! (Stockwell) ... $24.95
- ❒ STOCKWELL'S STAGE HYPNOSIS MADE EASY (Stockwell) ... $39.95
- ❒ THE SEARCH FOR COSMIC CONSCIOUSNESS: The Hypnosis Book Einstein Would Have Loved (McGill & Stockwell) ... $19.95
- ❒ THE SECRETS OF HYPNOTIZING WOMEN (McGill & Stockwell) ... $19.95
- ❒ TIME TRAVEL: The Do It Yourself Past Life Journey Handbook (Stockwell) ... $19.95

AUDIO CASSETTES

- ❒ AUTOMATIC WRITING & HEIROSCRIPTING ... $10.00
- ❒ CALMING ALPHA MUSIC ... $10.00
- ❒ ENTRANCING MUSIC (CD $25) ... $10.00
- ❒ EVERYTHING YOU EVER WANTED TO KNOW ABOUT EVERYTHING ... $10.00
- ❒ GREAT GOLF ... $10.00
- ❒ I LOVE EXERCISE (CD $25) ... $10.00
- ❒ KUNDALINI RISING ... $10.00
- ❒ LOSE WEIGHT ... $10.00
- ❒ MAGNETIC MIND TONING ... $10.00
- ❒ MEET YOUR ANGEL ... $10.00
- ❒ MER-KA-BA: Ascension to the 4th Dimension ... $10.00
- ❒ NO MORE ALCOHOL ... $10.00
- ❒ NO MORE SUGAR JUNKIE ... $10.00
- ❒ PEACE AND CALM ... $10.00
- ❒ QUIT SMOKING ... $10.00
- ❒ SANDY BEACH MEDITATION ... $10.00
- ❒ SERENITY RESONANCE SOUND (CD $25) ... $20.00
- ❒ SEX & OTHER TOUCHY SUBJECTS ... $10.00
- ❒ SLEEP, BEAUTIFUL SLEEP ... $10.00
- ❒ THE MONEY TAPE ... $10.00
- ❒ THE VIOLET FLAME ... $10.00
- ❒ THE WELLNESS TAPE ... $10.00
- ❒ TIME TRAVEL ... $10.00
- ❒ YES, I CAN! ... $10.00
- ❒ YOGA NIDRA/ HYPNO YOGA. ... $10.00

VIDEOS

- ❒ HOW TO TIME TRAVEL: Past Life Regression/ Future Life Progression ... $29.95
- ❒ HOW TO HYPNOTIZE IN 30 SECONDS: Stockwell's Rapid & Instant Inductions ... $29.95
- ❒ HYPNOTICALLY YOURS: Stockwell Interviews Ormond McGill, America's Most Beloved Hypnotist ... $19.95
- ❒ MASTER SECRETS OF STAGE HYPNOSIS: Ormond McGill Show ... $49.95
- ❒ MASTER SECRETS OF STAGE HYPNOSIS: Jerry Valley Show ... $49.95
- ❒ McGILL'S SECRETS OF MAGIC & STAGE HYPNOSIS ... $19.95
- ❒ STOCKWELL'S HYPNOSIS FOR WEIGHT CONTROL SEMINAR ... $34.95
- ❒ STOCKWELL'S JOY THERAPY SEMINAR ... $29.95
- ❒ STOCKWELL'S SECRETS OF THE MIND ... $19.95
- ❒ THE SECRET LIVES OF ORMOND McGILL: A Past Life Journey ... $19.95
- ❒ TRANCE-FORMATIONS: Hypnosis, Channeling & Past Life Regression ... $19.95

BOXED SETS

- ❒ STOCKWELL'S WEIGHT CONTROL: 1 BOOK, 1 VIDEO, 4 AUDIOTAPES ... $99.00
- ❒ STOCKWELL'S WEIGHT CONTROL: 1 INSTRUCTORS MANUAL, 1 BOOK, 1 VIDEO, 4 AUDIOTAPES ... $135.00

HEALTH DRINK

- ❒ GREEN MAGMA, JAPAN: Dried rice and barley greens (5.3 oz. jar) ... $35.00

SUBTOTAL ________

POSTAGE & HANDLING: Order $10 to $49 add $5--Order $50 to $99 add $10--Order $100 and above add $25 ________

California residents add 8.25% tax. Foreign countries add additional $6.00 per item ________

TOTAL ________

To order, check the products you want on the left side of this order form.

We are proud to offer you the highest quality of helpful tools that make life terrific. Please complete this order form and send to: Creativity Unlimited® *the company that loves you!*

Phone Orders: (310) 541-4844

Type or Print Clearly

Name on Card: ______________________________

Address: ______________________________

City: ______________________ State: _____ Zip: __________

Phone: (_______)_______________ E-Mail Address: ____________________

Pay by: ❐ Check ❐ Money Order ❐ Visa ❐ MasterCard ❐ American Express

Credit Card #: ______________________ Exp Date: _______

Signature: ______________________ Date: ______________

CREATIVITY UNLIMITED PRESS®
30819 Casilina Drive
Rancho Palos Verdes, CA 90275
(310) 541-4844

sstockwell@earthlink.net
www.hypnosisfederation.com

Two-Page Great Products Order Form (page 1)

Check your helpful products and complete the order form to the right. ☛

BOOKS

- ❐ AUTOMATIC WRITING & HEIROSCRIPTING: Tap Unlimited Creativity & Guidance (Stockwell) $9.95
- ❐ DENIAL IS NOT A RIVER IN EGYPT: Overcome Addiction, Compulsion & Depression (Stockwell) $24.95
- ❐ EVERYTHING YOU EVER WANTED TO KNOW ABOUT EVERYTHING (McGill & Stockwell) $14.95
- ❐ HYPNOSIS: How To Put A Smile On Your Face & Money In Your Pocket (Stockwell) $19.95
- ❐ INSIDES OUT: Love Yourself Poetry (Stockwell) $6.95
- ❐ LAVELLE'S: 101 HYPNOSIS SCRIPTS $45.00
- ❐ McGILL'S: THE COMPLETE ENCYCLOPEDIA OF STAGE HYPNOSIS $55.00
- ❐ NEVES: HYPNOSIS SCRIPTS, NLP INTERVENTIONS AND COLLECTED THOUGHTS $35.00
- ❐ PRIMER TO THE LIGHT: A Spiritual Book for Beginners (Galletti) $14.95
- ❐ SEX & OTHER TOUCHY SUBJECTS (Stockwell) $14.95
- ❐ STOCKWELL'S HYPNOSIS FOR WEIGHT CONTROL: 10 Easy Steps to a New You! (Stockwell) $24.95
- ❐ STOCKWELL'S STAGE HYPNOSIS MADE EASY (Stockwell) $39.95
- ❐ THE SEARCH FOR COSMIC CONSCIOUSNESS: The Hypnosis Book Einstein Would Have Loved (McGill & Stockwell) $19.95
- ❐ THE SECRETS OF HYPNOTIZING WOMEN (McGill & Stockwell) $19.95
- ❐ TIME TRAVEL: The Do It Yourself Past Life Journey Handbook (Stockwell) $19.95

AUDIO CASSETTES

- ❐ AUTOMATIC WRITING & HEIROSCRIPTING $10.00
- ❐ CALMING ALPHA MUSIC $10.00
- ❐ ENTRANCING MUSIC (CD $25) $10.00
- ❐ EVERYTHING YOU EVER WANTED TO KNOW ABOUT EVERYTHING $10.00
- ❐ GREAT GOLF $10.00
- ❐ I LOVE EXERCISE (CD $25) $10.00
- ❐ KUNDALINI RISING $10.00
- ❐ LOSE WEIGHT $10.00
- ❐ MAGNETIC MIND TONING $10.00
- ❐ MEET YOUR ANGEL $10.00
- ❐ MER-KA-BA: Ascension to the 4th Dimension $10.00
- ❐ NO MORE ALCOHOL $10.00
- ❐ NO MORE SUGAR JUNKIE $10.00
- ❐ PEACE AND CALM $10.00
- ❐ QUIT SMOKING $10.00
- ❐ SANDY BEACH MEDITATION $10.00
- ❐ SERENITY RESONANCE SOUND (CD $25) $20.00
- ❐ SEX & OTHER TOUCHY SUBJECTS $10.00
- ❐ SLEEP, BEAUTIFUL SLEEP $10.00
- ❐ THE MONEY TAPE $10.00
- ❐ THE VIOLET FLAME $10.00
- ❐ THE WELLNESS TAPE $10.00
- ❐ TIME TRAVEL $10.00
- ❐ YES, I CAN! $10.00
- ❐ YOGA NIDRA/ HYPNO YOGA. $10.00

VIDEOS

- ❐ HOW TO TIME TRAVEL: Past Life Regression/ Future Life Progression $29.95
- ❐ HOW TO HYPNOTIZE IN 30 SECONDS: Stockwell's Rapid & Instant Inductions $29.95
- ❐ HYPNOTICALLY YOURS: Stockwell Interviews Ormond McGill, America's Most Beloved Hypnotist $19.95
- ❐ MASTER SECRETS OF STAGE HYPNOSIS: Ormond McGill Show $49.95
- ❐ MASTER SECRETS OF STAGE HYPNOSIS: Jerry Valley Show $49.95
- ❐ McGILL'S SECRETS OF MAGIC & STAGE HYPNOSIS $19.95
- ❐ STOCKWELL'S HYPNOSIS FOR WEIGHT CONTROL SEMINAR $34.95
- ❐ STOCKWELL'S JOY THERAPY SEMINAR $29.95
- ❐ STOCKWELL'S SECRETS OF THE MIND $19.95
- ❐ THE SECRET LIVES OF ORMOND McGILL: A Past Life Journey $19.95
- ❐ TRANCE-FORMATIONS: Hypnosis, Channeling & Past Life Regression $19.95

BOXED SETS

- ❐ STOCKWELL'S WEIGHT CONTROL: 1 BOOK, 1 VIDEO, 4 AUDIOTAPES $99.00
- ❐ STOCKWELL'S WEIGHT CONTROL: 1 INSTRUCTORS MANUAL, 1 BOOK, 1 VIDEO, 4 AUDIOTAPES $135.00

HEALTH DRINK

- ❐ GREEN MAGMA, JAPAN: Dried rice and barley greens (5.3 oz. jar) $35.00

SUBTOTAL ______

POSTAGE & HANDLING: Order $10 to $49 add $5--Order $50 to $99 add $10--Order $100 and above add $25 ______

California residents add 8.25% tax. Foreign countries add additional $6.00 per item ______

TOTAL ______

Two-Page Great Products Order Form (page 2)

 *To order, check the products you want on the left side of this order form.*

We are proud to offer you the highest quality of helpful tools that make life terrific. Please complete this order form and send to: Creativity Unlimited® ***the company that loves you!***

Phone Orders: (310) 541-4844

Type or Print Clearly

Name on Card: ______________________________

Address: ______________________________

City: ____________________ State: _____ Zip: _________

Phone: (_______)______________ E-Mail Address: ______________

Pay by: ❒ Check ❒ Money Order ❒ Visa ❒ MasterCard ❒ American Express

Credit Card #: ______________________________ Exp Date: ______

Signature: ______________________________ Date: ______________

CREATIVITY UNLIMITED PRESS®
30819 Casilina Drive
Rancho Palos Verdes, CA 90275
(310) 541-4844

sstockwell@earthlink.net
www.hypnosisfederation.com

ALL OF OUR SELF-HYPNOSIS AUDIO CASSETTES...

AUTOMATIC WRITING & HEIROSCRIPTING
Tap your subconsciousness by writing and drawing.
ISBN #0-912559-60-8

ENTRANCING MUSIC
Relax Your Mind.
ISBN #0-912559-37-3

EVERYTHING YOU EVER WANTED TO KNOW ABOUT EVERYTHING
10 STEPS TO SUPER CONSCIOUSNESS
Book on Tape. ISBN #0-912559-44-6

GREAT GOLF
Build confidence, play focused, relaxed & improve your score!
ISBN #0-912559-20-9

GREAT TENNIS
Improve your game, play focused & have fun! ISBN #0-912559-41-1

I LOVE EXERCISE
Motivation is fun—gets you moving again!
ISBN #0-912559-40-3 Tape
ISBN #0-912559-55-1 CD

KUNDALINI RISING
The ancient rite of enlightenment. A wonderful experience.
ISBN #0-912559-38-1

LOSE WEIGHT!
Lose unwanted pounds forever, gaining energy and confidence.
ISBN #0-912559-02-0

MAGNETIC MIND TONING
Profound Hypnotic relaxation.
ISBN #0-912559-56-X

MEET YOUR ANGEL
Connect with your higher self, your guides and angels.
ISBN #0-912559-35-7

MER-KA-BA: ASCENSION TO THE 4TH DIMENSION
Powerful consciousness expansion for highest good. ISBN #0-912559-27-6

NO MORE ALCOHOL
Break free of alcohol. Feel your life again. ISBN #0-912559-10-1

NO MORE SUGAR JUNKIE
Bust the sugar blues. Feel alive and terrific!
ISBN #0-912559-03-9

PEACE AND CALM
The perfect stress reducer. You need no tranquilizers.
ISBN #0-912559-08-X

QUIT SMOKING
Save money, breathe again and feel healthy.
ISBN #0-912559-04-7

SANDY BEACH MEDITATION
Beautiful closed-eye meditation.
ISBN #0-912559-57-8

SERENITY RESONANCE SOUND
Alpha and theta brain waves.
ISBN #0-912559-53-5 Tape
ISBN #0-912559-54-3 CD

SEX & OTHER TOUCHY SUBJECTS
17 Songs from Book Book on Tape.
ISBN #0-912559-13-6

SLEEP, BEAUTIFUL SLEEP
Sleep soundly & feel rested, at home or away. Great stress buster.
ISBN #0-912559-01-2

THE MONEY TAPE
Create energy that lets you manifest opportunity & money.
ISBN #0-912559-37-3

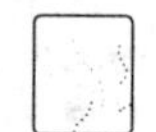

THE VIOLET FLAME
The most beautiful meditation in the world. ISBN #0-912559-33-0

THE WELLNESS TAPE
Tap your body's innate ability to renew, heal & revitalize!
ISBN #0-912559-32-2

TIME TRAVEL
Access your past & future lives. Discover your life's purpose.
ISBN #0-912559-21-7

YES, I CAN!
Achieve your personal goals & highest potentials.
ISBN #0-912559-09-8

YOGA NIDRA/HYPNOYOGA
The ancient Oriental method for advancing to cosmic consciousness.
ISBN #0-912559-34-9

A Gift For Yourself!

Please print your name & address:

Name: ______________________________

Address: ______________________________

City/Zip: ______________________________

Phone: (______) ______________________________

E-mail Address: ______________________________

A Gift for A Friend!

Make someone happy! Send them a book or tape today!

If the order is for a friend, please print their name, address and any greeting you wish to send, and we will mail it to them from you!

To:

Name: ______________________________

Friend's Address: ______________________________

City/Zip: ______________________________

Friend's Phone: (______) ______________________________

Greeting: ______________________________

____

To order additional gifts for yourself or friends, feel free to use a separate sheet of paper or xerox this form.

Pay by: ☐ Check ☐ Money Order ☐ Credit Card:

Name on Credit Card ______________________________

Credit Card # ______________________________

Exp. Date ______________________________

Signature ______________________________

SEND TO:

30819 Casilina Drive, Rancho Palos Verdes, CA 90275 U.S.A.
OR CALL: (310) 541-4844